# TABLE OF LAPLACE TRANSFORMS

by

G. E. ROBERTS

SENIOR MEMBER SCIENTIFIC STAFF
RCA VICTOR COMPANY, LTD.

and

H. KAUFMAN

PROFESSOR OF MATHEMATICS
MCGILL UNIVERSITY

W. B. SAUNDERS COMPANY

*Philadelphia and London*

RECID = 1691-1

Table of Laplace Transforms

 Press of W. B. Saunders Company. Library of Congress catalog card number 65-23098.

to

*Mary and Sylvia*

# PREFACE

The motivation for the present work lies in our belief that an ideal collection of Laplace transforms should combine the following features: comprehensiveness, a statement of validity conditions on the parameters, a tabulation of both direct and inverse transforms, and an effective key to the individual entries. We have been particularly concerned with the construction of a simple but effective indexing system. A detailed description of this system is given immediately following the table of contents.

We define the Laplace transform g(s) of a function f(t) by the integral

$$g(s) = \int_0^\infty e^{-st} f(t)\,dt$$

where s is a complex variable. The function f(t) is referred to as the inverse Laplace transform of g(s).

The inversion integral, expressing f(t) in terms of g(s), is given by

$$f(t) = \frac{1}{2\pi i} \int_{c-i\infty}^{c+i\infty} g(s) e^{st}\,ds$$

where g(s) is analytic in the half-plane Re $s \geqslant c$.

Our debt to the major collections of Erdelyi,[1] Doetsch,[2] McLachlan and Humbert,[3] and McLachlan, Humbert and Poli[4] will be apparent; other sources were Gardner and Barnes,[5] Nixon,[6] and Doetsch.[7] New transforms given by Poli,[8] Klamkin,[9] and Ragab[10, 11] have also been incorporated. We have omitted transforms of Mathieu functions, a topic which is adequately covered in reference 4. Although it was impossible to rederive every entry, great care was taken to crosscheck entries and to eliminate errors and inconsistencies. Since it is too much to hope that none of the latter remain, we shall be grateful to our readers for bringing any errors to our attention.

We wish to express our thanks to the RCA Victor Company, Ltd., for their unstinted cooperation and to Mrs. Shirley Pierrepoint for undertaking the arduous task of typing the manuscript.

G. E. Roberts
H. Kaufman

# REFERENCES


1. Erdelyi, A. (Editor), Tables of Integral Transforms, Vol. I (McGraw-Hill, 1954).
2. Doetsch, G., Tabellen zur Laplace-Transformation und Anleitung zum Gebrauch (Springer, 1947).
3. McLachlan, N. W., and Humbert, P., Formulaire pour le calcul symbolique, Mémorial des Sciences Mathématiques, Fascicule 100 (Gauthier-Villars, 1950).
4. McLachlan, N. W., Humbert, P., and Poli, L., Supplement au formulaire pour le calcul symbolique, Mémorial des Sciences Mathématiques, Fascicule 103 (Gauthier-Villars, 1950).
5. Gardner, M. F., and Barnes, J. L., Transients in Linear Systems (Wiley, 1947).
6. Nixon, F. E., Handbook of Laplace Transformation (Prentice-Hall, 1960).
7. Doetsch, G., Guide to the Applications of Laplace Transforms (Van Nostrand, 1961).
8. Poli, L., Quelques images symboliques, Annales de la Soc. Sci. Bruxelles (1), Vol. 68, 13-22, (1954).
9. Klamkin, M. S., An Application of the Gauss Multiplication Theorem, Amer. Math. Monthly, Vol. 64, 661-663 (1957).
10. Ragab, F. M., The Inverse Laplace Transform of an Exponential Function, Comm. Pure and Appl. Math., Vol. 11, 115-127, (1958).
11. Ragab, F. M., The Inverse Laplace Transform of the Product

$$\exp[-\tfrac{1}{2} a^{1/n} p^{1/n}] K_{n\nu}[\tfrac{1}{2} a^{1/n} p^{1/n}], n = 2,3,4,\ldots,$$

Boll. Un. Mat. Ital. (3), Vol. 19, 26-30 (1964).

# CONTENTS

# HOW TO USE THE BOOK

The book consists of two parts: Part I, Direct Transforms, and Part II, Inverse Transforms.

Each part is again divided into two sections. Section 1 of each part is a table of operations. The operations are grouped into convenient subsections with self-explanatory titles and are serially numbered for reference purposes. By means of the operations many transform pairs not listed in this book may be derived.

Section 2 of each part, comprising the bulk of this book, is a list of transform pairs. They are arranged in order according to an indexing system which will enable any particular entry to be quickly located. The indexing system applies to both the direct and inverse transform pairs.

All mathematical functions occurring in the transforms have been divided into 37 categories as shown in the Function Index, each category having a code number. To find a particular entry in the tables, select all the code numbers corresponding to the functional forms in the entry of interest and arrange them in descending numerical order. Look up this combined code number directly in the tables and select the required transform pair from those listed. Under each combined code number, transform pairs are given a serial number for reference.

"Function" as used here refers to a function of t in the direct transform pairs and s in the inverse transform pairs. There is one exception. When the function is given as an integral,

$$\text{i.e.} \quad \int f(u,t)\,du \text{ or } \int f(u,s)\,du$$

the coding of the entry is based on f considered as a function of u, with t and s being treated only as parameters (see example 6 following).

The user is advised to become familiar with the code numbers of the 37 categories, or at least with the more commonly used ones, as this will greatly facilitate the efficient use of the coding system.

The expressions *at* or *as,* although strictly rational algebraic functions, are not considered as such in the present context because they occur as basic quantities in all transforms and would invalidate the use of code number 1. Some examples follow.

Example 1. $f(t) = \dfrac{t^{\nu}}{t+a}$ has code number 2.1 since $t^{\nu}$ is in category 2 and $t+a$ is in category 1.

Example 2. $f(t) = e^{-at}$ has code number 3 since $e^{-at}$ is in category 3 and $-at$ is not considered as a rational function.

Example 3. $g(s) = \frac{1}{s^{\nu}} \operatorname{cosech}(as)\, I_{\nu}(as)$ has code number 12.7.2 since $I_{\nu}(as)$ is in category 12, cosech(as) is in category 7 and $\frac{1}{s^{\nu}}$ is in category 2.

Example 4. $f(t) = \begin{cases} 1 & na < t < na + b \\ 0 & na+b < t < (n+1)a \quad n = 0,1,2,\ldots \end{cases}$

has code number 35 since it is piecewise defined.

Example 5. $f(t) = \begin{cases} 0 & 0 < t < b \\ \left(\frac{t-b}{t+b}\right)^{\frac{\nu}{2}} e^{-(a+b)t} I_{\nu}[a(t^2-b^2)^{\frac{1}{2}}] & t > b \end{cases}$

has code number 36.12.3.2 since it is a delayed function, category 36, $I_{\nu}[a(t^2-b^2)^{\frac{1}{2}}]$ is in category 12, $e^{-(a+b)t}$ is in category 3, and $\left(\frac{t-b}{t+b}\right)^{\frac{\nu}{2}}$ and $a(t^2-b^2)^{\frac{1}{2}}$ are both in category 2.

Example 6. $f(t) = \int_0^{at} \frac{\sinh u}{u}\, du$ has code number 7 since sinh u is in category 7.

For convenience of reference, functions of the form $|f(t)|$ are placed both in the category corresponding to f(t) and in the category of piecewise defined functions (35).

Example 7. $|\cos(at)|$ has code numbers 5 and 35.5.

In Part II, Section 2, a large number of functions fall into code 1, polynomials in s. In this category the entries have been arranged under a special subcoding system which is explained at the start of Part II, Section 2.

In the case of a few categories containing a large number of entries, some descriptive subheadings have been introduced as guides.

# FUNCTION INDEX

*Note:* In the Function Index, x is to be considered as any function of t in the direct transforms or of s in the inverse transforms. The symbol y stands for t in the direct transforms and for s in the inverse transforms.

| Code Number | Types of Functions |
|---|---|
| 1. | RATIONAL ALBEGRAIC FUNCTIONS |
| | $\frac{P(y)}{Q(y)}$ where P(y) and Q(y) are polynomials in y. |
| | $\delta(y)$ and 1 are also included in this category. |
| 2. | IRRATIONAL ALBEGRAIC FUNCTIONS |
| | $[P(y)]^{\nu}$ where P(y) is a polynomial in y and $\nu$ is not an integer. |
| 3. | EXPONENTIAL FUNCTIONS |
| | $e^x$ $a^x$ |
| 4. | LOGARITHMIC FUNCTIONS |
| | $\log_b x$ where b is any base. |
| 5. | TRIGONOMETRIC FUNCTIONS |
| | sin x cos x tan x cosec x sec x cot x |
| 6. | INVERSE TRIGONOMETRIC FUNCTIONS |
| | $\sin^{-1} x$ $\cos^{-1} x$ $\tan^{-1} x$ $\mathrm{cosec}^{-1} x$ $\sec^{-1} x$ $\cot^{-1} x$ |

# FUNCTION INDEX

| Code Number | Types of Functions |
|---|---|

7. HYPERBOLIC FUNCTIONS

$\sinh x \quad \cosh x \quad \tanh x \quad \mathrm{cosech}\, x \quad \mathrm{sech}\, x \quad \coth x$

8. INVERSE HYPERBOLIC FUNCTIONS

$\sinh^{-1} x \quad \cosh^{-1} x \quad \tanh^{-1} x \quad \mathrm{cosech}^{-1} x \quad \mathrm{sech}^{-1} x \quad \cosh^{-1} x$

9. POLYNOMIALS

$A_n(x) \quad A_{n,\nu}(x) \quad A_n(a,x) \quad C_n^{\nu}(x) \quad He_n(x)$

$H_n(x) \quad L_n(x) \quad L_n^a(x) \quad O_o(x) \quad O_n(x)$

$\mathcal{Q}_n(x) \quad P_n(x) \quad P_n^{a,b}(x) \quad p_n(a;x) \quad Q_n(x)$

$S_n(x) \quad T_a^{(n)}(x) \quad T_n(x) \quad U_n(x)$

10. BESSEL FUNCTIONS

$J_\nu(x) \quad Y_\nu(x)$

11. HANKEL FUNCTIONS

$H_\nu^{(1)}(x) \quad H_\nu^{(2)}(x)$

12. MODIFIED BESSEL FUNCTIONS

$I_\nu(x)$

13. MODIFIED HANKEL FUNCTIONS

$K_\nu(x)$

14. ELLIPTIC INTEGRALS

$B(x) \quad D(x) \quad E(x) \quad F(x) \quad G(x) \quad K(x)$

15. THETA FUNCTIONS

$\theta_1(\nu|x) \quad \theta_2(\nu|x) \quad \theta_3(\nu|x) \quad \theta_4(\nu|x)$

$\hat{\theta}_1(\nu|x) \quad \hat{\theta}_2(\nu|x) \quad \hat{\theta}_3(\nu|x) \quad \hat{\theta}_4(\nu|x)$

## FUNCTION INDEX

| Code Number | Types of Functions |
|---|---|
| 16. | ERROR FUNCTIONS |
| | $\mathrm{Erf}(x)$ $\mathrm{Erfc}(x)$ |
| 17. | FRESNEL INTEGRALS |
| | $C(x)$ $S(x)$ |
| 18. | SINE AND COSINE INTEGRALS |
| | $\mathrm{Ci}(x)$ $\mathrm{ci}(x)$ $\mathrm{Si}(x)$ $\mathrm{si}(x)$ |
| 19. | EXPONENTIAL INTEGRALS |
| | $\mathrm{Ei}(-x)$ $\overline{\mathrm{Ei}}(x)$ |
| 20. | LOGARITHMIC INTEGRALS |
| | $\mathrm{li}(x)$ |
| 21. | GAMMA FUNCTIONS AND RELATED FUNCTIONS |
| | $B(x,a)$ $\Gamma(x)$ $\Gamma(a,x)$ $\gamma(a,x)$ $\binom{x}{a}$ |
| | $\psi(x)$ $\psi^{(n)}(x)$ |
| 22. | ZETA FUNCTIONS |
| | $\zeta(x)$ $\zeta(a,x)$ $\zeta'(x)$ |
| 23. | LEGENDRE FUNCTIONS |
| | $P_\nu^\mu(x)$ $Q_\nu^\mu(x)$ $P_\nu(x)$ $Q_\nu(x)$ |
| 24. | KELVIN FUNCTIONS AND RELATED FUNCTIONS |
| | $\mathrm{ber}_\nu(x)$ $\mathrm{ber}(x)$ $\mathrm{bei}_\nu(x)$ $\mathrm{bei}(x)$ |
| | $\mathrm{ker}_\nu(x)$ $\mathrm{ker}(x)$ $\mathrm{kei}_\nu(x)$ $\mathrm{kei}(x)$ |
| | $V_\nu^{(b)}(x)$ $W_\nu^{(b)}(x)$ $X_\nu^{(b)}(x)$ $Z_\nu^{(b)}(x)$ |

| Code Number | Types of Functions |
|---|---|

25. STRUVE FUNCTIONS

$H_\nu(x)$ $L_\nu(x)$

26. ANGER-WEBER FUNCTIONS

$J_\nu(x)$ $E_\nu(x)$

27. PARABOLIC CYLINDER FUNCTIONS

$D_\nu(x)$ $D_n(x)$

28. LOMMEL FUNCTIONS

$s_{\mu,\nu}(x)$ $S_{\mu,\nu}(x)$ $U_\nu(x,a)$ $V_\nu(x,a)$

29. BESSEL INTEGRAL FUNCTIONS

$Ii_\nu(x)$ $Ji_\nu(x)$ $Ki_\nu(x)$ $Yi_\nu(x)$

30. CONFLUENT HYPERGEOMETRIC FUNCTIONS

${}_1F_1\,[a;c;x]$ $k_\nu(x)$ $M_{\mu,\nu}(x)$ $W_{\mu,\nu}(x)$

$\Phi_1(a,b,c;x,z)$ $\Phi_2(a,b,c;x,z)$ $\Phi_2(b_1,\ldots,b_n;c;x_1,\ldots,x_n)$

$\Phi_3(b,c;x,z)$ $\Psi_1(a,b,c,d;x,z)$ $\Psi_2(a,c,d;x,z)$

$\Psi_2(a;b_1,\ldots,b_n;x_1,\ldots,x_n)$ $\Xi_1(a,b,c,d;x,z)$ $\Xi_2(a,b,c;x,z)$

31. HYPERGEOMETRIC FUNCTIONS

${}_2F_1\,[a,b;c;x]$ $F_1(a;b,c;d;x,z)$ $F_2(a;b,c;d,e;x,z)$

$F_3(a,b,c,d;e;x,z)$ $F_4(a,b;c,d;x,z)$

| Code Number | Types of Functions |
|---|---|

32. GENERALIZED HYPERGEOMETRIC FUNCTIONS

$$ {}_pF_q\left[\begin{matrix}(a)_p ; \\ (b)_q ;\end{matrix}\; x\right] \equiv {}_pF_q\left[\begin{matrix}a_1,\ldots,a_p ; \\ b_1,\ldots,b_p ;\end{matrix}\; x\right] $$

$$ E(m;a_i:n;b_j:x) \equiv E(a_1,\ldots,a_m:b_1,\ldots,b_n:x) $$

$$ S_n(a_1,a_2,a_3,a_4;x) $$

$$ F_A(a;b_1,\ldots,b_n;c_1,\ldots,c_n;x_1,\ldots,x_n) $$

33. WINDOW FUNCTIONS

All functions which are zero outside a finite time (t) interval.

34. JUMP FUNCTIONS

$$ \left[f(t) = f(n) \quad n < t < n+1 \quad n = 0,1,2,\ldots\right. $$

35. PIECEWISE DEFINED FUNCTIONS

Functions defined by different functional forms over different ranges of the variable (t) (excluding those which fall into category 33 or 34).

36. DELAYED FUNCTIONS

Functions which are zero for $-\infty < t < b$ where b is positive (excluding those which fall into category 33 or 34).

37. MISCELLANEOUS FUNCTIONS

| | | | | |
|---|---|---|---|---|
| $\mathrm{Cih}(x)$ | $I(a,b;x)$ | $J_n^m(x)$ | $Q^{\mu,\nu}(x)$ | $S(\nu,x)$ |
| $U^{m,n}(x)$ | $V_n(x)$ | $\mu(x,a)$ | $\nu(x)$ | $\nu(x,a)$ |

# FUNCTION DEFINITIONS

| | | |
|---|---|---|
| $A_n(x)$ | Appell polynomial | Defined by $e^{-x}(1+xu)^{\frac{1}{u}} = \sum_{n=o}^{\infty} (-1)^n A_n(x) u^n$ |
| $A_n(a,x)$ | Rainville polynomial | $= {}_2F_0[-n,n+a;\ ;x] \quad n=0,1,2,\ldots$ |
| $A_{n,\nu}(x)$ | Gegenbauer polynomial | Defined by $\frac{u^\nu}{x-u} = \sum_{n=o}^{\infty} A_{n,\nu}(x) J_{\nu+n}(u)$ |
| $B(x)$ | Elliptic integral | $= \int_o^{\frac{\pi}{2}} \frac{\cos^2\theta\, d\theta}{(1-x^2\sin^2\theta)^{\frac{1}{2}}}$ |
| $B(x,a)$ | Beta function | $= \frac{\Gamma(x)\Gamma(a)}{\Gamma(x+a)}$ |
| $bei(x)$ | Kelvin function | $bei_o(x)$ |
| $bei_\nu(x)$ | Kelvin function | $= \frac{1}{2i}[J_\nu(xe^{\frac{3\pi i}{4}}) - J_\nu(xe^{-\frac{3\pi i}{4}})]$ |
| $ber(x)$ | Kelvin function | $ber_o(x)$ |
| $ber_\nu(x)$ | Kelvin function | $= \frac{1}{2}[J_\nu(xe^{\frac{3\pi i}{4}}) + J_\nu(xe^{-\frac{3\pi i}{4}})]$ |

# FUNCTION DEFINITIONS

| | | | |
|---|---|---|---|
| $C(x)$ | Fresnel integral | $= \frac{1}{(2\pi)^{\frac{1}{2}}} \int_0^x \frac{\cos u \, du}{u^{\frac{1}{2}}}$ | |
| $C_n^{\nu}(x)$ | Gegenbauer polynomial | $= \frac{(-2)^n (\nu)_n}{n!(n+2\nu)_n} (1-x^2)^{\frac{1}{2}-\nu} \frac{d^n}{dx^n} (1-x^2)^{n+\nu-\frac{1}{2}}$ | $n = 0,1,2,\ldots$ |
| $Ci(x)$ | Cosine integral | $= -\int_x^{\infty} \frac{\cos u \, du}{u}$ | |
| $ci(x)$ | Cosine integral | $= \int_x^{\infty} \frac{\cos u \, du}{u}$ | |
| $Cih(x)$ | Hyperbolic cosine integral | $= \gamma + \log x + \int_0^x \frac{\cosh u - 1}{u} du$ | |
| $D(x)$ | Elliptic integral | $= \int_0^{\frac{\pi}{2}} \frac{\sin^2\theta \, d\theta}{(1-x^2 \sin^2\theta)^{\frac{1}{2}}}$ | |
| $D_n(x)$ | Parabolic cylinder function | $= (-1)^n e^{\frac{x^2}{4}} \frac{d^n}{dx^n} \left(e^{-\frac{x^2}{2}}\right)$ | $n = 0,1,2,\ldots$ |
| $D_{\nu}(x)$ | Parabolic cylinder function | $= \frac{2^{\frac{\nu}{2}+\frac{1}{4}}}{x^{\frac{1}{2}}} W_{\frac{\nu}{2}+\frac{1}{4},\frac{1}{4}}\left(\frac{x^2}{2}\right)$ | |
| $E(x)$ | Elliptic integral | $= \int_0^{\frac{\pi}{2}} (1-x^2 \sin^2\theta)^{\frac{1}{2}} d\theta$ | |
| $\mathbf{E}_{\nu}(x)$ | Weber function | $= \frac{1}{\pi} \int_0^{\pi} \sin(\nu\theta - x \sin\theta) \, d\theta$ | |

$E(m;a_i:n;b_j:x)$
$E(a_1,\ldots,a_m:b_1,\ldots,b_n:x)$ (MacRobert's E-function)

$$= \sum_{i=1}^{m} \frac{\prod_{j=1}^{m}{}^{*}\,\Gamma(a_j-a_i)}{\prod_{k=1}^{n}\Gamma(b_k-a_i)}\,\Gamma(a_i)\,x^{a_i}\;{}_{n+1}F_{m-1}\left[\begin{matrix}a_i, a_i-b_1+1,\ldots,a_i-b_n+1;\\ a_i-a_1+1,\ldots,*,\ldots,a_i-a_m+1;\end{matrix}(-1)^{m+n}x\right]$$

if $m \geqslant n+1$, with $|x| < 1$ if $m = n+1$;

$$= \frac{\prod_{i=1}^{m}\Gamma(a_i)}{\prod_{j=1}^{n}\Gamma(b_j)}\;{}_mF_n\left[\begin{matrix}a_1,\ldots,a_m;\\ b_1,\ldots,b_n;\end{matrix}\ -\frac{1}{x}\right] \qquad (x \neq 0)$$

if $m \leqslant n+1$, with $|x| > 1$ if $m = n+1$.

The asterisks denote that the term containing $a_i - a_i$ corresponding to $j = i$ is to be omitted.

| | | | |
|---|---|---|---|
| $Ei(-x)$ | Exponential integral | $= -\int_x^\infty e^{-u}\frac{du}{u}$ | $-\pi < \arg x < \pi$ |
| $\overline{Ei}(x)$ | Exponential integral | $= \frac{1}{2}[Ei(x+i0) + Ei(x-i0)]$ | $x > 0$ |
| $Erf(x)$ | Error function | $= \frac{2}{\pi^{\frac{1}{2}}}\int_0^x e^{-u^2}du$ | |
| $Erfc(x)$ | Complementary error function | $= \frac{2}{\pi^{\frac{1}{2}}}\int_x^\infty e^{-u^2}du$ | |
| $F(x,a)$ | Incomplete elliptic integral | $= \int_0^a \frac{d\theta}{(1-x^2\sin^2\theta)^{\frac{1}{2}}}$ | |
| ${}_1F_1[a;c;x]$ | Kummer function | $= \sum_{n=0}^{\infty}\frac{(a)_n}{(c)_n}\frac{x^n}{n!}$ | |

| | | |
|---|---|---|
| ${}_2F_1[a,b;c;x]$ | Gauss hypergeometric function | $=\sum_{n=0}^{\infty} \frac{(a)_n(b)_n}{(c)_n} \frac{x^n}{n!}$ |
| ${}_pF_q\left[\begin{matrix}(a)_p ; \\ (b)_q ;\end{matrix} x\right]$ <br> ${}_pF_q\left[\begin{matrix}a_1,\ldots,a_p ; \\ b_1,\ldots,b_q ;\end{matrix} x\right]$ | Hypergeometric function | $=\sum_{n=0}^{\infty} \frac{(a_1)_n\cdots(a_p)_n}{(b_1)_n\cdots(b_q)_n} \frac{x^n}{n!}$ |

$F_A(a;b_1,\ldots,b_n;c_1,\ldots,c_n;x_1,\ldots,x_n)$ Generalized hypergeometric function

$$=\sum \frac{(a)_{m_1+\cdots+m_n}(b_1)_{m_1}\cdots(b_n)_{m_n}}{(c_1)_{m_1}\cdots(c_n)_{m_n} m_1!\cdots m_n!} x_1^{m_1}\cdots x_n^{m_n}$$

where $\sum$ represents an n-fold summation in $m_1,\ldots,m_n$, each running from 0 to $\infty$.

| | | |
|---|---|---|
| $F_1(a;b,c;d;x,z)$ | Hypergeometric function of two variables | $=\sum_{m,n=0}^{\infty} \frac{(a)_{m+n}(b)_m(c)_n}{(d)_{m+n}m!n!} x^m z^n$ |
| $F_2(a;b,c;d,e;x,z)$ | Hypergeometric function of two variables | $=\sum_{m,n=0}^{\infty} \frac{(a)_{m+n}(b)_m(c)_n}{(d)_m(e)_n m!n!} x^m z^n$ |
| $F_3(a,b,c,d;e;x,z)$ | Hypergeometric function of two variables | $=\sum_{m,n=0}^{\infty} \frac{(a)_m(b)_n(c)_m(d)_n}{(e)_{m+n}m!n!} x^m z^n$ |
| $F_4(a,b;c,d;x,z)$ | Hypergeometric function of two variables | $=\sum_{m,n=0}^{\infty} \frac{(a)_{m+n}(b)_{m+n}}{(c)_m(d)_n m!n!} x^m z^n$ |
| $G(x)$ | Elliptic integral | $=\int_0^{\frac{\pi}{2}} \frac{\sin^2\theta\cos^2\theta}{(1-x^2\sin^2\theta)^{\frac{3}{2}}} d\theta$ |
| $H_n(x)$ | Hermite polynomial | $=(-1)^n e^{x^2} \frac{d^n}{dx^n} e^{-x^2} \quad n=0,1,2,\ldots$ |

$\mathbf{H}_\nu(x)$ Struve function $= \sum_{n=0}^{\infty} \frac{(-1)^n (\frac{x}{2})^{\nu+2n+1}}{\Gamma(n+\frac{3}{2})\Gamma(\nu+n+\frac{3}{2})}$

$H_\nu^{(1)}(x)$ Hankel function $= J_\nu(x) + i\, Y_\nu(x)$

$H_\nu^{(2)}(x)$ Hankel function $= J_\nu(x) - i\, Y_\nu(x)$

$He_n(x)$ Hermite polynomial $= (-1)^n e^{\frac{x^2}{2}} \frac{d^n}{dx^n} (e^{-\frac{x^2}{2}})$ $n = 0,1,2,\ldots$

$I(a,b;x)$ J. C. Jaeger, Proc. Roy. Soc. Edin. A, v.61, 1941-43. $= \int_0^\infty \frac{e^{-xu^2}}{[auJ_1(u)+bJ_0(u)]^2+[auY_1(u)+bY_0(u)]^2} \frac{du}{u}$

$I_\nu(x)$ Modified Bessel function $= \sum_{n=0}^{\infty} \frac{(\frac{x}{2})^{\nu+2n}}{n!\Gamma(\nu+n+1)}$

$Ii_\nu(x)$ Bessel integral function $= \int_x^\infty I_\nu(u) \frac{du}{u}$

$J_n^m(x)$ Bourget function $= \frac{1}{\pi}\int_0^\pi (2\cos\theta)^m \cos(n\theta - x\sin\theta)\, d\theta$

$J_\nu(x)$ Bessel function $= \sum_{n=0}^{\infty} \frac{(-1)^n (\frac{x}{2})^{\nu+2n}}{n!\Gamma(\nu+n+1)}$

$\mathbf{J}_\nu(x)$ Anger function $= \frac{1}{\pi}\int_0^\pi \cos(\nu\theta - x\sin\theta)\, d\theta$

$Ji_\nu(x)$ Bessel integral function $= \int_x^\infty J_\nu(u) \frac{du}{u}$

$K(x)$ Elliptic integral $= \int_0^{\frac{\pi}{2}} \frac{d\theta}{(1-x^2\sin^2\theta)^{\frac{1}{2}}}$

| | | |
|---|---|---|
| $K_\nu(x)$ | Modified Hankel function | $=\frac{\pi}{2}\frac{I_{-\nu}(x)-I_\nu(x)}{\sin(\nu\pi)}$ |
| $k_\nu(x)$ | Bateman function | $=\frac{W_{\frac{\nu}{2},\frac{1}{2}}(2x)}{\Gamma(\frac{\nu}{2}+1)}$ |
| $\mathrm{kei}(x)$ | Modified Kelvin function | $=\mathrm{kei}_o(x)$ |
| $\mathrm{kei}_\nu(x)$ | Modified Kelvin function | $=\frac{1}{2i}[K_\nu(xe^{\frac{\pi i}{4}})-K_\nu(xe^{-\frac{\pi i}{4}})]$ |
| $\mathrm{ker}(x)$ | Modified Kelvin function | $=\mathrm{ker}_o(x)$ |
| $\mathrm{ker}_\nu(x)$ | Modified Kelvin function | $=\frac{1}{2}[K_\nu(xe^{\frac{\pi i}{4}})+K_\nu(xe^{-\frac{\pi i}{4}})]$ |
| $\mathrm{Ki}_\nu(x)$ | Bessel integral function | $=\int_x^\infty K_\nu(u)\,\frac{du}{u}$ |
| $L_n(x)$ | Laguerre polynomial | $=L_n^o(x)$ |
| $L_n^a(x)$ | Laguerre polynomial | $=\frac{e^x}{x^a n!}\frac{d^n}{dx^n}(e^{-x}x^{n+a})$ |
| $\mathbf{L}_\nu(x)$ | Struve function | $=e^{-(\nu+1)\frac{\pi i}{2}}\,\mathbf{H}_\nu(xe^{\frac{\pi i}{2}})$ |
| $\mathrm{li}(x)$ | Logarithmic integral | $=\int_o^x\frac{du}{\log u}$ |
| $M_{\mu,\nu}(x)$ | Whittaker function | $=x^{\frac{1}{2}+\nu}\,e^{-\frac{x}{2}}\,{}_1F_1[\frac{1}{2}+\nu-\mu;2\nu+1;x]$ |

| | | |
|---|---|---|
| $O_0(x)$ | Neumann polynomial | $= \frac{1}{x}$ |
| $O_n(x)$ | Neumann polynomial | $= \frac{1}{4}\sum_{m=0}^{[\frac{n}{2}]} \frac{n(n-m-1)!}{m!(\frac{x}{2})^{n-2m+1}} \quad n=1,2,3,\ldots$ |
| $O_{-n}(x)$ | Neumann polynomial | $= (-1)^n O_n(x) \quad n=1,2,3,\ldots$ |
| $P_n(x)$ | Legendre polynomial | $= \frac{1}{2^n n!}\frac{d^n}{dx^n}(x^2-1)^n \quad n=0,1,2,\ldots$ |
| $P_n^{a,b}(x)$ | Jacobi polynomial | $= \frac{(-1)^n}{2^n n!(1-x)^a(1+x)^b}\frac{d^n}{dx^n}[(1-x)^{n+a}(1+x)^{n+b}] \quad n=0,1,2,\ldots$ |
| $p_n(a;x)$ | Charlier polynomial | $= n!a^{-n}L_n^{x-a}(a) \quad n=0,1,2,\ldots$ |
| $P_\nu(x)$ | Legendre function | $= P_\nu^0(x)$ |
| $P_\nu^\mu(x)$ | Legendre function | $= \frac{1}{\Gamma(1-\mu)}\left(\frac{x+1}{x-1}\right)^{\frac{\mu}{2}} {}_2F_1[-\nu,\nu+1;1-\mu;\frac{1-x}{2}]$ with x in the complex plane cut along the real axis from -1 to 1. |
| | | $= \frac{1}{\Gamma(1-\mu)}\left(\frac{1+x}{1-x}\right)^{\frac{\mu}{2}} {}_2F_1[-\nu,\nu+1;1-\mu;\frac{1-x}{2}] \quad -1<x<1$ |
| $Q_n(x)$ | Legendre polynomial | $= \frac{(x^2-1)^n}{2^n n!}\log\frac{x+1}{x-1} - \frac{1}{2}\log\frac{x+1}{x-1}P_n(x) \quad \lvert x\rvert > 1$ |
| $Q_\nu(x)$ | Legendre function | $= Q_\nu^0(x)$ |

| | | |
|---|---|---|
| $Q^{\mu}_{\nu}(x)$ | Legendre function | $= \dfrac{e^{\mu\pi i}\pi^{\frac{1}{2}}\Gamma(\mu+\nu+1)}{2^{\nu+1}\Gamma(\nu+\frac{3}{2})}\dfrac{(x^2-1)^{\frac{\mu}{2}}}{x^{\mu+\nu+1}}\,{}_2F_1\left[\dfrac{\mu+\nu+1}{2},\dfrac{\mu+\nu+2}{2};\nu+\dfrac{3}{2};\dfrac{1}{x^2}\right]$ with x in the complex plane cut along the real axis from -1 to 1. |
| | | $= \dfrac{1}{2}\left[e^{-\frac{3}{2}\mu\pi i}Q^{\mu}_{\nu}(x+i0) + e^{-\frac{1}{2}\mu\pi i}Q^{\mu}_{\nu}(x-i0)\right] \qquad -1 < x < 1$ |
| $Q^{\mu,\nu}(x)$ | Ultraspherical function | $= \pi^{\frac{1}{2}}2^{2\mu-1}\displaystyle\sum_{n=0}^{\infty}\frac{\Gamma(\nu+2\mu+2n)}{n!\Gamma(\nu+\mu+n+1)(2x)^{\nu+2\mu+2n}}$ |
| $S(x)$ | Fresnel integral | $= \dfrac{1}{(2\pi)^{\frac{1}{2}}}\displaystyle\int_0^x \sin u\,\frac{du}{u^{\frac{1}{2}}}$ |
| $S(\nu,x)$ | Schlömilch function | $= \displaystyle\int_0^{\infty} e^{-xu}\frac{du}{(1+u)^{\nu}}$ |
| $S_{\mu,\nu}(x)$ | Lommel function | $= s_{\mu,\nu}(x) + 2^{\mu-1}\Gamma\left(\dfrac{\mu-\nu+1}{2}\right)\Gamma\left(\dfrac{\mu+\nu+1}{2}\right)\left[\sin\left(\dfrac{\mu-\nu}{2}\pi\right)J_{\nu}(x) - \cos\left(\dfrac{\mu-\nu}{2}\pi\right)Y_{\nu}(x)\right]$ |
| $s_{\mu,\nu}(x)$ | Lommel function | $= \dfrac{x^{\mu+1}}{(\mu-\nu+1)(\mu+\nu+1)}\,{}_1F_2\left[\begin{matrix}1\,;\\ \frac{\mu-\nu+3}{2},\frac{\mu+\nu+3}{2};\end{matrix}\;-\dfrac{x^2}{4}\right]$ |
| $S_n(x)$ | Schläfli polynomial | $= \displaystyle\int_0^{\infty} e^{-xu}\left[[u+(u^2+1)^{\frac{1}{2}}]^n - [u-(u^2+1)^{\frac{1}{2}}]^n\right]\frac{du}{(u^2+1)^{\frac{1}{2}}}$ |

$S_n(a_1, a_2, a_3, a_4; x)$ Generalized hypergeometric function

$$= \sum_{r=1}^{n} \frac{\prod_{j=1}^{n} {}^{*}\Gamma(b_j - b_r)}{\prod_{j=n+1}^{4} \Gamma(1+b_r-b_j)} x^{1+2b_r} {}_0F_3\left[\begin{matrix} ; \\ 1+b_r-b_1, \ldots, *, \ldots, 1+b_r-b_4 ; \end{matrix} (-1)^n x^2\right]$$

where the asterisks denote that the term containing $b_r - b_n$ is to be omitted.
For n = 1 the product $\Pi$ in the numerator is to be replaced by 1.
For n = 4 the product $\Pi$ in the denominator is to be replaced by 1.

$Si(x)$ Sine integral $= \int_0^x \frac{\sin u}{u} du$

$si(x)$ Sine integral $= -\int_x^\infty \frac{\sin u}{u} du$

$T_n(x)$ Tchebichef polynomial $= \cos(n \cos^{-1} x)$ $n = 0, 1, 2, \ldots$

$T_a^{(n)}(x)$ Sonine polynomial $= \frac{(-1)^n}{\Gamma(a+n+1)} L_n^a(x)$ $n = 0, 1, 2, \ldots$

$U^{m,n}(x)$ Defined by $\frac{e^{-ax} I_0(bx)}{(1-h)(1-k)} = \sum_{m,n=0}^{\infty} h^m k^n U^{m,n}(x)$

where $a+b = \left(\frac{1+h}{1-h}\right)^2$, $a-b = \left(\frac{1+k}{1-k}\right)^2$

$U_n(x)$ Tchebichef polynomial $= \frac{\sin[(n+1)\cos^{-1} x]}{\sin(\cos^{-1} x)}$ $n = 0, 1, 2, \ldots$

$U_\nu(x,a)$ Lommel function of two variables $= \sum_{n=0}^{\infty} (-1)^n \left(\frac{x}{a}\right)^{\nu+2n} J_{\nu+2n}(a)$

$V_n(x)$ Defined by $\frac{1}{1-u} e^{-\frac{1+u}{1-u}x} = \sum_{n=0}^{\infty} (n+\tfrac{1}{2}) V_n(x) P_n(u)$

| | | |
|---|---|---|
| $V_{\nu}(x,a)$ | Lommel function of two variables | $= \cos\left(\frac{x}{2} + \frac{a^2}{2x} + \frac{\nu\pi}{2}\right) + U_{2-\nu}(x,a)$ |
| $V_{\nu}^{(b)}$ | Kelvin function | $=[\mathrm{ber}'_{\nu}(x)]^2 + [\mathrm{bei}'_{\nu}(x)]^2$ |
| $W_{\mu,\nu}(x)$ | Whittaker function | $= \frac{\Gamma(-2\nu)M_{\mu,\nu}(x)}{\Gamma(\frac{1}{2}-\nu-\mu)} + \frac{\Gamma(2\nu)M_{\mu,-\nu}(x)}{\Gamma(\frac{1}{2}+\nu-\mu)}$ |
| $W_{\nu}^{(b)}(x)$ | Kelvin function | $= \mathrm{ber}_{\nu}(x)\mathrm{bei}'_{\nu}(x) - \mathrm{bei}_{\nu}(x)\mathrm{ber}'_{\nu}(x)$ |
| $X_{\nu}^{(b)}(x)$ | Kelvin function | $= \mathrm{ber}^2\nu(x) + \mathrm{bei}^2_{\nu}(x)$ |
| $Y_{\nu}(x)$ | Bessel function | $= \mathrm{cosec}(\nu\pi)[J_{\nu}(x)\cos(\nu\pi) - J_{-\nu}(x)]$ |
| $Yi_{\nu}(x)$ | Bessel integral function | $= \int_x^{\infty} Y_{\nu}(u)\,\frac{du}{u}$ |
| $Z_{\nu}^{(b)}(x)$ | Kelvin function | $= 2\,[\mathrm{ber}_{\nu}(x)\mathrm{bei}'_{\nu}(x) + \mathrm{bei}_{\nu}(x)\mathrm{ber}'_{\nu}(x)]$ |
| $\Gamma(x)$ | Gamma function | $= \int_0^{\infty} e^{-u}\,u^{x-1}\,du$ |
| $\Gamma(a,x)$ | Incomplete gamma function | $= \int_x^{\infty} e^{-u}\,u^{a-1}\,du$ |
| $\gamma(a,x)$ | Incomplete gamma function | $= \int_0^{x} e^{-u}\,u^{a-1}\,du$ |
| $\delta(x)$ | Dirac delta function | |

# FUNCTION DEFINITIONS

| | | |
|---|---|---|
| $\zeta(x)$ | Zeta function | $= \sum_{n=1}^{\infty} \frac{1}{n^x}$ |
| $\zeta(a,x)$ | Zeta function | $= \sum_{n=0}^{\infty} \frac{1}{(n+x)^a}$ |
| $\theta_1(\nu\|x)$ | Theta function | $= \frac{1}{(\pi x)^{\frac{1}{2}}} \sum_{n=-\infty}^{\infty} (-1)^n e^{-\frac{1}{x}(\nu-\frac{1}{2}+n)^2}$ |
| $\theta_2(\nu\|x)$ | Theta function | $= \frac{1}{(\pi x)^{\frac{1}{2}}} \sum_{n=-\infty}^{\infty} (-1)^n e^{-\frac{1}{x}(\nu+n)^2}$ |
| $\theta_3(\nu\|x)$ | Theta function | $= \frac{1}{(\pi x)^{\frac{1}{2}}} \sum_{n=-\infty}^{\infty} e^{-\frac{1}{x}(\nu+n)^2}$ |
| $\theta_4(\nu\|x)$ | Theta function | $= \frac{1}{(\pi x)^{\frac{1}{2}}} \sum_{n=-\infty}^{\infty} e^{-\frac{1}{x}(\nu+\frac{1}{2}+n)^2}$ |
| $\hat{\theta}_1(\nu\|x)$ | Modified theta function | $= \frac{1}{(\pi x)^{\frac{1}{2}}} \left[ \sum_{n=0}^{\infty} (-1)^n e^{-\frac{1}{x}(\nu-\frac{1}{2}+n)^2} - \sum_{n=-1}^{-\infty} (-1)^n e^{-\frac{1}{x}(\nu-\frac{1}{2}+n)^2} \right]$ |
| $\hat{\theta}_2(\nu\|x)$ | Modified theta function | $= \frac{1}{(\pi x)^{\frac{1}{2}}} \left[ \sum_{n=0}^{\infty} (-1)^n e^{-\frac{1}{x}(\nu+n)^2} - \sum_{n=-1}^{-\infty} (-1)^n e^{-\frac{1}{x}(\nu+n)^2} \right]$ |
| $\hat{\theta}_3(\nu\|x)$ | Modified theta function | $= \frac{1}{(\pi x)^{\frac{1}{2}}} \left[ \sum_{n=0}^{\infty} e^{-\frac{1}{x}(\nu+n)^2} - \sum_{n=-1}^{-\infty} e^{-\frac{1}{x}(\nu+n)^2} \right]$ |
| $\hat{\theta}_4(\nu\|x)$ | Modified theta function | $= \frac{1}{(\pi x)^{\frac{1}{2}}} \left[ \sum_{n=0}^{\infty} e^{-\frac{1}{x}(\nu+\frac{1}{2}+n)^2} - \sum_{n=-1}^{-\infty} e^{-\frac{1}{x}(\nu+\frac{1}{2}+n)^2} \right]$ |

$\mu(x,a)$ $= \int_0^\infty \frac{x^u u^a}{\Gamma(u+1)} du$

$\nu(x)$ $= \int_0^\infty \frac{x^u}{\Gamma(u+1)} du$

$\nu(x,a)$ $= \int_0^\infty \frac{x^{u+a}}{\Gamma(u+a+1)} du$

$\Phi_1(a,b,c;x,z)$ Hypergeometric function of two variables $= \sum_{m,n=0}^\infty \frac{(a)_{m+n}(b)_m}{(c)_{m+n} m! n!} x^m z^n$

$\Phi_2(a,b,c;x,z)$ Hypergeometric function of two varaables $= \sum_{m,n=0}^\infty \frac{(a)_m(b)_n}{(c)_{m+n} m! n!} x^m z^n$

$\Phi_2(b_1,\ldots,b_n;c;x_1,\ldots,x_n)$ Generalized hypergeometric function $= \sum \frac{(b_1)_{m_1}\cdots(b_n)_{m_n}}{(c)_{m_1+\cdots+m_n} m_1!\cdots m_n!} x_1^{m_1}\cdots x_n^{m_n}$

where $\Sigma$ represents an n-fold summation in $m_1,\ldots,m_n$, each running from 0 to $\infty$.

$\Phi_3(b,c;x,z)$ Hypergeometric function of two variables $= \sum_{m,n=0}^\infty \frac{(b)_m}{(c)_{m+n} m! n!} x^m z^n$

$\psi(x)$ Logarithmic derivative of the gamma function $= \frac{\Gamma'(x)}{\Gamma(x)}$

$\Psi_1(a,b,c,d;x,z)$ Confluent hypergeometric function of two variables $= \sum_{m,n=0}^\infty \frac{(a)_{m+n}(b)_m}{(c)_m(d)_n m! n!} x^m z^n$

$\Psi_2(a,c,d;x,z)$ Confluent hypergeometric function of two variables $= \sum_{m,n=0}^\infty \frac{(a)_{m+n}}{(c)_m(d)_n m! n!} x^m z^n$

$\Psi_2(a;b_1,\ldots,b_n;x_1,\ldots,x_n)$ Confluent hypergeometric function of n variables $= \sum \frac{(a)_{m_1+\cdots+m_n}}{(b_1)_{m_1}\cdots(b_n)_{m_n} m_1!\cdots m_n!} x_1^{m_1}\cdots x_n^{m_n}$

where $\Sigma$ represents an n-fold summation in $m_1,\ldots,m_n$, each running from 0 to $\infty$.

$\Xi_1(a,b,c,d;x,z)$ Confluent hypergeometric function of two variables $= \sum_{m,n=0}^{\infty} \frac{(a)_m(b)_n(c)_m}{(d)_{m+n}\, m!n!} x^m z^n$

$\Xi_2(a,b,c;x,z)$ Confluent hypergeometric function of two variables $= \sum_{m,n=0}^{\infty} \frac{(a)_m(b)_m}{(c)_{m+n}\, m!n!} x^m z^n$

# MISCELLANEOUS NOTATIONS

| | |
|---|---|
| $a, b, c, d, x, y, \theta, \mu, \nu$ | Arbitrary constants; an exception is the use of x and y in the Function Index |
| $f^{(n)}$ | $n^{th}$ derivative |
| Im | Imaginary part of |
| log | Logarithm to base e |
| Re | Real part of |
| $\Delta_a^n$ | Difference operator<br>$\Delta_a g(s) = g(s+a) - g(s)$<br>$\Delta_a^2 g(s) = g(s+2a) - 2g(s+a) + g(s)$, etc. |
| $(a)_n$ | $a(a+1)(a+2)\ldots(a+n-1) \quad n = 1,2,3,\ldots \quad (a)_0 = 1$ |
| $\binom{x}{a}$ | Binomial coefficient $\dfrac{\Gamma(x)}{\Gamma(a)\Gamma(x-a)}$ |
| $[n]$ | The largest integer $\leq n$ |
| $\gamma$ | Euler constant $= e^C$ where $C = \lim_{n \to \infty} \left( \sum_{m=1}^{n} \frac{1}{m} - \log n \right) = .57722\ldots$ |
| $*$ | Convolution, defined by $f_1(t) * f_2(t) = \int_0^t f_1(u) f_2(t-u)\,du$ |
| $\Big\lceil\!\!\Big\rfloor$ | Jump function designation (See Function Definitions) |

Note: In certain entries with piecewise defined functions the symbol $n = 0,1,2,\ldots$(or $n = 1,2,3,\ldots$), which really forms part of the definition of $f(t)$, has for convenience been placed in the last column. In these cases the symbol is underlined, $\underline{n = 0,1,2,\ldots}$(or $\underline{n = 1,2,3,\ldots}$), to avoid confusion with the use of the same symbol as a parameter in the functional definitions.

# Part I

# DIRECT TRANSFORMS

# Section 1 • Operations

| | f(t) | g(s) | |
|---|---|---|---|
| Linearity, Scale Change & Translation | | | |
| 1. | $a\,f(t)$ | $a\,g(s)$ | |
| 2. | $f_1(t) \pm f_2(t)$ | $g_1(s) \pm g_2(s)$ | |
| 3. | $f(at)$ | $\frac{1}{a}\,g(\frac{s}{a})$ | $a > 0$ |
| 4. | $f(t+a)$ | $e^{as}[g(s) - \int_0^a e^{-su} f(u)\,du]$ | $a \geq 0$ |
| 5. | $0 \quad 0 < t < \frac{b}{a}$<br>$f(at-b) \quad t > \frac{b}{a}$ | $\frac{1}{a} e^{-\frac{bs}{a}} g(\frac{s}{a})$ | $a,b > 0$ |

| | $f(t)$ | $g(s)$ | |
|---|---|---|---|
| **Multiplication by a Function** | | | |
| 6. | $\frac{1}{t} f(t)$ | $\int_s^\infty g(u)\,du$ | |
| 7. | $\frac{1}{t^n} f(t)$ | $\int_s^\infty \cdots \int_s^\infty g(u)(du)^n$ | $n = 1,2,3,\ldots$ |
| 8. | $t^n f(t)$ | $(-1)^n \frac{d^n g(s)}{ds^n}$ | $n = 0,1,2,3,\ldots$ |
| 9. | $e^{\frac{b}{a}t} f(\frac{t}{a})$ | $a\,g(as-b)$ | $a > o$ |
| 10. | $(e^{-at}-1) f(t)$ | $g(s+a)-g(s)$ | |
| 11. | $(e^{-at}-1)^n f(t)$ | $\Delta_a^n\, g(s)$ | $n = 1,2,3,\ldots$ |
| 12. | $f(t)\ \sin at$ | $\frac{1}{2i}[g(s-ia)-g(s+ia)]$ | |
| 13. | $f(t)\ \cos at$ | $\frac{1}{2}[g(s-ia)+g(s+ia)]$ | |
| 14. | $f(t)\ \sinh at$ | $\frac{1}{2}[g(s-a)-g(s+a)]$ | |
| 15. | $f(t)\ \cosh at$ | $\frac{1}{2}[g(s-a)+g(s+a)]$ | |
| 16. | $f_1(t) f_2(t)$ | $\frac{1}{2\pi i} \int_{c-i\infty}^{c+i\infty} g_1(u)\, g_2(s-u)\,du$ where c is a line parallel to the imaginary axis and to the right of all the singularities of the integrand | |

| | f(t) | g(s) | |
|---|---|---|---|
| **Composite Functions** | | | |
| 17. | $f(\frac{1}{t})$ | $\frac{1}{s^{\frac{1}{2}}}\int_0^\infty u^{\frac{1}{2}} J_1(2s^{\frac{1}{2}}u^{\frac{1}{2}})g(u)\,du$ | |
| 18. | $\frac{1}{t}f(\frac{1}{t})$ | $\int_0^\infty J_0(2s^{\frac{1}{2}}u^{\frac{1}{2}})g(u)\,du$ | |
| 19. | $t^{\nu-1}f(\frac{1}{t})$ | $s^{-\frac{\nu}{2}}\int_0^\infty u^{\frac{\nu}{2}} J_\nu(2u^{\frac{1}{2}}s^{\frac{1}{2}})g(u)\,du$ | $\mathrm{Re}\,\nu > -1$ |
| 20. | $f(t^2)$ | $\frac{1}{\pi^{\frac{1}{2}}}\int_0^\infty e^{-\frac{s^2}{4u^2}} g(u^2)\,du$ <br> $= \frac{1}{2\pi^{\frac{1}{2}}}\int_0^\infty u^{-\frac{1}{2}} e^{-\frac{s^2}{4u}} g(u)\,du$ | |
| 21. | $t\,f(t^2)$ | $\frac{s}{4\pi^{\frac{1}{2}}}\int_0^\infty u^{-\frac{3}{2}} e^{-\frac{s^2}{4u}} g(u)\,du$ | |
| 22. | $t^n f(t^2)$ | $\frac{1}{2^{\frac{n}{2}}\pi^{\frac{1}{2}}}\int_0^\infty u^{n-2} e^{-\frac{s^2u^2}{4}} He_n(2^{-\frac{1}{2}}su)\,g(u^{-2})\,du$ | $n = 0,1,2,\ldots$ |
| 23. | $t^\nu f(t^2)$ | $\frac{1}{(2\pi)^{\frac{1}{2}}}\int_0^\infty u^{\nu-2} e^{-\frac{s^2u^2}{4}} D_\nu(su)\,g(\frac{1}{2u^2})\,du$ | |
| 24. | $f(ae^t - a)$ | $\frac{1}{a\Gamma(s+1)}\int_0^\infty e^{-u}u^s g(\frac{u}{a})\,du$ | $a > 0$ |
| 25. | $f(a \sinh t)$ | $\int_0^\infty J_s(au)\,g(u)\,du$ | $a > 0$ |
| 26. | $f[w(t)]$ | $\int_{w(0)}^{w(\infty)} r(s,u)\,g(u)\,du$ <br> where $r(a,t)$ is the inverse transform of $h'(s)e^{-ah(s)}$ and $h(s)$ is the reciprocal function of $w(s)$ | |

| | $f(t)$ | $g(s)$ | |
|---|---|---|---|

Differentiation

| | | | |
|---|---|---|---|
| 27. | $\frac{df(t)}{dt}$ | $sg(s)-f(o)$ | |
| 28. | $\frac{d^2f(t)}{dt^2}$ | $s^2g(s)-sf(o)-f'(o)$ | |
| 29. | $f^{(n)}(t)$ | $s^n g(s)-s^{n-1}f(o)-s^{n-2}f'(o)-\ldots -f^{(n-1)}(o)$ | $n=1,2,\ldots$ |
| 30. | $\left(t\frac{d}{dt}\right)^n f(t)$ | $\left(-\frac{d}{ds}s\right)^n g(s)$ | $n=0,1,2,\ldots$ |
| 31. | $\left(\frac{d}{dt}t\right)^n f(t)$ | $\left(-s\frac{d}{ds}\right)^n g(s)$ | $n=0,1,2,\ldots$ |
| 32. | $\left(\frac{1}{t}\frac{d}{dt}\right)^n f(t)$ if $\left(\frac{1}{t}\frac{d}{dt}\right)^k f(t)=0$ for $t=0$ $k=0,1,\ldots,n-1$ | $\int_s^\infty u\int_s^\infty \ldots u\int_s^\infty u\,g(u)(du)^n$ | |
| 33. | $t^m f^{(n)}(t)$ | $\left(-\frac{d}{ds}\right)^m[s^n g(s)]$ | $m\geqslant n$ $m,n=0,1,2,\ldots$ |
| 34. | $t^m f^{(n)}(t)$ | $\left(-\frac{d}{ds}\right)^m[s^n g(s)]+(-1)^{m-1}\left[\frac{(n-1)!}{(n-m-1)!}s^{n-m-1}f(o)+\frac{(n-2)!}{(n-m-2)!}s^{n-m-2}f'(o)+\ldots+m!f^{(n-m-1)}(o)\right]$ | $m<n$ $m,n=0,1,2,\ldots$ |
| 35. | $\frac{d^n}{dt^n}[t^m f(t)]$ | $(-1)^m s^n g^{(m)}(s)$ | $m\geqslant n$ $m,n=0,1,2,\ldots$ |
| 36. | $\frac{d^n}{dt^n}[t^m f(t)]$ | $(-1)^m s^n g^{(m)}(s)-m!s^{n-m-1}f(o)-\frac{(m+1)!}{1!}s^{n-m-2}f'(o)-\ldots-\frac{(n-1)!}{(n-m-1)!}f^{(n-m-1)}(o)$ | $m<n$ $m,n=0,1,2,\ldots$ |

| | $f(t)$ | $g(s)$ | |
|---|---|---|---|
| 37. | $\left(e^{t}\frac{d}{dt}\right)^{n} f(t)$ if $f^{(k)}(o)=0$ for $k=0,1,\ldots,n-1$ | $(s-1)\ldots(s-n)\,g(s-n)$ | $n=1,2,3,\ldots$ |
| 38. | $\frac{\partial}{\partial a} f(t,a)$ | $\frac{\partial}{\partial a} g(s,a)$ | |

Integration

| | | | |
|---|---|---|---|
| 39. | $\int_{a_0}^{a} f(t,u)\,du$ | $\int_{a_0}^{a} g(s,v)\,dv$ | |
| 40. | $\int_{0}^{t} f_1(u) f_2(t-u)\,du$ $= f_1(t) * f_2(t)$ | $g_1(s) g_2(s)$ | |
| 41. | $\int_{0}^{t}\cdots\int_{0}^{t} f(u)\,(du)^{n}$ | $s^{-n} g(s)$ | $n=1,2,3,\ldots$ |
| 42. | $\int_{a}^{t} f(u)\,du$ | $s^{-1} g(s) + s^{-1}\int_{a}^{0} f(u)\,du$ | |
| 43. | $\int_{t}^{\infty} u^{-1} f(u)\,du$ | $s^{-1}\int_{0}^{s} g(v)\,dv$ | |
| 44. | $\int_{0}^{t} u^{-1} f(u)\,du$ | $s^{-1}\int_{s}^{\infty} g(v)\,dv$ | |
| 45. | $\int_{0}^{\infty} \frac{t^{au-1}}{\Gamma(au)} f(u)\,du$ | $g(\log s^{a})$ | |
| 46. | $\int_{0}^{\infty} \frac{t^{u}}{\Gamma(u+1)} f(u)\,du$ | $s^{-1} g(\log s)$ | |
| 47. | $t^{-\frac{1}{2}}\int_{0}^{\infty} e^{-\frac{u^2}{4t}} f(u)\,du$ | $\left(\frac{\pi}{s}\right)^{\frac{1}{2}} g(s^{\frac{1}{2}})$ | |
| 48. | $t^{-\frac{3}{2}}\int_{0}^{\infty} u\, e^{-\frac{u^2}{4t}} f(u)\,du$ | $2\pi^{\frac{1}{2}} g(s^{\frac{1}{2}})$ | |

| | f(t) | g(s) | |
|---|---|---|---|
| 49. | $\int_0^t u(t-u)^{-\frac{3}{2}} e^{-\frac{u^2}{4(t-u)}} f(u)\,du$ | $2\pi^{\frac{1}{2}} g(s+s^{\frac{1}{2}})$ | |
| 50. | $\int_0^t (t-u)^{-\frac{1}{2}} e^{-\frac{u^2}{4(t-u)}} f(u)\,du$ | $(\frac{\pi}{s})^{\frac{1}{2}} g(s+s^{\frac{1}{2}})$ | |
| 51. | $\int_0^\infty u^{-\frac{1}{2}} \sin(2t^{\frac{1}{2}}u^{\frac{1}{2}}) f(u)\,du$ | $\frac{\pi^{\frac{1}{2}}}{s^{\frac{3}{2}}} g(\frac{1}{s})$ | |
| 52. | $t^{-\frac{1}{2}} \int_0^\infty \cos(2t^{\frac{1}{2}}u^{\frac{1}{2}}) f(u)\,du$ | $(\frac{\pi}{s})^{\frac{1}{2}} g(\frac{1}{s})$ | |
| 53. | $\int_0^\infty u^{-\frac{1}{2}} \sinh(2t^{\frac{1}{2}}u^{\frac{1}{2}}) f(u)\,du$ | $\frac{\pi^{\frac{1}{2}}}{s^{\frac{3}{2}}} g(-\frac{1}{s})$ | |
| 54. | $t^{-\frac{1}{2}} \int_0^\infty \cosh(2t^{\frac{1}{2}}u^{\frac{1}{2}}) f(u)\,du$ | $(\frac{\pi}{s})^{\frac{1}{2}} g(-\frac{1}{s})$ | |
| 55. | $\int_0^t J_0[a(t^2-u^2)^{\frac{1}{2}}] f(u)\,du$ | $\frac{g[(s^2+a^2)^{\frac{1}{2}}]}{(s^2+a^2)^{\frac{1}{2}}}$ | |
| 56. | $\int_0^t J_0[2(t-u)^{\frac{1}{2}}u^{\frac{1}{2}}] f(u)\,du$ | $\frac{1}{s} g(s+\frac{1}{s})$ | |
| 57. | $\int_0^\infty J_0(2t^{\frac{1}{2}}u^{\frac{1}{2}}) f(u)\,du$ | $\frac{1}{s} g(\frac{1}{s})$ | |
| 58. | $f(t)-a\int_0^t f[(t^2-u^2)^{\frac{1}{2}}] J_1(au)\,du$ | $g[(s^2+a^2)^{\frac{1}{2}}]$ | |
| 59. | $f(t)-at\int_0^t (t^2-u^2)^{-\frac{1}{2}} J_1[a(t^2-u^2)^{\frac{1}{2}}] f(u)\,du$ | $\frac{s}{(s^2+a^2)^{\frac{1}{2}}} g[(s^2+a^2)^{\frac{1}{2}}]$ | |
| 60. | $t^{-\frac{1}{2}} \int_0^\infty e^{-bu}(t+2u)^{-\frac{1}{2}} J_1[a(t^2+2tu)^{\frac{1}{2}}]\, u f(u)\,du$ | $\frac{1}{a} g(b) - \frac{1}{a} g[b+(s^2+a^2)^{\frac{1}{2}} - s]$ | |
| 61. | $t^{\nu} \int_0^\infty J_{2\nu}(2t^{\frac{1}{2}}u^{\frac{1}{2}}) u^{-\nu} f(u)\,du$ | $s^{-2\nu-1} g(\frac{1}{s})$ | $\mathrm{Re}\,\nu > -\frac{1}{2}$ |
| 62. | $\int_0^t \left(\frac{t-u}{au}\right)^{\nu} J_{2\nu}[2(atu-au^2)^{\frac{1}{2}}] f(u)\,du$ | $s^{-2\nu-1} g(s+\frac{a}{s})$ | |

| | $f(t)$ | $g(s)$ | |
|---|---|---|---|
| 63. | $\int_0^t \left(\frac{t-u}{t+u}\right)^{\nu} J_{2\nu}[a(t^2-u^2)^{\frac{1}{2}}]\, f(u)\,du$ | $\frac{a^{2\nu}\, g[(s^2+a^2)^{\frac{1}{2}}]}{(s^2+a^2)^{\frac{1}{2}}[(s^2+a^2)^{\frac{1}{2}}+s]^{2\nu}}$ | $\mathrm{Re}\,\nu > -\frac{1}{2}$ |
| 64. | $t^{\nu}\int_0^\infty (t+2u)^{-\nu} J_{2\nu}[a(t^2+2tu)^{\frac{1}{2}}]\, f(u)\,du$ | $\frac{[(s^2+a^2)^{\frac{1}{2}}-s]^{2\nu}\, g[(s^2+a^2)^{\frac{1}{2}}-s]}{a^{2\nu}(s^2+a^2)^{\frac{1}{2}}}$ | $\mathrm{Re}\,\nu > -\frac{1}{2}$ |
| 65. | $t^{\nu}\int_0^\infty (1-2u)^{-\nu} J_{2\nu}[a(t^2-2tu)^{\frac{1}{2}}]\, f(u)\,du$ | $\frac{[(s^2+a^2)^{\frac{1}{2}}-s]^{2\nu}\, g[s-(s^2+a^2)^{\frac{1}{2}}]}{a^{2\nu}(s^2+a^2)^{\frac{1}{2}}}$ | $\mathrm{Re}\,\nu > -\frac{1}{2}$ |
| 66. | $\int_0^t \left(\frac{t-u}{t+u}\right)^{\nu} I_{2\nu}[a(t^2-u^2)^{\frac{1}{2}}]\, f(u)\,du$ | $\frac{a^{2\nu}\, g[(s^2-a^2)^{\frac{1}{2}}]}{(s^2-a^2)^{\frac{1}{2}}[s+(s^2-a^2)^{\frac{1}{2}}]^{2\nu}}$ | $\mathrm{Re}\,\nu > -\frac{1}{2}$ |
| 67. | $\int_0^t I_0[a(t^2-u^2)^{\frac{1}{2}}]\, f(u)\,du$ | $\frac{g[(s^2-a^2)^{\frac{1}{2}}]}{(s^2-a^2)^{\frac{1}{2}}}$ | |
| 68. | $f(t)+a\int_0^t f[(t^2-u^2)^{\frac{1}{2}}]\, I_1(u)\,du$ | $g[(s^2-a^2)^{\frac{1}{2}}]$ | |
| 69. | $f(t)+at\int_0^t (t^2-u^2)^{-\frac{1}{2}} I_1[a(t^2-u^2)^{\frac{1}{2}}]\, f(u)\,du$ | $\frac{s\, g[(s^2-a^2)^{\frac{1}{2}}]}{(s^2-a^2)^{\frac{1}{2}}}$ | |
| 70. | $t^{-\frac{1}{2}}\int_0^\infty e^{-bu}(t+2u)^{-\frac{1}{2}} I_1[at^{\frac{1}{2}}(t+2u)^{\frac{1}{2}}]\, u\, f(u)\,du$ | $\frac{1}{a}\, g[b+(s^2-a^2)^{\frac{1}{2}}-s] - \frac{1}{a}\, g(b)$ | |
| 71. | $t^{\nu}\int_0^\infty (t+2u)^{-\nu} I_{2\nu}[a(t^2+2tu)^{\frac{1}{2}}]\, f(u)\,du$ | $\frac{[s-(s^2-a^2)^{\frac{1}{2}}]^{2\nu}\, g[(s^2-a^2)^{\frac{1}{2}}-s]}{a^{2\nu}(s^2-a^2)^{\frac{1}{2}}}$ | $\mathrm{Re}\,\nu > -\frac{1}{2}$ |
| 72. | $t^{\nu}\int_0^\infty (t-2u)^{-\nu} I_{2\nu}[a(t^2-2tu)^{\frac{1}{2}}]\, f(u)\,du$ | $\frac{[s-(s^2-a^2)^{\frac{1}{2}}]^{2\nu}\, g[s-(s^2-a^2)^{\frac{1}{2}}]}{a^{2\nu}(s^2-a^2)^{\frac{1}{2}}}$ | $\mathrm{Re}\,\nu > -\frac{1}{2}$ |
| 73. | $t^{-\frac{n+1}{2}}\int_0^\infty e^{-\frac{u^2}{4t}} He_n\left[\frac{u}{(2t)^{\frac{1}{2}}}\right] f(u)\,du$ | $2^{\frac{n}{2}}\pi^{\frac{1}{2}}s^{\frac{n-1}{2}}\, g(s^{\frac{1}{2}})$ | $n = 0, 1, 2, \ldots$ |
| 74. | $t^{-\nu-1}\int_0^\infty e^{-\frac{u^2}{8t}} D_{2\nu+1}\left(\frac{u}{2^{\frac{1}{2}}t^{\frac{1}{2}}}\right) f(u)\,du$ | $2^{\nu+\frac{1}{2}}\pi^{\frac{1}{2}}s^{\nu}\, g(s^{\frac{1}{2}})$ | |

| | f(t) | g(s) | |
|---|---|---|---|
| 75. | $\int_0^\infty {}_0F_n\left[\frac{1}{n},\frac{2}{n},\ldots,\frac{n-1}{n},1;\ ;\ \frac{-ut^n}{n^n}\right] f(u)\,du$ | $\frac{1}{s}\,g\left(\frac{1}{s^n}\right)$ | $n=1,2,3,\ldots$ |
| 76. | $\int_0^\infty r(u,t)f(u)\,du$ | $g[w(s)]$ | |

where the direct transform of $r(u,t)$ is $e^{-uw(s)}$

Miscellaneous

| | f(t) | g(s) | |
|---|---|---|---|
| 77. | $f(t+a)=f(t)$ | $(1-e^{-as})^{-1}\int_0^a e^{-su}f(u)\,du$ | $a>0$ |
| 78. | $f(t+a)=-f(t)$ | $(1+e^{-as})^{-1}\int_0^a e^{-su}f(u)\,du$ | $a>0$ |
| 79. | $\rfloor f(t+1)$ | $e^{s}\left[g(s)-f(0)\,\frac{1-e^{-s}}{s}\right]$ | |
| 80. | $\lim_{a\to a_0} f(t,a)$ | $\lim_{a\to a_0} g(s,a)$ | |
| 81. | $\lim_{t\to 0} f(t)$ | $\lim_{s\to\infty} s\,g(s)$ | |
| 82. | $\lim_{t\to\infty} f(t)$ | $\lim_{s\to 0} s\,g(s)$ if $s\,g(s)$ is analytic on the imaginary axis and in the right half-plane | |
| 83. | $\sum_{n=1}^{\infty}\frac{1}{n}\,f\left(\frac{t}{n}\right)$ | $\int_0^\infty (e^{su}-1)^{-1}f(u)\,du$ | |

# Section 2 • Direct Transform Pairs

| | | $f(t)$ | $g(s)$ | |
|---|---|---|---|---|
| 1 | 1 | $\delta(t-a)$ | $e^{-as}$ | $a \geq 0$<br>$\mathrm{Re}\, s > -\infty$ |
| | 2 | $1$ | $\frac{1}{s}$ | $\mathrm{Re}\, s > 0$ |
| | 3 | $t^n$ | $n!\, s^{-n-1}$ | $n = 0,1,2,\ldots$<br>$\mathrm{Re}\, s > 0$ |
| | 4 | $\frac{1}{t+a}$ | $-e^{as}\,\mathrm{Ei}(-as)$ | $\lvert \arg a \rvert < \pi$<br>$\mathrm{Re}\, s > 0$ |
| | 5 | $\frac{1}{t-a}$ | $-e^{-as}\,\overline{\mathrm{Ei}}(as)$<br>Cauchy Principal Value of integral | $a \geq 0$<br>$\mathrm{Re}\, s > 0$ |
| | 6 | $\frac{1}{(t+a)^2}$ | $se^{as}\,\mathrm{Ei}(-as) + \frac{1}{a}$ | $a \neq 0$<br>$\lvert \arg a \rvert < \pi$<br>$\mathrm{Re}\, s \geq 0$ |

| | | f(t) | g(s) | |
|---|---|---|---|---|
| 1 (Contd.) | 7 | $\frac{1}{(t+a)^n}$ | $\sum_{m=1}^{n-1}\frac{(m-1)!\,(-s)^{n-m-1}}{(n-1)!\quad a^m} - \frac{(-s)^{n-1}}{(n-1)!}e^{as}\,\mathrm{Ei}(-as)$ | $\lvert \arg a \rvert < \pi$<br>$n = 2,3,4,\ldots$<br>Re $s \geqslant 0$ |
| | 8 | $\frac{t^n}{t+a}$ | $(-1)^{n-1}a^n e^{as}\,\mathrm{Ei}(-as) + \sum_{m=1}^{n}(m-1)!(-a)^{n-m}s^{-m}$ | $\lvert \arg a \rvert < \pi$<br>$n = 1,2,3,\ldots$<br>Re $s > 0$ |
| | 9 | $\frac{1}{t^2+a^2}$ | $-a^{-1}[\mathrm{ci}(as)\sin(as)+\mathrm{si}(as)\cos(as)]$ | Re $a > 0$<br>Re $s > 0$ |
| | 10 | $\frac{t}{t^2+a^2}$ | $\mathrm{ci}(as)\cos(as)-\mathrm{si}(as)\sin(as)$ | Re $a > 0$<br>Re $s > 0$ |
| | 11 | $\frac{bt+c}{t^2+a^2}$ | $[b\cos(as) - \frac{c}{a}\sin(as)]\mathrm{ci}(as) - [b\sin(as) + \frac{c}{a}\cos(as)]\mathrm{si}(as)$ | $\lvert \arg(\pm ia) \rvert <$<br>Re $s > 0$ |
| | 12 | $\frac{bt+c}{t^2-a^2}$ | $-\frac{1}{2}(b-\frac{c}{a})e^{-as}\,\mathrm{Ei}(-as) - \frac{1}{2}(b+\frac{c}{a})e^{-as}\,\overline{\mathrm{Ei}}(as)$<br>Cauchy Principal Value of integral | $a > 0$<br>Re $s > 0$ |
| | 13 | $\frac{bt+c}{t^2-a^2}$ | $-\frac{1}{2}(b-\frac{c}{a})e^{as}\,\mathrm{Ei}(-as) - \frac{1}{2}(b+\frac{c}{a})e^{-as}\,\mathrm{Ei}(as)$ | $\lvert \arg(\pm a) \rvert <$<br>Re $s > 0$ |

Functions of t only

| | | | | |
|---|---|---|---|---|
| 2 | 1 | $t^{\frac{1}{2}}$ | $\frac{\pi^{\frac{1}{2}}}{2s^{\frac{3}{2}}}$ | Re $s > 0$ |
| | 2 | $\frac{1}{t^{\frac{1}{2}}}$ | $(\frac{\pi}{s})^{\frac{1}{2}}$ | Re $s > 0$ |
| | 3 | $t^{n-\frac{1}{2}}$ | $\pi^{\frac{1}{2}}(\frac{1}{2})(\frac{3}{2})\ldots(\frac{2n-1}{2})s^{-\frac{2n+1}{2}}$ | $n = 1,2,3,\ldots$<br>Re $s > 0$ |
| | 4 | $t^{\nu}$ | $\frac{\Gamma(\nu+1)}{s^{\nu+1}}$ | Re $\nu > -1$<br>Re $s > 0$ |

2 (Contd.)

Functions of t, (t±a)

| | $f(t)$ | $g(s)$ | |
|---|---|---|---|
| 5 | $\dfrac{1}{(t+a)^{\frac{1}{2}}}$ | $\left(\dfrac{\pi}{s}\right)^{\frac{1}{2}} e^{as}\,\mathrm{Erfc}\,(a^{\frac{1}{2}}s^{\frac{1}{2}})$ | $\lvert\arg a\rvert < \pi$<br>$\mathrm{Re}\ s > 0$ |
| 6 | $\dfrac{1}{(t+a)^{\frac{3}{2}}}$ | $2a^{-\frac{1}{2}} - 2\pi^{\frac{1}{2}}s^{\frac{1}{2}}e^{as}\,\mathrm{Erfc}(a^{\frac{1}{2}}s^{\frac{1}{2}})$ | $\lvert\arg a\rvert < \pi$<br>$\mathrm{Re}\ s \geq 0$ |
| 7 | $(t+a)^{\nu}$ | $\dfrac{e^{as}\Gamma(\nu+1,as)}{s^{\nu+1}}$<br>$= a^{\nu+1}S(-\nu,as)$ | $\lvert\arg a\rvert < \pi$<br>$\mathrm{Re}\ s > 0$ |
| 8 | $\dfrac{t^{\nu-1}}{(t+a)^{\nu+\frac{1}{2}}}$ | $2^{\nu}\,\Gamma(\nu)a^{-\frac{1}{2}}e^{\frac{as}{2}}D_{-2\nu}(2^{\frac{1}{2}}a^{\frac{1}{2}}s^{\frac{1}{2}})$ | $\mathrm{Re}\,\nu > 0$<br>$\lvert\arg a\rvert < \pi$<br>$\mathrm{Re}\ s \geq 0$ |
| 9 | $\dfrac{t^{\nu-1}}{(t+a)^{\nu-\frac{1}{2}}}$ | $2^{\nu-\frac{1}{2}}\Gamma(\nu)s^{-\frac{1}{2}}e^{\frac{as}{2}}D_{1-2\nu}(2^{\frac{1}{2}}a^{\frac{1}{2}}s^{\frac{1}{2}})$ | $\mathrm{Re}\,\nu > 0$<br>$\lvert\arg a\rvert < \pi$<br>$\mathrm{Re}\ s \geq 0$ |
| 10 | $t^{\mu}(a+t)^{\nu}$ | $\Gamma(\mu+1)a^{\frac{\mu+\nu}{2}}s^{-\frac{\mu+\nu+2}{2}}e^{\frac{as}{2}}W_{\frac{\nu-\mu}{2},\frac{\mu+\nu+1}{2}}(as)$ | $\lvert\arg a\rvert < \pi$<br>$\mathrm{Re}\ \mu > -1$<br>$\mathrm{Re}\ s > 0$ |

Functions of $(t^2+a^2)$

| | $f(t)$ | $g(s)$ | |
|---|---|---|---|
| 11 | $(t^2+a^2)^{\frac{1}{2}}-a$ | $\dfrac{\pi^{\frac{1}{2}}e^{a^2s}}{2s^{\frac{3}{2}}}\,\mathrm{erfc}(as^{\frac{1}{2}})$ | $\mathrm{Re}\ s > 0$ |
| 12 | $\dfrac{1}{(1+t^2)^{\frac{1}{2}}}$ | $S_{0,0}(s)$<br>$= -\frac{\pi}{2}[\mathbf{E}_0(s) + Y_0(s)]$<br>$= \frac{\pi}{2}[\mathbf{H}_0(s) - Y_0(s)]$ | $\mathrm{Re}\ s > 0$ |
| 13 | $(t^2+a^2)^{\nu}$ | $2^{\nu-\frac{1}{2}}\pi^{\frac{1}{2}}a^{\nu+\frac{1}{2}}\Gamma(\nu+1)s^{-\nu-\frac{1}{2}}[\mathbf{H}_{\nu+\frac{1}{2}}(as) - Y_{\nu+\frac{1}{2}}(as)]$ | $\mathrm{Re}\ a > 0$<br>$-2 < \mathrm{Re}\,\nu < 0$<br>$\mathrm{Re}\ s > 0$ |

| | f(t) | g(s) | |
|---|---|---|---|

2 (Contd.)

Functions of $(t^2 \pm at)$ only

| | | | |
|---|---|---|---|
| 14 | $(t^2+at)^{\frac{1}{2}}$ | $\frac{a}{2s} e^{\frac{as}{2}} K_1(\frac{as}{2})$ | $\lvert \arg a \rvert < \pi$<br>$\mathrm{Re}\, s > 0$ |
| 15 | $\frac{1}{(t^2+at)^{\frac{1}{2}}}$ | $e^{\frac{as}{2}} K_0(\frac{as}{2})$ | $\lvert \arg a \rvert < \pi$<br>$\mathrm{Re}\, s > 0$ |
| 16 | $(t^2+at)^{\nu}$ | $\pi^{-\frac{1}{2}}\Gamma(\nu+1)(\frac{a}{s})^{\nu+\frac{1}{2}} e^{\frac{as}{2}} K_{\nu+\frac{1}{2}}(\frac{as}{2})$ | $\lvert \arg a \rvert < \pi$<br>$\mathrm{Re}\, \nu > -1$<br>$\mathrm{Re}\, s > 0$ |
| 17 | $(t^2+it)^{\nu}$ | $-\frac{i\pi^{\frac{1}{2}}}{2}\Gamma(\nu+1)s^{-\nu-\frac{1}{2}} e^{\frac{is}{2}} H^{(2)}_{\nu+\frac{1}{2}}(\frac{s}{2})$ | $\mathrm{Re}\, \nu > -1$<br>$\mathrm{Re}\, s > 0$ |
| 18 | $(t^2+ait)^{\nu}$ | $-\frac{i}{2}\pi^{\frac{1}{2}} a^{\nu+\frac{1}{2}}\Gamma(\nu+1)s^{-\nu-\frac{1}{2}} e^{\frac{ias}{2}} H^{(2)}_{\nu+\frac{1}{2}}(\frac{as}{2})$ | $\mathrm{Re}\, \nu > -1$<br>$-\frac{3\pi}{2} < \arg a < \frac{\pi}{2}$<br>$\mathrm{Re}\, s > 0$ |
| 19 | $(t^2-it)^{\nu}$ | $\frac{i\pi^{\frac{1}{2}}}{2}\Gamma(\nu+1)s^{-\nu-\frac{1}{2}} e^{-\frac{is}{2}} H^{(1)}_{\nu+\frac{1}{2}}(\frac{s}{2})$ | $\mathrm{Re}\, \nu > -1$<br>$\mathrm{Re}\, s > 0$ |
| 20 | $(t^2-ait)^{\nu}$ | $\frac{i}{2}\pi^{\frac{1}{2}} a^{\nu+\frac{1}{2}}\Gamma(\nu+1)s^{-\nu-\frac{1}{2}} e^{-\frac{ias}{2}} H^{(1)}_{\nu+\frac{1}{2}}(\frac{as}{2})$ | $\mathrm{Re}\, \nu > -1$<br>$-\frac{\pi}{2} < \arg a < \frac{3\pi}{2}$<br>$\mathrm{Re}\, s > 0$ |

Functions of $[(t^2+a^2)^{\frac{1}{2}} \pm t]$

| | | | |
|---|---|---|---|
| 21 | $[(t^2+1)^{\frac{1}{2}}+t]^{\nu}$ | $s^{-1}S_{1,\nu}(s)+\nu s^{-1}S_{0,\nu}(s)$ | $\mathrm{Re}\, s > 0$ |
| 22 | $[(t^2+1)^{\frac{1}{2}}-t]^{\nu}$ | $s^{-1}S_{1,\nu}(s)-\nu s^{-1}S_{0,\nu}(s)$ | $\mathrm{Re}\, s > 0$ |
| 23 | $[(t^2+1)^{\frac{1}{2}}+t]^{\nu}+[(t^2+1)^{\frac{1}{2}}-t]^{\nu}$ | $\frac{2}{s}S_{1,\nu}(s)$ | $\mathrm{Re}\, s > 0$ |

| | | $f(t)$ | $g(s)$ | |
|---|---|---|---|---|
| 2 (Contd.) | 24 | $[(t^2+1)^{\frac{1}{2}}+t]^{\nu}-[(t^2+1)^{\frac{1}{2}}-t]^{\nu}$ | $-\frac{2\nu}{\nu^2-1}\left[\frac{1}{s}S_{2,\nu}(s)-1\right]$ | Re s > o |
| | 25 | $\frac{[(t^2+1)^{\frac{1}{2}}-t]^{\nu}}{(t^2+1)^{\frac{1}{2}}}$ | $S_{o,\nu}(s)-\nu S_{-1,\nu}(s)$ <br> $=[\mathbf{J}_{\nu}(s)-J_{\nu}(s)]\pi\operatorname{cosec}(\nu\pi)$ | Re s > o |
| | 26 | $\frac{[(t^2+1)^{\frac{1}{2}}+t]^{\nu}+[(t^2+1)^{\frac{1}{2}}-t]^{\nu}}{(t^2+1)^{\frac{1}{2}}}$ | $2S_{o,\nu}(s)$ | Re s > o |
| | 27 | $\frac{[(t^2+1)^{\frac{1}{2}}+t]^{\nu}-[(t^2+1)^{\frac{1}{2}}-t]^{\nu}}{(t^2+1)^{\frac{1}{2}}}$ | $2\nu S_{-1,\nu}(s)$ | Re s > o |
| | 28 | $\frac{[a^2t^2+1)^{\frac{1}{2}}+at]^{\nu}+\cos(\nu\pi)[(a^2t^2+1)^{\frac{1}{2}}-at]^{\nu}}{(a^2t^2+1)^{\frac{1}{2}}}$ | $-a^{-1}[\mathbf{E}_{\nu}(\frac{s}{a})+Y_{\nu}(\frac{s}{a})]$ | Re s > o |
| | 29 | $\left[\frac{t+(t^2+a^2)^{\frac{1}{2}}}{t(t^2+a^2)}\right]^{\frac{1}{2}}$ | $\frac{\pi}{2^{\frac{1}{2}}}[\sin(\frac{as}{2})J_0(\frac{as}{2})-\cos(\frac{as}{2})Y_0(\frac{as}{2})]$ | Re a > o <br> Re s > o |
| | 30 | $\left[\frac{(t^2+a^2)^{\frac{1}{2}}-t}{t(t^2+a^2)}\right]^{\frac{1}{2}}$ | $\frac{\pi}{2^{\frac{1}{2}}}[\cos(\frac{as}{2})J_0(\frac{as}{2})+\sin(\frac{as}{2})Y_0(\frac{as}{2})]$ | Re a > o <br> Re s > o |
| | 31 | $\frac{[t+(t^2+a^2)^{\frac{1}{2}}]^{\frac{3}{2}}}{t^{\frac{1}{2}}(t^2+a^2)^{\frac{1}{2}}}$ | $\frac{\pi a}{2^{\frac{1}{2}}}[\sin(\frac{as}{2})J_1(\frac{as}{2})-\cos(\frac{as}{2})Y_1(\frac{as}{2})]$ | Re a > o <br> Re s > o |
| | 32 | $\frac{[(t^2+a^2)^{\frac{1}{2}}-t]^{\frac{3}{2}}}{t^{\frac{1}{2}}(t^2+a^2)^{\frac{1}{2}}}$ | $-\frac{\pi a}{2^{\frac{1}{2}}}[\cos(\frac{as}{2})J_1(\frac{as}{2})+\sin(\frac{as}{2})Y_1(\frac{as}{2})]$ | Re a > o <br> Re s > o |
| | 33 | $\frac{[t+(t^2+a^2)^{\frac{1}{2}}]^{\nu}}{t^{\frac{1}{2}}(t^2+a^2)^{\frac{1}{2}}}$ | $(\frac{\pi}{2})^{\frac{3}{2}}a^{\nu}s^{\frac{1}{2}}[J_{-\frac{\nu}{2}+\frac{1}{4}}(\frac{as}{2})Y_{-\frac{\nu}{2}-\frac{1}{4}}(\frac{as}{2})$ <br> $-J_{-\frac{\nu}{2}-\frac{1}{4}}(\frac{as}{2})Y_{-\frac{\nu}{2}+\frac{1}{4}}(\frac{as}{2})]$ | Re a > o <br> Re s > o |
| Miscellaneous | | | | |
| | 34 | $\frac{[1+(t^2+1)^{\frac{1}{2}}]^{\nu+\frac{1}{2}}}{t^{\nu+1}(t^2+1)^{\frac{1}{2}}}$ | $2^{\frac{1}{2}}\Gamma(-\nu)D_{\nu}[(2is)^{\frac{1}{2}}]D_{\nu}[(-2is)^{\frac{1}{2}}]$ | Re $\nu$ < o <br> Re s ⩾ o |

| | | f(t) | g(s) | |
|---|---|---|---|---|
| 2 (Contd.) | 35 | $[(t+a)^{\frac{1}{2}}+t^{\frac{1}{2}}]^{\nu}-[(t+a)^{\frac{1}{2}}-t^{\frac{1}{2}}]^{\nu}$ | $\nu a^{\frac{\nu}{2}} s^{-1} e^{\frac{as}{2}} K_{\frac{\nu}{2}}(\frac{as}{2})$ | $\|\arg a\| < \pi$<br>$\mathrm{Re}\, s > 0$ |
| 2.1 | 1 | $\frac{1+at}{t^{\frac{1}{2}}}$ | $\frac{\pi^{\frac{1}{2}}(s+\frac{a}{2})}{s^{\frac{3}{2}}}$ | $\mathrm{Re}\, s > 0$ |
| | 2 | $\frac{t^{\frac{1}{2}}}{t+a}$ | $\pi^{\frac{1}{2}} s^{-\frac{1}{2}} - \pi a^{\frac{1}{2}} e^{as}\,\mathrm{Erfc}(a^{\frac{1}{2}} s^{\frac{1}{2}})$ | $\|\arg a\| < \pi$<br>$\mathrm{Re}\, s > 0$ |
| | 3 | $\frac{1}{t^{\frac{1}{2}}(t+a)}$ | $\pi a^{-\frac{1}{2}} e^{as}\,\mathrm{Erfc}(a^{\frac{1}{2}} s^{\frac{1}{2}})$ | $\|\arg a\| < \pi$<br>$\mathrm{Re}\, s \geqslant 0$ |
| | 4 | $\frac{t^{\nu}}{t+a}$ | $\Gamma(\nu+1) a^{\nu} e^{as} \Gamma(-\nu, as)$ | $\|\arg a\| < \pi$<br>$\mathrm{Re}\,\nu > -1$<br>$\mathrm{Re}\, s > 0$ |
| | 5 | $(t^2+a^2)^{\frac{1}{2}}-t$ | $\frac{a\pi}{2s}[\mathbf{H}_1(as) - Y_1(as)] - \frac{1}{as^2}$ | $\|\arg a\| < \frac{\pi}{2}$<br>$\mathrm{Re}\, s > 0$ |
| | 6 | $\frac{t}{(t^2+a^2)^{\frac{1}{2}}}$ | $\frac{\pi a}{2}[\mathbf{H}_1(as) - Y_1(as)] - a$ | $\|\arg a\| < \frac{\pi}{2}$<br>$\mathrm{Re}\, s > 0$ |
| | 7 | $\frac{t^{\nu}}{1+t^2}$ | $\pi \operatorname{cosec}[(\nu+1)\pi] V_{\nu+1}(2s, 0)$ | $\mathrm{Re}\,\nu > -1$<br>$\mathrm{Re}\, s > 0$ |
| | 8 | $\frac{t+a}{(t^2+2at)^{\frac{1}{2}}}$ | $a e^{as} K_1(as)$ | $\|\arg a\| < \pi$<br>$\mathrm{Re}\, s > 0$ |
| | 9 | $\frac{1}{(1+t+\cos\theta)(t^2+2t)^{\frac{1}{2}}}$ | $e^{2s\cos^2\frac{\theta}{2}}\left[\frac{\theta}{\sin\theta} - \int_0^s K_0(u) e^{-u\cos\theta}\, du\right]$ | $\mathrm{Re}\, s > 0$ |
| | 10 | $\frac{[t+(1+t^2)^{\frac{1}{2}}]^n}{(1+t^2)^{\frac{1}{2}}}$ | $\frac{1}{2}[S_n(s) - \pi \mathbf{E}_n(s) - \pi Y_n(s)]$ | $n = 0, 1, 2, \ldots$<br>$\mathrm{Re}\, s > 0$ |
| | 11 | $\frac{[t-(1+t^2)^{\frac{1}{2}}]^n}{(1+t^2)^{\frac{1}{2}}}$ | $-\frac{1}{2}[S_n(s) + \pi \mathbf{E}_n(s) + \pi Y_n(s)]$ | $n = 0, 1, 2, \ldots$<br>$\mathrm{Re}\, s > 0$ |
| | 12 | $[at+(1+a^2t^2)^{\frac{1}{2}}]^n + [at-(1+a^2t^2)^{\frac{1}{2}}]^n$ | $\frac{2}{a} O_n(\frac{s}{a})$ | $n = 0, 1, 2, \ldots$<br>$a > 0$<br>$\mathrm{Re}\, s > 0$ |

| | | f(t) | g(s) | |
|---|---|---|---|---|
| 2.1 (Contd.) | 13 | $\frac{[at+(1+a^2t^2)^{\frac{1}{2}}]^n - [at-(1+a^2t^2)^{\frac{1}{2}}]^n}{(1+a^2t^2)^{\frac{1}{2}}}$ | $\frac{1}{a}S_n\left(\frac{s}{a}\right)$ | $n=0,1,2,\ldots$<br>$a>0$<br>$\text{Re } s>0$ |
| 3 | 1 | $a^t$ | $\frac{1}{s-\log a}$ | $\text{Re } a>0$<br>$\text{Re } s>\text{Re } \log\lvert a\rvert$ |
| | 2 | $e^{-at}$ | $\frac{1}{s+a}$ | $\text{Re } s>-\text{Re } a$ |
| | 3 | $te^{-at}$ | $\frac{1}{(s+a)^2}$ | $\text{Re } s>-\text{Re } a$ |
| | 4 | $\frac{1}{t}e^{-\frac{a}{t}}$ | $2K_0(2a^{\frac{1}{2}}s^{\frac{1}{2}})$ | $\text{Re } a\geqslant 0$<br>$a\neq 0$<br>$\text{Re } s>0$ |
| | 5 | $e^{bt}-e^{at}$ | $\frac{b-a}{(s-a)(s-b)}$ | $\text{Re } s>\text{Max Re } a, \text{Re } b$ |
| | 6 | $be^{bt}-ae^{at}$ | $\frac{(b-a)s}{(s-a)(s-b)}$ | $\text{Re } s>\text{Max Re } a, \text{Re } b$ |
| | 7 | $(b-c)e^{at}+(c-a)e^{bt}+(a-b)e^{ct}$ | $-\frac{(a-b)(b-c)(c-a)}{(s-a)(s-b)(s-c)}$ | $\text{Re } s>\text{Max Re } a, \text{Re } b, \text{Re } c$ |
| | 8 | $e^{-at}+\omega e^{-\omega at}+\omega^2e^{-\omega^2at}$<br>where $\omega=-\frac{1}{2}+i\frac{3^{\frac{1}{2}}}{2}$ | $\frac{3a^2}{s^3+a^3}$ | $\text{Re } s>\text{Max} -\text{Re } a,$<br>$\frac{1}{2}(\text{Re } a+3^{\frac{1}{2}}\lvert\text{Im } a\rvert)$ |
| | 9 | $e^{-at}+\omega^2e^{-\omega at}+\omega e^{-\omega^2at}$<br>where $\omega=-\frac{1}{2}+i\frac{3^{\frac{1}{2}}}{2}$ | $\frac{-3as}{s^3+a^3}$ | $\text{Re } s>\text{Max} -\text{Re } a,$<br>$\frac{1}{2}(\text{Re } a+3^{\frac{1}{2}}\lvert\text{Im } a\rvert)$ |
| | 10 | $e^{-at}+e^{-\omega at}+e^{-\omega^2at}$<br>where $\omega=-\frac{1}{2}+i\frac{3^{\frac{1}{2}}}{2}$ | $\frac{3s^2}{s^3+a^3}$ | $\text{Re } s>\text{Max} -\text{Re } a,$<br>$\frac{1}{2}(\text{Re } a+3^{\frac{1}{2}}\lvert\text{Im } a\rvert)$ |
| | 11 | $\exp(-ae^t)$ | $a^s\Gamma(-s,a)$ | $\text{Re } a>0$<br>$\text{Re } s>-\infty$ |
| | 12 | $\exp(-ae^{-t})$ | $a^{-s}\gamma(s,a)$ | $\text{Re } s>0$ |

| | | f(t) | g(s) | |
|---|---|---|---|---|
| 3 (Contd.) | 13 | $e^{-\frac{a}{t}}$ | $2a^{\frac{1}{2}}s^{-\frac{1}{2}}K_1(2a^{\frac{1}{2}}s^{\frac{1}{2}})$ | Re a ⩾ o<br>Re s > o |
| | 14 | $e^{at}-1$ | $\frac{a}{s(s-a)}$ | Re s > Max o, Re a |
| | 15 | $(1-e^{-\frac{t}{a}})^n$ | $\frac{n!}{s(as+1)_n}$ | Re s > Max o, −n Re $\frac{1}{a}$<br>n = 0,1,2,... |
| | 16 | $(1-e^{-\frac{t}{a}})^\nu$ | $aB(as,\nu+1)$ | Re a > o<br>Re ν > − 1<br>Re s > o |
| | 17 | $1-4at\,e^{-at}$ | $\frac{(s-a)^2}{s(s+a)^2}$ | Re s > Max o, − Re a |
| | 18 | $t(1-e^{-t})^a$ | $B(s,a+1)[\psi(s+a+1)-\psi(s)]$ | Re a > − 1<br>Re s > o |
| | 19 | $1+2\frac{a+b}{a-b}(e^{-at}-e^{-bt})$ | $\frac{(s-a)(s-b)}{s(s+a)(s+b)}$ | Re s > Max o, − Re a, − Re b |
| | 20 | $\frac{1-e^{at}}{t}$ | $\log\frac{s-a}{s}$ | Re s > Max o, Re a |
| | 21 | $\frac{e^{-at}-e^{-bt}}{t}$ | $\log\frac{s+b}{s+a}$ | Re s > Max − Re a, − Re b |
| | 22 | $\frac{1}{1+e^{-t}}$ | $\frac{1}{2}\psi(\frac{s+1}{2})-\frac{1}{2}\psi(\frac{s}{2})$ | Re s > o |
| | 23 | $\frac{t}{1-e^{-t}}$ | $\psi'(s)$<br>$=\zeta(2,s)$ | Re s > o |
| | 24 | $\frac{1}{t}-\frac{a}{1-e^{-at}}$ | $\psi(\frac{s}{a})-\log\frac{s}{a}$ | Re s > o |
| | 25 | $(1-e^{-t})^\nu\exp(ae^{-t})$ | $\frac{\Gamma(\nu+1)\Gamma(s)}{\Gamma(\nu+s+1)}a^{-\frac{\nu+s+1}{2}}e^{\frac{a}{2}}M_{\frac{\nu-s+1}{2},\frac{\nu+s}{2}}(a)$ | Re ν > − 1<br>Re s > o |

| | | f(t) | g(s) | |
|---|---|---|---|---|
| 3 (Contd.) | 26 | $(1-e^{-t})^{\nu}\exp(-ae^{t})$ | $\Gamma(\nu+1)a^{\frac{s-1}{2}}e^{-\frac{a}{2}}W_{-\frac{1+s+2\nu}{2},\,-\frac{s}{2}}(a)$ | $\operatorname{Re} a>0$<br>$\operatorname{Re}\nu>-1$<br>$\operatorname{Re} s>-\infty$ |
| | 27 | $(e^{t}-1)^{\nu}\exp\left[-\frac{a}{e^{t}-1}\right]$ | $\Gamma(s-\nu)e^{\frac{a}{2}}a^{\frac{\nu}{2}}W_{\frac{\nu-2s}{2},\,\frac{\nu+1}{2}}(a)$ | $\operatorname{Re} a>0$<br>$\operatorname{Re} s>\operatorname{Re}\nu$ |
| | 28 | $e^{(\mu-1)t}(1-e^{-t})^{\mu-\frac{1}{2}}[(1-e^{-t})\sin\theta$<br>$\mp(1-e^{-t})\cos\theta]^{\mu-\frac{1}{2}}$ | $\frac{2^{\mu-1}\Gamma(\mu+\frac{1}{2})\Gamma(s-\mu+1)}{\pi^{\frac{1}{2}}\Gamma(s+\mu+1)}\sin^{\mu}\theta\cdot$<br>$\cdot e^{\pm(s+\frac{1}{2})i\theta\pm(\frac{\mu}{2}-\frac{1}{4})\pi i}\cdot$<br>$\cdot[\pi P_{\nu}^{\mu}(\cos\theta)\pm 2iQ_{\nu}^{\mu}(\cos\theta)]$ | $\operatorname{Re}\mu>-\frac{1}{2}$<br>$\operatorname{Re} s>\operatorname{Re}(\mu-1)$ |
| | 29 | $\frac{1-e^{-at}}{1-e^{-t}}$ | $\psi(s+a)-\psi(s)$ | $\operatorname{Re} s>\operatorname{Max} 0,\ -\operatorname{Re} a$ |
| | 30 | $\frac{e^{-ct}-e^{-bt}}{1-e^{-at}}$ | $\frac{1}{a}[\psi(\frac{s+b}{a})-\psi(\frac{s+c}{a})]$ | $\operatorname{Re} a>0$<br>$\operatorname{Re} s>\operatorname{Max}-\operatorname{Re} b,\ -\operatorname{Re} c$ |
| | 31 | $\frac{(1-e^{-at})(1-e^{-bt})}{1-e^{-t}}$ | $\psi(s+a)+\psi(s+b)-\psi(s+a+b)-\psi(s)$ | $\operatorname{Re} s>\operatorname{Max} 0,\ -\operatorname{Re} a,\ -\operatorname{Re} b,$<br>$-\operatorname{Re}(a+b)$ |
| | 32 | $\frac{1-e^{-at}}{t(1+e^{-t})}$ | $\log\frac{\Gamma(\frac{s}{2})\Gamma(\frac{a+s+1}{2})}{\Gamma(\frac{s+1}{2})\Gamma(\frac{a+s}{2})}$ | $\operatorname{Re} s>\operatorname{Max} 0,\ -\operatorname{Re} a$ |
| | 33 | $\frac{e^{-at}-e^{-bt}}{t(1+e^{-\frac{t}{2}})}$ | $\log\frac{\Gamma(s+a)\Gamma(s+b+\frac{1}{2})}{\Gamma(s+a+\frac{1}{2})\Gamma(s+b)}$ | $\operatorname{Re} s>\operatorname{Max}-\operatorname{Re} a,\ -\operatorname{Re} b$ |
| | 34 | $\frac{1-e^{t}+t\,e^{2t}}{t(e^{2t}-1)}$ | $\log\frac{\Gamma(1+\frac{s}{2})}{\Gamma(\frac{1+s}{2})}-\frac{1}{2}\psi(\frac{s}{2})$ | $\operatorname{Re} s>0$ |
| | 35 | $\frac{(1-e^{-at})(1-e^{-bt})}{t(1-e^{-t})}$ | $\log\frac{\Gamma(s)\Gamma(s+a+b)}{\Gamma(s+a)\Gamma(s+b)}$ | $\operatorname{Re} s>\operatorname{Max} 0,\ -\operatorname{Re} a,\ -\operatorname{Re} b,$<br>$-\operatorname{Re}(a+b)$ |
| | 36 | $\frac{(e^{-at}-e^{-bt})(1-e^{-ct})}{t(1-e^{-t})}$ | $\log\frac{\Gamma(s+a)\Gamma(s+b+c)}{\Gamma(s+a+c)\Gamma(s+b)}$ | $\operatorname{Re} s>\operatorname{Max}-\operatorname{Re} a,\ -\operatorname{Re} b,$<br>$-\operatorname{Re}(a+c),\ -\operatorname{Re}(b+c)$ |

| | | f(t) | g(s) | |
|---|---|---|---|---|
| 3(Contd.) | 37 | $\dfrac{(1-e^{-at})(1-e^{-bt})(1-e^{-ct})}{t(1-e^{-t})}$ | $\log\dfrac{\Gamma(s)\Gamma(s+a+b)\Gamma(s+b+c)\Gamma(s+c+a)}{\Gamma(s+a)\Gamma(s+b)\Gamma(s+c)\Gamma(s+a+b+c)}$ | $2\,\mathrm{Re}\,s > \lvert\mathrm{Re}\,a\rvert+\lvert\mathrm{Re}\,b\rvert+\lvert\mathrm{Re}\,c\rvert$ |
| | 38 | $\dfrac{1}{1-e^{-at}}\left[\dfrac{e^{-bt}-e^{-ct}}{t}+(b-c)e^{-dt}\right]$ | $\log\dfrac{\Gamma(\frac{s+b}{a})}{\Gamma(\frac{s+c}{a})}+\dfrac{c-b}{a}\psi(\frac{s+d}{a})$ | $\mathrm{Re}\,a>0$<br>$\mathrm{Re}\,s>\mathrm{Max}-\mathrm{Re}\,b,\ -\mathrm{Re}\,c,\ -\mathrm{Re}\,d$ |
| | 39 | $\dfrac{[a+(1-e^{-t})^{\frac{1}{2}}]^{\nu}+[a-(1-e^{-t})^{\frac{1}{2}}]^{\nu}}{(1-e^{-t})^{\frac{1}{2}}}$ | $2^{s+1}e^{(s+\nu)\pi i}\dfrac{\Gamma(s)}{\Gamma(-\nu)}(a^2-1)^{\frac{s+\nu}{2}}Q_{s-1}^{-\nu-s}(a)$<br>$=2^{s+\frac{1}{2}}\pi^{\frac{1}{2}}\Gamma(s)(a^2-1)^{\frac{s+\nu}{2}-\frac{1}{4}}P_{\nu+s-\frac{1}{2}}^{\frac{1}{2}-s}\left[\dfrac{a}{(a^2-1)^{\frac{1}{2}}}\right]$ | $\mathrm{Re}\,s>0$ |
| | 40 | $\dfrac{(1-e^{-t})^{\nu}}{(1-c\,e^{-t})^{\mu}}$ | $B(s,\nu+1)\,{}_2F_1[\mu,s;s+\nu+1;c]$ | $\mathrm{Re}\,\nu>-1$<br>$\lvert\arg(1-c)\rvert<\pi$<br>$\mathrm{Re}\,s>0$ |
| | 41 | $\dfrac{(1-e^{-t})^{\nu}}{(1-c\,e^{-t})^{\mu}}\exp(a\,e^{-t})$ | $\dfrac{\Gamma(\nu+1)\Gamma(s)}{\Gamma(\nu+s+1)}\Phi_1(s,\mu,\nu+1;c,a)$ | $\mathrm{Re}\,\nu>-1$<br>$\lvert\arg(1-c)\rvert<\pi$<br>$\mathrm{Re}\,s>0$ |
| | 42 | $\dfrac{e^{t}(e^{t}-1)^{\nu}}{[1-a(1-e^{-t})]^{\mu}}$ | $B(\nu+1,s-\nu-1)\,{}_2F_1[\mu,\nu+1;s;a]$ | $\lvert a\rvert<1$<br>$\mathrm{Re}\,\nu>-1$<br>$\mathrm{Re}\,s>\mathrm{Re}\,(\nu+1)$ |
| 3.1 | 1 | $t^n e^{-at}$ | $\dfrac{n!}{(s+a)^{n+1}}$ | $\mathrm{Re}\,s>-\mathrm{Re}\,a$ |
| | 2 | $e^{-\frac{t^2}{a}}$ | $\frac{1}{2}(\pi a)^{\frac{1}{2}}e^{\frac{as^2}{4}}\,\mathrm{Erfc}\,\dfrac{a^{\frac{1}{2}}s}{2}$ | $\mathrm{Re}\,a>0$<br>$\mathrm{Re}\,s>-\infty$ |
| | 3 | $t\,e^{-\frac{t^2}{a}}$ | $\dfrac{a}{s}-\dfrac{\pi^{\frac{1}{2}}}{4}a^{\frac{3}{2}}\,s\,e^{\frac{as^2}{4}}\,\mathrm{Erfc}\,\dfrac{a^{\frac{1}{2}}s}{2}$ | $\mathrm{Re}\,a>0$<br>$\mathrm{Re}\,s>-\infty$ |
| | 4 | $\dfrac{1}{t^2}e^{-\frac{a}{t}}$ | $2(\frac{s}{a})^{\frac{1}{2}}K_1(2a^{\frac{1}{2}}s^{\frac{1}{2}})$ | $\mathrm{Re}\,a>0$<br>$\mathrm{Re}\,s>0$ |

| | | f(t) | g(s) | |
|---|---|---|---|---|
| 3.1 (Contd.) | 5 | $1-e^{-at}\left[1+\frac{at}{1!}+\cdots+\frac{(at)^n}{n!}\right]$ | $\frac{a^{n+1}}{s(s+a)^{n+1}}$ | $n=0,1,2,\ldots$<br>$\mathrm{Re}\, s > \mathrm{Max}\ 0, -\mathrm{Re}\, a$ |
| | 6 | $(1+bt)e^{-at}$ | $\frac{s+b+a}{(s+a)^2}$ | $\mathrm{Re}\, s > -\mathrm{Re}\, a$ |
| | 7 | $e^{at}-[1+(a-b)t]e^{bt}$ | $\frac{(a-b)^2}{(s-a)(s-b)^2}$ | $\mathrm{Re}\, s > \mathrm{Max}\ \mathrm{Re}\, a, \mathrm{Re}\, b$ |
| | 8 | $\frac{(at+1)e^{-at}-1}{t^2}$ | $s\log\left(2+\frac{a}{s}\right)-a$ | $\mathrm{Re}\, s > -\mathrm{Re}\, a$ |
| | 9 | $\frac{1}{t^2}(1-e^{-at})^2$ | $(s+2a)\log(s+2a)+s\log s$<br>$-2(s+a)\log(s+a)$ | $\mathrm{Re}\, s \geq \mathrm{Max}\ 0, -\mathrm{Re}\, 2a$ |
| | 10 | $e^{-at}\frac{at+1}{t^2}-e^{-bt}\frac{bt+1}{t^2}$ | $s\log\frac{s+a}{s+b}+b-a$ | $\mathrm{Re}\, s > \mathrm{Max} -\mathrm{Re}\, a, -\mathrm{Re}\, b$ |
| | 11 | $\frac{t^n}{1-e^{-\frac{t}{a}}}$ | $(-a)^{n+1}\psi^{(n)}(as)$ | $\mathrm{Re}\, a > 0$<br>$n=0,1,2,\ldots$<br>$\mathrm{Re}\, s > 0$ |
| | 12 | $\frac{a}{t}-\frac{(at+2)(1-e^{-at})}{2t^2}$ | $\left(s+\frac{a}{2}\right)\log\left(1+\frac{a}{s}\right)-a$ | $\mathrm{Re}\, s > -\mathrm{Re}\, a$ |
| | 13 | $\frac{1}{t}\left(\frac{1}{1-e^{-t}}-\frac{1}{t}-\frac{1}{2}\right)$ | $\log\frac{e^s\Gamma(s)}{(2\pi)^{\frac{1}{2}}s^{s-\frac{1}{2}}}$ | $\mathrm{Re}\, s > 0$ |
| | 14 | $\frac{1}{1+e^{-t}}\left(\frac{1}{2}-\frac{1}{t}+\frac{t}{e^t-1}\right)$ | $\log(2\pi)^{\frac{1}{2}}-\log B\left(\frac{s}{2},\frac{1}{2}\right)-\frac{1}{2}\psi(s)$ | $\mathrm{Re}\, s > 0$ |
| | 15 | $\frac{1}{1-e^{-t}}\left(\frac{1}{e^t-1}-\frac{1}{t}+\frac{1}{2}\right)$ | $\sum_{k=0}^{\infty}\left[\log(s+k)-\psi(s+k)-\frac{1}{2(s+k)}\right]$ | $\mathrm{Re}\, s > 0$ |
| | 16 | $(e^t-1)^{\nu}\exp\left[-\frac{a}{2}+\mu t-\frac{a}{e^t-1}\right]$ | $a^{\frac{\nu}{2}}\Gamma(\mu+s)W_{-\mu-\frac{\nu}{2}-s,\ \frac{\nu+1}{2}}(a)$ | $\mathrm{Re}\, a > 0$<br>$\mathrm{Re}\, s > \mathrm{Re}(\mu+\nu)$ |

| | | $f(t)$ | $g(s)$ | |
|---|---|---|---|---|
| 3.1 (Contd.) | 17 | $\dfrac{\exp[-\mu t-a(e^t-\frac{1}{2})]}{(e^t-1)^\nu}$ | $\Gamma(1-\nu)a^{\frac{\nu-\mu+s-1}{2}} W_{\frac{\nu+\mu-1-s}{2},\frac{\nu-\mu+s}{2}}(a)$ | Re $\nu < 1$<br>Re $a > 0$<br>Re $s > -\infty$ |
| | 18 | $\dfrac{d^n}{dt^n}\left(e^{-\frac{t^2}{2}}t^n\right)$ | $n!\,s^n e^{\frac{s^2}{4}} D_{-n-1}(s)$ | $n = 0,1,2,\ldots$<br>Re $s > -\infty$ |
| 3.2 | 1 | $\dfrac{1}{t^{\frac{1}{2}}}e^{-at}$ | $\dfrac{\pi^{\frac{1}{2}}}{(s+a)^{\frac{1}{2}}}$ | Re $s > -$ Re $a$ |
| | 2 | $t^{n-\frac{1}{2}}e^{-at}$ | $\dfrac{\pi^{\frac{1}{2}}\cdot\frac{1}{2}\cdot\frac{3}{2}\cdots(n-\frac{1}{2})}{(s+a)^{n+\frac{1}{2}}}$ | $n = 1,2,3,\ldots$<br>Re $s > -$ Re $a$ |
| | 3 | $t^\nu e^{-at}$ | $\dfrac{\Gamma(\nu+1)}{(s+a)^{\nu+1}}$ | Re $\nu > -1$<br>Re $s > -$ Re $a$ |
| | 4 | $\dfrac{e^{bt}-e^{at}}{t^{\frac{3}{2}}}$ | $2\pi^{\frac{1}{2}}[(s-a)^{\frac{1}{2}}-(s-b)^{\frac{1}{2}}]$ | Re $s >$ Max Re $a$, Re $b$ |
| | 5 | $t^{\frac{1}{2}}e^{-\frac{a}{t}}$ | $\dfrac{\pi^{\frac{1}{2}}(1+2a^{\frac{1}{2}}s^{\frac{1}{2}})}{2s^{\frac{3}{2}}e^{2a^{\frac{1}{2}}s^{\frac{1}{2}}}}$ | Re $a \geq 0$<br>Re $s > 0$ |
| | 6 | $\dfrac{1}{t^{\frac{1}{2}}}e^{-\frac{a}{t}}$ | $(\frac{\pi}{s})^{\frac{1}{2}}e^{-2a^{\frac{1}{2}}s^{\frac{1}{2}}}$ | Re $a \geq 0$<br>Re $s > 0$ |
| | 7 | $\dfrac{1}{t^{\frac{3}{2}}}e^{-\frac{a}{t}}$ | $(\frac{\pi}{a})^{\frac{1}{2}}e^{-2a^{\frac{1}{2}}s^{\frac{1}{2}}}$ | Re $a > 0$<br>Re $s > 0$ |
| | 8 | $t^\nu e^{-\frac{a}{t}}$ | $2(\frac{a}{s})^{\frac{\nu+1}{2}} K_{\nu+1}(2a^{\frac{1}{2}}s^{\frac{1}{2}})$ | Re $a > 0$<br>Re $s > 0$ |
| | 9 | $\dfrac{1}{t^{\frac{1}{2}}}(e^{-\frac{a}{t}}-1)$ | $(\frac{\pi}{s})^{\frac{1}{2}}(e^{-2a^{\frac{1}{2}}s^{\frac{1}{2}}}-1)$ | Re $a \geq 0$<br>Re $s \geq 0$ |
| | 10 | $e^{-at^{\frac{1}{2}}}$ | $\dfrac{1}{s}-\dfrac{\pi^{\frac{1}{2}}a}{2s^{\frac{3}{2}}}e^{\frac{a^2}{4s}}\,\mathrm{Erfc}\,\dfrac{a}{2s^{\frac{1}{2}}}$ | Re $a > 0$<br>Re $s > 0$ |

| | | f(t) | g(s) | |
|---|---|---|---|---|
| 3.2 (Contd.) | 11 | $t^{\frac{1}{2}} e^{-at^{\frac{1}{2}}}$ | $\frac{\pi^{\frac{1}{2}}(a^2+2s)e^{\frac{a^2}{4s}}}{4s^{\frac{5}{2}}}\mathrm{Erfc}\,\frac{a}{2s^{\frac{1}{2}}} - \frac{a}{2s^2}$ | $\mathrm{Re}\, a > 0$<br>$\mathrm{Re}\, s > 0$ |
| | 12 | $\frac{1}{t^{\frac{1}{2}}} e^{-at^{\frac{1}{2}}}$ | $\left(\frac{\pi}{s}\right)^{\frac{1}{2}} e^{\frac{a^2}{4s}}\,\mathrm{Erfc}\,\frac{a}{2s^{\frac{1}{2}}}$ | $\mathrm{Re}\, a > 0$<br>$\mathrm{Re}\, s > 0$ |
| | 13 | $\frac{1}{t^{\frac{3}{4}}} e^{-at^{\frac{1}{2}}}$ | $\frac{a}{2^{\frac{3}{4}} s^{\frac{1}{2}}} e^{\frac{a^2}{8s}} K_{\frac{1}{4}}\left(\frac{a^2}{8s}\right)$ | $\mathrm{Re}\, a > 0$<br>$\mathrm{Re}\, s > 0$ |
| | 14 | $t^{\nu} e^{-at^{\frac{1}{2}}}$ | $\frac{\Gamma(2\nu+2)}{2^{\nu} s^{\nu+1}} e^{\frac{a^2}{8s}} D_{-2\nu-2}\left[\left(\frac{a^2}{2s}\right)^{\frac{1}{2}}\right]$ | $\mathrm{Re}\, a > 0$<br>$\mathrm{Re}\, \nu > -1$<br>$\mathrm{Re}\, s > 0$ |
| | 15 | $\frac{t^{\nu}}{1+e^{t}}$ | $\Gamma(\nu+1)\sum_{k=1}^{\infty}\frac{(-1)^{k-1}}{(s+k)^{\nu+1}}$ | $\mathrm{Re}\, \nu > 0$<br>$\mathrm{Re}\, s > -1$ |
| | 16 | $\frac{t^{\nu}}{e^{t}-1}$ | $\Gamma(\nu+1)\sum_{k=1}^{\infty}\frac{1}{(s+k)^{\nu+1}}$ | $\mathrm{Re}\, \nu > 0$<br>$\mathrm{Re}\, s > -1$ |
| | 17 | $\frac{t^{\nu}}{1-a\,e^{-t}}$ | $\Gamma(\nu+1)\sum_{k=0}^{\infty}\frac{a^{k}}{(s+k)^{\nu+1}}$ | $\mathrm{Re}\, \nu > -1$<br>$\lvert a \rvert < 1$<br>$\mathrm{Re}\, s > 0$ |
| | 18 | $\frac{t^{\nu}}{1-e^{-at}}$ | $\frac{\Gamma(\nu+1)\zeta(\nu+1, \frac{s}{a})}{a^{\nu+1}}$ | $\mathrm{Re}\, a > 0$<br>$\mathrm{Re}\, \nu > 0$<br>$\mathrm{Re}\, s > 0$ |
| | 19 | $\frac{1}{t^{\frac{1}{2}}}\frac{d^n}{da^n} e^{-\frac{a^2}{4t}}$ | $(-1)^n \pi^{\frac{1}{2}} s^{\frac{n-1}{2}} e^{-as^{\frac{1}{2}}}$ | $\mathrm{Re}\, s > 0$ |
| | 20 | $\frac{e^{at}}{t^{\frac{1}{2}}} * \frac{e^{bt}}{t^{\frac{1}{2}}} * \frac{e^{ct}}{t^{\frac{1}{2}}}$ | $\frac{\pi^{\frac{3}{2}}}{[(s-a)(s-b)(s-c)]^{\frac{1}{2}}}$ | $\mathrm{Re}\, s > \mathrm{Max}\ \mathrm{Re}\, a, \mathrm{Re}\, b, \mathrm{Re}\, c$ |
| | 21 | $1-e^{-at^{\frac{1}{2}}}$ | $\frac{a\pi^{\frac{1}{2}}}{2s^{\frac{3}{2}}} e^{\frac{a^2}{4s}}\,\mathrm{Erfc}\left(\frac{a}{2s^{\frac{1}{2}}}\right)$ | $\mathrm{Re}\, s > 0$ |
| 3.2.1 | 1 | $\frac{1}{t^{\frac{1}{2}}}\left[e^{-\frac{(a-b)^2}{4t}} - e^{-\frac{(a+b)^2}{4t}}\right]$ | $2\left(\frac{\pi}{s}\right)^{\frac{1}{2}} e^{-as^{\frac{1}{2}}} \sinh(bs^{\frac{1}{2}})$ | $0 \leq b \leq a$<br>$\mathrm{Re}\, s > 0$ |

| | | f(t) | g(s) | |
|---|---|---|---|---|
| 3.2.1 (Contd.) | 2 | $\frac{1}{t^{\frac{1}{2}}} e^{-at^2}$ | $\frac{s^{\frac{1}{2}}}{2a^{\frac{1}{2}}} e^{\frac{s^2}{8a}} K_{\frac{1}{4}}\left(\frac{s^2}{8a}\right)$ | $\text{Re } s > \begin{cases} -\infty \text{ for } \lvert\arg a\rvert < \frac{\pi}{4}, \frac{3\pi}{4} < \arg a < \frac{5\pi}{4} \\ 0 \text{ for } \arg a = \frac{\pi}{4}, \frac{3\pi}{4}, \frac{5\pi}{4}, \frac{7\pi}{4} \\ \infty \text{ otherwise} \end{cases}$ |
| | 3 | $t^{\nu} e^{-at^2}$ | $\frac{\Gamma(\nu+1)}{(2a)^{\frac{\nu+1}{2}}} e^{\frac{s^2}{8a}} D_{-\nu-1}\left(\frac{s}{2^{\frac{1}{2}} a^{\frac{1}{2}}}\right)$ | $\text{Re } s > \begin{cases} -\infty \text{ for } \lvert\arg a\rvert < \frac{\pi}{4}, \frac{3\pi}{4} < \arg a < \frac{5\pi}{4} \\ 0 \text{ for } \arg a = \frac{\pi}{4}, \frac{3\pi}{4}, \frac{5\pi}{4}, \frac{7\pi}{4} \\ \infty \text{ otherwise} \end{cases}$ <br> $\text{Re } \nu > -1$ |
| | 4 | $\frac{1}{t^{\frac{5}{2}}}\left(a - \frac{t}{2}\right) e^{-\frac{a}{t}}$ | $\pi^{\frac{1}{2}} s^{\frac{1}{2}} e^{-2a^{\frac{1}{2}} s^{\frac{1}{2}}}$ | Re a > o <br> Re s > o |
| | 5 | $\frac{1}{t^{\frac{5}{2}}}\left(\frac{2a}{t} - 3\right) e^{-\frac{a}{t}}$ | $\frac{2\pi^{\frac{1}{2}}}{a^{\frac{1}{2}}} s\, e^{-2a^{\frac{1}{2}} s^{\frac{1}{2}}}$ | Re a > o <br> Re s > o |
| | 6 | $\frac{e^{-\frac{a}{t}}}{t^{\frac{9}{2}}}(4a^2 - 6at + 3t^2)$ | $4\pi^{\frac{1}{2}} s^{\frac{3}{2}} e^{-2a^{\frac{1}{2}} s^{\frac{1}{2}}}$ | Re s > o <br> Re a > o |
| | 7 | $\frac{1}{t^{\frac{1}{2}}}\left(e^{-\frac{b}{t}} - e^{-\frac{a}{t}}\right)$ | $2\left(\frac{\pi}{s}\right)^{\frac{1}{2}} e^{(b^{\frac{1}{2}} - a^{\frac{1}{2}}) s^{\frac{1}{2}}} \sinh[(a^{\frac{1}{2}} + b^{\frac{1}{2}}) s^{\frac{1}{2}}]$ | Re a ⩾ o <br> Re b ⩾ o <br> Re s > o |
| 4 | 1 | $\log t$ | $-\frac{1}{s} \log(\gamma s)$ | Re s > o |
| | 2 | $(\log t)^2$ | $\frac{1}{s}\left\{\frac{\pi^2}{6} + [\log(\gamma s)]^2\right\}$ | Re s > o |
| | 3 | $\frac{\log(\gamma t) - 1}{t}$ | $-\frac{\log s}{s^2}$ | Re s > o |
| | 4 | $t\left\{[1 - \log(\gamma t)]^2 + 1 - \frac{\pi^2}{6}\right\}$ | $\left(\frac{\log s}{s}\right)^2$ | Re s > o |
| | 5 | $-[\log(\gamma t)]^3 + \frac{\pi^2}{2}\log(\gamma t) + \psi''(1)$ | $\frac{(\log s)^3}{s}$ | Re s > o |
| | 6 | $t\left[\left\{1 - \log(\gamma t)\right\}^3 + \left(\frac{\pi^2}{2} - 3\right)\log(\gamma t) + 5 - \frac{\pi^2}{2} + \psi''(1)\right]$ | $\frac{(\log s)^3}{s^2}$ | Re s > o |

| | | f(t) | g(s) | |
|---|---|---|---|---|
| 4.1 | 1 | $t^n \log t$ | $\frac{n!}{s^{n+1}}[1+\frac{1}{2}+\frac{1}{3}+\dots+\frac{1}{n}-\log(\gamma s)]$ | $n=1,2,3,\dots$<br>$\mathrm{Re}\, s>0$ |
| | 2 | $t^n[1+\frac{1}{2}+\frac{1}{3}+\dots+\frac{1}{n}-\log(\gamma t)]$ | $\frac{n!\,\log s}{s^{n+1}}$ | $n=1,2,3,\dots$<br>$\mathrm{Re}\, s>0$ |
| | 3 | $\log(t+a)$ | $\frac{1}{s}[\log a - e^{as}\,\mathrm{Ei}(-as)]$ | $\lvert\arg a\rvert<\pi$<br>$\mathrm{Re}\, s>0$ |
| | 4 | $\log(1+at)$ | $-\frac{1}{s}e^{\frac{s}{a}}\,\mathrm{Ei}(-\frac{s}{a})$ | $\lvert\arg a\rvert<\pi$<br>$\mathrm{Re}\, s>0$ |
| | 5 | $\log\lvert b-t\rvert$ | $\frac{1}{s}[\log b - e^{-bs}\,\overline{\mathrm{Ei}}(bs)]$ | $b>0$<br>$\mathrm{Re}\, s>0$ |
| | 6 | $\log(t^2-a^2)$ | $\frac{1}{s}[\log(a^2)-e^{as}\,\mathrm{Ei}(-as)-e^{-as}\,\mathrm{Ei}(as)]$ | $\lvert\mathrm{Im}\, a\rvert>0$<br>$\mathrm{Re}\, s>0$ |
| | 7 | $\log(1+\frac{t^2}{a^2})$ | $\frac{2}{s}[\mathrm{ci}(as)\cos(as)-\mathrm{si}(as)\sin(as)]$ | $\mathrm{Re}\, a>0$<br>$\mathrm{Re}\, s>0$ |
| | 8 | $\log(t^2+a^2)$ | $\frac{2}{s}[\log a - \mathrm{ci}(as)\cos(as)-\mathrm{si}(as)\sin(as)]$ | $\mathrm{Re}\, s>0$ |
| | 9 | $\log\lvert t^2-a^2\rvert$ | $\frac{1}{s}[\log(a^2)-e^{as}\,\mathrm{Ei}(-as)-e^{-as}\,\overline{\mathrm{Ei}}(as)]$ | $\mathrm{Re}\, s>0$<br>$\mathrm{Re}\, a>0$ |
| | 10 | $\frac{1}{t}\log(1+a^2t^2)$ | $[\mathrm{ci}(\frac{s}{a})]^2+[\mathrm{si}(\frac{s}{a})]^2$ | $\mathrm{Re}\, s>0$ |
| | 11 | $\frac{1}{t}\log\lvert 1-a^2t^2\rvert$ | $\overline{\mathrm{Ei}}(\frac{s}{a})\,\mathrm{Ei}(-\frac{s}{a})$ | $\mathrm{Re}\, s>0$ |
| | 12 | $\frac{1}{t}\log(1-t^2)$ | $-S(1,s)\,S(1,-s)$ | $\mathrm{Re}\, s>0$ |
| | 13 | $\frac{\log[(t+a)(t+b)]}{t+a+b}$ | $e^{(a+b)s}[\mathrm{Ei}(-as)\,\mathrm{Ei}(-bs)$<br>$-\log(ab)\,\mathrm{Ei}(-as-bs)]$ | $\lvert\arg(a+b)\rvert<\pi$<br>$a\neq 0$<br>$b\neq 0$<br>$\mathrm{Re}\, s>0$ |

| | | f(t) | g(s) | |
|---|---|---|---|---|
| 4.1 (Contd.) | 14 | $\dfrac{\log \frac{(t+a)(t+b)}{ab}}{t+a+b}$ | $e^{(a+b)s}\,Ei(-as)Ei(-bs)$ | $\lvert\arg(a+b)\rvert < \pi$<br>$a \neq o$<br>$b \neq o$<br>Re $s > o$ |
| 4.2 | 1 | $\frac{1}{t^{\frac{1}{2}}}\log t$ | $-(\frac{\pi}{s})^{\frac{1}{2}}\log(4\gamma s)$ | Re $s > o$ |
| | 2 | $t^{n-\frac{1}{2}}\log t$ | $\frac{\pi^{\frac{1}{2}}\,1.3.5.\cdots(2n-1)}{s^{n+\frac{1}{2}}2^n}\left[2(1+\frac{1}{3}+\frac{1}{5}+\cdots+\frac{1}{2n-1}) - \log(4\gamma s)\right]$ | $n = 1,2,3,\ldots$<br>Re $s > o$ |
| | 3 | $t^{n-\frac{1}{2}}[2(1+\frac{1}{3}+\cdots+\frac{1}{2n-1})-\log(4\gamma t)]$ | $\frac{1.3.5.\cdots(2n-1)\pi^{\frac{1}{2}}\log s}{2^n s^{n+\frac{1}{2}}}$ | $n = 1,2,3,\ldots$<br>Re $s > o$ |
| | 4 | $t^{\nu}\log t$ | $\Gamma(\nu+1)s^{-\nu-1}[\psi(\nu+1)-\log s]$ | Re $\nu > -1$<br>Re $s > o$ |
| | 5 | $t^{\nu}[\psi(\nu+1)-\log t]$ | $\Gamma(\nu+1)\,\frac{\log s}{s^{\nu+1}}$ | Re $\nu > -1$<br>Re $s > o$ |
| | 6 | $\log\frac{t^{\frac{1}{2}}+(t+a)^{\frac{1}{2}}}{a^{\frac{1}{2}}}$ | $\frac{1}{2s}e^{\frac{as}{2}}K_o(\frac{as}{2})$ | $\lvert\arg a\rvert < \pi$<br>Re $s > o$ |
| | 7 | $\log\frac{(t+ib)^{\frac{1}{2}}+(t-ib)^{\frac{1}{2}}}{(2b)^{\frac{1}{2}}}$ | $\frac{\pi}{4s}[H_o(bs)-Y_o(bs)]$ | $b > o$<br>Re $s > o$ |
| 4.3 | 1 | $\log\frac{1+e^t}{2}$ | $\frac{1}{2s}[\psi(\frac{s+1}{2})-\psi(\frac{s}{2})]$ | Re $s > o$ |
| | 2 | $\log[\gamma(e^{\frac{t}{a}}-1)]$ | $-\frac{1}{s}\psi(as)$ | Re $a > o$<br>Re $s > o$ |
| | 3 | $\log\frac{at}{e^{at}-1}$ | $\frac{1}{s}[\psi(\frac{s}{a})-\log\frac{s}{a}]$ | Re $s > o$ |

| | | f(t) | g(s) | |
|---|---|---|---|---|
| 4.3 (Contd.) | 4 | $\frac{\log(1+e^{-t})}{1+e^{-t}}$ | $\sum_{k=1}^{\infty}\frac{(-1)^{k-1}}{s+k}[\psi(k+1)+\log\gamma]$ | Re s > o |
| | 5 | $t^{\nu}\frac{\log\frac{1+e^{-t}}{2}}{1-e^{-t}}$ | $\Gamma(\nu+1)\sum_{k=1}^{\infty}\frac{(-1)^{k}}{n}[\zeta(\nu+1,s)-\zeta(\nu+1,s+k)]$ | Re s > o |
| | 6 | $\frac{\log(1-e^{-t})}{1+e^{-t}}$ | $\sum_{k=1}^{\infty}\frac{(-1)^{k}}{s+k}[1-\frac{1}{2}+\frac{1}{3}-\cdots+\frac{(-1)^{k-1}}{k}]$ | Re s > o |
| | 7 | $[\log\gamma(e^{t}-1)]^{2}-\frac{\pi^{2}}{6}-t\log(e^{t}-1)+1*\log(e^{t}-1)$ | $\frac{\psi^{2}(s)}{s}$ | Re s > o |
| 5 | 1 | $\sin(at)$ | $\frac{a}{s^{2}+a^{2}}$ | Re s > \|Im a\| |
| | 2 | $\frac{1}{t}\sin(at)$ | $\tan^{-1}(\frac{a}{s})$ <br> $=\cot^{-1}(\frac{s}{a})$ <br> $=\sin^{-1}\frac{a}{(s^{2}+a^{2})^{\frac{1}{2}}}$ <br> $=\cos^{-1}\frac{s}{(s^{2}+a^{2})^{\frac{1}{2}}}$ | Re s > \|Im a\| |
| | 3 | $\|\sin(at)\|$ | $\frac{a}{s^{2}+a^{2}}\coth(\frac{\pi s}{2a})$ <br> $=\frac{a}{s^{2}+a^{2}}\cdot\frac{1+e^{-\frac{\pi s}{a}}}{1-e^{-\frac{\pi s}{a}}}$ | Re s > \|Im a\| |
| | 4 | $\frac{1}{t}\sin^{2}(at)$ | $\frac{1}{4}\log(1+\frac{4a^{2}}{s^{2}})$ | Re s > 2\|Im a\| |
| | 5 | $\sin^{3}(at)$ | $\frac{6a^{3}}{(s^{2}+a^{2})(s^{2}+9a^{2})}$ | Re s > 3\|Im a\| |
| | 6 | $\frac{1}{t}\sin^{3}(at)$ | $\frac{3}{4}\tan^{-1}\frac{a}{s}-\frac{1}{4}\tan^{-1}\frac{3a}{s}$ | Re s > 3\|Im a\| |

| | | f(t) | g(s) | |
|---|---|---|---|---|
| 5 (Contd.) | 7 | $\frac{1}{t}\sin^4(at)$ | $\frac{1}{8}\log\frac{(s^2+4a^2)^2}{s^3}-\frac{1}{16}\log(s^2+16a^2)$ | Re s > 4\|Im a\| |
| | 8 | $\frac{1}{t}\sin^5(at)$ | $\frac{5}{8}\tan^{-1}\frac{a}{s}-\frac{5}{16}\tan^{-1}\frac{3a}{s}+\frac{1}{16}\tan^{-1}\frac{5a}{s}$ | Re s > 5\|Im a\| |
| | 9 | $\sin^{2n}(at)$ | $\frac{(2n)!a^{2n}}{s[s^2+(2a)^2][s^2+(4a)^2]\dots[s^2+(2na)^2]}$ | n = 1,2,3,... <br> Re s > 2n\|Im a\| |
| | 10 | $\sin^{2n+1}(at)$ | $\frac{(2n+1)!\ a^{2n+1}}{[s^2+a^2][s^2+(3a)^2]\cdots[s^2+((2n+1)a)^2]}$ | n = 0,1,2,... <br> Re s > (2n+1)\|Im a\| |
| | 11 | $\sin^{\frac{1}{2}}t$ | $\frac{\pi^{\frac{1}{2}}\Gamma(-\frac{1}{4}-\frac{is}{2})}{(i-1)(1-2is)\Gamma(\frac{1}{4}-\frac{is}{2})}$ | Re s > o |
| | 12 | $\sin^{\nu}(at)$ | $\frac{\Gamma(\nu+1)\Gamma\left(-\frac{a\nu+is}{2a}\right)}{(2i)^{\nu+1}\Gamma\left(1+\frac{a\nu-is}{2a}\right)}$ | Re$\nu$ > - 1 <br> Re s > Max 2 Im a + Im a $\nu$, - Im a $\nu$ |
| | 13 | $\|\sin(at)\|^{\nu}$ | $\frac{B(1+\frac{is}{2a},1-\frac{is}{2a})}{(\nu+1)2^{\nu}s\,B(\frac{\nu}{2}+1+\frac{is}{2a},\frac{\nu}{2}+1-\frac{is}{2a})}$ | Re s > \|Im a\| <br> Re$\nu$ > - 1 |
| | 14 | 1 - 2sin(at) | $\frac{(s-a)^2}{s(s^2+a^2)}$ | Re s > \|Im a\| |
| | 15 | sin at + \|sin (at)\| | $\frac{2a}{s^2+a^2}\ \frac{1}{1-e^{-\frac{\pi}{a}s}}$ | Re s > \|Im a\| |
| | 16 | \|sin(at)\|-sin(at) | $\frac{2a}{s^2+a^2}\ \frac{1}{e^{\frac{\pi}{a}s}-1}$ | Re s > \|Im a\| |
| | 17 | a sin(at) - b sin(bt) | $\frac{(a^2-b^2)s^2}{(s^2+a^2)(s^2+b^2)}$ | Re s > Max \|Im a\|, \|Im b\| |

| | f(t) | g(s) | |
|---|---|---|---|
| 5 (Contd.) 18 | $a\sin(bt) - b\sin(at)$ | $\dfrac{ab(a^2-b^2)}{(s^2+a^2)(s^2+b^2)}$ | $\mathrm{Re}\, s > \mathrm{Max}\,\lvert \mathrm{Im}\, a\rvert, \lvert \mathrm{Im}\, b\rvert$ |
| 19 | $\dfrac{\sin(at)+\sin(bt)}{t}$ | $\dfrac{1}{2}\log\dfrac{s^2+a^2}{s^2+b^2}$ | $\mathrm{Re}\, s > \mathrm{Max}\,\lvert \mathrm{Im}\, a\rvert, \lvert \mathrm{Im}\, b\rvert$ |
| 20 | $\sin(at)\sin(bt)$ | $\dfrac{2abs}{[s^2+(a+b)^2][s^2+(a-b)^2]}$ | $\mathrm{Re}\, s \geqslant \lvert \mathrm{Im}(\pm a \pm b)\rvert$ |
| 21 | $\dfrac{\sin(at)\sin(bt)}{t}$ | $\dfrac{1}{4}\log\dfrac{s^2+(a+b)^2}{s^2+(a-b)^2}$ | $\mathrm{Re}\, s > \lvert \mathrm{Im}(\pm a \pm b)\rvert$ |
| 22 | $\displaystyle\sum_{n=1}^{\infty}\frac{(-1)^{n-1}}{n-\frac{1}{2}}\sin\frac{(n-\frac{1}{2})\pi b}{a}\sin\frac{(n-\frac{1}{2})\pi t}{a}$ | $\dfrac{\pi\sinh(bs)}{2s\cosh(as)}$ | $0 \leqslant b \leqslant a$<br>$\mathrm{Re}\, s > 0$ |
| 23 | $\dfrac{\sin[(2n+1)t]}{\sin t}$ | $\displaystyle\frac{1}{s} + \sum_{m=1}^{n}\frac{2s}{s^2+4m^2}$ | $n = 1, 2, 3, \ldots$<br>$\mathrm{Re}\, s > 0$ |
| 24 | $\cos(at)$ | $\dfrac{s}{s^2+a^2}$ | $\mathrm{Re}\, s > \lvert \mathrm{Im}\, a\rvert$ |
| 25 | $\lvert\cos(at)\rvert$ | $\dfrac{s + a\,\mathrm{cosech}(\frac{\pi s}{2a})}{s^2+a^2}$<br>$= \dfrac{a}{s^2+a^2}\left(\dfrac{s}{a} + \dfrac{2e^{-\frac{\pi s}{2a}}}{1-e^{-\frac{\pi s}{a}}}\right)$ | $\mathrm{Re}\, s > \lvert \mathrm{Im}\, a\rvert$ |
| 26 | $\cos^2(at)$ | $\dfrac{s^2+2a^2}{s(s^2+4a^2)}$ | $\mathrm{Re}\, s > 2\lvert \mathrm{Im}\, a\rvert$ |
| 27 | $\cos^3(at)$ | $\dfrac{s(s^2+7a^2)}{(s^2+a^2)(s^2+9a^2)}$ | $\mathrm{Re}\, s > 3\lvert \mathrm{Im}\, a\rvert$ |
| 28 | $\cos^{2n}(at)$ | $\dfrac{(2n)!\,a^{2n}\left\{1+\dfrac{s^2}{2!\,a^2}+\cdots+\dfrac{s^2[s^2+4a^2]\cdots[s^2+4(na-a)^2]}{(2n)!\,a^{2n}}\right\}}{s[s^2+(2a)^2][s^2+(4a)^2]\cdots[s^2+(2na)^2]}$ | $n = 1, 2, 3, \ldots$<br>$\mathrm{Re}\, s > 2n\lvert \mathrm{Im}\, a\rvert$ |

| | f(t) | g(s) | |
|---|---|---|---|
| 5 (Contd.) 29 | $\cos^{2n+1}(at)$ | $\dfrac{(2n+1)!a^{2n}s\left\{1+\dfrac{s^2+a^2}{3!a^2}+\dots+\dfrac{[s^2+a^2][s^2+(3a)^2]\cdots[s^2+(2na-a)^2]}{(2n+1)!a^{2n}}\right\}}{[s^2+a^2][s^2+(3a)^2]\cdots[s^2+(2na+a)^2]}$ | $n=0,1,2,\dots$ Re $s > (2n+1)\lvert \text{Im } a\rvert$ |
| 30 | $1-\cos(at)$ | $\dfrac{a^2}{s(s^2+a^2)}$ | Re $s > \lvert \text{Im } a\rvert$ |
| 31 | $\frac{1}{t}(1-\cos at)$ | $\frac{1}{2}\log(1+\frac{a^2}{s^2})$ | Re $s > \lvert \text{Im } a\rvert$ |
| 32 | $\cos(bt)-\cos(at)$ | $\dfrac{s(a^2-b^2)}{(s^2+a^2)(s^2+b^2)}$ | Re $s >$ Max$\lvert \text{Im } a\rvert, \lvert \text{Im } b\rvert$ |
| 33 | $a^2\cos(at)-b^2\cos(bt)$ | $\dfrac{(a^2-b^2)s^3}{(s^2+a^2)(s^2+b^2)}$ | Re $s >$ Max$\lvert \text{Im } a\rvert, \lvert \text{Im } b\rvert$ |
| 34 | $\sin(at)-at\cos(at)$ | $\dfrac{2a^3}{(s^2+a^2)^2}$ | Re $s > \lvert \text{Im } a\rvert$ |
| 35 | $\dfrac{\cos(at)-\cos(bt)}{t}$ | $\frac{1}{2}\log\dfrac{s^2+b^2}{s^2+a^2}$ | Re $s >$ Max$\lvert \text{Im } a\rvert, \lvert \text{Im } b\rvert$ |
| 36 | $\lvert\cos(at)\rvert-\cos(at)$ | $\dfrac{a\,\text{cosech}\,\frac{\pi s}{2a}}{s^2+a^2}$ | Re $s > \lvert \text{Im } a\rvert$ |
| 37 | $\cos(at)\cos(bt)$ | $\dfrac{s(s^2+a^2+b^2)}{[s^2+(a+b)^2][s^2+(a-b)^2]}$ | Re $s > \lvert \text{Im}(\pm a\pm b)\rvert$ |
| 38 | $1+\dfrac{2}{\pi}\sum_{n=1}^{\infty}\dfrac{(-1)^n}{n-\frac{1}{2}}\cos\dfrac{(n-\frac{1}{2})\pi b}{a}\cos\dfrac{(n-\frac{1}{2})\pi t}{a}$ | $\dfrac{\cosh(bs)}{s\cosh(as)}$ | $-a \leq b \leq a$ Re $s > 0$ |
| 39 | $\cos(at)\sin(bt)$ | $\dfrac{b(s^2-a^2+b^2)}{[s^2+(a+b)^2][s^2+(a-b)^2]}$ | Re $s > \lvert \text{Im}(\pm a\pm b)\rvert$ |
| 40 | $\dfrac{\sin(at)\cos(bt)}{t}$ | $\frac{1}{2}\tan^{-1}\dfrac{2as}{s^2-a^2+b^2}$ | Re $>$ Max$\lvert \text{Im}(a+b)\rvert, \lvert \text{Im}(a-b)\rvert$ |

| | | f(t) | g(s) | |
|---|---|---|---|---|
| 5 (Contd.) | 41 | $\frac{\sin^2(at)\cos(bt)}{t}$ | $\frac{1}{8}\log\frac{[s^2+(2a+b)^2][s^2+(2a-b)^2]}{(s^2+b^2)^2}$ | Re s > Max \| Im(2a+b) \|, \| Im(2a-b) \|, \| Im b \| |
| | 42 | $\tan t\cos[(2n+1)t]$ | $\frac{2n+1}{s^2+(2n+1)^2}+2\sum_{m=0}^{n-1}\frac{(-1)^m(2m+1)}{s^2+(2m+1)^2}$ | n = 1,2,3,... Re s > o |
| 5.1 | 1 | $t^n\sin(at)$ | $n!\frac{s^{n+1}}{(s^2+a^2)^{n+1}}\sum_{o\le 2m\le n}(-1)^m\binom{n+1}{2m+1}\left(\frac{a}{s}\right)^{2m+1}$ | n = 0,1,2,... Re s > \| Im a \| |
| | 2 | $\frac{1}{t^2}\sin^2(at)$ | $a\tan^{-1}\frac{2a}{s}-\frac{s}{4}\log(1+\frac{4a^2}{s^2})$ | Re s ⩾ 2\| Im a \| |
| | 3 | $\frac{1}{t^2}\sin^3(at)$ | $\frac{s}{4}\tan^{-1}\frac{3a}{s}-\frac{3s}{4}\tan^{-1}\frac{a}{s}+\frac{3a}{8}\log\frac{s^2+3a^2}{s^2+a^2}$ | Re s ⩾ 3\| Im a \| |
| | 4 | $\sin(at+b)$ | $\frac{\sin(b+\tan^{-1}\frac{a}{s})}{(s^2+a^2)^{\frac{1}{2}}}$ $=\frac{s\sin b+a\cos b}{s^2+a^2}$ | Re s > \| Im a \| |
| | 5 | $\frac{1}{t}\sin(t^2)$ | $\frac{\pi}{2}[\frac{1}{2}-C(\frac{s^2}{4})]^2+\frac{\pi}{2}[\frac{1}{2}-S(\frac{s^2}{4})]^2$ $=\frac{1}{2}D_{-1}[(\frac{i}{2})^{\frac{1}{2}}s]D_{-1}[(-\frac{i}{2})^{\frac{1}{2}}s]$ | Re s > o |
| | 6 | $\sin(t^2)$ | $\left(\frac{\pi}{2}\right)^{\frac{1}{2}}\left[\cos(\frac{s^2}{4})\left\{\frac{1}{2}-C(\frac{s^2}{4})\right\}+\sin(\frac{s^2}{4})\left\{\frac{1}{2}-S(\frac{s^2}{4})\right\}\right]$ | Re s > o |
| | 7 | $\frac{\sin(at)\sin(bt)}{t^2}$ | $\frac{a}{2}\tan^{-1}\frac{2bs}{s^2+a^2-b^2}+\frac{b}{2}\tan^{-1}\frac{2as}{s^2-a^2+b^2}+\frac{s}{4}\log\frac{s^2+(a-b)^2}{s^2+(a+b)^2}$ | Re s ⩾ \| Im(±a±b) \| |
| | 8 | $t^n\cos(at)$ | $\frac{n!s^{n+1}}{(s^2+a^2)^{n+1}}\sum_{o\le 2m\le n+1}(-1)^m\binom{n+1}{2m}\left(\frac{a}{s}\right)^{2m}$ | n = 0,1,2,... Re s > \| Im a \| |
| | 9 | $\cos(at+b)$ | $\frac{\cos(b+\tan^{-1}\frac{a}{s})}{(s^2+a^2)^{\frac{1}{2}}}=\frac{s\cos b-a\sin b}{s^2+a^2}$ | Re s > \| Im a \| |

| | | f(t) | g(s) | |
|---|---|---|---|---|
| 5.1 (Contd.) | 10 | $\cos(t^2)$ | $(\frac{\pi}{2})^{\frac{1}{2}}\left[\cos(\frac{s^2}{4})\left\{\frac{1}{2}-S(\frac{s^2}{4})\right\}-\sin(\frac{s^2}{4})\left\{\frac{1}{2}-C(\frac{s^2}{4})\right\}\right]$ | Re s > o |
| | 11 | $\frac{1-\cos(at)}{t^2}$ | $a\tan^{-1}\frac{a}{s}-\frac{s}{2}\log(1+\frac{a^2}{s^2})$ | Re s > \|Im a\| |
| | 12 | $\frac{\cos(at)-\cos(bt)}{t^2}$ | $\frac{s}{2}\log\frac{s^2+a^2}{s^2+b^2}+b\tan^{-1}\frac{b}{s}-a\tan^{-1}\frac{a}{s}$ | Re s ⩾ Max \|Im a\|,\|Im b\| |
| | 13 | $t\sin(at)-at^2\cos(at)$ | $\frac{8a^3 s}{(s^2+a^2)^3}$ | Re s > \|Im a\| |
| | 14 | $(3-a^2t^2)\sin(at)-3at\cos(at)$ | $\frac{8a^5}{(s^2+a^2)^3}$ | Re s > \|Im a\| |
| | 15 | $(1+a^2t^2)\sin(at)-at\cos(at)$ | $\frac{8a^3s^2}{(s^2+a^2)^3}$ | Re s > \|Im a\| |
| | 16 | $\frac{at\cos(at)-\sin(at)}{t^2}$ | $s\tan^{-1}\frac{a}{s}-a$ | Re s > \|Im a\| |
| | 17 | $\frac{\cos(at)-1}{t^2}+\frac{a\sin(at)}{t}$ | $\frac{s}{2}\log\frac{s^2+a^2}{s^2}$ | Re s > \|Im a\| |
| | 18 | $\frac{\sin at[2at\cos(at)-\sin(at)]}{t^2}$ | $\frac{s}{4}\log\left(1+\frac{4a^2}{s^2}\right)$ | Re s > 2\|Im a\| |
| | 19 | $\frac{1}{t^2}[\cos(bt)+bt\sin(bt)-\cos(at)-at\sin(at)]$ | $\frac{s}{2}\log\frac{s^2+b^2}{s^2+a^2}$ | Re s > Max \|Im a\|,\|Im b\| |
| 5.2 | 1 | $\frac{1}{t^{\frac{1}{2}}}\sin at$ | $(\frac{\pi}{2})^{\frac{1}{2}}[\frac{(s^2+a^2)^{\frac{1}{2}}-s}{s^2+a^2}]^{\frac{1}{2}}$ | Re s > \|Im a\| |
| | 2 | $\frac{1}{t^{\frac{3}{2}}}\sin(at)$ | $(2\pi)^{\frac{1}{2}}[(s^2+a^2)^{\frac{1}{2}}-s]^{\frac{1}{2}}$ | Re s > \|Im a\| |

| | | f(t) | g(s) | |
|---|---|---|---|---|
| 5.2 (Contd.) | 3 | $t^{\nu}\sin(at)$ | $\frac{i}{2}\Gamma(\nu+1)[(s+ia)^{-\nu-1}-(s-ia)^{-\nu-1}]$ $=\Gamma(\nu+1)(s^2+a^2)^{-\frac{\nu+1}{2}}\sin[(\nu+1)\tan^{-1}(\frac{a}{s})]$ | $\mathrm{Re}\,\nu>-2$ $\mathrm{Re}\,s>\lvert\mathrm{Im}\,a\rvert$ |
| | 4 | $\sin(at^{\frac{1}{2}})$ | $\frac{a\pi^{\frac{1}{2}}}{2}s^{-\frac{3}{2}}e^{-\frac{a^2}{4s}}$ | $\mathrm{Re}\,s>0$ |
| | 5 | $t^{\frac{1}{2}}\sin(at^{\frac{1}{2}})$ | $\frac{a}{2s^2}-\frac{i\pi^{\frac{1}{2}}}{s^{\frac{5}{2}}}(\frac{s}{2}-\frac{a^2}{4})e^{-\frac{a^2}{4s}}\mathrm{Erf}\left(\frac{ia}{2s^{\frac{1}{2}}}\right)$ | $\mathrm{Re}\,s>0$ |
| | 6 | $\frac{1}{t^{\frac{1}{2}}}\sin(at^{\frac{1}{2}})$ | $-\frac{i\pi^{\frac{1}{2}}}{s^{\frac{1}{2}}}e^{-\frac{a^2}{4s}}\mathrm{Erf}\left(\frac{ia}{2s^{\frac{1}{2}}}\right)$ | $\mathrm{Re}\,s>0$ |
| | 7 | $\frac{1}{t^{\frac{3}{4}}}\sin(at^{\frac{1}{2}})$ | $\pi(\frac{a}{2})^{\frac{1}{2}}s^{-\frac{1}{2}}e^{-\frac{a^2}{8s}}I_{\frac{1}{4}}(\frac{a^2}{8s})$ | $\mathrm{Re}\,s>0$ |
| | 8 | $\frac{1}{t}\sin(at^{\frac{1}{2}})$ | $\pi\,\mathrm{Erf}(\frac{a}{2s^{\frac{1}{2}}})$ | $\mathrm{Re}\,s>0$ |
| | 9 | $t^{\nu}\sin(at^{\frac{1}{2}})$ | $-\frac{\pi^{\frac{1}{2}}\sec(\nu\pi)}{2^{\nu+\frac{3}{2}}s^{\nu+1}}e^{-\frac{a^2}{8s}}\left[D_{2\nu+1}\left(-\frac{a}{2^{\frac{1}{2}}s^{\frac{1}{2}}}\right)-D_{2\nu+1}\left(\frac{a}{2^{\frac{1}{2}}s^{\frac{1}{2}}}\right)\right]$ | $\mathrm{Re}\,\nu>-\frac{3}{2}$ $\mathrm{Re}\,s>0$ |
| | 10 | $t^{\nu}\sin(\nu\pi-at^{\frac{1}{2}})$ | $-\frac{\pi^{\frac{1}{2}}}{2^{\nu+\frac{3}{2}}s^{\nu+1}}e^{\frac{a^2}{8s}}D_{2\nu+1}\left(\frac{a}{2^{\frac{1}{2}}s^{\frac{1}{2}}}\right)$ | $\mathrm{Re}\,\nu>0$ $\mathrm{Re}\,s>0$ |
| | 11 | $\frac{1}{t^{\frac{1}{2}}}\sin\frac{a}{t}$ | $(\frac{\pi}{s})^{\frac{1}{2}}e^{-(2as)^{\frac{1}{2}}}\sin[(2as)^{\frac{1}{2}}]$ | $\mathrm{Re}\,s>0$ |
| | 12 | $\frac{\sin[a(t^2+2bt)^{\frac{1}{2}}]}{(t+2b)^{\frac{1}{2}}}$ | $\frac{a\pi^{\frac{1}{2}}e^{b[s-(s^2+a^2)^{\frac{1}{2}}]}}{2^{\frac{1}{2}}(s^2+a^2)^{\frac{1}{2}}[s+(s^2+a^2)^{\frac{1}{2}}]^{\frac{1}{2}}}$ | $\mathrm{Re}\,s>\lvert\mathrm{Im}\,a\rvert$ |
| | 13 | $\frac{\sin(at^{\frac{1}{2}})\sin(bt^{\frac{1}{2}})}{t^{\frac{1}{2}}}$ | $(\frac{\pi}{s})^{\frac{1}{2}}e^{-\frac{a^2+b^2}{4s}}\sinh(\frac{ab}{2s})=\frac{\pi}{2}\frac{(ab)^{\frac{1}{2}}}{s}e^{-\frac{a^2+b^2}{4s}}I_{\frac{1}{2}}(\frac{ab}{2s})$ | $\mathrm{Re}\,s>0$ |

| | f(t) | g(s) | |
|---|---|---|---|
| 5.2 (Contd.) 14 | $\frac{1}{t^{\frac{1}{2}}}\cos(at)$ | $(\frac{\pi}{2})^{\frac{1}{2}} \frac{[s+(s^2+a^2)^{\frac{1}{2}}]^{\frac{1}{2}}}{(s^2+a^2)^{\frac{1}{2}}}$ | Re s > \|Im a\| |
| 15 | $t^{\nu}\cos(at)$ | $\frac{1}{2}\Gamma(\nu+1)[(s-ia)^{-\nu-1}+(s+ia)^{-\nu-1}]$ $= \frac{\Gamma(\nu+1)\cos[(\nu+1)\tan^{-1}\frac{a}{s}]}{(s^2+a^2)^{\frac{\nu+1}{2}}}$ | Re ν > − 1 <br> Re s > \|Im a\| |
| 16 | $\cos(at^{\frac{1}{2}})$ | $\frac{1}{s} + \frac{i\pi^{\frac{1}{2}}a}{2s^{\frac{3}{2}}} e^{-\frac{a^2}{4s}} \mathrm{Erf}\left(\frac{ia}{2s^{\frac{1}{2}}}\right)$ | Re s > o |
| 17 | $t^{\frac{1}{2}}\cos(at^{\frac{1}{2}})$ | $\frac{\pi^{\frac{1}{2}}}{s^{\frac{5}{2}}} (\frac{s}{2} - \frac{a^2}{4}) e^{-\frac{a^2}{4s}}$ | Re s > o |
| 18 | $\frac{1}{t^{\frac{1}{2}}}\cos(at^{\frac{1}{2}})$ | $(\frac{\pi}{s})^{\frac{1}{2}} e^{-\frac{a^2}{4s}}$ | Re s > o |
| 19 | $\frac{1}{t^{\frac{3}{4}}}\cos(at^{\frac{1}{2}})$ | $\pi (\frac{a}{2})^{\frac{1}{2}} s^{-\frac{1}{2}} e^{-\frac{a^2}{8s}} I_{-\frac{1}{4}}(\frac{a^2}{8s})$ | Re s > o |
| 20 | $t^{n-\frac{1}{2}}\cos(at^{\frac{1}{2}})$ | $\frac{\pi^{\frac{1}{2}}}{(-2)^n s^{n+\frac{1}{2}}} e^{-\frac{a^2}{4s}} He_{2n}\left(\frac{a}{2^{\frac{1}{2}}s^{\frac{1}{2}}}\right)$ $= \frac{\pi^{\frac{1}{2}}}{(-2)^n s^{n+\frac{1}{2}}} e^{-\frac{a^2}{8s}} D_{2n}\left(\frac{a}{2^{\frac{1}{2}}s^{\frac{1}{2}}}\right)$ | n = 0,1,2,... <br> Re s > o |
| 21 | $t^{\nu}\cos(at^{\frac{1}{2}})$ | $-\frac{\pi^{\frac{1}{2}}\operatorname{cosec}(\nu\pi)}{2^{\nu+\frac{3}{2}} s^{\nu+1}} e^{-\frac{a^2}{8s}} \left[D_{2\nu+1}\left(\frac{a}{2^{\frac{1}{2}}s^{\frac{1}{2}}}\right) + D_{2\nu+1}\left(-\frac{a}{2^{\frac{1}{2}}s^{\frac{1}{2}}}\right)\right]$ | Re ν > − 1 <br> Re s > o |
| 22 | $t^{\nu}\cos(2^{\frac{1}{2}}t^{\frac{1}{2}})$ | $\frac{\Gamma(2\nu+2)}{(2s)^{\nu+1}} e^{-\frac{1}{4s}} \left[D_{-2\nu-2}\left(\frac{i}{s^{\frac{1}{2}}}\right) + D_{-2\nu-2}\left(\frac{-i}{s^{\frac{1}{2}}}\right)\right]$ | Re ν > − 1 <br> Re s > o |
| 23 | $\frac{1}{t^{\frac{1}{2}}}\cos\frac{a}{t}$ | $(\frac{\pi}{s})^{\frac{1}{2}} e^{-(2as)^{\frac{1}{2}}} \cos[(2as)^{\frac{1}{2}}]$ | Re s > o |

| | | f(t) | g(s) | |
|---|---|---|---|---|
| 5.2 (Contd.) | 24 | $\dfrac{\cos[a(t^2+2bt)^{\frac{1}{2}}]}{(t+2b)^{\frac{1}{2}}}$ | $(\frac{\pi}{2})^{\frac{1}{2}}\dfrac{[s+(s^2+a^2)^{\frac{1}{2}}]^{\frac{1}{2}}e^{b[s-(s^2+a^2)^{\frac{1}{2}}]}}{(s^2+a^2)^{\frac{1}{2}}}$ | $\mathrm{Re}\, s > \lvert \mathrm{Im}\, a \rvert$ |
| | 25 | $\dfrac{\cos(at^{\frac{1}{2}})\cos(bt^{\frac{1}{2}})}{t^{\frac{1}{2}}}$ | $(\frac{\pi}{s})^{\frac{1}{2}} e^{-\frac{a^2+b^2}{4s}} \cosh(\frac{ab}{2s})$ <br> $= \frac{\pi}{2}\,\frac{(ab)^{\frac{1}{2}}}{s}\, e^{-\frac{a^2+b^2}{4s}} I_{-\frac{1}{2}}(\frac{ab}{2s})$ | $\mathrm{Re}\, s > 0$ |
| | 26 | $\frac{1}{a}\sin(at^{\frac{1}{2}}) - t^{\frac{1}{2}}\cos(at^{\frac{1}{2}})$ | $\dfrac{\pi^{\frac{1}{2}}a^2}{4s^{\frac{5}{2}}} e^{-\frac{a^2}{4s}}$ | $\mathrm{Re}\, s > 0$ |
| | 27 | $\frac{1}{t^{\frac{3}{4}}}\sin(at^{\frac{1}{2}}) - \frac{1}{at^{\frac{5}{4}}}\cos(at^{\frac{1}{2}})$ | $\pi(\frac{a}{2s})^{\frac{1}{2}} e^{-\frac{a^2}{8s}} I_{-\frac{3}{4}}(\frac{a^2}{8s})$ | $\mathrm{Re}\, s > 0$ |
| | 28 | $\frac{1}{at^{\frac{5}{4}}}\sin(at^{\frac{1}{2}}) - \frac{1}{t^{\frac{3}{4}}}\cos(at^{\frac{1}{2}})$ | $(\frac{a}{2s})^{\frac{1}{2}} e^{-\frac{a^2}{8s}} I_{\frac{3}{4}}(\frac{a^2}{8s})$ | $\mathrm{Re}\, s > 0$ |
| 5.2.1 | 1 | $t^n \sin(at^{\frac{1}{2}})$ | $\dfrac{(-1)^n\pi^{\frac{1}{2}}}{2^{n+\frac{1}{2}}s^{n+1}} e^{-\frac{a^2}{4s}} He_{2n+1}\left(\dfrac{a}{2^{\frac{1}{2}}s^{\frac{1}{2}}}\right)$ <br> $= \dfrac{(-1)^n\pi^{\frac{1}{2}}e^{-\frac{a^2}{8s}}}{2^{n+\frac{1}{2}}s^{n+1}} D_{2n+1}\left(\dfrac{a}{2^{\frac{1}{2}}s^{\frac{1}{2}}}\right)$ | $n = 0,1,2,\ldots$ <br> $\mathrm{Re}\, s > 0$ |
| | 2 | $(\frac{3}{8t}-1)\dfrac{\sin[(8t)^{\frac{1}{2}}]}{(2t^3)^{\frac{1}{4}}} - \dfrac{3\cos[(8t)^{\frac{1}{2}}]}{2t(8t)^{\frac{1}{4}}}$ | $\dfrac{\pi}{s^{\frac{1}{2}}} e^{-\frac{1}{s}} I_{\frac{5}{4}}(\frac{1}{s})$ | $\mathrm{Re}\, s > 0$ |
| | 3 | $(\frac{3}{8t}-1)\dfrac{\cos[(8t)^{\frac{1}{2}}]}{(2t^3)^{\frac{1}{4}}} + \dfrac{3\sin[(8t)^{\frac{1}{2}}]}{2t(8t)^{\frac{1}{4}}}$ | $\dfrac{\pi}{s^{\frac{1}{2}}} e^{-\frac{1}{s}} I_{-\frac{5}{4}}(\frac{1}{s})$ | $\mathrm{Re}\, s > 0$ |
| 5.3 | 1 | $e^{-at}\sin(bt)$ | $\dfrac{b}{(s+a)^2+b^2}$ | $\mathrm{Re}\, s > \lvert \mathrm{Im}\, b \rvert - \mathrm{Re}\, a$ |
| | 2 | $\dfrac{e^{at}-1}{t}\sin(bt)$ | $\cot^{-1}\dfrac{s^2-as+b}{ab}$ | $\mathrm{Re}\, s > \mathrm{Max} \lvert \mathrm{Im}\, b \rvert,$ <br> $\lvert \mathrm{Im}\, b \rvert + \mathrm{Re}\, a$ |
| | 3 | $(1-e^{-t})^{\nu}\sin(at)$ | $\frac{i}{2}B(\nu+1, s+ia) - \frac{i}{2}B(\nu+1, s-ia)$ | $\mathrm{Re}\,\nu > -2$ <br> $\mathrm{Re}\, s > \lvert \mathrm{Im}\, a \rvert$ |

| | | f(t) | g(s) | |
|---|---|---|---|---|
| 5.3 (Contd.) | 4 | $\frac{\sin(at)}{e^t-1}$ | $\frac{i}{2}\psi(s-ia+1)-\frac{i}{2}\psi(s+ia+1)$ | $\mathrm{Re}\, s > \lvert \mathrm{Im}\, a \rvert - 1$ |
| | 5 | $\frac{\sin(at)}{1-e^{-t}}$ | $\frac{i}{2}\psi(s-ia)-\frac{i}{2}\psi(s+ia)$ | $\mathrm{Re}\, s > \lvert \mathrm{Im}\, a \rvert$ |
| | 6 | $\sin(a e^{-t})$ | $\frac{\Gamma(s)}{a^s}[U_s(2a,o)\sin a - U_{s+1}(2a,o)\cos a]$ | $\mathrm{Re}\, s > o$ |
| | 7 | $\sin[a(1-e^{-t})]$ | $\frac{\Gamma(s)}{a^s}U_{s+1}(2a,o)$ | $\mathrm{Re}\, s > o$ |
| | 8 | $\frac{\sin[a(1-e^{-t})^{\frac{1}{2}}]}{(e^t-1)^{\frac{1}{2}}}$ | $\pi^{\frac{1}{2}}\Gamma(s+\frac{1}{2})(\frac{2}{a})^s\, \mathbf{H}_s(a)$ | $\mathrm{Re}\, s > -\frac{1}{2}$ |
| | 9 | $\frac{\sin[a(e^t-1)^{\frac{1}{2}}]}{(1-e^{-t})^{\frac{1}{2}}}$ | $\pi^{\frac{1}{2}}\Gamma(\frac{1}{2}-s)(\frac{a}{2})^s[I_s(a)-\mathbf{L}_{-s}(a)]$ | $a > o$<br>$\mathrm{Re}\, s > -\frac{1}{2}$ |
| | 10 | $e^{-at}\cos(bt)$ | $\frac{s+a}{(s+a)^2+b^2}$ | $\mathrm{Re}\, s > \lvert \mathrm{Im}\, b \rvert - \mathrm{Re}\, a$ |
| | 11 | $\frac{1}{t}\cos(ct)(e^{-bt}-e^{-at})$ | $\frac{1}{2}\log\frac{(s+a)^2+c^2}{(s+b)^2+c^2}$ | $\mathrm{Re}\, s > \lvert \mathrm{Im}\, c \rvert - \mathrm{Min}\ \mathrm{Re}\, a, \mathrm{Re}\, b$ |
| | 12 | $(1-e^{-t})^\nu\cos(at)$ | $\frac{1}{2}B(\nu+1,s-ia)+\frac{1}{2}B(\nu+1,s+ia)$ | $\mathrm{Re}\, \nu > -1$<br>$\mathrm{Re}\, s > \lvert \mathrm{Im}\, a \rvert$ |
| | 13 | $\cos(a e^{-t})$ | $\frac{\Gamma(s)}{a^s}[U_s(2a,o)\cos a + U_{s+1}(2a,o)\sin a]$ | $\mathrm{Re}\, s > o$ |
| | 14 | $\cos[a(1-e^{-t})]$ | $\frac{\Gamma(s)}{a^s}U_s(2a,o)$ | $\mathrm{Re}\, s > o$ |
| | 15 | $\frac{\cos[a(1-e^{-t})^{\frac{1}{2}}]}{(e^t-1)^{\frac{1}{2}}}$ | $\pi^{\frac{1}{2}}\Gamma(s+\frac{1}{2})(\frac{2}{a})^s\, J_s(a)$ | $\mathrm{Re}\, s > -\frac{1}{2}$ |

| | | f(t) | g(s) | |
|---|---|---|---|---|
| 5.3 (Contd.) | 16 | $\frac{\cos[a(e^{t}-1)^{\frac{1}{2}}]}{(1-e^{-t})^{\frac{1}{2}}}$ | $\frac{2\pi^{\frac{1}{2}}(\frac{a}{2})^{s}}{\Gamma(s+\frac{1}{2})}K_{s}(a)$ | Re s > $-\frac{1}{2}$<br>a > o |
| | 17 | $e^{-at}[\cos(bt)+c\sin(bt)]$ | $\frac{s+bc+a}{(s+a)^{2}+b^{2}}$ | Re s > \|Im b\| − Re a |
| 5.3.2.1 | 1 | $t^{\nu}e^{-at^{2}}\sin(bt)$ | $\frac{i\Gamma(\nu+1)}{2(2a)^{\frac{\nu+1}{2}}}e^{\frac{s^{2}-b^{2}}{8a}}\left\{e^{\frac{ibs}{4a}}D_{-\nu-1}\left[\frac{s+ib}{(2a)^{\frac{1}{2}}}\right]-e^{-\frac{ibs}{4a}}D_{-\nu-1}\left[\frac{s-ib}{(2a)^{\frac{1}{2}}}\right]\right\}$ | Re(s±ib) > $\begin{cases}-\infty \text{ where } \|\arg a\|<\frac{\pi}{2}\\ o \text{ where } \arg a=\frac{\pi}{2},\frac{3\pi}{2}\\ +\infty \text{ otherwise}\end{cases}$<br>Re a > o<br>Re ν > − 2 |
| | 2 | $t^{\nu}e^{-at^{2}}\cos(bt)$ | $\frac{i\Gamma(\nu+1)}{2(2a)^{\frac{\nu+1}{2}}}e^{\frac{s^{2}-b^{2}}{8a}}\left\{e^{\frac{ibs}{4a}}D_{-\nu-1}\left[\frac{s+ib}{(2a)^{\frac{1}{2}}}\right]+e^{-\frac{ibs}{4a}}D_{-\nu-1}\left[\frac{s-ib}{(2a)^{\frac{1}{2}}}\right]\right\}$ | Re(s±ib) > $\begin{cases}-\infty \text{ where } \|\arg a\|<\frac{\pi}{2}\\ o \text{ where } \arg a=\frac{\pi}{2},\frac{3\pi}{2}\\ +\infty \text{ otherwise}\end{cases}$<br>Re a > o<br>Re ν > − 1 |
| 5.4 | 1 | $\log t\sin(at)$ | $\frac{s\tan^{-1}\frac{a}{s}-a\log[\gamma(s^{2}+a^{2})^{\frac{1}{2}}]}{s^{2}+a^{2}}$ | Re s > \|Im a\| |
| | 2 | $\frac{1}{t}\log t\sin(at)$ | $-\log[\gamma(s^{2}+a^{2})^{\frac{1}{2}}]\tan^{-1}\frac{a}{s}$ | Re s > \|Im a\| |
| | 3 | $\log t\sin^{2}\frac{at}{2}$ | $\frac{a s\tan^{-1}\frac{a}{s}+s^{2}\log(s^{2}+a^{2})^{\frac{1}{2}}-(s^{2}+a^{2})\log s-a^{2}\log\gamma}{s(s^{2}+a^{2})}$ | Re s > \|Im a\| |
| | 4 | $\log(2\sin\frac{at}{2})$ | $-s\sum_{k=1}^{\infty}\frac{1}{k(s^{2}+k^{2}a^{2})}$ | a ≠ o<br>Re s > o |
| | 5 | $\log t\cos(at)$ | $-\frac{a\tan^{-1}\frac{a}{s}+s\log[\gamma(s^{2}+a^{2})^{\frac{1}{2}}]}{s^{2}+a^{2}}$ | Re s > \|Im a\| |
| | 6 | $\log(2\cos\frac{at}{2})$ | $s\sum_{k=1}^{\infty}\frac{(-1)^{k-1}}{k(s^{2}+k^{2}a^{2})}$ | Re s > o |

| | | f(t) | g(s) | |
|---|---|---|---|---|
| 5.4 (Contd.) | 7 | $\log\cot\frac{at}{2}$ | $2s\sum_{k=1}^{\infty}\frac{1}{(2k-1)[s^2+(2k-1)^2a^2]}$ | Re s > o |
| | 8 | $\cos(at) * \frac{\sin(at)}{t} - \log\frac{t}{\gamma}\sin(at)$ | $\frac{a}{2}\frac{\log(s^2+a^2)}{s^2+a^2}$ | Re s > \|Im a\| |
| 5.4.2 | 1 | $t^{\nu}\log t\sin(at)$ | $\frac{\Gamma(\nu+1)}{(s^2+a^2)^{\frac{\nu+1}{2}}}\sin[(\nu+1)\tan^{-1}\frac{a}{s}]\left\{\psi(\nu+1)-\frac{1}{2}\log(s^2+a^2)+\tan^{-1}\frac{a}{s}\cot[(\nu+1)\tan^{-1}\frac{a}{s}]\right\}$ | Re ν > - 2<br>Re s > \|Im a\| |
| | 2 | $t^{\nu}\log t\cos(at)$ | $\frac{\Gamma(\nu+1)}{(s^2+a^2)^{\frac{\nu+1}{2}}}\cos[(\nu+1)\tan^{-1}\frac{a}{s}]\left\{\psi(\nu+1)-\frac{1}{2}\log(s^2+a^2)-\tan^{-1}\frac{a}{s}\tan[(\nu+1)\tan^{-1}\frac{a}{s}]\right\}$ | Re ν > - 1<br>Re s > \|Im a\| |
| 6 | 1 | $\tan^{-1}(at)$ | $-\frac{1}{s}[\mathrm{ci}(\frac{s}{a})\sin(\frac{s}{a})+\mathrm{si}(\frac{s}{a})\cos(\frac{s}{a})]$ | Re a > o<br>Re s > o |
| | 2 | $\cot^{-1}(at)$ | $\frac{1}{s}[\frac{\pi}{2}+\mathrm{ci}(\frac{s}{a})\sin(\frac{s}{a})+\mathrm{si}(\frac{s}{a})\cos(\frac{s}{a})]$ | Re s > o |
| | 3 | $t\tan^{-1}(at)$ | $\frac{1}{s^2}[-\mathrm{ci}(\frac{s}{a})\sin(\frac{s}{a})-\mathrm{si}(\frac{s}{a})\cos(\frac{s}{a})]+\frac{a}{s}[\mathrm{ci}(\frac{s}{a})\cos(\frac{s}{a})-\mathrm{si}(\frac{s}{a})\sin(\frac{s}{a})]$ | Re s > o |
| | 4 | $t\cot^{-1}(at)$ | $\frac{1}{s^2}[\frac{\pi}{2}+\mathrm{ci}(\frac{s}{a})\sin(\frac{s}{a})+\mathrm{si}(\frac{s}{a})\cos(\frac{s}{a})]+\frac{a}{s}[\mathrm{si}(\frac{s}{a})\sin(\frac{s}{a})-\mathrm{ci}(\frac{s}{a})\cos(\frac{s}{a})]$ | Re s > o |
| 6.3.2 | 1 | $t^{2\nu}(1+t^2)^{\nu}e^{-2i\nu\cot^{-1}t}$ | $\frac{i\pi^{\frac{1}{2}}}{2\Gamma(2\nu+1)}s^{-2\nu-\frac{1}{2}}e^{-\frac{is}{2}}H^{(1)}_{2\nu+\frac{1}{2}}(\frac{s}{2})$ | Re ν > $-\frac{1}{2}$<br>Re s > o |
| 6.5.2 | 1 | $t^{\nu}(t^2+a^2)^{\frac{\nu}{2}}\sin[\nu\cot^{-1}(\frac{t}{a})+b]$ | $\frac{\pi^{\frac{1}{2}}a^{\nu+\frac{1}{2}}\Gamma(\nu+1)}{-2s^{\nu+\frac{1}{2}}}[\cos(\frac{as}{2}+b)J_{\nu+\frac{1}{2}}(\frac{as}{2})+\sin(\frac{as}{2}+b)Y_{\nu+\frac{1}{2}}(\frac{as}{2})]$ | Re ν > - 1<br>Re a > o<br>Re s > o |
| | 2 | $t^{\nu}(t^2+a^2)^{\frac{\nu}{2}}\cos[\nu\cot^{-1}(\frac{t}{a})+b]$ | $\frac{\pi^{\frac{1}{2}}a^{\nu+\frac{1}{2}}\Gamma(\nu+1)}{2s^{\nu+\frac{1}{2}}}[\sin(\frac{as}{2}+b)J_{\nu+\frac{1}{2}}(\frac{as}{2})-\cos(\frac{as}{2}+b)Y_{\nu+\frac{1}{2}}(\frac{as}{2})]$ | Re ν > - 1<br>Re a > o<br>Re s > o |

| | | f(t) | g(s) | |
|---|---|---|---|---|
| 6.5.2.1 | 1 | $\dfrac{\cos(\nu \cos^{-1}\frac{1}{1+t})}{[t(t+1)(t+2)]^{\frac{1}{2}}}$ | $\pi^{\frac{1}{2}} e^{s} D_{\nu-\frac{1}{2}}(2^{\frac{1}{2}}s^{\frac{1}{2}}) D_{-\nu-\frac{1}{2}}(2^{\frac{1}{2}}s^{\frac{1}{2}})$ | Re s > o |
| 6.5.3 | 1 | $\dfrac{\cos[\nu \cos^{-1}(e^{-t})]}{(1-e^{-2t})^{\frac{1}{2}}}$ | $\dfrac{\pi}{2^{s} s\, B\left(\frac{s+\nu+1}{2}, \frac{s-\nu+1}{2}\right)}$ | Re s > o |
| 7 | 1 | $\sinh(at)$ | $\dfrac{a}{s^2-a^2}$ | Re s > \|Re a\| |
| | 2 | $\dfrac{\sinh(at)}{t}$ | $\dfrac{1}{2}\log\dfrac{s+a}{s-a}$ <br> $= \coth^{-1}\dfrac{s}{a}$ | Re s > \|Re a\| |
| | 3 | $\sinh^2(at)$ | $\dfrac{2a^2}{s(s^2-4a^2)}$ | Re s > 2\|Re a\| |
| | 4 | $\sinh^{2n}(at)$ | $\dfrac{(2n)!(a)^{2n}}{s[s^2-(2a)^2][s^2-2^2(2a)^2]\cdots[s^2-n^2(2a)^2]}$ | n = 1,2,3,... <br> Re s > n\| Re a\| |
| | 5 | $\sinh^{2n+1}(at)$ | $\dfrac{(2n+1)!a^{2n+1}}{[s^2-a^2][s^2-3^2a^2]\cdots[s^2-(2n+1)^2a^2]}$ | n = 0,1,2,... <br> Re s > (2n+1) \| Re a\| |
| | 6 | $\sinh^{\nu}(at)$ | $\dfrac{B\left(\frac{s}{2a}-\frac{\nu}{2}, \nu+1\right)}{2^{\nu+1}a}$ | Re a > o <br> Re $\nu$ > - 1 <br> Re s > Re($a\nu$) |
| | 7 | $a\sinh(at)-b\sinh(bt)$ | $\dfrac{(a^2-b^2)s^2}{(s^2-a^2)(s^2-b^2)}$ | Re s > Max \| Re a\| ,\|Re b\| |
| | 8 | $b\sinh(at)-a\sinh(bt)$ | $\dfrac{ab(a^2-b^2)}{(s^2-a^2)(s^2-b^2)}$ | Re s > Max \| Re a\| ,\|Re b\| |
| | 9 | $\dfrac{1}{t}-\operatorname{cosech} t$ | $\psi(\frac{s+1}{2}) - \log\frac{s}{2}$ | Re s > o |
| | 10 | $\cosh(at)$ | $\dfrac{s}{s^2-a^2}$ | Re s > \|Re a\| |

| | | f(t) | g(s) | |
|---|---|---|---|---|
| 7 (Contd.) | 11 | $\frac{1-\cosh(at)}{t}$ | $\frac{1}{2}\log\frac{s^2-a^2}{s^2}$ | Re s > \|Re a\| |
| | 12 | $\cosh^2(at)$ | $\frac{s^2-2a^2}{s(s^2-4a^2)}$ | Re s > 2\| Re a\| |
| | 13 | $[\cosh(at)-1]^{\nu}$ | $\frac{B(\frac{s}{a}-\nu,2\nu+1)}{2^{\nu}a}$ | Re a > o<br>Re $\nu$ > $-\frac{1}{2}$<br>Re s > Re($a\nu$) |
| | 14 | $\cosh(at)-\cosh(bt)$ | $\frac{(a^2-b^2)s}{(s^2-a^2)(s^2-b^2)}$ | Re s > Max\| Re a \|,\|Re b\| |
| | 15 | $a^2\cosh(at)-b^2\cosh(bt)$ | $\frac{(a^2-b^2)s^3}{(s^2-a^2)(s^2-b^2)}$ | Re s > Max\| Re a \|,\|Re b\| |
| | 16 | $\text{sech}(at)$ | $\frac{1}{2a}\psi(\frac{s+3a}{4a})-\frac{1}{2a}\psi(\frac{s+a}{4a})$ | Re s > Max - Re a , -Re 3a |
| | 17 | $\frac{1-\text{sech}\, t}{t}$ | $2\log\frac{\Gamma(\frac{s+3}{4})}{\Gamma(\frac{s+1}{4})}-\log\frac{s}{4}$ | Re s > o |
| | 18 | $\text{sech}^2 t$ | $\frac{s}{2}[\psi(\frac{s+2}{4})-\psi(\frac{s}{4})]-1$ | Re s > o |
| | 19 | $at\cosh(at)-\sinh(at)$ | $\frac{2a^3}{(s^2-a^2)^2}$ | Re s> \|Re a\| |
| | 20 | $\tanh t$ | $\frac{1}{2}[\psi(\frac{s+2}{4})-\psi(\frac{s}{4})]-\frac{1}{s}$ | Re s > o |
| | 21 | $\frac{\tanh t}{t}$ | $\log\frac{s}{4}+2\log\frac{\Gamma(\frac{s}{4})}{\Gamma(\frac{s+2}{4})}$ | Re s > o |
| | 22 | $\frac{1}{t}-\coth t$ | $\psi(\frac{s}{2})+\frac{1}{s}-\log\frac{s}{2}$ | Re s> o |

| | | f(t) | g(s) | |
|---|---|---|---|---|
| 7 (Contd.) | 23 | $\int_0^{at} \frac{\sinh u}{u}\, du$ | $\frac{\tanh^{-1}\frac{s}{a}}{s}$ <br> $= \frac{\log \frac{s+a}{s-a}}{2s}$ | $\mathrm{Re}\, s > \lvert \mathrm{Re}\, a \rvert$ |
| 7.1 | 1 | $[\sinh \frac{t}{2} \sinh(a+\frac{t}{2})]^{\mu}$ | $\frac{\Gamma(\mu+1)\, e^{(\mu+\frac{1}{2})\pi i} \sinh^{\mu+\frac{1}{2}} a}{2^{\mu-\frac{1}{2}}}\, e^{as}\, Q^{-\mu-\frac{1}{2}}_{s-\frac{1}{2}}(\cosh a)$ | $\mathrm{Re}\, \mu > -1$ <br> $\lvert \arg a \rvert < \pi$ <br> $\mathrm{Re}\, s > \mathrm{Re}\, \mu$ |
| | 2 | $at^2 \cosh(at) - t \sinh(at)$ | $\frac{8a^3 s}{(s^2-a^2)^3}$ | $\mathrm{Re}\, s > \lvert \mathrm{Re}\, a \rvert$ |
| | 3 | $at \cosh(at) - (1-a^2t^2) \sinh(at)$ | $\frac{8a^3 s^2}{(s^2-a^2)^3}$ | $\mathrm{Re}\, s > \lvert \mathrm{Re}\, a \rvert$ |
| | 4 | $(3+a^2t^2) \sinh(at) - 3at \cosh(at)$ | $\frac{8a^5}{(s^2-a^2)^3}$ | $\mathrm{Re}\, s > \lvert \mathrm{Re}\, a \rvert$ |
| | 5 | $\frac{\cosh(at)-1}{t^2} - \frac{a \sinh(at)}{t}$ | $\frac{s}{2} \log \frac{s^2-a^2}{s^2}$ | $\mathrm{Re}\, s > \lvert \mathrm{Re}\, a \rvert$ |
| 7.2 | 1 | $\frac{1}{t^{\frac{1}{2}}} \sinh(at)$ | $(\frac{\pi}{2})^{\frac{1}{2}} \left[ \frac{s-(s^2-a^2)^{\frac{1}{2}}}{s^2-a^2} \right]^{\frac{1}{2}}$ | $\mathrm{Re}\, s > \lvert \mathrm{Re}\, a \rvert$ |
| | 2 | $t^{\nu} \sinh(at)$ | $\frac{\Gamma(\nu+1)}{2} [(s-a)^{-\nu-1} - (s+a)^{-\nu-1}]$ | $\mathrm{Re}\, \nu > -1$ <br> $\mathrm{Re}\, s > \lvert \mathrm{Re}\, a \rvert$ |
| | 3 | $\sinh(at^{\frac{1}{2}})$ | $\frac{\pi^{\frac{1}{2}} a}{2s^{\frac{3}{2}}} e^{\frac{a^2}{4s}}$ | $\mathrm{Re}\, s > 0$ |
| | 4 | $t^{\frac{1}{2}} \sinh(at^{\frac{1}{2}})$ | $\pi^{\frac{1}{2}} s^{-\frac{5}{2}} (\frac{s}{2} + \frac{a^2}{4}) e^{\frac{a^2}{4s^2}} \mathrm{Erf}(\frac{a}{2s^{\frac{1}{2}}}) - \frac{a}{2s^2}$ | $\mathrm{Re}\, s > 0$ |
| | 5 | $\frac{1}{t^{\frac{1}{2}}} \sinh(at^{\frac{1}{2}})$ | $(\frac{\pi}{s})^{\frac{1}{2}} e^{\frac{a^2}{4s}} \mathrm{Erf}(\frac{a}{2s^{\frac{1}{2}}})$ | $\mathrm{Re}\, s > 0$ |
| | 6 | $\frac{1}{t^{\frac{3}{4}}} \sinh(at^{\frac{1}{2}})$ | $\pi (\frac{a}{2s})^{\frac{1}{2}} e^{\frac{a^2}{8s}} I_{\frac{1}{4}}(\frac{a^2}{8s})$ | $\mathrm{Re}\, s > 0$ |

| | | f(t) | g(s) | |
|---|---|---|---|---|
| 7.2 (Contd.) | 7 | $t^{\nu}\sinh(at^{\frac{1}{2}})$ | $\frac{\Gamma(2\nu+2)}{(2s)^{\nu+1}} e^{\frac{a^2}{8s}}\left[D_{-2\nu-2}\left(-\frac{a}{2^{\frac{1}{2}}s^{\frac{1}{2}}}\right)-D_{-2\nu-2}\left(\frac{a}{2^{\frac{1}{2}}s^{\frac{1}{2}}}\right)\right]$ | $\mathrm{Re}\,\nu > -\frac{3}{2}$<br>$\mathrm{Re}\,s > 0$ |
| | 8 | $\frac{1}{t^{\frac{1}{2}}}\sinh^2(at^{\frac{1}{2}})$ | $\frac{\pi^{\frac{1}{2}}}{2s^{\frac{1}{2}}}(e^{\frac{a^2}{s}}-1)$ | $\mathrm{Re}\,s > 0$ |
| | 9 | $\frac{\sinh[a(t^2+bt)^{\frac{1}{2}}]}{(t+b)^{\frac{1}{2}}}$ | $(\frac{\pi}{2})^{\frac{1}{2}} e^{\frac{b}{2}[s-(s^2-a^2)^{\frac{1}{2}}]}\left[\frac{s-(s^2-a^2)^{\frac{1}{2}}}{s^2-a^2}\right]^{\frac{1}{2}}$ | $\mathrm{Re}\,s > \|\mathrm{Re}\,a\|$ |
| | 10 | $t^{\nu}\,\mathrm{cosech}\,t$ | $2^{-\nu}\Gamma(\nu+1)\zeta(\nu+1, \frac{s+1}{2})$ | $\mathrm{Re}\,\nu > 0$<br>$\mathrm{Re}\,s > -1$ |
| | 11 | $\frac{1}{t^{\frac{1}{2}}}\cosh(at)$ | $(\frac{\pi}{2})^{\frac{1}{2}}\left[\frac{s+(s^2-a^2)^{\frac{1}{2}}}{s^2-a^2}\right]^{\frac{1}{2}}$ | $\mathrm{Re}\,s > \|\mathrm{Re}\,a\|$ |
| | 12 | $t^{\nu}\cosh(at)$ | $\frac{\Gamma(\nu+1)}{2}[(s-a)^{-\nu-1}+(s+a)^{-\nu-1}]$ | $\mathrm{Re}\,\nu > -1$<br>$\mathrm{Re}\,s > \|\mathrm{Re}\,a\|$ |
| | 13 | $\cosh(at^{\frac{1}{2}})$ | $\frac{\pi^{\frac{1}{2}}a}{2s^{\frac{3}{2}}} e^{\frac{a^2}{4s}}\,\mathrm{Erf}\left(\frac{a}{2s^{\frac{1}{2}}}\right)+\frac{1}{s}$ | $\mathrm{Re}\,s > 0$ |
| | 14 | $t^{\frac{1}{2}}\cosh(at^{\frac{1}{2}})$ | $\pi^{\frac{1}{2}}s^{-\frac{5}{2}}(\frac{s}{2}+\frac{a^2}{4})e^{\frac{a^2}{4s}}$ | $\mathrm{Re}\,s > 0$ |
| | 15 | $\frac{1}{t^{\frac{1}{2}}}\cosh(at^{\frac{1}{2}})$ | $(\frac{\pi}{s})^{\frac{1}{2}} e^{\frac{a^2}{4s}}$ | $\mathrm{Re}\,s > 0$ |
| | 16 | $\frac{1}{t^{\frac{3}{4}}}\cosh(at^{\frac{1}{2}})$ | $\pi(\frac{a}{2s})^{\frac{1}{2}} e^{\frac{a^2}{8s}} I_{-\frac{1}{4}}(\frac{a^2}{8s})$ | $\mathrm{Re}\,s > 0$ |
| | 17 | $t^{\nu}\cosh(at^{\frac{1}{2}})$ | $\frac{\Gamma(2\nu+2)}{(2s)^{\nu+1}} e^{\frac{a^2}{8s}}\left[D_{-2\nu-2}\left(-\frac{a}{2^{\frac{1}{2}}s^{\frac{1}{2}}}\right)+D_{-2\nu-2}\left(\frac{a}{2^{\frac{1}{2}}s^{\frac{1}{2}}}\right)\right]$ | $\mathrm{Re}\,\nu > -1$<br>$\mathrm{Re}\,s > 0$ |
| | 18 | $\frac{1}{t^{\frac{1}{2}}}\cosh^2(at^{\frac{1}{2}})$ | $\frac{\pi^{\frac{1}{2}}}{2s^{\frac{1}{2}}}(e^{\frac{a^2}{s}}+1)$ | $\mathrm{Re}\,s > 0$ |
| | 19 | $\frac{\cosh[a(t^2+bt)^{\frac{1}{2}}]}{(t+b)^{\frac{1}{2}}}$ | $(\frac{\pi}{2})^{\frac{1}{2}} e^{\frac{b}{2}[s-(s^2-a^2)^{\frac{1}{2}}]}\left[\frac{(s^2-a^2)^{\frac{1}{2}}+s}{s^2-a^2}\right]^{\frac{1}{2}}$ | $\mathrm{Re}\,s > \|\mathrm{Re}\,a\|$ |

| | | f(t) | g(s) | |
|---|---|---|---|---|
| 7.2 (Contd.) | 20 | $t^{\nu}\coth t$ | $\Gamma(\nu+1)[2^{-\nu}\zeta(\nu+1\,,\frac{s}{2})-s^{-\nu-1}]$ | Re $\nu$ > o<br>Re s > o |
| | 21 | $t^{\nu}(\coth t-1)$ | $2^{-\nu}\Gamma(\nu+1)\zeta(\nu+1\,,\frac{s}{2}+1)$ | Re $\nu$ > o<br>Re s > - 2 |
| | 22 | $\frac{1}{t^{\frac{3}{4}}}\sinh(at^{\frac{1}{2}})-\frac{1}{at^{\frac{5}{4}}}\cosh(at^{\frac{1}{2}})$ | $\pi(\frac{a}{2s})^{\frac{1}{2}}e^{\frac{a^2}{8s}}\,I_{-\frac{3}{4}}(\frac{a^2}{8s})$ | Re s > o |
| | 23 | $\frac{1}{t^{\frac{3}{4}}}\cosh(at^{\frac{1}{2}})-\frac{1}{at^{\frac{5}{4}}}\sinh(at^{\frac{1}{2}})$ | $\pi(\frac{a}{2s})^{\frac{1}{2}}e^{\frac{a^2}{8s}}\,I_{\frac{3}{4}}(\frac{a^2}{8s})$ | Re s > o |
| | 24 | $t^{\frac{1}{2}}\cosh(at^{\frac{1}{2}})-\frac{1}{a}\sinh(at^{\frac{1}{2}})$ | $\dfrac{a^2\pi^{\frac{1}{2}}\,e^{\frac{a^2}{4s}}}{4s^{\frac{5}{2}}}$ | Re s > o |
| 7.2.1 | 1 | $t^{\frac{1}{2}}\sinh(at^{\frac{1}{2}})-\frac{1}{a}\cosh(at^{\frac{1}{2}})-(\frac{at}{2}-\frac{1}{a})$ | $\frac{a^2\pi^{\frac{1}{2}}}{4s^{\frac{5}{2}}}\,e^{\frac{a^2}{4s}}\,\mathrm{Erf}(\frac{a}{2s^{\frac{1}{2}}})$ | Re s > o |
| | 2 | $(\frac{3}{t}+1)\frac{\sinh(t^{\frac{1}{2}})}{t^{\frac{3}{4}}}-\frac{3\cosh(t^{\frac{1}{2}})}{t^{\frac{5}{4}}}$ | $\dfrac{\pi\,e^{\frac{1}{8s}}\,I_{\frac{5}{4}}(\frac{1}{8s})}{(2s)^{\frac{1}{2}}}$ | Re s > o |
| | 3 | $(\frac{3}{t}+1)\frac{\cosh(t^{\frac{1}{2}})}{t^{\frac{3}{4}}}-\frac{3\sinh(t^{\frac{1}{2}})}{t^{\frac{5}{4}}}$ | $\dfrac{\pi\,e^{\frac{1}{8s}}\,I_{-\frac{5}{4}}(\frac{1}{8s})}{(2s)^{\frac{1}{2}}}$ | Re s > o |
| 7.3 | 1 | $e^{-a\sinh t}$ | $\pi\,\mathrm{cosec}(\pi s)[\,\mathbf{J}_s(a)-J_s(a)]$ | Re a > o<br>Re s > - $\infty$ |
| | 2 | $\dfrac{\sinh[a(1-e^{-t})^{\frac{1}{2}}]}{(e^{t}-1)^{\frac{1}{2}}}$ | $\pi^{\frac{1}{2}}\Gamma(s+\frac{1}{2})(\frac{2}{a})^{s}\,\mathbf{L}_s(a)$ | Re s > - $\frac{1}{2}$ |
| | 3 | $e^{-a\cosh t}$ | $\mathrm{cosec}(s\pi)\left[\int_0^{\pi}e^{a\cos\theta}\cos(s\theta)\,d\theta-\pi\,I_s(a)\right]$ | Re a > o<br>Re s > - $\infty$ |
| | 4 | $\dfrac{\cosh[a(1-e^{-t})^{\frac{1}{2}}]}{(e^{t}-1)^{\frac{1}{2}}}$ | $\pi^{\frac{1}{2}}\Gamma(s+\frac{1}{2})(\frac{2}{a})^{s}\,I_s(a)$ | Re s > - $\frac{1}{2}$ |

| | | f(t) | g(s) | |
|---|---|---|---|---|
| 7.3 (Contd.) | 5 | $\frac{1}{t}e^{-at}[1-\operatorname{sech}\frac{t}{4}]$ | $\log\left[\frac{1}{s+a}\left(\frac{\Gamma(s+a+\frac{3}{4})}{\Gamma(s+a+\frac{1}{4})}\right)^2\right]$ | Re s > - Re a |
| | 6 | $\frac{1}{t}e^{-at}\tanh\frac{t}{4}$ | $\log\left[(s+a)\left(\frac{\Gamma(s+a)}{\Gamma(s+a+\frac{1}{2})}\right)^2\right]$ | Re s > - Re a |
| | 7 | $\frac{e^t(t-2e^{\frac{t}{2}}\cosh\frac{t}{2})}{t(\cosh t+1)}$ | $2\log\frac{\Gamma(\frac{s}{2})}{\Gamma(\frac{s-1}{2})}-\psi(\frac{s}{2})$ | Re s > 1 |
| | 8 | $\tanh[\frac{\pi}{2}(e^{2t}-1)^{\frac{1}{2}}]$ | $\frac{\zeta(s-1)}{2^s}$ | Re s > 0 |
| | 9 | $\sinh^{2b}\frac{t}{2}\,e^{-2a\coth\frac{t}{2}}$ | $\frac{1}{2}a^{\frac{b-1}{2}}\Gamma(s-b)[W_{-s+\frac{1}{2},b}(4a)-(s-b)W_{-s-\frac{1}{2},b}(4a)]$ | Re a > 0<br>Re s > Re b |
| | 10 | $e^{-bt}[\cosh(ct)+a\sinh(ct)]$ | $\frac{s+ac+b}{(s+b)^2-c^2}$ | Re s > Max - Re(c+b), - Re(b-c |
| 7.3.1 | 1 | $e^{-a\sinh(t+ib)}$ | $\operatorname{cosec}(s\pi)\left[\int_0^{\pi}e^{ia\sin b\cos\theta}\cos(s\theta-a\cos b\sin\theta)\,d\theta-\pi e^{ibs}J_s(a)\right]$ | $-\frac{\pi}{2}<b<\frac{\pi}{2}$<br>$\lvert\arg a\rvert<\frac{\pi}{2}-b$<br>Re s > $-\infty$ |
| | 2 | $\frac{t-e^t+1}{2t\sinh t}$ | $\log\frac{\Gamma(\frac{s+1}{2})}{\Gamma(\frac{s}{2})}-\frac{1}{2}\psi(\frac{s+1}{2})$ | Re s > 0 |
| | 3 | $\frac{t-e^t+1}{2t\sinh t}+e^t$ | $\log\frac{\Gamma(\frac{s+1}{2})}{\Gamma(\frac{s}{2})}-\frac{1}{2}\psi(\frac{s-1}{2})$ | Re s > 1 |
| 7.4 | 1 | $\log\sinh t-\log t$ | $s^{-1}[\log\frac{s}{2}-\frac{1}{2s}-\psi(\frac{s}{2})]$ | Re s > 0 |
| | 2 | $\log\frac{2\sinh\frac{t}{2}}{t}$ | $\frac{1}{s}\frac{d}{ds}[\log\Gamma(s)-(s-\frac{1}{2})\log s+s-\log(2\pi)^{\frac{1}{2}}]$ | Re s > 0 |
| | 3 | $\log(\frac{t}{\gamma})\sinh(at)$ | $\frac{s\tanh^{-1}\frac{a}{s}-\frac{a}{2}\log(s^2-a^2)}{s^2-a^2}$ | Re s > $\lvert$Re a$\rvert$ |

| | | f(t) | g(s) | |
|---|---|---|---|---|
| 7.4 (Contd.) | 4 | $\log\cosh t$ | $\frac{1}{2s}[\psi(\frac{s+2}{4}) - \psi(\frac{s}{4})] - \frac{1}{s^2}$ | Re s > o |
| | 5 | $\log(\frac{\gamma}{t})\cosh(at)$ | $\frac{\frac{s}{2}\log(s^2-a^2) - a\tanh^{-1}\frac{a}{s}}{s^2-a^2}$ | Re s > \|Re a\| |
| | 6 | $\log(\frac{\gamma}{t})\sinh(at) + \cosh(at)*\frac{\sinh(at)}{t}$ | $\frac{a\log(s^2-a^2)}{2(s^2-a^2)}$ | Re s > \|Re a\| |
| | 7 | $\log(\frac{\gamma}{t})\cosh(at) + \sinh(at)*\frac{\sinh(at)}{t}$ | $\frac{s\log(s^2-a^2)}{2(s^2-a^2)}$ | Re s > \|Re a\| |
| 7.5 | 1 | $\sinh(at) + \sin(at)$ | $\frac{2as^2}{s^4-a^4}$ | Re s > Max \|Re a\|, \|Im a\| |
| | 2 | $\sinh(at) - \sin(at)$ | $\frac{2a^3}{s^4-a^4}$ | Re s > Max \|Re a\|, \|Im a\| |
| | 3 | $\sin(at)\sinh(at)$ | $\frac{2a^2s}{s^4+4a^4}$ | Re s > \|Re a\| + \|Im a\| |
| | 4 | $\cos(at)\sinh(at)$ | $\frac{a(s^2-2a^2)}{s^4+4a^4}$ | Re s > \|Re a\| + \|Im a\| |
| | 5 | $\frac{\cos(bt)\sinh(at)}{t}$ | $\frac{1}{4}\log\frac{s^2+2as+(a^2+b^2)}{s^2-2as+(a^2+b^2)}$ | Re s > \|Im b\| + \|Re a\| |
| | 6 | $\sin(at)\cosh(at)$ | $\frac{a(s^2+2a^2)}{s^4+4a^4}$ | Re s > \|Re a\| + \|Im a\| |
| | 7 | $\frac{\sin(bt)\cosh(at)}{t}$ | $\frac{1}{2}\tan^{-1}\frac{2bs}{s^2-(a^2+b^2)}$ | Re s > \|Im b\| + \|Re a\| |
| | 8 | $\cosh(at)+\cos(at)$ | $\frac{2s^3}{s^4-a^4}$ | Re s > Max \|Re a\|, \|Im a\| |
| | 9 | $\cosh(at)-\cos(at)$ | $\frac{2a^2s}{s^4-a^4}$ | Re s > Max \|Re a\|, \|Im a\| |
| | 10 | $\cos(at)\cosh(at)$ | $\frac{s^3}{s^4+4a^4}$ | Re s > \|Re a\| + \|Im a\| |

| | | f(t) | g(s) | |
|---|---|---|---|---|
| 7.5 (Contd.) | 11 | $\cosh(at)\sin(at) + \sinh(at)\cos(at)$ | $\frac{2as^2}{s^4+4a^4}$ | Re s > \|Re a\| + \|Im a\| |
| | 12 | $\cosh(at)\sin(at) - \sinh(at)\cos(at)$ | $\frac{4a^3}{s^4+4a^4}$ | Re s> \|Re a\| + \|Im a\| |
| 7.5.2 | 1 | $\frac{1}{t^{\frac{1}{2}}} \sinh(at^{\frac{1}{2}})\sin(at^{\frac{1}{2}})$ | $\frac{\pi^{\frac{1}{2}}\sin\frac{a^2}{2s}}{s^{\frac{1}{2}}}$ | Re s > o |
| | 2 | $\sinh(at^{\frac{1}{2}})+\sin(at^{\frac{1}{2}})$ | $\frac{a\pi^{\frac{1}{2}}}{s^{\frac{3}{2}}}\cosh\frac{a^2}{4s}$ | Re s > o |
| | 3 | $\sinh(at^{\frac{1}{2}})-\sin(at^{\frac{1}{2}})$ | $\frac{a\pi^{\frac{1}{2}}}{s^{\frac{3}{2}}}\sinh\frac{a^2}{4s}$ | Re s > o |
| | 4 | $\frac{\sinh(t^{\frac{1}{2}}) + \sin(t^{\frac{1}{2}})}{t^{\frac{3}{4}}}$ | $(\frac{2}{s})^{\frac{1}{2}}\pi \cosh\frac{1}{8s} I_{\frac{1}{4}}(\frac{1}{8s})$ | Re s > o |
| | 5 | $\frac{\sinh(t^{\frac{1}{2}})-\sin(t^{\frac{1}{2}})}{t^{\frac{3}{4}}}$ | $(\frac{2}{s})^{\frac{1}{2}}\pi \sinh\frac{1}{8s} I_{\frac{1}{4}}(\frac{1}{8s})$ | Re s > o |
| | 6 | $\sinh(at^{\frac{1}{2}})\cos(at^{\frac{1}{2}})$ | $\frac{\pi^{\frac{1}{2}}a}{2^{\frac{1}{2}}s^{\frac{3}{2}}}\cos\frac{a^2}{2s}$ | Re s > o |
| | 7 | $\frac{1}{t^{\frac{1}{2}}} \cosh(at^{\frac{1}{2}})\cos(at^{\frac{1}{2}})$ | $\frac{\pi^{\frac{1}{2}}}{s^{\frac{1}{2}}}\cos\frac{a^2}{2s}$ | Re s > o |
| | 8 | $\frac{1}{t^{\frac{1}{2}}}[\cosh(at^{\frac{1}{2}})+\cos(at^{\frac{1}{2}})]$ | $\frac{2\pi^{\frac{1}{2}}}{s^{\frac{1}{2}}}\cosh\frac{a^2}{4s}$ | Re s > o |
| | 9 | $\frac{1}{t^{\frac{1}{2}}}[\cosh(at^{\frac{1}{2}})-\cos(at^{\frac{1}{2}})]$ | $\frac{2\pi^{\frac{1}{2}}}{s^{\frac{1}{2}}}\sinh\frac{a^2}{4s}$ | Re s > o |
| | 10 | $\frac{\cosh(t^{\frac{1}{2}})+\cos(t^{\frac{1}{2}})}{t^{\frac{3}{4}}}$ | $(\frac{2}{s})^{\frac{1}{2}}\pi\cosh\frac{1}{8s} I_{-\frac{1}{4}}(\frac{1}{8s})$ | Re s > o |
| | 11 | $\frac{\cosh(t^{\frac{1}{2}})-\cos(t^{\frac{1}{2}})}{t^{\frac{3}{4}}}$ | $(\frac{2}{s})^{\frac{1}{2}}\pi\sinh\frac{1}{8s} I_{-\frac{1}{4}}(\frac{1}{8s})$ | Re s > o |

| | | f(t) | g(s) | |
|---|---|---|---|---|
| 7.5.2 (Contd.) | 12 | $\cosh(at^{\frac{1}{2}})\sin(at^{\frac{1}{2}})$ | $\frac{\pi^{\frac{1}{2}}a}{2^{\frac{1}{2}}s^{\frac{3}{2}}}\sin\frac{a^2}{2s}$ | Re s > o |
| | 13 | $t^{\frac{1}{2}}[\cosh(at^{\frac{1}{2}})+\cos(at^{\frac{1}{2}})]-\frac{1}{a}[\sinh(at^{\frac{1}{2}})+\sin(at^{\frac{1}{2}})]$ | $\frac{a^2\pi^{\frac{1}{2}}}{2s^{\frac{5}{2}}}\sinh\frac{a^2}{4s}$ | Re s > o |
| | 14 | $t^{\frac{1}{2}}[\cosh(at^{\frac{1}{2}})-\cos(at^{\frac{1}{2}})]-\frac{1}{a}[\sinh(at^{\frac{1}{2}})-\sin(at^{\frac{1}{2}})]$ | $\frac{a^2\pi^{\frac{1}{2}}}{2s^{\frac{5}{2}}}\cosh\frac{a^2}{4s}$ | Re s > o |
| | 15 | $\frac{\sinh a}{t^{\frac{1}{2}}[\cosh a-\cos(t^{\frac{1}{2}})]}$ | $2\pi e^{a^2 s}[\theta_3(2as\vert 4s)+\hat{\theta}_3(2as\vert 4s)]-(\frac{\pi}{s})^{\frac{1}{2}}$ | Re s > o |
| 8 | 1 | $\sinh^{-1}(at)$ | $\frac{\pi}{2}s^{-1}[H_0(\frac{s}{a})-Y_0(\frac{s}{a})]$ | Re s > o |
| | 2 | $t\sinh^{-1}t$ | $\frac{\pi}{2s^2}[H_0(s)-Y_0(s)+sH_1(s)-sY_1(s)]-\frac{1}{s}$ | Re s > o |
| 8.1 | 1 | $\cosh^{-1}(1+at)$ | $\frac{1}{s}e^{\frac{s}{a}}K_0(\frac{s}{a})$ | $\vert\arg a\vert<\pi$<br>Re s > o |
| 8.2 | 1 | $(1+t^2)^{\frac{1}{2}}-t\sinh^{-1}t$ | $\frac{S_{2,0}(s)}{s^2}$ | Re s > o |
| | 2 | $\sinh^{-1}[(\frac{t}{a})^{\frac{1}{2}}]$ | $s^{-1}e^{as}K_0(as)$ | $\vert\arg a\vert<\pi$<br>Re s > o |
| 8.3.2 | 1 | $\frac{e^{n\sinh^{-1}t}}{(1+t^2)^{\frac{1}{2}}}$ | $\frac{1}{2}[S_n(s)-\pi E_n(s)-\pi Y_n(s)]$ | n = 0,1,2,...<br>Re s > o |
| | 2 | $\frac{e^{-n\sinh^{-1}t}}{(1+t^2)^{\frac{1}{2}}}$ | $\frac{1}{2}(-1)^{n+1}[S_n(s)+\pi E_n(s)+\pi Y_n(s)]$ | n = 0,1,2,...<br>Re s > o |
| | 3 | $\frac{e^{-\nu\sinh^{-1}t}}{(1+t^2)^{\frac{1}{2}}}$ | $\frac{\pi}{\sin(\nu\pi)}[J_\nu(s)-J_\nu(s)]$ | Re s > o |
| | 4 | $\frac{e^{\nu\sinh^{-1}\frac{t}{a}}}{t^{\frac{1}{2}}(t^2+a^2)^{\frac{1}{2}}}$ | $(\frac{\pi}{2})^{\frac{3}{2}}s^{\frac{1}{2}}[J_{\frac{\nu}{2}+\frac{1}{4}}(\frac{as}{2})J_{\frac{\nu}{2}-\frac{1}{4}}(\frac{as}{2})+Y_{\frac{\nu}{2}+\frac{1}{4}}(\frac{as}{2})Y_{\frac{\nu}{2}-\frac{1}{4}}(\frac{as}{2})]$ | Re a > o<br>Re s > o |

| | | f(t) | g(s) | |
|---|---|---|---|---|
| 8.3.2 (Contd.) | 5 | $\dfrac{e^{-\nu \sinh^{-1}\frac{t}{a}}}{t^{\frac{1}{2}}(t^2+a^2)^{\frac{1}{2}}}$ | $(\frac{\pi}{2})^{\frac{3}{2}} s^{\frac{1}{2}} [ J_{\frac{\nu}{2}+\frac{1}{4}}(\frac{as}{2}) Y_{\frac{\nu}{2}-\frac{1}{4}}(\frac{as}{2}) - J_{\frac{\nu}{2}-\frac{1}{4}}(\frac{as}{2}) Y_{\frac{\nu}{2}+\frac{1}{4}}(\frac{as}{2})]$ | Re a > o<br>Re s > o |
| | 6 | $\dfrac{\sin[(\nu+\frac{1}{4})\pi] e^{-2\nu \sinh^{-1}\frac{t}{a}} - \cos[(\nu+\frac{1}{4})\pi] e^{2\nu \sinh^{-1}\frac{t}{a}}}{t^{\frac{1}{2}}(t^2+a^2)^{\frac{1}{2}}}$ | $(\frac{\pi}{2})^{\frac{3}{2}} s^{\frac{1}{2}} [ J_{\frac{1}{4}+\nu}(\frac{as}{2}) Y_{\frac{1}{4}-\nu}(\frac{as}{2}) - J_{\frac{1}{4}-\nu}(\frac{as}{2}) Y_{\frac{1}{4}+\nu}(\frac{as}{2})]$ | Re a > o<br>Re s > o |
| | 7 | $\dfrac{\cos[(\nu+\frac{1}{4})\pi] e^{-2\nu \sinh^{-1}\frac{t}{a}} + \sin[(\nu+\frac{1}{4})\pi] e^{2\nu \sinh^{-1}\frac{t}{a}}}{t^{\frac{1}{2}}(t^2+a^2)^{\frac{1}{2}}}$ | $(\frac{\pi}{2})^{\frac{3}{2}} s^{\frac{1}{2}} [ J_{\frac{1}{4}+\nu}(\frac{as}{2}) J_{\frac{1}{4}-\nu}(\frac{as}{2}) + Y_{\frac{1}{4}+\nu}(\frac{as}{2}) Y_{\frac{1}{4}-\nu}(\frac{as}{2})]$ | Re a > o<br>Re s > o |
| 8.7 | 1 | $\sinh[(2n+1)\sinh^{-1} t]$ | $O_{2n+1}(s)$ | n = 0,1,2,..<br>Re s > o |
| | 2 | $\sinh(\nu \sinh^{-1} at)$ | $\frac{\nu}{\nu^2-1}[\frac{1}{s} S_{2,\nu}(\frac{s}{a}) - \frac{1}{a}] = \frac{\nu}{s} S_{0,\nu}(\frac{s}{a})$ | Re s > o |
| | 3 | $\cosh(2n \sinh^{-1} t)$ | $O_{2n}(s)$ | n = 0,1,2,.. |
| | 4 | $\cosh(\nu \sinh^{-1} t)$ | $\frac{1}{s} S_{1,\nu}(s)$ | Re s > o |
| | 5 | $\int_0^t \sinh(\nu \sinh^{-1} u)\, du$ | $\frac{\nu}{(\nu^2-1)s}[\frac{1}{s} S_{2,\nu}(s) - 1]$ | Re s > o |
| 8.7.1 | 1 | $\sinh[\nu \cosh^{-1}(1+\frac{t}{a})]$ | $\frac{\nu}{s} e^{as} K_\nu(as)$ | \|arg a\| < π<br>Re s > o |
| 8.7.2 | 1 | $\dfrac{\sinh(\nu \sinh^{-1} t)}{(1+t^2)^{\frac{1}{2}}}$ | $\nu S_{-1,\nu}(s)$ | Re s > o |
| | 2 | $\dfrac{\sinh(\nu \sinh^{-1}\frac{t}{a})}{t^{\frac{1}{2}}(t^2+a^2)^{\frac{1}{2}}}$ | $\frac{\pi^{\frac{3}{2}} s^{\frac{1}{2}}}{8i}[e^{\frac{i\nu\pi}{2}} H^{(1)}_{\frac{1+\nu}{2}}(\frac{as}{2}) H^{(2)}_{\frac{1-\nu}{2}}(\frac{as}{2}) - e^{-\frac{i\nu\pi}{2}} H^{(1)}_{\frac{1-\nu}{2}}(\frac{as}{2}) H^{(2)}_{\frac{1+\nu}{2}}(\frac{as}{2})]$ | \|arg a\| < π<br>Re s > o |

| | | f(t) | g(s) | |
|---|---|---|---|---|
| 8.7.2 (Contd.) | 3 | $\sinh[\nu \sinh^{-1}(\frac{t^{\frac{1}{2}}}{a^{\frac{1}{2}}})]$ | $\frac{\nu}{s} e^{as} K_{\nu}(as)$ | $\lvert \arg a \rvert < \pi$<br>$\mathrm{Re}\, s > 0$ |
| | 4 | $\frac{\cosh(\nu \sinh^{-1} t)}{(1+t^2)^{\frac{1}{2}}}$ | $S_{0,\nu}(s)$ | $\mathrm{Re}\, s > 0$ |
| | 5 | $\frac{\cosh(\nu \sinh^{-1} \frac{t}{a})}{t^{\frac{1}{2}}(t^2+a^2)^{\frac{1}{2}}}$ | $\frac{\pi^{\frac{3}{2}} s^{\frac{1}{2}}}{8}[e^{\frac{i\nu\pi}{2}} H^{(1)}_{\frac{1+\nu}{2}}(\frac{as}{2}) H^{(2)}_{\frac{1-\nu}{2}}(\frac{as}{2}) + e^{-\frac{i\nu\pi}{2}} H^{(1)}_{\frac{1-\nu}{2}}(\frac{as}{2}) H^{(2)}_{\frac{1+\nu}{2}}(\frac{as}{2})]$ | $\lvert \arg a \rvert < \pi$<br>$\mathrm{Re}\, s > 0$ |
| | 6 | $\frac{\cosh(\nu \sinh^{-1} \frac{t^{\frac{1}{2}}}{a^{\frac{1}{2}}})}{(t^2+2at)^{\frac{1}{2}}}$ | $e^{as} K_{\nu}(as)$ | $\mathrm{Re}\, s > 0$<br>$\lvert \arg a \rvert < \pi$ |
| | 7 | $\frac{\cosh(\nu \sinh^{-1} \frac{t^{\frac{1}{2}}}{a^{\frac{1}{2}}})}{[t(t+a)(t+2a)]^{\frac{1}{2}}}$ | $(\frac{s}{2\pi})^{\frac{1}{2}} e^{as} K_{\frac{\nu}{2}+\frac{1}{4}}(\frac{as}{2}) K_{\frac{\nu}{2}-\frac{1}{4}}(\frac{as}{2})$ | $\lvert \arg a \rvert < \pi$<br>$\mathrm{Re}\, s > 0$ |
| | 8 | $\frac{\cosh(\nu \sinh^{-1} \frac{t}{a}) + i \sinh(\nu \sinh^{-1} \frac{t}{a})}{t^{\frac{1}{2}}(t^2+a^2)^{\frac{1}{2}}}$ | $\frac{\pi^{\frac{3}{2}}}{4} e^{\frac{\nu\pi i}{2}} s^{\frac{1}{2}} H^{(1)}_{\frac{1+\nu}{2}}(\frac{as}{2}) H^{(2)}_{\frac{1-\nu}{2}}(\frac{as}{2})$ | $\mathrm{Re}\, a > 0$<br>$\mathrm{Re}\, s > 0$ |
| 8.7.2.1 | 1 | $\frac{\cosh[\nu \cosh^{-1}(1+\frac{t}{a})]}{(t^2+2at)^{\frac{1}{2}}}$ | $e^{as} K_{\nu}(as)$ | $\lvert \arg a \rvert < \pi$<br>$\mathrm{Re}\, s > 0$ |
| | 2 | $\frac{\cosh[\nu \cosh^{-1}(1+\frac{t}{a})]}{[t(t+a)(t+2a)]^{\frac{1}{2}}}$ | $(\frac{s}{2\pi})^{\frac{1}{2}} e^{as} K_{\frac{\nu}{2}+\frac{1}{4}}(\frac{as}{2}) K_{\frac{\nu}{2}-\frac{1}{4}}(\frac{as}{2})$ | $\lvert \arg a \rvert < \pi$<br>$\mathrm{Re}\, s > 0$ |
| 9 | 1 | $A_n(at)$ | $\frac{1}{s}(\frac{a}{s}-1)(\frac{a}{s}-\frac{1}{2})\cdots(\frac{a}{s}-\frac{1}{n})$ | $n = 1,2,3,\ldots$<br>$\mathrm{Re}\, s > 0$ |
| | 2 | $C_n^{\nu}(-it)$ | $\frac{A_{n,\nu}(s)}{2^{\nu} i^n (n+\nu)\Gamma(\nu)}$ | $n = 0,1,2,\ldots$<br>$\mathrm{Re}\, s > 0$ |
| | 3 | $H_{2n}(t)$ | $\frac{(2n-1)!}{(-2)^n (n-1)!\, s} A_n(1-n, \frac{2}{s^2})$ | $n = 0,1,2,\ldots$<br>$\mathrm{Re}\, s > 0$ |

| | | f(t) | g(s) | |
|---|---|---|---|---|
| 9 (Contd.) | 4 | $He_{2n+1}(t)$ | $\frac{(2n+1)!}{(-2)^n n! s^2} A_n(1-n, \frac{2}{s^2})$ | n = 0,1,2,... Re s > 0 |
| | 5 | $L_n(t)$ | $\frac{(s-1)^n}{s^{n+1}}$ | n = 0,1,2,... Re s > 0 |
| | 6 | $L_n^a(t)$ | $\sum_{m=0}^{n} \binom{a+m-1}{m} \frac{(s-1)^{n-m}}{s^{n-m+1}}$ | n = 0,1,2,... Re s > 0 |
| | 7 | $L_n(at)L_n(bt)$ | $\frac{(s-a-b)^n}{s^{n+1}} P_n\left[\frac{s^2-(a+b)s+2ab}{s(s-a-b)}\right]$ | n = 0,1,2,... Re s > 0 |
| | 8 | $L_n[(a-b)t]L_n[(a+b)t]$ | $\frac{(s-2a)^n}{s^{n+1}} P_n\left[\frac{s^2+2(1-2a)(a^2-b^2)}{s(s-2a)}\right]$ | Re s > 0 |
| | 9 | $T_a^{(n)}(t)$ | $\frac{(1-s)^n}{n! s^{n+a+1}}$ | Re a > − 1 Re s > 0 |
| 9.1 | 1 | $t^n L_n(t)$ | $\frac{n!}{s^{n+1}} P_n(1-\frac{2}{s})$ | n = 0,1,2,... Re s > 0 |
| | 2 | $P_n(1+t)$ | $(\frac{2}{\pi s})^{\frac{1}{2}} e^s K_{n+\frac{1}{2}}(s)$ | n = 0,1,2,... Re s > 0 |
| | 3 | $P_n(1-t)$ | $e^{-s}(\frac{1}{s}\frac{d}{ds})^n(\frac{e^s}{s})$ $= s^n(1+\frac{1}{2}\frac{d}{ds})^n(\frac{1}{s^{n+1}})$ $=\frac{1}{s}\,{}_2F_0[-n, n+1; \quad ; \frac{1}{2s}]$ $=\frac{1}{s} A_n(1, \frac{1}{2s})$ | n = 0,1,2,... Re s > 0 |
| | 4 | $(t+1)^n P_n(\frac{t-1}{t+1})$ | $\frac{n!}{s^{n+1}} L_n(s)$ | n = 0,1,2,... Re s > 0 |

| | | $f(t)$ | $g(s)$ | |
|---|---|---|---|---|
| 9.1 (Contd.) | 5 | $t^m p_n(m;t)$ | $m!\dfrac{(s-1)^n}{s^{m+1}}$ | $n,m = 0,1,2,\ldots$<br>$\mathrm{Re}\, s > 0$ |
| 9.2 | 1 | $\dfrac{1}{t^{\frac{1}{2}}} C^{\nu}_{2n}(t^{\frac{1}{2}})$ | $(-1)^n \left(\dfrac{\pi}{s}\right)^{\frac{1}{2}} \dfrac{\Gamma(n+\nu)}{n!\Gamma(\nu)} A_n\left(\nu, \dfrac{1}{s}\right)$ | $n = 0,1,2,\ldots$<br>$\mathrm{Re}\, s > 0$ |
| | 2 | $\dfrac{1}{t^{\frac{1}{2}}} C^{\nu}_{2n+1}(t^{\frac{1}{2}})$ | $\dfrac{(-1)^n \Gamma(n+\nu+1)\pi^{\frac{1}{2}}}{n!\Gamma(\nu) s^{\frac{3}{2}}} A_n\left(\nu+1, \dfrac{1}{s}\right)$ | $n = 0,1,2,\ldots$<br>$\mathrm{Re}\, s > 0$ |
| | 3 | $He_{2n+1}(t^{\frac{1}{2}})$ | $\dfrac{\pi^{\frac{1}{2}}}{2^{n+1}} \dfrac{(2n+1)!}{n!} \dfrac{(\frac{1}{2} - s)^n}{s^{n+\frac{3}{2}}}$ | $n = 0,1,2,\ldots$<br>$\mathrm{Re}\, s > 0$ |
| | 4 | $\dfrac{1}{t^{\frac{1}{2}}} He_{2n}(t^{\frac{1}{2}})$ | $\dfrac{\pi^{\frac{1}{2}}}{2^n} \dfrac{(2n)!}{n!} \dfrac{(\frac{1}{2}-s)^n}{s^{n+\frac{1}{2}}}$ | $n = 0,1,2,\ldots$<br>$\mathrm{Re}\, s > 0$ |
| | 5 | $t^{n+\frac{1}{2}} He_{2n+1}(t^{\frac{1}{2}})$ | $\dfrac{(2n+1)!}{2^n s^{n+2}} U_{n+1}\left(\dfrac{1}{s} - 1\right)$ | $n = 0,1,2,\ldots$<br>$\mathrm{Re}\, s > 0$ |
| | 6 | $t^{\frac{n-1}{2}} He_n(t^{\frac{1}{2}})$ | $\dfrac{\pi^{\frac{1}{2}} n!}{2^{\frac{n}{2}} s^{\frac{n+1}{2}}} P_n\left[\dfrac{1}{(2s)^{\frac{1}{2}}}\right]$ | $n = 0,1,2,\ldots$<br>$\mathrm{Re}\, s > 0$ |
| | 7 | $t^{\frac{n}{2}+\nu} He_n[(2t)^{\frac{1}{2}}]$ | $\dfrac{n!\Gamma(\nu+1)}{2^{\frac{n}{2}} s^{\frac{n}{2}+\nu+1}} C_n^{\nu+1}\left(\dfrac{1}{s^{\frac{1}{2}}}\right)$ | $n = 0,1,2,\ldots$<br>$\mathrm{Re}\, s > 0$ |
| | 8 | $t^{a-1} He_n(t)$ | $\displaystyle\sum_{m=0}^{[\frac{n}{2}]} \dfrac{n!\Gamma(a+n-2m)}{m!(n-2m)!} \left(-\tfrac{1}{2}\right)^m s^{2m-a-n}$ | $n = 0,1,2,\ldots$<br>$\mathrm{Re}\, a > 0$ for $n$ even<br>$\mathrm{Re}\, a > -1$ for $n$ odd<br>$\mathrm{Re}\, s > 0$ |
| | 9 | $t^{a-\frac{n}{2}-1} He_n(t^{\frac{1}{2}})$ | $\dfrac{\Gamma(a)}{s^a} {}_2F_1\left[-\dfrac{n}{2}, \dfrac{1-n}{2}; 1-a; 2s\right]$<br>If $a$ is an integer take the first $1 + [\frac{n}{2}]$ terms of the series | $n = 0,1,2,\ldots$<br>$\mathrm{Re}\, a > \dfrac{n}{2}$ for $n$ even<br>$\mathrm{Re}\, a > \dfrac{n-1}{2}$ for $n$ odd<br>$\mathrm{Re}\, s > 0$ |

| | | f(t) | g(s) | |
|---|---|---|---|---|
| 9.2 (Contd.) | 10 | $\frac{1}{t^{\frac{1}{2}}} He_{2n}[(2at)^{\frac{1}{2}}]He_{2m}[(2bt)^{\frac{1}{2}}]$ | $\frac{\pi^{\frac{1}{2}}(2m+2n)!}{(-2)^{m+n}(m+n)!}\frac{(s-a)^n(s-b)^m}{s^{m+n+\frac{1}{2}}}\cdot$ $\cdot\ {}_2F_1[-m,-n;-m-n+\frac{1}{2};\frac{s(s-a-b)}{(s-a)(s-b)}]$ | $m,n=0,1,2,\ldots$ Re $s>0$ |
| | 11 | $\frac{1}{t^{\frac{1}{2}}} He_{2n+1}[(2at)^{\frac{1}{2}}]He_{2m+1}[(2bt)^{\frac{1}{2}}]$ | $\frac{(ab)^{\frac{1}{2}}(2m+2n+2)!}{\pi^{\frac{1}{2}}(-2)^{m+n+1}(m+n+1)!}\frac{(s-a)^n(s-b)^m}{s^{m+n+\frac{3}{2}}}\cdot$ $\cdot\ {}_2F_1\left[-m,-n;-m-n-\frac{1}{2};\frac{s(s-a-b)}{(s-a)(s-b)}\right]$ | $m,n=0,1,2,\ldots$ Re $s>0$ |
| | 12 | $\frac{1}{t^{\frac{1}{2}}} He_n[(at)^{\frac{1}{2}}]He_n[(-at)^{\frac{1}{2}}]$ | $\frac{n!\,i^n\pi^{\frac{1}{2}}P_n(\frac{a}{2s})}{s^{\frac{1}{2}}}$ | $n=0,1,2,\ldots$ Re $s>0$ |
| | 13 | $\frac{1}{t^{\frac{1}{2}}}\left[He_n\left(\frac{a+t^{\frac{1}{2}}}{b}\right)+He_n\left(\frac{a-t^{\frac{1}{2}}}{b}\right)\right]$ | $(\frac{2\pi}{s})^{\frac{1}{2}}\left(1-\frac{1}{2b^2s}\right)^{\frac{n}{2}} He_n\left[\frac{a}{(b^2-\frac{1}{2s})^{\frac{1}{2}}}\right]$ | $n=0,1,2,\ldots$ Re $s>0$ |
| | 14 | $\frac{1}{t^{\frac{1}{2}}}\left[He_m\left(\frac{a+t^{\frac{1}{2}}}{c}\right)He_n\left(\frac{b+t^{\frac{1}{2}}}{d}\right)+He_m\left(\frac{a-t^{\frac{1}{2}}}{c}\right)He_n\left(\frac{b-t^{\frac{1}{2}}}{d}\right)\right]$ | $\frac{2\pi^{\frac{1}{2}}}{c^md^n(2s)^{\frac{m+n+1}{2}}}\sum_{k=0}^{n}\left\{\binom{m}{k}\binom{n}{k}k!\cdot\right.$ $\cdot\ (2c^2s-1)^{\frac{m+k}{2}}(2d^2s-1)^{\frac{n+k}{2}}\cdot$ $\left.\cdot\ He_{m-k}\left[\frac{a}{(c^2-\frac{1}{2s})^{\frac{1}{2}}}\right]He_{n-k}\left[\frac{b}{(d^2-\frac{1}{2s})^{\frac{1}{2}}}\right]\right\}$ | $m,n=0,1,2,\ldots$ $m\geq n$ Re $s>0$ |
| | 15 | $t^aL_n^a(t)$ | $\frac{\Gamma(a+n+1)}{n!}\frac{(s-1)^n}{s^{a+n+1}}$ | Re $a>-1$ $n=0,1,2,\ldots$ Re $s>0$ |
| | 16 | $t^bL_n^a(t)$ | $\frac{\Gamma(b+n+1)}{n!}\frac{(s-1)^n}{s^{b+n+1}}\ {}_2F_1[-n,a-b;-b-n;\frac{s}{s-1}]$ $=\frac{\Gamma(a+n+1)\Gamma(b+1)}{n!\Gamma(a+1)s^{b+1}}\ {}_2F_1[-n,b+1;a+1;\frac{1}{s}]$ | Re $b>-1$ $n=0,1,2,\ldots$ Re $s>0$ |

| | | f(t) | g(s) | |
|---|---|---|---|---|
| 9.2 (Contd.) | 17 | $t^{n+2a}\,L_n^a(t)$ | $\dfrac{\Gamma(2a+1)\Gamma(n+a+1)}{\Gamma(a+1)\,s^{n+2a+1}}C_n^{a+\frac{1}{2}}(1-\frac{2}{s})$ | $n=0,1,2,\ldots$<br>$\mathrm{Re}\ a>-\frac{1+n}{2}$<br>$\mathrm{Re}\ s>0$ |
| | 18 | $t^{b+n}\,L_n^a(t)$ | $\dfrac{\Gamma(b+n+1)}{s^{b+n+1}}P_n^{a,b-a}(1-\frac{2}{s})$ | $n=0,1,2,\ldots$<br>$\mathrm{Re}\,b>-1-n$<br>$\mathrm{Re}\ s>0$ |
| | 19 | $t^a\,L_n^a(bt)L_m^a(ct)$ | $\dfrac{\Gamma(m+n+a+1)}{m!n!}\,\dfrac{(s-b)^n(s-c)^m}{s^{m+n+a+1}}\,{}_2F_1\left[-m,-n;-m-n-a;\ \dfrac{s(s-b-c)}{(s-b)(s-c)}\right]$ | $\mathrm{Re}\ a>-1$<br>$n,m=0,1,2,\ldots$<br>$\mathrm{Re}\ s>0$ |
| | 20 | $t^{2a}\,L_n^a(bt)L_n^a(ct)$ | $\dfrac{\Gamma(2a+1)\Gamma(n+a+1)}{n!s^{2a+1}}\displaystyle\sum_{r=0}^{\infty}\left\{\frac{(-1)^r(1-\frac{b+c}{2s})^{n-r}}{r!\,\Gamma(a-r+1)}C_{n+r}^{a+\frac{1}{2}}\left[\frac{s^2-(b+c)s+2bc}{s(s-b-c)}\right]\right\}$ | $\mathrm{Re}\ a>-\frac{1}{2}$<br>$n=0,1,2,\ldots$<br>$\mathrm{Re}\ s>0$ |
| | 21 | $t^{2a}[L_n^a(t)]^2$ | $\dfrac{2^{2a}\Gamma(a+\frac{1}{2})\Gamma(n+\frac{1}{2})}{\pi(n!)^2s^{2a+1}}\,{}_2F_1[-n,a+\frac{1}{2};\frac{1}{2}-n;(1-\frac{2}{s})^2]$ | $\mathrm{Re}\ a>-\frac{1}{2}$<br>$n=0,1,2,\ldots$<br>$\mathrm{Re}\ s>0$ |
| | 22 | $P_{2n+1}(t^{\frac{1}{2}})$ | $\dfrac{(-1)^n\pi^{\frac{1}{2}}(2n+1)!}{2s^{\frac{3}{2}}}A_n(\frac{3}{2},\frac{1}{s})$ | $n=0,1,2,\ldots$<br>$\mathrm{Re}\ s>0$ |
| | 23 | $\dfrac{1}{t^{\frac{1}{2}}}P_{2n}(t^{\frac{1}{2}})$ | $(-1)^n(2n)!(\frac{\pi}{s})^{\frac{1}{2}}A_n(\frac{1}{2},\frac{1}{s})$ | $n=0,1,2,\ldots$<br>$\mathrm{Re}\ s>0$ |
| | 24 | $t^{a-1}\,p_n(m,t)$ | $\dfrac{m!\Gamma(a-n)}{(m-n)!s^{a-n}}\,{}_2F_1[-n,a-n;m-n+1;\ \dfrac{(s^2+a^2)^{\frac{1}{2}}}{s}]$ | $\mathrm{Re}\ a>\min(n,m)$<br>$n,m=0,1,2,\ldots$<br>$\mathrm{Re}\ s>0$ |
| 9.2.1 | 1 | $t^{\nu-\frac{1}{2}}C_n^{\nu}(2t-1)$ | $\dfrac{(-1)^n\Gamma(2\nu+n)\Gamma(\nu+\frac{1}{2})}{n!\Gamma(2\nu)\,s^{\nu+\frac{1}{2}}}A_n(2\nu,\frac{1}{s})$ | $n=0,1,2,\ldots$<br>$\mathrm{Re}\ \nu>-\frac{1}{2}$<br>$\mathrm{Re}\ s>0$ |
| | 2 | $t^{n-1}\,He_{2n}(t^{\frac{1}{2}})$ | $\dfrac{\Gamma(2n)}{2^{n-1}(-s)^n}T_n(1-\frac{1}{s})$ | $n=1,2,3,\ldots$<br>$\mathrm{Re}\ s>0$ |

| | | $f(t)$ | $g(s)$ | |
|---|---|---|---|---|
| 9.2.1 (Contd.) | 3 | $t^a(1+t)^b P_n^{a,b}(1+2t)$ | $\frac{\Gamma(n+a+1)}{n!}\frac{e^{\frac{s}{2}}}{s^{\frac{a+b}{2}+1}}W_{b-a,\frac{a+b+1}{2}+n}(s)$ | $n=0,1,2,\ldots$ <br> $\mathrm{Re}\ a>-1$ <br> $\mathrm{Re}\ s>0$ |
| | 4 | $t^b(1+t)^n P_n^{a,b}(\frac{t-1}{t+1})$ | $\frac{\Gamma(n+b+1)}{s^{n+b+1}}L_n^a(s)$ | $n=0,1,2,\ldots$ <br> $\mathrm{Re}\ b>-1$ <br> $\mathrm{Re}\ s>0$ |
| | 5 | $\frac{(1+t)^n}{t^{\frac{1}{2}}}T_n(\frac{1-t}{1+t})$ | $\frac{\pi^{\frac{1}{2}}}{2^n s^{n+\frac{1}{2}}}He_{2n}[(2s)^{\frac{1}{2}}]$ | $n=0,1,2,\ldots$ <br> $\mathrm{Re}\ s>0$ |
| | 6 | $\frac{1}{t^{\frac{1}{2}}}T_n(1-2t)$ | $(\frac{\pi}{s})^{\frac{1}{2}}A_n(o,\frac{1}{s})$ | $n=0,1,2,\ldots$ <br> $\mathrm{Re}\ s>0$ |
| | 7 | $t^{\frac{1}{2}}U_n(2t-1)$ | $(-1)^{n-1}\frac{n\pi^{\frac{1}{2}}}{2s^{\frac{3}{2}}}A_{n-1}(2,\frac{1}{s})$ | $n=0,1,2,\ldots$ <br> $\mathrm{Re}\ s>0$ |
| | 8 | $t^{\frac{1}{2}}(t+1)^n U_{n+1}(\frac{1-t}{1+t})$ | $\frac{\pi^{\frac{1}{2}}(n+1)}{2^{n+\frac{3}{2}}s^{n+2}}He_{2n+1}[(2s)^{\frac{1}{2}}]$ | $n=0,1,2,\ldots$ <br> $\mathrm{Re}\ s>0$ |
| 9.3 | 1 | $He_{2n+1}[a^{\frac{1}{2}}(1-e^{-t})^{\frac{1}{2}}]$ | $(-2)^n a^{\frac{1}{2}}B(s,n+\frac{3}{2})n!\,L_n^{s+\frac{1}{2}}(\frac{a}{2})$ | $n=0,1,2,\ldots$ <br> $\mathrm{Re}\ s>0$ |
| | 2 | $\frac{He_{2n}[a^{\frac{1}{2}}(1-e^{-t})^{\frac{1}{2}}]}{(e^t-1)^{\frac{1}{2}}}$ | $(-2)^n B(s+\frac{1}{2},n+\frac{1}{2})n!\,L_n^{s}(\frac{a}{2})$ | $n=0,1,2,\ldots$ <br> $\mathrm{Re}\ s>-\frac{1}{2}$ |
| | 3 | $e^{-at}L_n(2at)$ | $\frac{(s-a)^n}{(s+a)^{n+1}}$ | $n=0,1,2,\ldots$ <br> $\mathrm{Re}\ s>-\mathrm{Re}\ a$ |
| | 4 | $e^{-t}\sum_{m=0}^{n}a_{mn}L_m(2t)$ <br> where $a_{mn}$ is given by <br> $P_n(x)=\sum_{m=o}^{n}a_{mn}x^m$ | $\frac{1}{s+1}P_n(\frac{s-1}{s+1})$ | $\mathrm{Re}\ s>-1$ |

| | | f(t) | g(s) | |
|---|---|---|---|---|
| 9.3 (Contd.) | 5 | $P_n(e^{-t})$ | $\frac{(s-1)(s-2)\ldots(s-n+1)}{(s+n)(s+n-2)\ldots(s-n+2)}$ | $n=2,3,4,\ldots$ <br> Re $s>0$ |
| | 6 | $\frac{[1-(1-e^{-t})^{\frac{1}{2}}]^a+(-1)^n[1+(1-e^{-t})^{\frac{1}{2}}]^a}{(1-e^{-t})^{\frac{1}{2}}}P_n[(1-e^{-t})^{\frac{1}{2}}]$ | $2^{2s+a}B(s,s+a)\,{}_3F_2\left[\begin{matrix}-n,n+1,s+a;\\ 1,2s+a;\end{matrix}\;1\right]$ | $n=0,1,2,\ldots$ <br> Re $s>0$ |
| | 7 | $\frac{T_n(e^{-t})}{(1-e^{-2t})^{\frac{1}{2}}}$ | $\frac{\pi\Gamma(s)}{2^s\Gamma(\frac{s-n+1}{2})\Gamma(\frac{s+n+1}{2})}$ | $n=0,1,2,\ldots$ <br> Re $s>0$ |
| 9.3.1 | 1 | $t^n e^{-bt}L_n(at)$ | $\frac{n!P_n(\frac{s+b-2a}{s+b})}{(s+b)^{n+1}}$ | $n=0,1,2,\ldots$ <br> Re $s>-$ Re $b$ |
| | 2 | $\frac{e^{-\frac{b}{t}}L_n^a(\frac{b}{t})}{t^n}$ | $\frac{(-1)^n\,2\,s^{\frac{a}{2}+n}}{n!\,b^{\frac{a}{2}}}K_a(2b^{\frac{1}{2}}s^{\frac{1}{2}})$ | Re $b>0$ <br> Re $s>0$ |
| 9.3.2 | 1 | $\frac{e^{-\frac{a}{2t}}He_n(\frac{a^{\frac{1}{2}}}{t^{\frac{1}{2}}})}{t^{\frac{n+1}{2}}}$ | $2^{\frac{n}{2}}\pi^{\frac{1}{2}}s^{\frac{n-1}{2}}e^{-(2as)^{\frac{1}{2}}}$ | Re $a>0$ <br> $n=0,1,2,\ldots$ <br> Re $s>0$ |
| | 2 | $\frac{1}{t^{\frac{1}{2}}}e^{bt}He_{2n}(at^{\frac{1}{2}})$ | $(-2)^{-n}\pi^{\frac{1}{2}}\frac{(2n)!}{n!}\frac{(s-b-\frac{a^2}{2})^n}{(s-b)^{n+\frac{1}{2}}}$ | $n=0,1,2,\ldots$ <br> Re $s>$ Re $b$ |
| | 3 | $e^{bt}He_{2n+1}(at^{\frac{1}{2}})$ | $-(-2)^{n-1}\pi^{\frac{1}{2}}a\frac{(2n+1)!}{n!}\frac{(s-b-\frac{a^2}{2})^n}{(s-b)^{n+\frac{3}{2}}}$ | $n=0,1,2,\ldots$ <br> Re $s>$ Re $b$ |
| | 4 | $\frac{1}{t^{\frac{1}{2}}}e^{-(a+b)t}He_n[(4at)^{\frac{1}{2}}]\;He_n[(4bt)^{\frac{1}{2}}]$ | $\pi^{\frac{1}{2}}n!\,\frac{(a+b-s)^{\frac{n}{2}}}{(a+b+s)^{\frac{n+1}{2}}}P_n\left[\frac{2a^{\frac{1}{2}}b^{\frac{1}{2}}}{[(a+b)^2-s^2]^{\frac{1}{2}}}\right]$ | $n=0,1,2,\ldots$ <br> Re $s>-$ Re$(a+b)$ |
| | 5 | $t^a e^{bt}L_n^a(ct)$ | $\frac{\Gamma(a+n+1)}{n!}\frac{(s-c-b)^n}{(s-b)^{a+n+1}}$ | Re $a>-1$ <br> $n=0,1,2,\ldots$ <br> Re $s>$ Re $b$ |

| | | f(t) | g(s) | |
|---|---|---|---|---|
| 9.5 | 1 | $P_{2n}[\cos(at)]$ | $\frac{[s^2+a^2][s^2+(3a)^2]\cdots[s^2+(2na-a)^2]}{s[s^2+(2a)^2][s^2+(4a)^2]\cdots[s^2+(2na)^2]}$ | $n=1,2,3,\ldots$ <br> a Real <br> $\mathrm{Re}\, s > 0$ |
| | 2 | $P_{2n+1}[\cos(at)]$ | $\frac{s[s^2+(2a)^2][s^2+(4a)^2]\cdots[s^2+(2na)^2]}{[s^2+a^2][s^2+(3a)^2]\cdots[s^2+(2na+a)^2]}$ | $n=1,2,3,\ldots$ <br> a Real <br> $\mathrm{Re}\, s > 0$ |
| 9.7 | 1 | $P_{2n}[\cosh(at)]$ | $\frac{[s^2-a^2][s^2-(3a)^2]\cdots[s^2-(2na-a)^2]}{s[s^2-(2a)^2][s^2-(4a)^2]\cdots[s^2-(2na)^2]}$ | $n=1,2,3,\ldots$ <br> a Real <br> $\mathrm{Re}\, s > 2n\lvert a\rvert$ |
| | 2 | $P_{2n+1}[\cosh(at)]$ | $\frac{s[s^2-(2a)^2][s^2-(4a)^2]\cdots[s^2-(2na)^2]}{[s^2-a^2][s^2-(3a)^2]\cdots[s^2-(2na+a)^2]}$ | $n=1,2,3,\ldots$ <br> a Real <br> $\mathrm{Re}\, s > (2n+1)\lvert a\rvert$ |
| 10 | 1 | $J_0(at)$ | $\frac{1}{(s^2+a^2)^{\frac{1}{2}}}$ | $\mathrm{Re}\, s > \lvert \mathrm{Im}\, a\rvert$ |
| | 2 | $J_0^2(at)$ | $\frac{2K\left[\frac{2a}{(s^2+4a^2)^{\frac{1}{2}}}\right]}{\pi(s^2+4a^2)^{\frac{1}{2}}}$ | $\mathrm{Re}\, s > 2\lvert \mathrm{Im}\, a\rvert$ |
| | 3 | $J_0(at)J_0(bt)$ | $\frac{1}{\pi}\int_{-a}^{a}\frac{du}{(a^2-u^2)^{\frac{1}{2}}[b^2+(s+iu)^2]^{\frac{1}{2}}}$ | $\mathrm{Re}\, s > \lvert \mathrm{Im}\, a\rvert + \lvert \mathrm{Im}\, b\rvert$ |
| | 4 | $J_1^2(at)$ | $\frac{(s^2+4a^2)^{\frac{1}{2}}}{\pi a^2}\left\{\frac{s^2+2a^2}{s^2+4a^2}K\left[\frac{2a}{(s^2+4a^2)^{\frac{1}{2}}}\right]-E\left[\frac{2a}{(s^2+4a^2)^{\frac{1}{2}}}\right]\right\}$ | $\mathrm{Re}\, s > 2\lvert \mathrm{Im}\, a\rvert$ |
| | 5 | $J_0^2(at)+J_1^2(at)$ | $\frac{4}{\pi}\frac{D\left[\frac{2a}{(s^2+4a^2)^{\frac{1}{2}}}\right]}{(s^2+4a^2)^{\frac{1}{2}}}$ | $\mathrm{Re}\, s > \lvert \mathrm{Im}\, a\rvert$ |
| | 6 | $J_0^2(at)-J_1^2(at)$ | $\frac{4}{\pi}\frac{B\left[\frac{2a}{(s^2+4a^2)^{\frac{1}{2}}}\right]}{(s^2+4a^2)^{\frac{1}{2}}}$ | $\mathrm{Re}\, s > \lvert \mathrm{Im}\, a\rvert$ |
| | 7 | $t\,J_0(at)J_1(at)$ | $\frac{K\left[\frac{2a}{(s^2+4a^2)^{\frac{1}{2}}}\right]-E\left[\frac{2a}{(s^2+4a^2)^{\frac{1}{2}}}\right]}{\pi a(s^2+4a^2)^{\frac{1}{2}}}$ | $\mathrm{Re}\, s > 2\lvert \mathrm{Im}\, a\rvert$ |

| | | f(t) | g(s) | |
|---|---|---|---|---|
| 0 Contd.) | 8 | $\frac{J_0(at)J_1(bt)}{t}$ | $\frac{1}{b\pi}\int_{-b}^{b}\frac{(b^2-u^2)^{\frac{1}{2}}du}{[a^2+(s+iu)^2]^{\frac{1}{2}}}$ | Re s > \|Im a\|+\|Im b\| |
| | 9 | $J_0(at)[J_0(at)-2atJ_1(at)]$ | $\frac{2\,E\left[\frac{2a}{(s^2+4a^2)^{\frac{1}{2}}}\right]}{\pi(s^2+4a^2)^{\frac{1}{2}}}$ | Re s > \|Im a\| |
| | 10 | $J_{\frac{1}{2}}(at)$ | $\left[\frac{(s^2+a^2)^{\frac{1}{2}}-s}{a(s^2+a^2)}\right]^{\frac{1}{2}}$ | Re s > \|Im a\| |
| | 11 | $J_{-\frac{1}{2}}(at)$ | $\left[\frac{(s^2+a^2)^{\frac{1}{2}}+s}{a(s^2+a^2)}\right]^{\frac{1}{2}}$ | Re s > \|Im a\| |
| | 12 | $J_n^2(at)$ | $(-1)^n\,\frac{2}{\pi}\int_0^{\frac{\pi}{2}}\frac{\cos 2n\theta\,d\theta}{[s^2+4a^2\cos^2\theta]^{\frac{1}{2}}}$ | n an integer<br>Re s > 2\|Im a\| |
| | 13 | $t\,J_\nu(at)$ | $\frac{a^\nu[s+\nu(s^2+a^2)^{\frac{1}{2}}]}{(s^2+a^2)^{\frac{3}{2}}[s+(s^2+a^2)^{\frac{1}{2}}]^\nu}$ | Re ν > − 2<br>Re s > \|Im a\| |
| | 14 | $J_\nu(at)$ | $\frac{a^\nu}{(s^2+a^2)^{\frac{1}{2}}[s+(s^2+a^2)^{\frac{1}{2}}]^\nu}$<br>$=\frac{e^{-\nu\sinh^{-1}\frac{s}{a}}}{(s^2+a^2)^{\frac{1}{2}}}$ | Re ν > − 1<br>Re s > \|Im a\| |
| | 15 | $t\,J_\nu^2(at)$ | $\frac{2^{2\nu+1}a^{2\nu}(\nu+\frac{1}{2})}{\pi s^{2\nu+2}}B(\nu+\frac{1}{2},\nu+\frac{1}{2})\;{}_2F_1[\nu+\frac{1}{2},\nu+\frac{3}{2};2\nu+1;-\frac{4a^2}{s^2}]$ | Re ν > − 1<br>Re s > 2\|Im a\| |
| | 16 | $\frac{1}{t}J_\nu(at)$ | $\frac{a^\nu}{\nu[s+(s^2+a^2)^{\frac{1}{2}}]^\nu}$ | Re ν > 0<br>Re s ≥ \|Im a\| |
| | 17 | $\frac{1}{t}J_\nu(\frac{a}{t})$ | $2\,J_\nu[(2as)^{\frac{1}{2}}]K_\nu[(2as)^{\frac{1}{2}}]$ | a > 0<br>Re s > 0 |
| | 18 | $J_\nu(at)J_\nu(bt)$ | $\frac{1}{\pi a^{\frac{1}{2}}b^{\frac{1}{2}}}Q_{\nu-\frac{1}{2}}\left(\frac{s^2+a^2+b^2}{2\,ab}\right)$ | Re ν > $-\frac{1}{2}$<br>Re s > \|Im a\|+\|Im b\| |

| | | $f(t)$ | $g(s)$ | |
|---|---|---|---|---|
| 10 (Contd.) | 19 | $J_{\nu-1}(at)-J_{\nu+1}(at)$ | $\dfrac{2a^{\nu-1}s}{(s^2+a^2)^{\frac{1}{2}}[s+(s^2+a^2)^{\frac{1}{2}}]^{\nu}}$ | $\text{Re}\,\nu > 0$<br>$\text{Re } s > \lvert\text{Im}$ |
| | 20 | $Y_0(at)$ | $-\dfrac{2\sinh^{-1}(\frac{s}{a})}{\pi(s^2+a^2)^{\frac{1}{2}}}$<br>$= -\dfrac{2}{\pi}\dfrac{1}{(s^2+a^2)^{\frac{1}{2}}}\log\dfrac{s+(s^2+a^2)^{\frac{1}{2}}}{a}$ | $\text{Re } s > \lvert\text{Im } a\rvert$ |
| | 21 | $t\,Y_0(at)$ | $\dfrac{2\left[1-\dfrac{s}{(s^2+a^2)^{\frac{1}{2}}}\log\dfrac{s+(s^2+a^2)^{\frac{1}{2}}}{a}\right]}{\pi(s^2+a^2)}$ | $\text{Re } s > \lvert\text{Im } a\rvert$ |
| | 22 | $t\,Y_1(at)$ | $-\dfrac{2s}{\pi a(s^2+a^2)}-\dfrac{2a\log\dfrac{s+(s^2+a^2)^{\frac{1}{2}}}{a}}{\pi(s^2+a^2)^{\frac{3}{2}}}$ | $\text{Re } s > \lvert\text{Im } a\rvert$ |
| | 23 | $Y_{-n-\frac{1}{2}}(at)$ | $\dfrac{(-1)^n[(s^2+a^2)^{\frac{1}{2}}-s]^{n+\frac{1}{2}}}{a^{n+\frac{1}{2}}(s^2+a^2)^{\frac{1}{2}}}$ | $n$ an integer<br>$\text{Re } s > \lvert\text{Im } a\rvert$ |
| | 24 | $Y_{\nu}(at)$ | $\dfrac{\cot(\nu\pi)[(s^2+a^2)^{\frac{1}{2}}-s]^{\nu}-\text{cosec}(\nu\pi)[(s^2+a^2)^{\frac{1}{2}}+s]^{\nu}}{a^{\nu}(s^2+a^2)^{\frac{1}{2}}}$ | $\lvert\text{Re}\,\nu\rvert < 1$<br>$\text{Re } s > \lvert\text{Im } a\rvert$ |
| | 25 | $\dfrac{Y_{\nu}(\frac{a}{t})}{t}$ | $2Y_{\nu}[(2as)^{\frac{1}{2}}]K_{\nu}[(2as)^{\frac{1}{2}}]$ | $a > 0$<br>$\text{Re } s > 0$ |
| | 26 | $\log a\,J_0(at)-\frac{\pi}{2}Y_0(at)$ | $\dfrac{\log[s+(s^2+a^2)^{\frac{1}{2}}]}{(s^2+a^2)^{\frac{1}{2}}}$ | $\text{Re } s > \lvert\text{Im } a\rvert$ |
| 10.1 | 1 | $\dfrac{1}{t^2}J_1^2(at)$ | $\dfrac{a}{2\pi}\displaystyle\int_0^{\pi}\left[\left(\frac{s^2}{a^2}+2-2\cos\theta\right)^{\frac{1}{2}}-\frac{s}{a}\right](1+\cos\theta)\,d\theta$ | $\text{Re } s > 0$ |
| | 2 | $t^nJ_n(at)$ | $\dfrac{1.3.5\ldots(2n-1)a^n}{(s^2+a^2)^{n+\frac{1}{2}}}$ | $n=1,2,3,\ldots$<br>$\text{Re } s > \lvert\text{Im } a\rvert$ |

| | | f(t) | g(s) | |
|---|---|---|---|---|
| 10.1 (Contd.) | 3 | $J_\nu(at^2)$ | $\frac{\Gamma(\nu+\frac{1}{2})}{(2\pi a)^{\frac{1}{2}}} D_{-\nu-\frac{1}{2}}\left[\frac{s\,e^{\frac{\pi i}{4}}}{(2a)^{\frac{1}{2}}}\right] D_{-\nu-\frac{1}{2}}\left[\frac{s\,e^{-\frac{\pi i}{4}}}{(2a)^{\frac{1}{2}}}\right]$ | $\mathrm{Re}\,\nu > -\frac{1}{2}$<br>$\mathrm{Re}\,s > 0$ |
| | 4 | $t^2 J_\nu(at)$ | $\frac{[(s^2+a^2)^{\frac{1}{2}}-s]^\nu}{a^\nu (s^2+a^2)^{\frac{3}{2}}}\left[\nu^2-1+\frac{3s[s+\nu(s^2+a^2)^{\frac{1}{2}}]}{s^2+a^2}\right]$ | $\mathrm{Re}\,\nu > -3$<br>$\mathrm{Re}\,s > \lvert\mathrm{Im}\,a\rvert$ |
| | 5 | $\frac{a}{t} J_{\nu-1}(at) - \frac{\nu+1}{t^2} J_\nu(at)$ | $\frac{s}{\nu a^\nu}[(s^2+a^2)^{\frac{1}{2}}-s]^\nu$ | $\mathrm{Re}\,\nu > 1$<br>$\mathrm{Re}\,s \geqslant \lvert\mathrm{Im}\,a\rvert$ |
| | 6 | $\frac{1}{t^2} J_\nu(at)$ | $\frac{[(s^2+a^2)^{\frac{1}{2}}-s]^{\nu-1}}{2\nu(\nu-1)a^{\nu-2}} + \frac{[(s^2+a^2)^{\frac{1}{2}}-s]^{\nu+1}}{2\nu(\nu+1)a^\nu}$ | $\mathrm{Re}\,\nu > 1$<br>$\mathrm{Re}\,s \geqslant \lvert\mathrm{Im}\,a\rvert$ |
| 10.2 | 1 | $J_0(at^{\frac{1}{2}})$ | $\frac{e^{-\frac{a^2}{4s}}}{s}$ | $\mathrm{Re}\,s > 0$ |
| | 2 | $J_0^2(at^{\frac{1}{2}})$ | $\frac{e^{-\frac{a^2}{2s}} M_{0,0}(\frac{a^2}{s})}{a\,s^{\frac{1}{2}}}$ | $\mathrm{Re}\,s > 0$ |
| | 3 | $J_0^2(at^{\frac{1}{2}})$ | $\frac{1}{s}\,{}_1F_1[\frac{1}{2};1;-\frac{a^2}{s}]$ | $\mathrm{Re}\,s > 0$ |
| | 4 | $t^\nu J_0(at^{\frac{1}{2}})$ | $\frac{\Gamma(\nu+1)e^{-\frac{a^2}{4s}}\,{}_1F_1[-\nu,1,\frac{a^2}{4s}]}{s^{\nu+1}}$ | $\mathrm{Re}\,\nu > -1$<br>$\mathrm{Re}\,s > 0$ |
| | 5 | $\sum_{n=0}^{\infty} J_0[2(nt)^{\frac{1}{2}}]$ | $\frac{1}{s(1-e^{-\frac{1}{s}})}$ | $\mathrm{Re}\,s > 0$ |
| | 6 | $J_0[a(t^2+bt)^{\frac{1}{2}}]$ | $\frac{e^{\frac{b}{2}[s-(s^2+a^2)^{\frac{1}{2}}]}}{(s^2+a^2)^{\frac{1}{2}}}$<br>$= \left(\frac{b}{\pi}\right)^{\frac{1}{2}} \frac{e^{\frac{bs}{2}} K_{\frac{1}{2}}[\frac{b}{2}(s^2+a^2)^{\frac{1}{2}}]}{(s^2+a^2)^{\frac{1}{4}}}$ | $\lvert\arg b\rvert < \pi$<br>$\mathrm{Re}\,s > \lvert\mathrm{Im}\,a\rvert$ |

| | | f(t) | g(s) | |
|---|---|---|---|---|
| 10.2 (Contd.) | 7 | $t^{\frac{1}{2}}J_1(at^{\frac{1}{2}})$ | $\frac{a}{2s^2}e^{-\frac{a^2}{4s}}$ | Re s > o |
| | 8 | $\frac{1}{t^{\frac{1}{2}}}J_1(at^{\frac{1}{2}})$ | $\frac{2}{a}(1-e^{-\frac{a^2}{4s}})$ | Re s > o |
| | 9 | $t^{n-\frac{1}{2}}J_1(at^{\frac{1}{2}})$ | $\frac{2(-1)^{n-1}n!}{a\,s^n}e^{-\frac{a^2}{8s}}k_{2n}(\frac{a^2}{8s})$ | n = 1,2,3,.. <br> Re s > o |
| | 10 | $\frac{J_1[a(t^2+2bt)^{\frac{1}{2}}]}{(t^2+2bt)^{\frac{1}{2}}}$ | $\frac{1-e^{-b[(s^2+a^2)^{\frac{1}{2}}-s]}}{ab}$ | Re s > \|Im a |
| | 11 | $\frac{1}{t^{\frac{1}{2}}}J_{\frac{1}{3}}\left(\frac{1}{t^{\frac{1}{3}}}\right)$ | $\frac{2^{\frac{1}{2}}}{3^{\frac{7}{6}}s^{\frac{2}{3}}}\left[e^{\frac{3}{2}(3s)^{\frac{1}{3}}}+\omega^2e^{\frac{3}{2}\omega(3s)^{\frac{1}{3}}}+\omega e^{\frac{3}{2}\omega^2(3s)^{\frac{1}{3}}}\right]$ <br> where $\omega=-\frac{1}{2}+i\frac{3^{\frac{1}{2}}}{2}$ | Re s > o |
| | 12 | $\frac{1}{t^{\frac{1}{2}}}J_{-\frac{1}{3}}\left(\frac{1}{t^{\frac{1}{3}}}\right)$ | $\frac{2^{\frac{1}{2}}}{3^{\frac{7}{6}}s^{\frac{2}{3}}}\left[e^{\frac{3}{2}(3s)^{\frac{1}{3}}}+e^{\frac{3}{2}\omega(3s)^{\frac{1}{3}}}+e^{\frac{3}{2}\omega^2(3s)^{\frac{1}{3}}}\right]$ <br> where $\omega=-\frac{1}{2}+i\frac{3^{\frac{1}{2}}}{2}$ | Re s > o |
| | 13 | $t^{\nu}J_{-n}(at)$ | $\frac{\Gamma(\nu-n+1)P_{\nu}^{n}\left[\frac{s}{(s^2+a^2)^{\frac{1}{2}}}\right]}{(s^2+a^2)^{\frac{\nu+1}{2}}}$ | n = 1,2,3,.. <br> Re $\nu$ > n − 1 <br> Re s > \|Im a |
| | 14 | $t^{\mu}J_{\nu}(at)$ | $\frac{\Gamma(\mu+\nu+1)}{\Gamma(\nu+1)}(\frac{a}{2})^{\nu}(s^2+a^2)^{-\frac{\mu+\nu+1}{2}}\,{}_2F_1[\frac{\mu+\nu+1}{2},\frac{\nu-\mu}{2};\nu+1;\frac{a^2}{s^2+a^2}]$ | Re($\mu+\nu$) > − <br> Re s > \|Im a |
| | 15 | $t^{\nu}J_{\nu}(at)$ | $\frac{(2a)^{\nu}\Gamma(\nu+\frac{1}{2})}{\pi^{\frac{1}{2}}(s^2+a^2)^{\nu+\frac{1}{2}}}$ | Re $\nu$ > $-\frac{1}{2}$ <br> Re s > \|Im a |
| | 16 | $t^{\nu+1}J_{\nu}(at)$ | $\frac{2^{\nu+1}a^{\nu}\Gamma(\nu+\frac{3}{2})s}{\pi^{\frac{1}{2}}(s^2+a^2)^{\nu+\frac{3}{2}}}$ | Re $\nu$ > − 1 <br> Re s > \|Im a |
| | 17 | $J_{\nu}(at^{\frac{1}{2}})$ | $\frac{a\pi^{\frac{1}{2}}}{4s^{\frac{3}{2}}}e^{-\frac{a^2}{8s}}\left[I_{\frac{\nu-1}{2}}\left(\frac{a^2}{8s}\right)-I_{\frac{\nu+1}{2}}\left(\frac{a^2}{8s}\right)\right]$ | Re $\nu$ > − 2 <br> Re s > o |

0.2 Contd.)

| | f(t) | g(s) | |
|---|---|---|---|
| 18 | $\frac{1}{t^{\frac{1}{2}}} J_\nu(at^{\frac{1}{2}})$ | $(\frac{\pi}{s})^{\frac{1}{2}} e^{-\frac{a^2}{8s}} I_{\frac{\nu}{2}}(\frac{a^2}{8s})$ | $\mathrm{Re}\,\nu > -1$<br>$\mathrm{Re}\,s > 0$ |
| 19 | $t^\mu J_\nu(at^{\frac{1}{2}})$ | $\frac{\Gamma(\mu+1+\frac{\nu}{2})a^\nu}{2^\nu\Gamma(\nu+1)s^{\mu+1+\frac{\nu}{2}}} {}_1F_1[\mu+1+\frac{\nu}{2};\nu+1;-\frac{a^2}{4s}]$<br>$= \frac{2\Gamma(\mu+1+\frac{\nu}{2})}{a\Gamma(\nu+1)s^{\mu+\frac{1}{2}}} e^{-\frac{a^2}{8s}} M_{\mu+\frac{1}{2},\frac{\nu}{2}}(\frac{a^2}{4s})$ | $\mathrm{Re}(\mu+\frac{\nu}{2}) > -1$<br>$\mathrm{Re}\,s > 0$ |
| 20 | $t^{\frac{\nu}{2}} J_\nu(at^{\frac{1}{2}})$ | $(\frac{a}{2})^\nu \frac{e^{-\frac{a^2}{4s}}}{s^{\nu+1}}$ | $\mathrm{Re}\,\nu > -1$<br>$\mathrm{Re}\,s > 0$ |
| 21 | $t^{\frac{\nu}{2}-1} J_\nu(at^{\frac{1}{2}})$ | $(\frac{2}{a})^\nu \gamma(\nu, \frac{a^2}{4s})$ | $\mathrm{Re}\,\nu > 0$<br>$\mathrm{Re}\,s > 0$ |
| 22 | $t^{\frac{\nu}{2}+n} J_\nu(at^{\frac{1}{2}})$ | $n!(\frac{a}{2})^\nu s^{-n-\nu-1} e^{-\frac{a^2}{4s}} L_n^\nu(\frac{a^2}{4s})$ | $\mathrm{Re}(\nu+n) > -1$<br>$n = 0,1,2,\ldots$<br>$\mathrm{Re}\,s > 0$ |
| 23 | $\frac{1}{t^{\frac{\nu}{2}}} J_\nu(at^{\frac{1}{2}})$ | $\frac{2^\nu e^{i\nu\pi} s^{\nu-1}}{a^\nu\Gamma(\nu)} e^{-\frac{a^2}{4s}} \gamma\left(\nu, \frac{a^2}{4s} e^{-i\pi}\right)$ | $\mathrm{Re}\,s > 0$ |
| 24 | $\sum_{n=0}^{\infty} J_{2\nu+2n+1}(t^{\frac{1}{2}})$ | $\frac{\pi^{\frac{1}{2}}}{(2s)^{\frac{3}{2}}} e^{-\frac{1}{8s}} I_\nu(\frac{1}{8s})$ | $\mathrm{Re}\,\nu > -\frac{3}{2}$<br>$\mathrm{Re}\,s > 0$ |
| 25 | $\frac{t^{\frac{\nu}{2}-1}}{(t+1)^{\frac{\nu}{2}}} J_\nu[a(t^2+t)^{\frac{1}{2}}]$ | $(\frac{2}{a})^\nu \gamma\left(\nu, \frac{(s^2+a^2)^{\frac{1}{2}}-s}{2}\right)$ | $\mathrm{Re}\,\nu > 0$<br>$\mathrm{Re}\,s > \lvert \mathrm{Im}\,a \rvert$ |
| 26 | $\frac{t^{b-\frac{\nu}{2}-1}}{(t+1)^{\frac{\nu}{2}}} J_\nu[a(t^2+t)^{\frac{1}{2}}]$ | $\frac{2^\nu}{a^\nu\Gamma(\nu-b+1)} \int_0^{\frac{(s^2+a^2)^{\frac{1}{2}}-s}{2}} e^{-u} u^{b-1} (\frac{a^2}{4} - su - u^2)^{\nu-b}\, du$ | $\mathrm{Re}(\nu+1) > \mathrm{Re}\,b > 0$<br>$\mathrm{Re}\,s > \lvert \mathrm{Im}\,a \rvert$ |
| 27 | $(t^2+bt)^{\frac{\nu}{2}} J_\nu[a(t^2+bt)^{\frac{1}{2}}]$ | $\pi^{-\frac{1}{2}}(\frac{a}{2})^\nu \frac{b^{\nu+\frac{1}{2}}}{(s^2+a^2)^{\frac{\nu}{2}+\frac{1}{4}}} e^{\frac{bs}{2}} K_{\nu+\frac{1}{2}}\left[\frac{b(s^2+a^2)^{\frac{1}{2}}}{2}\right]$ | $\mathrm{Re}\,\nu > -1$<br>$\lvert \arg b \rvert < \pi$<br>$\mathrm{Re}\,s > \lvert \mathrm{Im}\,a \rvert$ |

| | | $f(t)$ | $g(s)$ | |
|---|---|---|---|---|
| 10.2 (Contd.) | 28 | $\left(\frac{t}{t+b}\right)^{\frac{\nu}{2}} J_\nu[a(t^2+bt)^{\frac{1}{2}}]$ | $\frac{a^\nu e^{\frac{b}{2}[s-(s^2+a^2)^{\frac{1}{2}}]}}{(s^2+a^2)^{\frac{1}{2}}[s+(s^2+a^2)^{\frac{1}{2}}]^\nu}$ | $\operatorname{Re}\nu > -1$<br>$\lvert\arg b\rvert < \pi$<br>$\operatorname{Re} s > \lvert\operatorname{Im} a\rvert$ |
| | 29 | $(t^2+2it)^{\frac{\nu}{2}} J_\nu[a(t^2+2it)^{\frac{1}{2}}]$ | $-\frac{i\pi^{\frac{1}{2}} a^\nu e^{is} H^{(2)}_{\nu+\frac{1}{2}}[(s^2+a^2)^{\frac{1}{2}}]}{2^{\frac{1}{2}}(s^2+a^2)^{\frac{\nu}{2}+\frac{1}{4}}}$ | $\operatorname{Re}\nu > -1$<br>$\operatorname{Re} s > \lvert\operatorname{Im} a\rvert$ |
| | 30 | $(t^2+2it)^{b-\frac{\nu}{2}} J_\nu[a(t^2+2it)^{\frac{1}{2}}]$ | $\frac{2^{b-\nu-\frac{1}{2}}\pi^{\frac{1}{2}} e^{is}\Gamma(b+1)}{i(s^2+a^2)^{\frac{b}{2}+\frac{1}{4}}\Gamma(\nu-b)} \cdot \sum_{n=0}^{\infty} \frac{\Gamma(\nu-b+n)}{2^n n!\Gamma(\nu+n+1)(s^2+a^2)^{\frac{n}{2}}} H^{(2)}_{b+n+\frac{1}{2}}[(s^2+a^2)^{\frac{1}{2}}]$ | $\operatorname{Re} b > -1$<br>$\operatorname{Re} s > \lvert\operatorname{Im} a\rvert$ |
| | 31 | $t^{\nu-\frac{1}{2}}\left\{J_{2\mu}(at^{\frac{1}{2}})\cos[(\nu+\mu)\pi] - J_{-2\mu}(at^{\frac{1}{2}})\cos[(\nu-\mu)\pi]\right\}$ | $-\frac{2}{a}\sin(2\mu\pi)s^{-\nu} e^{-\frac{a^2}{8s}} W_{\nu,\mu}(\frac{a^2}{4s})$ | $\operatorname{Re}(\nu\pm\mu) > -\frac{1}{2}$<br>$\operatorname{Re} s > 0$ |
| | 32 | $t^{\frac{1}{2}} J_\nu^2(at)$ | $\frac{a\Gamma(2\nu+\frac{3}{2})}{2^{\nu+\frac{1}{2}} s^{\frac{1}{2}}(s^2+4a^2)^{\frac{1}{2}}} P^{-\nu}_{\frac{1}{4}}\left[\frac{(s^2+4a^2)^{\frac{1}{2}}}{s}\right] \cdot P^{-\nu}_{-\frac{1}{4}}\left[\frac{(s^2+4a^2)^{\frac{1}{2}}}{s}\right]$ | $\operatorname{Re}\nu > -\frac{3}{4}$<br>$\operatorname{Re} s > 2\lvert\operatorname{Im} a$ |
| | 33 | $\frac{1}{t^{\frac{1}{2}}} J_\nu^2(at)$ | $\frac{\Gamma(2\nu+\frac{1}{2})}{2^{\nu+\frac{1}{2}} s^{\frac{1}{2}}}\left\{P^{-\nu}_{-\frac{1}{4}}\left[\frac{(s^2+4a^2)^{\frac{1}{2}}}{s}\right]\right\}^2$ | $\operatorname{Re}\nu > -\frac{1}{4}$<br>$\operatorname{Re} s > 2\lvert\operatorname{Im} a$ |
| | 34 | $t^{2\nu} J_\nu^2(at)$ | $\frac{2^{4\nu} a^{2\nu}\Gamma(\nu+\frac{1}{2})\Gamma(2\nu+\frac{1}{2})}{\pi\Gamma(\nu+1)s^{4\nu+1}} {}_2F_1[\nu+\frac{1}{2}; 2\nu+\frac{1}{2}; \nu+1; -\frac{4a^2}{s^2}]$ | $\operatorname{Re}\nu > -\frac{1}{4}$<br>$\operatorname{Re} s > 2\lvert\operatorname{Im} a$ |
| | 35 | $J_\nu^2(at^{\frac{1}{2}})$ | $\frac{1}{s} e^{-\frac{a^2}{2s}} I_\nu(\frac{a^2}{2s})$ | $\operatorname{Re}\nu > -1$<br>$\operatorname{Re} s > 0$ |
| | 36 | $\frac{1}{t} J_\nu^2(at^{\frac{1}{2}})$ | $\nu^{-1} e^{-\frac{2a}{s}}[I_\nu(\frac{a^2}{2s}) + 2\sum_{n=1}^{\infty} I_{\nu+n}(\frac{a^2}{2s})]$ | $\operatorname{Re}\nu > 0$<br>$\operatorname{Re} s > 0$ |

| | | f(t) | g(s) | |
|---|---|---|---|---|
| 10.2 (Contd.) | 37 | $t^{\frac{1}{2}}J_{\nu}(at)J_{-\nu}(at)$ | $\frac{a\pi^{\frac{1}{2}}}{s^{\frac{1}{2}}(s^2+4a^2)^{\frac{1}{2}}}\left\{(\nu+\frac{1}{4})P^{\nu}_{-\frac{1}{4}}\left[\frac{(s^2+4a^2)^{\frac{1}{2}}}{s}\right]\cdot P^{-\nu}_{\frac{1}{4}}\left[\frac{(s^2+4a^2)^{\frac{1}{2}}}{s}\right]-(\nu-\frac{1}{4})P^{\nu}_{\frac{1}{4}}\left[\frac{(s^2+4a^2)^{\frac{1}{2}}}{s}\right]\cdot P^{-\nu}_{-\frac{1}{4}}\left[\frac{(s^2+4a^2)^{\frac{1}{2}}}{s}\right]\right\}$ | $\mathrm{Re}\, s > 2\,\lvert\mathrm{Im}\, a\rvert$ |
| | 38 | $\frac{1}{t^{\frac{1}{2}}}J_{\nu}(at)J_{-\nu}(at)$ | $\left(\frac{\pi}{2s}\right)^{\frac{1}{2}}P^{\nu}_{-\frac{1}{4}}\left[\frac{(s^2+4a^2)^{\frac{1}{2}}}{s}\right]P^{-\nu}_{-\frac{1}{4}}\left[\frac{(s^2+4a^2)^{\frac{1}{2}}}{s}\right]$ | $\mathrm{Re}\, s > 2\,\lvert\mathrm{Im}\, a\rvert$ |
| | 39 | $t^{\frac{1}{2}}J_{\nu}(at)J_{\nu+1}(at)$ | $\frac{\Gamma(2\nu+\frac{5}{2})}{2^{\nu+\frac{3}{2}}s^{\frac{1}{2}}(s^2+4a^2)^{\frac{1}{2}}}P^{-\nu}_{-\frac{1}{4}}\left[\frac{(s^2+4a^2)^{\frac{1}{2}}}{s}\right]P^{-\nu-1}_{-\frac{1}{4}}\left[\frac{(s^2+4a^2)^{\frac{1}{2}}}{s}\right]$ | $\mathrm{Re}\,\nu > -\frac{5}{4}$<br>$\mathrm{Re}\, s > 2\,\lvert\mathrm{Im}\, a\rvert$ |
| | 40 | $t^{\mu+\nu}J_{\mu}(at)J_{\nu}(at)$ | $\frac{2(4a)^{\mu+\nu}\Gamma(\mu+\nu+\frac{1}{2})}{\pi^{\frac{3}{2}}}\int_0^{\frac{\pi}{2}}\frac{\cos^{\mu+\nu}\theta\cos(\mu-\nu)\theta\,d\theta}{(s^2+4a^2\cos^2\theta)^{\mu+\nu+\frac{1}{2}}}$ | $\mathrm{Re}(\mu+\nu) > -\frac{1}{2}$<br>$\mathrm{Re}\, s > \lvert\mathrm{Im}\, a\rvert$ |
| | 41 | $t^{\mu-\nu}J_{\nu}(at)J_{\mu}(bt)$ | $\frac{a^{\nu}b^{\mu}\Gamma(2\mu+1)}{\pi^{\frac{1}{2}}2^{\mu+\nu}\Gamma(\nu+\frac{1}{2})}\int_{-1}^{1}\frac{(1-u^2)^{\nu-\frac{1}{2}}du}{[b^2+(s+iau)^2]^{\mu+\frac{1}{2}}}$<br>$=\frac{a^{\nu}b^{\mu}\Gamma(2\mu+1)}{\pi^{\frac{1}{2}}2^{\mu+\nu}\Gamma(\nu+\frac{1}{2})}\int_0^{\pi}\frac{\sin^{2\nu}\theta\,d\theta}{[b^2+(s+ia\cos\theta)^2]^{\mu+\frac{1}{2}}}$ | $\mathrm{Re}\,\mu > -\frac{1}{2}$<br>$\mathrm{Re}\, s > \lvert\mathrm{Im}\, a\rvert + \lvert\mathrm{Im}\, b\rvert$ |
| | 42 | $t^{\mu-2\nu-1}J_{\nu}(at)J_{\nu}(bt)$ | $\frac{(ab)^{\nu}\Gamma(\mu)}{\pi\Gamma(2\nu+1)s^{\mu}}\int_0^{\pi}{}_2F_1\left[\frac{\mu}{2},\frac{\mu+1}{2};\nu+1;-\frac{a^2-2ab\cos\theta+b^2}{s^2}\right]\cdot\sin^{2\nu}\theta\,d\theta$ | $\mathrm{Re}\,\mu > 0$<br>$\mathrm{Re}\, s > \lvert\mathrm{Im}\, a\rvert + \lvert\mathrm{Im}\, b\rvert$ |
| | 43 | $t^{2(\nu+1)}J_{\nu}(t)J_{-\nu-1}(t)$ | $\frac{2^{2\nu+1}}{\pi}\sum_{n=0}^{\infty}\frac{(-4)^n\Gamma(n+\frac{1}{2})\Gamma(\nu+n+\frac{3}{2})}{n!\Gamma(n-\nu)s^{2(\nu+n+1)}}$ | $\mathrm{Re}\, s > 0$ |
| | 44 | $J_{\nu}(at^{\frac{1}{2}})J_{\nu}(bt^{\frac{1}{2}})$ | $\frac{1}{s}e^{-\frac{a^2+b^2}{4s}}I_{\nu}(\frac{ab}{2s})$ | $\mathrm{Re}\,\nu > -1$<br>$\mathrm{Re}\, s > 0$ |

10.2 (Contd)

| | f(t) | g(s) | |
|---|---|---|---|
| 45 | $\frac{1}{t^{\frac{1}{2}}} J_\nu(at^{\frac{1}{2}}e^{\frac{i\pi}{4}})J_\nu(at^{\frac{1}{2}}e^{-\frac{i\pi}{4}})$ | $\frac{\Gamma(\nu+\frac{1}{2})}{[\Gamma(\nu+1)]^2}\frac{s^{\frac{1}{2}}}{2^{\nu-1}a^2}M_{\frac{1}{4},\frac{\nu}{2}}(\frac{a^2}{2s})\,M_{-\frac{1}{4},\frac{\nu}{2}}(\frac{a^2}{2s})$ | $\mathrm{Re}\,\nu > -\frac{1}{2}$ <br> $\mathrm{Re}\,s > 0$ |
| 46 | $J_\nu[(-it)^{\frac{1}{2}}]J_\nu[(it)^{\frac{1}{2}}]$ | $\frac{I_\nu(\frac{1}{2s})}{s}$ | $\mathrm{Re}\,\nu > -1$ <br> $\mathrm{Re}\,s > 0$ |
| 47 | $\frac{1}{t^{\frac{3}{2}}}J_\nu(t^{\frac{1}{2}})J_{1-\nu}(t^{\frac{1}{2}}) - \frac{\sin(\nu\pi)}{2\nu(1-\nu)\pi t}$ | $\frac{1}{2}\sum_{n=1}^{\infty}\frac{(2n+1)!}{n!(n+1)!\Gamma(\nu+n+1)\Gamma(2-\nu+n)(4s)^n}$ | $\mathrm{Re}\,s > 0$ |
| 48 | $t^\mu J_\nu(at^{\frac{1}{2}})J_\nu(bt^{\frac{1}{2}})$ | $\frac{(ab)^\nu\Gamma(\mu+\nu+1)}{\pi\Gamma(2\nu+1)s^{\mu+\nu+1}}\int_0^\pi e^{-\frac{a^2-2ab\cos\theta+b^2}{4s}}\cdot$ <br> $\cdot\,{}_1F_1\left[-\mu;\nu+1;\frac{a^2-2ab\cos\theta+b^2}{4s}\right]\sin^{2\nu}\theta\,d\theta$ | $\mathrm{Re}\,\nu > -\frac{1}{2}$ <br> $\mathrm{Re}(\mu+\nu) > -1$ <br> $\mathrm{Re}\,s > 0$ |
| 49 | $t^{b-1}J_{2\mu}(at^{\frac{1}{2}})J_{2\nu}(at^{\frac{1}{2}})$ | $\frac{\Gamma(b+\mu+\nu)a^{2\mu+2\nu}}{2^{2\mu+2\nu-1}\Gamma(2\mu+1)\Gamma(2\nu+1)}s^{-b-\mu-\nu}\cdot$ <br> $\cdot\,{}_3F_3\left[\begin{matrix}\mu+\nu+\frac{1}{2},\mu+\nu+1,b+\mu+\nu; & -\frac{a^2}{s}\\ 2\mu+1,2\nu+1,2\mu+2\nu+1; & \end{matrix}\right]$ | $\mathrm{Re}(b+\mu+\nu) > 0$ <br> $\mathrm{Re}\,s > 0$ |
| 50 | $J_\nu(t)J_{2\nu}(at^{\frac{1}{2}})$ | $\frac{e^{-\frac{a^2 s}{4(s^2+1)}}}{(s^2+1)^{\frac{1}{2}}}J_\nu\left[\frac{a^2}{4(s^2+1)}\right]$ | $\mathrm{Re}\,\nu > -\frac{1}{2}$ <br> $\mathrm{Re}\,s > 0$ |
| 51 | $t^\mu\prod_{r=1}^{n}J_{\nu_r}(a_r t)$ | $\frac{\Gamma(\mu+\nu+1)\prod_{r=1}^{n}a_r^{\nu_r}}{2^\nu\prod_{r=1}^{n}[\Gamma(\nu_r+1)](s+ia)^{\mu+\nu+1}}\cdot$ <br> $\cdot\,F_A\left(\mu+\nu+1;\nu_1+\frac{1}{2},\dots,\nu_n+\frac{1}{2};2\nu_1+1,\dots,2\nu_n+1;\frac{2a_1 i}{s+ia},\dots,\frac{2a_n i}{s+ia}\right)$ <br> If n=2 replace $F_A$ by $F_2$ | $n = 1,2,3,\dots$ <br> $\mathrm{Re}(\mu+\nu) > -1$ <br> $\nu = \sum_{r=1}^{n}\nu_r$ <br> $a = \sum_{r=1}^{a}a_r$ <br> $\mathrm{Re}(s\pm ia_1\pm\dots\pm ia_n) > 0$ |
| 52 | $t^\mu\prod_{r=1}^{n}J_{\nu_r}(a_r t^{\frac{1}{2}})$ | $\frac{\Gamma(\mu+\nu+1)}{s^{\mu+\nu+1}}\prod_{r=1}^{n}\left[\frac{a_r^{\nu_r}}{2^{\nu_r}\Gamma(\nu_r+1)}\right]\cdot$ <br> $\cdot\,\psi_2(\mu+\nu+1;\nu_1+1,\dots,\nu_n+1;\frac{a_1^2}{4s},\dots,\frac{a_n^2}{4s})$ | $n = 1,2,3,\dots$ <br> $\mathrm{Re}(\mu+\nu) > -1$ <br> $\nu = \frac{1}{2}\sum_{r=1}^{n}\nu_r$ <br> $\mathrm{Re}\,s > 0$ |

| | | f(t) | g(s) | |
|---|---|---|---|---|
| 10.2 (Contd) | 53 | $\frac{1}{t^{\frac{1}{2}}} Y_0(t^{\frac{1}{2}})$ | $-\frac{e^{-\frac{1}{8s}} K_0(\frac{1}{8s})}{(\pi s)^{\frac{1}{2}}}$ | Re s > o |
| | 54 | $t^{\mu} Y_{\nu}(at)$ | $(s^2+a^2)^{-\frac{\mu+1}{2}} \left\{ \Gamma(\mu+\nu+1)\cot(\nu\pi) \cdot P_{\mu}^{-\nu}\left[\left(\frac{s^2}{s^2+a^2}\right)^{\frac{1}{2}}\right] - \Gamma(\mu-\nu+1)\ \mathrm{cosec}(\nu\pi) P_{\mu}^{\nu}\left[\left(\frac{s^2}{s^2+a^2}\right)^{\frac{1}{2}}\right]\right\}$ | Re$(\mu\pm\nu) > -1$ <br> Re s > \|Im a\| |
| | 55 | $\frac{1}{t^{\frac{1}{2}}} Y_{\nu}(at^{\frac{1}{2}})$ | $-\left(\frac{\pi}{s}\right)^{\frac{1}{2}} e^{-\frac{a^2}{8s}} \left[\tan\left(\frac{\nu\pi}{2}\right) I_{\frac{\nu}{2}}\left(\frac{a^2}{8s}\right) + \frac{\sec\left(\frac{\nu\pi}{2}\right)}{\pi} K_{\frac{\nu}{2}}\left(\frac{a^2}{8s}\right)\right]$ | \|Re $\nu$\| < 1 <br> Re s > o |
| | 56 | $t^{\mu} Y_{\nu}(at^{\frac{1}{2}})$ | $\frac{2e^{-\frac{a^2}{8s}}}{as^{\mu+\frac{1}{2}}} \left\{ \frac{\tan[(\mu-\frac{\nu-1}{2})\pi]\Gamma(\mu+\frac{\nu}{2}+1)}{\Gamma(\nu+1)} M_{\mu+\frac{1}{2},\frac{\nu}{2}}\left(\frac{a^2}{4s}\right) - \sec[(\mu-\frac{\nu-1}{2})\pi] W_{\mu+\frac{1}{2},\frac{\nu}{2}}\left(\frac{a^2}{4s}\right) \right\}$ | Re$(\mu\pm\frac{\nu}{2}) > -1$ <br> Re s > o |
| | 57 | $(\log a) J_0[a(t^2+bt)^{\frac{1}{2}}] -\frac{\pi}{2} Y_0[a(t^2+bt^{\frac{1}{2}})]$ | $\frac{e^{\frac{b}{2}[s-(s^2+a^2)^{\frac{1}{2}}]} \log[s+(s^2+a^2)^{\frac{1}{2}}]}{(s^2+a^2)^{\frac{1}{2}}}$ | Re s > \|Im a\| |
| | 58 | $\frac{1}{t^{\frac{1}{2}}}[\sin(\frac{\nu\pi}{2}) J_{\nu}(at^{\frac{1}{2}}) + \cos(\frac{\nu\pi}{2}) Y_{\nu}(at^{\frac{1}{2}})]$ | $-\frac{e^{-\frac{a^2}{8s}}}{(\pi s)^{\frac{1}{2}}} K_{\frac{\nu}{2}}\left(\frac{a^2}{8s}\right)$ | \|Re $\nu$\| < 1 <br> Re s > o |
| | 59 | $t^{\mu}\left\{\sin[(\frac{\nu-1}{2}-\mu)\pi] J_{\nu}(at^{\frac{1}{2}}) + \cos[(\frac{\nu-1}{2}-\mu)\pi] Y_{\nu}(at^{\frac{1}{2}})\right\}$ | $-\frac{2}{as^{\mu+\frac{1}{2}}} e^{\frac{a^2}{8s}} W_{\mu+\frac{1}{2},\frac{\nu}{2}}\left(\frac{a^2}{4s}\right)$ | Re$(\mu\pm\frac{\nu}{2}) > -1$ <br> Re s > o |
| | 60 | $\frac{[at^{\frac{1}{2}} J_1(t^{\frac{1}{2}}) + bJ_0(t^{\frac{1}{2}})]^2}{t} + \frac{1}{t[at^{\frac{1}{2}} Y_1(t^{\frac{1}{2}}) + bY_0(t^{\frac{1}{2}})]^2}$ | $2\,I(a,b;s)$ | Re s > o |
| | 61 | $t^{\nu} \int_{\infty}^{(at)^{\frac{1}{2}}} u^{-\nu-1} J_{\nu}(2u)\,du$ | $\frac{\mathrm{Ei}(-\frac{a}{s})}{2s^{\nu+1}}$ | Re $\nu > -1$ <br> Re a > o <br> Re s > o |

| | | f(t) | g(s) | |
|---|---|---|---|---|
| 10.2 Contd.) | 62 | $t^{\frac{\nu}{2}-\mu-1}\int_{at}^{\infty} u^{\mu} J_{\nu}(2u^{\frac{1}{2}})\,du$ | $s^{\mu-\frac{\nu}{2}}\Gamma(\mu+1+\frac{\nu}{2},\frac{a}{s})$ | $Re\mu < \frac{3}{4}$<br>$Re(\mu-\frac{\nu}{2}) > 0$<br>$Re\, s > 0$ |
| | 63 | $t^{\frac{\nu}{2}-\mu-1}\int_{0}^{at} u^{\mu} J_{\nu}(2u^{\frac{1}{2}})\,du$ | $s^{\mu-\frac{\nu}{2}}\gamma(\mu+1+\frac{\nu}{2},\frac{a}{s})$ | $Re(\mu+\frac{\nu}{2}) > -1$<br>$Re\nu > -1$<br>$Re\, s > 0$ |
| | 64 | $t^{\nu}\int_{\infty}^{at} u^{-\frac{\nu}{2}-1} J_{\nu}[2(u-at)^{\frac{1}{2}}]\,du$ | $\frac{e^{\frac{a}{s}}\,Ei(-\frac{a}{s})}{s^{\nu+1}}$ | $Re\,\nu > -1$<br>$Re\, s > 0$ |
| | 65 | $\int_{0}^{t} J_0[2(tu-u^2)^{\frac{1}{2}}]J_0(2a^{\frac{1}{2}}u^{\frac{1}{2}})\,du$ | $\frac{e^{-\frac{as}{s^2+1}}}{s^2+1}$ | $Re\, s > 0$ |
| 10.2.1 | 1 | $t^{\frac{1}{2}}J_{\frac{1}{4}}(at^2)$ | $\frac{\pi^{\frac{1}{2}}s^{\frac{1}{2}}}{4a}\left[\mathbf{H}_{-\frac{1}{4}}\left(\frac{s^2}{4a}\right)-Y_{-\frac{1}{4}}\left(\frac{s^2}{4a}\right)\right]$ | $a > 0$<br>$Re\, s > 0$ |
| | 2 | $t^{\frac{1}{2}}J_{-\frac{1}{4}}(at^2)$ | $\frac{\pi^{\frac{1}{2}}s^{\frac{1}{2}}}{4a}\left[\mathbf{H}_{\frac{1}{4}}\left(\frac{s^2}{4a}\right)-Y_{\frac{1}{4}}\left(\frac{s^2}{4a}\right)\right]$ | $a > 0$<br>$Re\, s > 0$ |
| | 3 | $t^{\frac{3}{2}}J_{-\frac{1}{4}}(at^2)$ | $-\frac{\pi^{\frac{1}{2}}s^{\frac{3}{2}}}{8a^2}\left[\mathbf{H}_{-\frac{3}{4}}\left(\frac{s^2}{4a}\right)-Y_{-\frac{3}{4}}\left(\frac{s^2}{4a}\right)\right]$ | $a > 0$<br>$Re\, s > 0$ |
| | 4 | $t^{\frac{3}{2}}J_{-\frac{3}{4}}(at^2)$ | $\frac{\pi^{\frac{1}{2}}s^{\frac{3}{2}}}{8a^2}\left[\mathbf{H}_{-\frac{1}{4}}\left(\frac{s^2}{4a}\right)-Y_{-\frac{1}{4}}\left(\frac{s^2}{4a}\right)\right]$ | $a > 0$<br>$Re\, s > 0$ |
| | 5 | $t^{\frac{1}{2}}J_{\frac{1}{8}}(at^2)J_{-\frac{1}{8}}(at^2)$ | $\frac{\pi^{\frac{1}{2}}s^{\frac{1}{2}}}{2^{\frac{1}{2}}.16a\cos(\frac{\pi}{8})}H^{(1)}_{\frac{1}{8}}\left(\frac{s^2}{16a}\right)H^{(2)}_{\frac{1}{8}}\left(\frac{s^2}{16a}\right)$ | $a > 0$<br>$Re\, s > 0$ |
| | 6 | $\frac{t+b}{(t^2+2bt)^{\frac{1}{2}}}J_1[a(t^2+2bt)^{\frac{1}{2}}]$ | $\frac{1}{a}-\frac{s\,e^{b[s-(s^2+a^2)^{\frac{1}{2}}]}}{a(s^2+a^2)^{\frac{1}{2}}}$ | $Re\, s > \lvert Im\, a\rvert$ |
| | 7 | $t^{\frac{1}{2}}J_{\nu+\frac{1}{8}}(at^2)J_{\nu-\frac{1}{8}}(at^2)$ | $\frac{2^{\frac{1}{2}}\Gamma(\nu+\frac{3}{8})\Gamma(\nu+\frac{5}{8})}{(\pi s)^{\frac{3}{2}}}W_{-\nu,\frac{1}{8}}\left(\frac{e^{\frac{\pi i}{2}}s^2}{8a}\right)W_{-\nu,\frac{1}{8}}\left(\frac{e^{-\frac{\pi i}{2}}s^2}{8a}\right)$ | $Re\,\nu > -\frac{3}{8}$<br>$a > 0$<br>$Re\, s > 0$ |

| | | f(t) | g(s) | |
|---|---|---|---|---|
| 10.3 | 1 | $e^{-at} J_o(bt)$ | $\frac{1}{[(s+a)^2+b^2]^{\frac{1}{2}}}$ | Re s > − Re a + \| Im b \| |
| | 2 | $e^{ia(1-e^{-t})} J_\nu(ae^{-t})$ | $\frac{J_\nu(a)}{\nu+s} + 2\sum_{n=1}^{\infty} i^n \frac{(\nu-s+1)_{n-1}}{(\nu+s)_{n+1}} (\nu+n) J_{\nu+n}(a)$ | Re s > − Re ν |
| | 3 | $(1-e^{-t})^{\frac{\nu}{2}} J_\nu[a(1-e^{-t})^{\frac{1}{2}}]$ | $\Gamma(s)(\frac{2}{a})^s J_{\nu+s}(a)$ | Re ν > − 1<br>Re s > o |
| | 4 | $\frac{J_\nu[a(1-e^{-t})^{\frac{1}{2}}]}{(1-e^{-t})^{\frac{\nu}{2}}}$ | $\frac{s_{\nu+s-1,s-\nu}(a)}{2^\nu a^s \Gamma(\nu)}$ | Re s > o |
| | 5 | $(e^t-1)^\mu J_{2\nu}[2a(e^t-1)^{\frac{1}{2}}]$ | $\frac{a^{2\nu} B(\mu+\nu+1, s-\mu-\nu)}{\Gamma(2\nu+1)} {}_1F_2\left[\begin{matrix} \mu+\nu+1; a^2 \\ \mu+\nu+1-s, 2\nu+1; \end{matrix}\right]$<br>$+ \frac{a^{2s-2\mu}\Gamma(\mu+\nu-s)}{\Gamma(\nu-\mu+s+1)} {}_1F_2\left[\begin{matrix} s+1; a^2 \\ s+1+\nu-\mu, s+1-\mu-\nu; \end{matrix}\right]$ | a > o<br>Re(μ+ν) > − 1<br>Re s > Re μ $-\frac{7}{4}$ |
| | 6 | $(e^t-1)^{\frac{\nu}{2}} J_\nu[2a(e^t-1)^{\frac{1}{2}}]$ | $\frac{2a^s}{\Gamma(s+1)} K_{\nu-s}(2a)$ | a > o<br>Re ν > − 1<br>Re s > $\frac{1}{2}$ Re$(\nu - \frac{3}{2})$ |
| | 7 | $J_\mu(ae^{-t}) J_\nu[a(1-e^{-t})]$ | $(\frac{2}{a})^s \sum_{n=o}^{\infty} \frac{(-1)^n \Gamma(s+n)}{(\mu+n)n!B(s,\mu+n)} J_{\mu+\nu+s+2n}(a)$ | Re ν > − 1<br>Re s > − Re μ |
| 10.3.2 | 1 | $e^{-at} J_o[(b-a^2t)^{\frac{1}{2}}]$ | $\frac{1}{(s^2+2as+b)^{\frac{1}{2}}}$ | Re s > $\lvert \mathrm{Im}(b-a^2)^{\frac{1}{2}} \rvert$ − Re a |
| 10.3.2.1 | 1 | $\frac{1}{t^{\frac{3}{2}}} \int_o^\infty u^{1+\frac{\nu}{2}} e^{-\frac{u^2}{4t}} J_\nu(au^{\frac{1}{2}}) du$ | $\frac{\pi^{\frac{1}{2}} a^\nu e^{-\frac{a^2}{4s^{\frac{1}{2}}}}}{2^{\nu-1} s^{\frac{\nu+1}{2}}}$ | Re $a^2$ > o<br>Re ν > −1<br>Re s > o |
| | 2 | $\frac{1}{t^{\frac{3}{2}}} \int_o^\infty u e^{-\frac{u^2}{4t}} J_o(au^{\frac{1}{2}}) du$ | $2(\frac{\pi}{s})^{\frac{1}{2}} e^{-\frac{a^2}{4s^{\frac{1}{2}}}}$ | Re $a^2$ > o<br>Re s > o |
| 10.5 | 1 | $\frac{\sin(at) J_o(bt)}{t}$ | $\frac{1}{2}\int_{-a}^{a} \frac{du}{[b^2+(s+iu)^2]^{\frac{1}{2}}}$ | Re s > Max \| Im a \|, \| Im b \| |

| | | f(t) | g(s) | |
|---|---|---|---|---|
| 10.5 (Contd.) | 2 | $t[J_1(at)\log a - \frac{\pi}{2}Y_1(at)] - \frac{\cos(at)}{a}$ | $\frac{a\log[s+(s^2+a^2)^{\frac{1}{2}}]}{(s^2+a^2)^{\frac{3}{2}}}$ | Re $s > \|\text{Im } a\|$ |
| | 3 | $t[J_0(at)\log a - \frac{\pi}{2}Y_0(at)] + \frac{\sin(at)}{a}$ | $\frac{s}{(s^2+a^2)^{\frac{3}{2}}}\log[s+(s^2+a^2)^{\frac{1}{2}}]$ | Re $s > \|\text{Im } a\|$ |
| | 4 | $\int_0^t J_0(au)\sin u\,du$ | $-\frac{1}{s}\left[\frac{[(s^2+a^2-1)^2+4s^2]^{\frac{1}{2}}-s^2-a^2+1}{2(s^2+a^2-1)^2+8s^2}\right]^{\frac{1}{2}}$ | Re $s > \|\text{Im } a\|$ |
| | 5 | $\int_0^t J_0(au)\cos u\,du$ | $\frac{1}{s}\left[\frac{[(s^2+a^2-1)^2+4s^2]^{\frac{1}{2}}+s^2+a^2-1}{2(s^2+a^2-1)^2+8s^2}\right]^{\frac{1}{2}}$ | Re $s > \|\text{Im } a\|$ |
| 10.5.2 | 1 | $t^{\mu}\sin(at)J_{\mu}(at)$ | $\frac{\Gamma(\mu+1)a^{\mu+1}}{2^{\frac{1}{2}}\pi}\int_0^{\frac{\pi}{2}}\frac{\cos^{\mu+\frac{1}{2}}\theta\cos[(\mu-\frac{1}{2})\theta]d\theta}{(\frac{s^2}{4}+a^2\cos^2\theta)^{\mu+1}}$ | $a > 0$<br>Re $\mu > -1$<br>Re $s > 0$ |
| | 2 | $t^{\mu-1}\cos(at)J_{\mu}(at)$ | $\frac{\Gamma(\mu)a^{\mu}}{2^{\frac{1}{2}}\pi}\int_0^{\frac{\pi}{2}}\frac{\cos^{\mu-\frac{1}{2}}\theta\cos[(\mu+\frac{1}{2})\theta]d\theta}{(\frac{s^2}{4}+a^2\cos^2\theta)^{\mu}}$ | $a > 0$<br>Re $\mu > 0$<br>Re $s > 0$ |
| 10.5.3 | 1 | $\sin[a(1-e^{-t})]J_{\nu}(ae^{-t})$ | $2\sum_{n=0}^{\infty}\frac{(-1)^n(\nu-s+1)_{2n}}{(\nu+s)_{2n+2}}(\nu+2n-1)J_{\nu+2n+1}(a)$ | Re $s > -$ Re $\nu$ |
| | 2 | $\cos[a(1-e^{-t})]J_{\nu}(ae^{-t})$ | $\frac{J_{\nu}(a)}{\nu+s}+2\sum_{n=0}^{\infty}(-1)^n\frac{(\nu-s+1)_{2n-1}}{(\nu+s)_{2n+1}}(\nu+2n)J_{\nu+2n}(a)$ | Re $s > -$ Re $\nu$ |
| 10.7 | 1 | $\frac{\sinh(at)}{t}J_0(bt)$ | $\frac{1}{2}\int_{-a}^{a}\frac{du}{[b^2+(s-u)^2]^{\frac{1}{2}}}$ | Re $s >$ Max $\|\text{Im } b\|, \|\text{Re } a\|$ |
| | 2 | $J_0(a\sinh t)$ | $K_{\frac{s}{2}}(\frac{a}{2})I_{\frac{s}{2}}(\frac{a}{2})$ | Re $a > 0$<br>Re $s > -\frac{1}{2}$ |
| | 3 | $J_{\nu}(a\sinh t)$ | $I_{\frac{\nu+s}{2}}(\frac{a}{2})K_{\frac{\nu-s}{2}}(\frac{a}{2})$ | Re $\nu > -1$<br>Re $a > 0$<br>Re $s > -\frac{1}{2}$ |

| | | f(t) | g(s) | |
|---|---|---|---|---|
| 10.7 (Contd.) | 4 | $\operatorname{cosech} t\, J_\nu(a \operatorname{cosech} t)$ | $\dfrac{\Gamma(\frac{s+\nu+1}{2})}{a\Gamma(\nu+1)} W_{-\frac{s}{2},\frac{\nu}{2}}(a) M_{\frac{s}{2},\frac{\nu}{2}}(a)$ | $a > o$<br>$\operatorname{Re} s > -\operatorname{Re}(\nu+1)$ |
| 10.7.3 | 1 | $\operatorname{cosech}\frac{t}{2}\, e^{\frac{a-b}{2}\coth\frac{t}{2}} J_\nu[(ab)^{\frac{1}{2}}\operatorname{cosech}\frac{t}{2}]$ | $\dfrac{2\Gamma(s+\frac{\nu+1}{2})}{(ab)^{\frac{1}{2}}\Gamma(\nu+1)} M_{s,\frac{\nu}{2}}(a) W_{-s,\frac{\nu}{2}}(b)$ | $\operatorname{Re} a > o$<br>$\operatorname{Re} b > o$<br>$\operatorname{Re} s > -\operatorname{Re}\frac{\nu-1}{2}$ |
| 10.9.2 | 1 | $t^{\frac{\nu}{2}} L_n^\nu(t) J_\nu(at^{\frac{1}{2}})$ | $(\frac{a}{2})^\nu e^{-\frac{a^2}{4s}} \dfrac{(s-1)^n}{s^{\nu+n+1}} L_n^\nu\left[\dfrac{a^2}{4s(1-s)}\right]$ | $n = 0,1,2,\ldots$<br>$\operatorname{Re}\nu > -1$<br>$\operatorname{Re} s > o$ |
| 10.9.3.2 | 1 | $t^{\frac{\nu}{2}}\int_o^\infty e^{-bu} J_\nu(2t^{\frac{1}{2}}u^{\frac{1}{2}}) L_n^{(a)}(u) u^{a-\frac{\nu}{2}}\, du$ | $\dfrac{\Gamma(n+a+1)[1+(b-1)s]^n}{n!\, s^{\nu-a}(1+bs)^{n+a+1}}$ | $\operatorname{Re}\nu > -1$<br>$\operatorname{Re} a > -1$<br>$\operatorname{Re} s > \operatorname{Max} o, -\operatorname{Re}\frac{1}{b}$ |
| 11 | 1 | $H_o^{(1)}(at)$ | $\dfrac{1-\frac{2i}{\pi}\sinh^{-1}(\frac{s}{a})}{(s^2+a^2)^{\frac{1}{2}}}$<br>$= \dfrac{1-\frac{2i}{\pi}\log\frac{s+(s^2+a^2)^{\frac{1}{2}}}{a}}{(s^2+a^2)^{\frac{1}{2}}}$ | $\operatorname{Re} s > \lvert\operatorname{Im} a\rvert$ |
| | 2 | $t H_o^{(1)}(at)$ | $\dfrac{s}{(s^2+a^2)^{\frac{3}{2}}}\left(1-\frac{2i}{\pi}\log\frac{s+(s^2+a^2)^{\frac{1}{2}}}{a}\right)+\dfrac{2i}{\pi(s^2+a^2)}$ | $\operatorname{Re} s > \lvert\operatorname{Im} a\rvert$ |
| | 3 | $t H_1^{(1)}(at)$ | $\dfrac{a}{(s^2+a^2)^{\frac{3}{2}}}\left(1-\frac{2i}{\pi}\log\frac{s+(s^2+a^2)^{\frac{1}{2}}}{a}\right)-\dfrac{2is}{\pi a(s^2+a^2)}$ | $\operatorname{Re} s > \lvert\operatorname{Im} a\rvert$ |
| | 4 | $H_\nu^{(1)}(at)$ | $\dfrac{i\operatorname{cosec}(\nu\pi)}{(s^2+a^2)^{\frac{1}{2}}}\left\{\dfrac{e^{-i\nu\pi}a^\nu}{[s+(s^2+a^2)^{\frac{1}{2}}]^\nu}-\dfrac{[s+(s^2+a^2)^{\frac{1}{2}}]^\nu}{a^\nu}\right\}$ | $\lvert\operatorname{Re}\nu\rvert < 1$<br>$\operatorname{Re} s > \lvert\operatorname{Im} a\rvert$ |
| | 5 | $\frac{1}{t} H_\nu^{(1)}(\frac{a}{t})$ | $2H_\nu^{(1)}[(2as)^{\frac{1}{2}}] K_\nu[(2as)^{\frac{1}{2}}]$ | $a > o$<br>$\operatorname{Re} s > o$ |
| | 6 | $H_o^{(2)}(at)$ | $\dfrac{1+\frac{2i}{\pi}\sinh^{-1}(\frac{s}{a})}{(s^2+a^2)^{\frac{1}{2}}}$<br>$= \dfrac{1+\frac{2i}{\pi}\log\frac{s+(s^2+a^2)^{\frac{1}{2}}}{a}}{(s^2+a^2)^{\frac{1}{2}}}$ | $\operatorname{Re} s > \lvert\operatorname{Im} a\rvert$ |

| | | f(t) | g(s) | |
|---|---|---|---|---|
| 11 (Contd.) | 7 | $tH_0^{(2)}(at)$ | $\frac{s}{(s^2+a^2)^{\frac{3}{2}}}\left(1+\frac{2i}{\pi}\log\frac{s+(s^2+a^2)^{\frac{1}{2}}}{a}\right)-\frac{2i}{\pi(s^2+a^2)}$ | Re s > \|Im a\| |
| | 8 | $tH_1^{(2)}(at)$ | $\frac{a}{(s^2+a^2)^{\frac{3}{2}}}\left(1+\frac{2i}{\pi}\log\frac{s+(s^2+a^2)^{\frac{1}{2}}}{a}\right)+\frac{2is}{\pi a(s^2+a^2)}$ | Re s > \|Im a\| |
| | 9 | $H_\nu^{(2)}(at)$ | $\frac{i\,\mathrm{cosec}(\nu\pi)}{(s^2+a^2)^{\frac{1}{2}}}\left\{\frac{[s+(s^2+a^2)^{\frac{1}{2}}]^\nu}{a^\nu}-\frac{a^\nu e^{i\nu\pi}}{[s+(s^2+a^2)^{\frac{1}{2}}]^\nu}\right\}$ | \|Re ν\| < 1<br>Re s > \|Im a\| |
| | 10 | $\frac{1}{t}H_\nu^{(2)}(\frac{a}{t})$ | $2H_\nu^{(2)}[(2as)^{\frac{1}{2}}]K_\nu[(2as)^{\frac{1}{2}}]$ | a > 0<br>Re s > 0 |
| 11.2 | 1 | $t^\nu H_1^{(1)}(at^{\frac{1}{2}})$ | $\frac{\Gamma(\nu+\frac{3}{2})e^{-\frac{a^2}{8s}}}{is^{\nu+\frac{1}{2}}\sin[(\nu+\frac{1}{2})\pi]}k_{-2\nu-1}\left(\frac{a^2e^{-i\pi}}{8s}\right)$ | Re ν > $-\frac{1}{2}$<br>Re s > 0 |
| | 2 | $\frac{1}{t^{\frac{1}{2}}}H_\nu^{(1)}(at^{\frac{1}{2}})$ | $(\frac{\pi}{s})^{\frac{1}{2}}\sec(\frac{\nu\pi}{2})e^{-\frac{a^2}{8s}}[e^{-\frac{i\nu\pi}{2}}I_{\frac{\nu}{2}}(\frac{a^2}{8s})-\frac{i}{\pi}K_{\frac{\nu}{2}}(\frac{a^2}{8s})]$ | \|Re ν\| < 1<br>Re s > 0 |
| | 3 | $t^\mu H_\nu^{(1)}(at^{\frac{1}{2}})$ | $\frac{2\Gamma(\mu+\frac{\nu}{2}+1)\Gamma(\mu-\frac{\nu}{2}+1)}{\pi a e^{\frac{\nu\pi i}{2}+\frac{a^2}{8s}}s^{\mu+\frac{1}{2}}}W_{-\mu-\frac{1}{2},\frac{\nu}{2}}\left(\frac{a^2e^{-i\pi}}{4s}\right)$ | Re$(\mu\pm\frac{\nu}{2}) > -1$<br>Re s > 0 |
| | 4 | $\frac{1}{t^{\frac{\nu}{2}}}H_\nu^{(1)}(at^{\frac{1}{2}})$ | $\frac{2^\nu s^{\nu-1}e^{-\frac{a^2}{4s}}}{\pi i a^\nu}\Gamma(1-\nu)\Gamma(\nu,\frac{e^{i\pi}a^2}{4s})$ | Re ν < 1<br>Re s > 0 |
| | 5 | $t^\nu H_1^{(2)}(at^{\frac{1}{2}})$ | $\frac{i\Gamma(\nu+\frac{3}{2})}{s^{\nu+\frac{1}{2}}\cos(\nu\pi)}e^{-\frac{a^2}{8s}}k_{-2\nu-1}\left(\frac{a^2e^{i\pi}}{8s}\right)$ | Re ν > $-\frac{1}{2}$<br>Re s > 0 |
| | 6 | $\frac{1}{t^{\frac{1}{2}}}H_\nu^{(2)}(at^{\frac{1}{2}})$ | $(\frac{\pi}{s})^{\frac{1}{2}}e^{-\frac{a^2}{8s}}\sec(\frac{\nu\pi}{2})[e^{\frac{i\nu\pi}{2}}I_{\frac{\nu}{2}}(\frac{a^2}{8s})+\frac{i}{\pi}K_{\frac{\nu}{2}}(\frac{a^2}{8s})]$ | \|Re ν\| < 1<br>Re s > 0 |
| | 7 | $t^\mu H_\nu^{(2)}(at^{\frac{1}{2}})$ | $\frac{2\Gamma(\mu+\frac{\nu}{2}+1)\Gamma(\mu-\frac{\nu}{2}+1)}{\pi a e^{-\frac{\nu\pi i}{2}+\frac{a^2}{8s}}s^{\mu+\frac{1}{2}}}W_{-\mu-\frac{1}{2},\frac{\nu}{2}}\left(\frac{a^2e^{i\pi}}{4s}\right)$ | Re$(\mu\pm\frac{\nu}{2}) > -1$<br>Re s > 0 |

| | | f(t) | g(s) | |
|---|---|---|---|---|
| 11.2 (Contd.) | 8 | $t^{-\frac{\nu}{2}} H_{\nu}^{(2)}(at^{\frac{1}{2}})$ | $-\frac{2^{\nu} s^{\nu-1} e^{-\frac{a^2}{4s}}}{\pi i a^{\nu}} \Gamma(1-\nu)\Gamma(\nu, \frac{e^{i\pi} a^2}{4s})$ | Re $\nu < 1$ Re $s > 0$ |
| 12 | 1 | $I_0(at)$ | $\frac{1}{(s^2-a^2)^{\frac{1}{2}}}$ | Re $s > \|$Re $a\|$ |
| | 2 | $I_0^2(at)$ | $\frac{2}{\pi s} K(\frac{2a}{s})$ | Re $s > 2\|$Re $a\|$ |
| | 3 | $\frac{1}{t} I_1(at)$ | $\frac{s-(s^2-a^2)^{\frac{1}{2}}}{a}$ | Re $s > \|$Re $a\|$ |
| | 4 | $I_1^2(at)$ | $\frac{1}{\pi a^2}\left[\frac{s^2-2a^2}{s} K(\frac{2a}{s}) - s E(\frac{2a}{s})\right]$ | Re $s > 2\|$Re $a\|$ |
| | 5 | $I_{\frac{1}{2}}(at)$ | $\left[\frac{s-(s^2-a^2)^{\frac{1}{2}}}{a(s^2-a^2)}\right]^{\frac{1}{2}}$ | Re $s > \|$Re $a\|$ |
| | 6 | $I_{-\frac{1}{2}}(at)$ | $\left[\frac{(s^2-a^2)^{\frac{1}{2}}+s}{a(s^2-a^2)}\right]^{\frac{1}{2}}$ | Re $s > \|$Re $a\|$ |
| | 7 | $I_0(at)+I_1(at)$ | $\frac{1}{a}\left[\left(\frac{s+a}{s-a}\right)^{\frac{1}{2}} - 1\right]$ | Re $s > \|$Re $a\|$ |
| | 8 | $I_0^2(at)+I_1^2(at)$ | $\frac{s}{\pi a^2}[K(\frac{2a}{s}) - E(\frac{2a}{s})]$ | Re $s > 2\|$Re $a\|$ |
| | 9 | $I_0(at)I_1(at)$ | $\frac{1}{\pi a} K(\frac{2a}{s}) - \frac{1}{2a}$ | Re $s > 2\|$Re $a\|$ |
| | 10 | $\frac{1}{t} I_0(at)I_1(at)$ | $\frac{s}{\pi a}[\frac{\pi}{2} - E(\frac{2a}{s})]$ | Re $s > 2\|$Re $a\|$ |
| | 11 | $t I_0(at)I_1(at)$ | $\frac{sE(\frac{2a}{s})}{\pi a(s^2-4a^2)} - \frac{K(\frac{2a}{s})}{\pi as}$ | Re $s > 2\|$Re $a\|$ |
| | 12 | $t[I_0^2(at) + I_1^2(at)]$ | $\frac{1}{\pi a^2}\left[\frac{s^2}{s^2-4a^2} E(\frac{2a}{s}) - K(\frac{2a}{s})\right]$ | Re $s > 2\|$Re $a\|$ |

| | | f(t) | g(s) | |
|---|---|---|---|---|
| 12 (Contd.) | 13 | $I_0(at)[I_0(at)+2atI_1(at)]$ | $\frac{2}{\pi}\frac{s}{s^2-4a^2}E(\frac{2a}{s})$ | Re s > 2 \| Re a \| |
| | 14 | $I_0^2(at)+2I_1^2(at)+I_0(at)I_2(at)$ | $\frac{2s}{\pi a^2}[K(\frac{2a}{s})-\frac{\pi}{2}]$ | Re s > 2 \| Re a \| |
| | 15 | $I_\nu(at)$ | $\frac{[s-(s^2-a^2)^{\frac{1}{2}}]^\nu}{a^\nu(s^2-a^2)^{\frac{1}{2}}}$ | Re ν > − 1<br>Re s > \|Re a\| |
| | 16 | $t\,I_\nu(at)$ | $\frac{[s+\nu(s^2-a^2)^{\frac{1}{2}}][s-(s^2-a^2)^{\frac{1}{2}}]^\nu}{a^\nu(s^2-a^2)^{\frac{3}{2}}}$ | Re ν > −2<br>Re s > \|Re a \| |
| | 17 | $\frac{1}{t}I_\nu(at)$ | $\frac{[s-(s^2-a^2)^{\frac{1}{2}}]^\nu}{\nu a^\nu}$ | Re ν > o<br>Re s > \|Re a \| |
| | 18 | $I_{\nu-1}(at)+I_{\nu+1}(at)$ | $\frac{2s[s-(s^2-a^2)^{\frac{1}{2}}]^\nu}{a^{\nu+1}(s^2-a^2)^{\frac{1}{2}}}$ | Re ν > o<br>Re s > \|Re a\| |
| | 19 | $I_{\nu-1}(at)+2I_\nu(at)+I_{\nu+1}(at)$ | $\frac{4(s+a)^{\frac{1}{2}}[(s+a)^{\frac{1}{2}}-(s-a)^{\frac{1}{2}}]^{2\nu}}{(2a)^{\nu+1}(s-a)^{\frac{1}{2}}}$ | Re ν > o<br>Re s > \|Re a\| |
| 12.1 | 1 | $t^n I_n(at)$ | $\frac{1.3.5...(2n-1)a^n}{(s^2-a^2)^{n+\frac{1}{2}}}$ | n = 1,2,3,...<br>Re s > \|Re a \| |
| | 2 | $\frac{a}{t}I_{\nu-1}(at)-\frac{\nu+1}{t^2}I_\nu(at)$ | $\frac{s[s-(s^2-a^2)^{\frac{1}{2}}]^\nu}{\nu a^\nu}$ | Re ν > 1<br>Re s > \|Re a \| |
| | 3 | $\frac{1}{t^2}I_\nu(at)$ | $\frac{[s+\nu(s^2-a^2)^{\frac{1}{2}}][s-(s^2-a^2)^{\frac{1}{2}}]^\nu}{\nu(\nu^2-1)a^\nu}$ | Re ν > 1<br>Re s > \|Re a\| |
| | 4 | $I_\nu(t^2)$ | $\frac{(-1)^{\nu+\frac{1}{2}}\Gamma(\nu+\frac{1}{2})}{(2\pi)^{\frac{1}{2}}}D_{-\nu-\frac{1}{2}}(\frac{s}{2^{\frac{1}{2}}})D_{-\nu-\frac{1}{2}}(-\frac{s}{2^{\frac{1}{2}}})$ | Re ν > $-\frac{1}{2}$<br>Re s > o |
| 12.2 | 1 | $\frac{1}{t^{\frac{1}{2}}}I_1(at^{\frac{1}{2}})$ | $\frac{2}{a}(e^{\frac{a^2}{4s}}-1)$ | Re s > o |

12.2 (Contd.)

| | f(t) | g(s) | |
|---|---|---|---|
| 2 | $\dfrac{I_1[a(t^2+2bt)^{\frac{1}{2}}]}{(t^2+2bt)^{\frac{1}{2}}}$ | $\dfrac{e^{b[s-(s^2-a^2)^{\frac{1}{2}}]}-1}{ab}$ | Re s > \|Re a\| |
| 3 | $\dfrac{1}{t^{\frac{1}{2}}} I_\nu(at)$ | $\left(\dfrac{2}{a\pi}\right)^{\frac{1}{2}} Q_{\nu-\frac{1}{2}}\left(\dfrac{s}{a}\right)$ | Re $\nu > -\frac{1}{2}$<br>Re s > \|Re a\| |
| 4 | $t^\mu I_\nu(at)$ | $\left(\dfrac{2}{\pi a}\right)^{\frac{1}{2}} \dfrac{\sin[(\nu-\frac{1}{2})\pi]}{\sin[(\mu+\nu)\pi]} \dfrac{Q^{\mu+\frac{1}{2}}_{\nu-\frac{1}{2}}\left(\frac{s}{a}\right)}{(s^2-a^2)^{\frac{\mu}{2}+\frac{1}{4}}}$<br>$= \dfrac{a^\nu \Gamma(\mu+\nu+1)}{2^\mu \Gamma(\nu+1) s^{\mu+\nu+1}} {}_2F_1\left[\dfrac{\mu+\nu+1}{2}, \dfrac{\mu+\nu+2}{2}; \nu+1; \dfrac{a^2}{s^2}\right]$ | Re$(\mu+\nu) > -1$<br>Re $\nu > -1$<br>Re s > \|Re a\| |
| 5 | $t^\nu I_\nu(at)$ | $\dfrac{2^\nu \Gamma(\nu+\frac{1}{2}) a^\nu}{\pi^{\frac{1}{2}}(s^2-a^2)^{\nu+\frac{1}{2}}}$ | Re $\nu > -\frac{1}{2}$<br>Re s > \|Re a\| |
| 6 | $t^{\nu+1} I_\nu(at)$ | $\dfrac{2^{\nu+1}\Gamma(\nu+\frac{3}{2}) a^\nu s}{\pi^{\frac{1}{2}}(s^2-a^2)^{\nu+\frac{3}{2}}}$ | Re $\nu > -1$<br>Re s > \|Re a\| |
| 7 | $I_\nu(at^{\frac{1}{2}})$ | $\dfrac{a\pi^{\frac{1}{2}}}{4s^{\frac{3}{2}}} e^{\frac{a^2}{8s}} \left[I_{\frac{\nu-1}{2}}\left(\dfrac{a^2}{8s}\right) - I_{\frac{\nu+1}{2}}\left(\dfrac{a^2}{8s}\right)\right]$ | Re $\nu > -2$<br>Re s > 0 |
| 8 | $\dfrac{1}{t^{\frac{1}{2}}} I_\nu(at^{\frac{1}{2}})$ | $\left(\dfrac{\pi}{s}\right)^{\frac{1}{2}} e^{\frac{a^2}{8s}} I_{\frac{\nu}{2}}\left(\dfrac{a^2}{8s}\right)$ | Re $\nu > -1$<br>Re s > 0 |
| 9 | $t^\mu I_\nu(at^{\frac{1}{2}})$ | $\dfrac{2\Gamma(\mu+\frac{\nu}{2}+1)\, e^{\frac{a^2}{8s}}}{a\Gamma(\nu+1) s^{\mu+\frac{1}{2}}} M_{-\mu-\frac{1}{2},\frac{\nu}{2}}\left(\dfrac{a}{s}\right)$ | Re$(\mu+\frac{\nu}{2}) > -1$<br>Re s > 0 |
| 10 | $t^{\frac{\nu}{2}} I_\nu(at^{\frac{1}{2}})$ | $\left(\dfrac{a}{2}\right)^\nu s^{-\nu-1} e^{\frac{a^2}{4s}}$ | Re $\nu > -1$<br>Re s > 0 |
| 11 | $t^{-\frac{\nu}{2}} I_\nu(at^{\frac{1}{2}})$ | $\dfrac{2^\nu s^{\nu-1} e^{\frac{a^2}{4s}}}{a^\nu \Gamma(\nu)} \gamma\left(\nu, \dfrac{a^2}{4s}\right)$ | Re $\nu > 0$<br>Re s > 0 |
| 12 | $t^{\frac{\nu}{2}-1} I_\nu(at^{\frac{1}{2}})$ | $\left(\dfrac{-2}{a}\right)^\nu P\left(-\dfrac{a^2}{4s}, \nu\right)$ | Re $\nu > 0$<br>Re s > 0 |

| | $f(t)$ | $g(s)$ | |
|---|---|---|---|
| 12.2 (Contd.) 13 | $\sum_{n=0}^{\infty} I_{2\nu+2n+1}(at^{\frac{1}{2}})$ | $\frac{a\pi^{\frac{1}{2}}}{(2s)^{\frac{3}{2}}} e^{\frac{a^2}{8s}} I_\nu(\frac{a^2}{8s})$ | $\mathrm{Re}\,\nu > -\frac{3}{2}$ <br> $\mathrm{Re}\,s > 0$ |
| 14 | $(t^2+bt)^{\frac{\nu}{2}} I_\nu[a(t^2+bt)^{\frac{1}{2}}]$ | $\pi^{-\frac{1}{2}}(\frac{a}{2})^\nu \frac{b^{\nu+\frac{1}{2}}}{(s^2-a^2)^{\frac{\nu}{2}+\frac{1}{4}}} e^{\frac{bs}{2}} K_{\nu+\frac{1}{2}}\left[\frac{b(s^2-a^2)^{\frac{1}{2}}}{2}\right]$ | $\mathrm{Re}\,\nu > -1$ <br> $\lvert\arg b\rvert < \pi$ <br> $\mathrm{Re}\,s > \lvert\mathrm{Re}\,a\rvert$ |
| 15 | $\left(\frac{t}{t+b}\right)^{\frac{\nu}{2}} I_\nu[a(t^2+bt)^{\frac{1}{2}}]$ | $\frac{e^{\frac{b}{2}[s-(s^2-a^2)^{\frac{1}{2}}]}[s-(s^2-a^2)^{\frac{1}{2}}]^\nu}{a^\nu(s^2-a^2)^{\frac{1}{2}}}$ | $\mathrm{Re}\,\nu > -1$ <br> $\lvert\arg b\rvert < \pi$ <br> $\mathrm{Re}\,s > \lvert\mathrm{Re}\,a\rvert$ |
| 16 | $\frac{t^{\mu-1}}{(t+b)^\mu} I_\nu[a(t^2+bt)^{\frac{1}{2}}]$ | $\frac{2\Gamma(\mu+\frac{\nu}{2})\, e^{\frac{b}{2}s}}{ab\,\Gamma(\nu+1)} M_{\frac{1}{2}-\mu,\frac{\nu}{2}}\left[\frac{a^2 b}{2[s+(s^2-a^2)^{\frac{1}{2}}]}\right]\cdot$ <br> $W_{\frac{1}{2}-\mu,\frac{\nu}{2}}\left[\frac{b[s+(s^2-a^2)^{\frac{1}{2}}]}{2}\right]$ | $\mathrm{Re}(\mu+\frac{\nu}{2}) > 0$ <br> $\lvert\arg b\rvert < \pi$ <br> $\mathrm{Re}\,s > \lvert\mathrm{Re}\,a\rvert$ |
| 17 | $I_\nu^2(at^{\frac{1}{2}})$ | $\frac{1}{s} e^{\frac{a^2}{2s}} I_\nu(\frac{a^2}{2s})$ | $\mathrm{Re}\,\nu > -1$ <br> $\mathrm{Re}\,s > 0$ |
| 18 | $t^{\frac{1}{2}} I_{\nu-\frac{1}{4}}(t) I_{\nu+\frac{1}{4}}(t)$ | $\frac{1}{\pi(2s)^{\frac{1}{2}}} Q^{1,2\nu-1}(\frac{s}{2})$ | $\mathrm{Re}\,s > 1$ |
| 19 | $t^c I_\mu(at) I_\nu(bt)$ | $\frac{2^c a^\mu b^\nu \Gamma(\frac{c+\mu+\nu+1}{2})\Gamma(\frac{c+\mu+\nu+2}{2})}{\pi^{\frac{1}{2}}\Gamma(\mu+1)\Gamma(\nu+1)s^{c+\mu+\nu+1}}\cdot$ <br> $F_4(\frac{c+\mu+\nu+1}{2}, \frac{c+\mu+\nu+2}{2}; \mu+1, \nu+1; \frac{a^2}{s^2}, \frac{b^2}{s^2})$ | $\mathrm{Re}(c+\mu+\nu) > -$ <br> $\mathrm{Re}\,s > \lvert\mathrm{Re}\,a\rvert$ <br> $\lvert\mathrm{Re}\,b\rvert$ |
| 20 | $I_\nu(at^{\frac{1}{2}}) I_\nu(bt^{\frac{1}{2}})$ | $\frac{1}{s} e^{\frac{a^2+b^2}{4s}} I_\nu(\frac{ab}{2s})$ | $\mathrm{Re}\,\nu > -1$ <br> $\mathrm{Re}\,s > 0$ |
| 21 | $I_0[a(t^2+bt)^{\frac{1}{2}}]$ | $\frac{1}{(s^2-a^2)^{\frac{1}{2}}} e^{\frac{b}{2}[s-(s^2-a^2)^{\frac{1}{2}}]}$ | $\lvert\arg b\rvert < \pi$ <br> $\mathrm{Re}\,s > \lvert\mathrm{Re}\,a\rvert$ |
| 22 | $I_0(at^{\frac{1}{2}})$ | $\frac{1}{s} e^{\frac{a^2}{4s}}$ | $\mathrm{Re}\,s > 0$ |
| 23 | $\frac{1}{t^{\frac{1}{2}}} I_0(at^{\frac{1}{2}})$ | $(\frac{\pi}{s})^{\frac{1}{2}} e^{\frac{a^2}{8s}} I_0(\frac{a^2}{8s})$ | $\mathrm{Re}\,s > 0$ |

| | | f(t) | g(s) | |
|---|---|---|---|---|
| 12.2.1 | 1 | $\frac{t+b}{(t^2+2bt)^{\frac{1}{2}}} I_1[a(t^2+2bt)^{\frac{1}{2}}]$ | $\frac{1}{a}\left[\frac{s}{(s^2-a^2)^{\frac{1}{2}}} e^{b[s-(s^2-a^2)^{\frac{1}{2}}]} - 1\right]$ | Re s > \|Re a\| |
| 12.3 | 1 | $e^{-at} I_0(bt)$ | $\frac{1}{[(s+a+b)(s+a-b)]^{\frac{1}{2}}}$ | Re s > Max − Re(a+b), − Re(a−b) |
| | 2 | $\frac{1}{t} e^{-\frac{a}{t}} I_0(\frac{a}{t})$ | $2 I_0[(2as)^{\frac{1}{2}}] K_0[(2as)^{\frac{1}{2}}]$ | Re s > o |
| | 3 | $e^{-at} I_\nu(bt)$ | $\frac{[(s+a+b)^{\frac{1}{2}} - (s+a-b)^{\frac{1}{2}}]^{2\nu}}{(2b)^\nu [(s+a)^2-b^2]^{\frac{1}{2}}}$ | Re ν > − 1<br>Re s > Max Re(b−a), − Re(b+a) |
| | 4 | $\frac{1}{t} e^{-at} I_\nu(bt)$ | $\frac{[(s+a+b)^{\frac{1}{2}} - (s+a-b)^{\frac{1}{2}}]^{2\nu}}{\nu(2b)^\nu}$ | Re s > Max Re(b−a), − Re(b+a)<br>Re ν > o |
| | 5 | $e^{at} I_\nu(at)$ | $\frac{[s^{\frac{1}{2}}-(s-2a)^{\frac{1}{2}}]^{2\nu}}{(2a)^\nu s^{\frac{1}{2}}(s-2a)^{\frac{1}{2}}}$ | Re ν > − 1<br>Re s > Max o , Re a |
| | 6 | $e^{-at} I_\nu(at)$ | $\frac{[(s+2a)^{\frac{1}{2}}-s^{\frac{1}{2}}]^{2\nu}}{(2a)^\nu s^{\frac{1}{2}}(s+2a)^{\frac{1}{2}}}$ | Re ν > − 1<br>Re s > Max o , − Re a |
| | 7 | $\frac{1}{t} e^{-at} I_\nu(at)$ | $\frac{[(s+2a)^{\frac{1}{2}} - s^{\frac{1}{2}}]^{2\nu}}{\nu(2a)^\nu}$ | Re ν > o<br>Re s > Max o , − Re(2a) |
| | 8 | $\frac{1}{t} e^{-\frac{a+b}{2t}} I_\nu\left(\frac{a-b}{2t}\right)$ | $2K_\nu[(a^{\frac{1}{2}}+b^{\frac{1}{2}})s^{\frac{1}{2}}] I_\nu[(a^{\frac{1}{2}}-b^{\frac{1}{2}})s^{\frac{1}{2}}]$ | Re a ⩾ Re b > o<br>Re s > o |
| | 9 | $te^{-at}[I_0(bt)+I_1(bt)]$ | $\frac{1}{(s+a+b)^{\frac{1}{2}}(s+a-b)^{\frac{3}{2}}}$ | Re s > Max Re(b−a), − Re(b+a) |
| | 10 | $\exp[a(1-e^{-t})] I_\nu(ae^{-t})$ | $\frac{I_\nu(a)}{\nu+s} + \sum_{n=1}^{\infty} \frac{(\nu-s+1)_{n-1}}{(\nu+s)_{n+1}}(\nu+n) I_{\nu+n}(a)$ | Re s > − Re ν |
| | 11 | $e^{-at}[I'_\nu(at) - I_\nu(at)]$ | $\frac{2}{(2a)^{\nu+1}} \left(\frac{s}{s+2a}\right)^{\frac{1}{2}} \left[(s+2a)^{\frac{1}{2}}-s^{\frac{1}{2}}\right]^{2\nu}$ | Re ν > o<br>Re s > Max o, − Re(2a) |

| | | $f(t)$ | $g(s)$ | |
|---|---|---|---|---|
| 12.3 (Contd.) | 12 | $e^{-bt} I_0(at)+(b-a)\int_0^t e^{-bu} I_0(au)\,du$ | $\dfrac{(s+b-a)^{\frac{1}{2}}}{s(s+a+b)^{\frac{1}{2}}}$ | Re s > Max o, Re(a-b) - Re(a+b) |
| 12.3.1 | 1 | $e^{-\frac{t^2}{a}} I_0\left(\frac{t^2}{a}\right)$ | $\frac{1}{4}\left(\frac{2a}{\pi}\right)^{\frac{1}{2}} e^{\frac{as^2}{16}} K_0\left(\frac{as^2}{16}\right)$ | Re a > o<br>Re s > o |
| | 2 | $e^{-at}[(1+2bt)I_0(bt)+2bt\,I_1(bt)]$ | $\dfrac{(s+a+b)^{\frac{1}{2}}}{(s+a-b)^{\frac{3}{2}}}$ | Re s > Max - Re(a+b), Re(b-a) |
| 12.3.2 | 1 | $\dfrac{e^{at}}{t^{\frac{1}{2}}} * [I_0(bt)e^{ct}]$ | $\dfrac{\pi^{\frac{1}{2}}}{[(s-a)(s-b-c)(s+b-c)]^{\frac{1}{2}}}$ | Re s > Max Re a, Re(b+c), Re(c-b) |
| | 2 | $\frac{1}{t}\left[\dfrac{e^{at}}{t^{\frac{1}{2}}} * [I_0(bt)e^{ct}]\right]$ | $\pi^{\frac{1}{2}}\displaystyle\int_s^{\infty}\frac{du}{[(u-a)(u-b-c)(u+b-c)]^{\frac{1}{2}}}$ | Re s > Max Re a, Re(b+c), Re(c-b) |
| | 3 | $\dfrac{e^{t}}{t}\left[\dfrac{1}{t^{\frac{1}{2}}} * e^{(a-1)t} I_0(at)\right]$ | $2\pi^{\frac{1}{2}} F\left(2^{\frac{1}{2}}a^{\frac{1}{2}}, \sin^{-1}\frac{1}{s^{\frac{1}{2}}}\right)$ | Re s > o |
| | 4 | $\dfrac{e^{-\frac{a}{t}}}{t^{\frac{1}{2}}}\left[I_{\frac{1}{4}}\left(\frac{a}{t}\right) - I_{-\frac{1}{4}}\left(\frac{a}{t}\right)\right] + \dfrac{2^{\frac{5}{4}} a^{\frac{1}{4}}\Gamma\left(\frac{1}{4}\right)}{\pi t^{\frac{1}{4}}}$ | $4\left(\frac{\pi a}{s}\right)^{\frac{1}{2}}\left\{I_{\frac{1}{2}}[(8as)^{\frac{1}{2}}] - L_{\frac{1}{2}}[(8as)^{\frac{1}{2}}]\right\}$ | Re s > o |
| | 5 | $t^{\nu} e^{-at} I_{\nu}(bt)$ | $\dfrac{(2b)^{\nu}\,\Gamma\left(\nu+\frac{1}{2}\right)}{\pi^{\frac{1}{2}}(s+a+b)^{\nu+\frac{1}{2}}(s+a-b)^{\nu+\frac{1}{2}}}$ | Re $\nu > -\frac{1}{2}$<br>Re s > Max - Re(a+b) Re(b-a) |
| | 6 | $\dfrac{1}{t^{\frac{1}{2}}} e^{-\frac{a}{t}} I_0\left(\frac{a}{t}\right)$ | $\left(\frac{\pi}{s}\right)^{\frac{1}{2}}\left[I_0[(8as)^{\frac{1}{2}}] - L_0[(8as)^{\frac{1}{2}}]\right]$ | Re $a^{\frac{1}{2}} > o$<br>Re s > o |
| | 7 | $\left(\dfrac{t}{t+2c}\right)^{\frac{\nu}{2}} e^{-(a+b)t} I_{\nu}[a(t^2+2ct)^{\frac{1}{2}}]$ | $\dfrac{a^{\nu} e^{[cs-c(s+2a+b)^{\frac{1}{2}}(s+b)^{\frac{1}{2}}+c(a+b)]}}{(s+2a+b)^{\frac{1}{2}}(s+b)^{\frac{1}{2}}[s+(a+b)+(s+2a+b)^{\frac{1}{2}}(s+b)^{\frac{1}{2}}]^{\nu}}$ | Re $\nu > -1$<br>Re s > Max - Re b, - Re(2a+b) |
| 12.3.2.1 | 1 | $e^{-a(t+b)} I_0[c(t^2+2bt)^{\frac{1}{2}}]$ | $\dfrac{e^{b[s-(s+a+c)^{\frac{1}{2}}(s+a-c)^{\frac{1}{2}}]}}{[(s+a+c)(s+a-c)]^{\frac{1}{2}}}$ | Re s > Max - Re(a+c) Re(c-a) |

| | | $f(t)$ | $g(s)$ | |
|---|---|---|---|---|
| 2.3.2.1 (Contd.) | 2 | $t^{\frac{1}{2}} e^{-\frac{t^2}{a}} I_{\frac{1}{4}}\left(\frac{t^2}{a}\right)$ | $\left(\frac{a}{2s}\right)^{\frac{1}{2}} e^{\frac{as^2}{8}} \frac{\Gamma\left(\frac{1}{4}, \frac{as^2}{8}\right)}{\Gamma\left(\frac{1}{4}\right)}$ | Re a > o<br>Re s > o |
| | 3 | $t^{2\nu} e^{-\frac{t^2}{a}} I_\nu\left(\frac{t^2}{a}\right)$ | $2^{-\frac{11\nu}{2}} \frac{a^{\frac{\nu}{2}} \Gamma(4\nu+1)}{\Gamma(\nu+1)} s^{-\nu-1} e^{\frac{as^2}{16}} W_{-\frac{3\nu}{2}, \frac{\nu}{2}}\left(\frac{as^2}{8}\right)$ | Re a > o<br>Re $\nu > -\frac{1}{4}$<br>Re s > o |
| 2.7.2 | 1 | $t^\nu \sinh t\, I_\nu(t)$ | $\frac{Q^{\nu+1, -\nu-\frac{1}{2}}\left(\frac{s}{2}\right)}{(2\pi)^{\frac{1}{2}} (2s)^{\nu+\frac{1}{2}}}$ | Re s > 1 |
| | 2 | $t^\nu \cosh t\, I_\nu(t)$ | $\frac{Q^{\nu+1, -\nu-\frac{3}{2}}\left(\frac{s}{2}\right)}{\pi^{\frac{1}{2}} (4s)^{\nu+\frac{1}{2}}}$ | Re s > 1 |
| 2.10 | 1 | $J_0(at) * I_0(at)$ | $\frac{1}{(s^4-a^4)^{\frac{1}{2}}}$ | Re s > $\lvert$Re a$\rvert$ |
| | 2 | $\frac{1}{t}[J_0(at) * I_0(at)]$ | $a \int_s^\infty \frac{du}{(u^4-a^4)^{\frac{1}{2}}}$ | Re s > Max $\lvert$Re a$\rvert$, $\lvert$Re b$\rvert$ |
| 2.10.2 | 1 | $\frac{1}{t^{\frac{1}{2}}}[I_\nu(at^{\frac{1}{2}}) + J_\nu(at^{\frac{1}{2}})]$ | $2\pi^{\frac{1}{2}} s^{-\frac{1}{2}} \cosh \frac{a^2}{8s} I_{\frac{\nu}{2}}\left(\frac{a^2}{8s}\right)$ | Re $\nu > -1$<br>Re s > o |
| | 2 | $\frac{1}{t^{\frac{1}{2}}}[I_\nu(at^{\frac{1}{2}}) - J_\nu(at^{\frac{1}{2}})]$ | $2\pi^{\frac{1}{2}} s^{-\frac{1}{2}} \sinh \frac{a^2}{8s} I_{\frac{\nu}{2}}\left(\frac{a^2}{8s}\right)$ | Re $\nu > -1$<br>Re s > o |
| | 3 | $t^{\frac{\nu}{2}}[I_\nu(at^{\frac{1}{2}}) + J_\nu(at^{\frac{1}{2}})]$ | $2\left(\frac{a}{2}\right)^\nu s^{-\nu-1} \cosh \frac{a^2}{4s}$ | Re $\nu > -1$<br>Re s > o |
| | 4 | $t^{\frac{\nu}{2}}[I_\nu(at^{\frac{1}{2}}) - J_\nu(at^{\frac{1}{2}})]$ | $2\left(\frac{a}{2}\right)^\nu s^{-\nu-1} \sinh \frac{a^2}{4s}$ | Re $\nu > -2$<br>Re s > o |
| | 5 | $J_\nu(at^{\frac{1}{2}}) I_\nu(at^{\frac{1}{2}})$ | $\frac{1}{s} J_\nu\left(\frac{a^2}{2s}\right)$ | Re $\nu > -1$<br>Re s > o |
| | 6 | $J_\nu(bt^{\frac{1}{2}}) I_\nu(at^{\frac{1}{2}})$ | $\frac{1}{s} e^{\frac{a^2-b^2}{4s}} J_\nu\left(\frac{ab}{2s}\right)$ | Re $\nu > -1$<br>Re s > o |

| | | $f(t)$ | $g(s)$ | |
|---|---|---|---|---|
| 12.10.2 (Contd.) | 7 | $I_\nu(at^{\frac{1}{2}})I_\nu(bt^{\frac{1}{2}})+J_\nu(at^{\frac{1}{2}})J_\nu(bt^{\frac{1}{2}})$ | $\frac{2}{s}\cosh\frac{a^2+b^2}{4s}I_\nu\left(\frac{ab}{2s}\right)$ | Re $\nu > -1$<br>Re $s > 0$ |
| | 8 | $I_\nu(at^{\frac{1}{2}})I_\nu(bt^{\frac{1}{2}})-J_\nu(at^{\frac{1}{2}})J_\nu(bt^{\frac{1}{2}})$ | $\frac{2}{s}\sinh\frac{a^2+b^2}{4s}I_\nu\left(\frac{ab}{2s}\right)$ | Re $\nu > -1$<br>Re $s > 0$ |
| | 9 | $I_\nu^2[(2t)^{\frac{1}{2}}]+J_\nu^2[(2t)^{\frac{1}{2}}]$ | $\frac{2}{s}I_\nu(\frac{1}{s})\cosh\frac{1}{s}$ | Re $\nu > -1$<br>Re $s > 0$ |
| | 10 | $I_\nu^2[(2t)^{\frac{1}{2}}]-J_\nu^2[(2t)^{\frac{1}{2}}]$ | $\frac{2}{s}I_\nu(\frac{1}{s})\sinh\frac{1}{s}$ | Re $\nu > -1$<br>Re $s > 0$ |
| 13 | 1 | $K_0(at)$ | $\dfrac{\log\frac{s+(s^2-a^2)^{\frac{1}{2}}}{a}}{(s^2-a^2)^{\frac{1}{2}}}$<br>$=\dfrac{\sinh^{-1}\left[\left(\frac{s^2}{a^2}-1\right)^{\frac{1}{2}}\right]}{(s^2-a^2)^{\frac{1}{2}}}$<br>$=\dfrac{\cosh^{-1}\frac{s}{a}}{(s^2-a^2)^{\frac{1}{2}}}$ | Re $s > -$ Re |
| | 2 | $tK_0(at)$ | $\dfrac{s\log\frac{s+(s^2-a^2)^{\frac{1}{2}}}{a}}{(s^2-a^2)^{\frac{3}{2}}}-\dfrac{1}{s^2-a^2}$ | Re $s > -$ Re |
| | 3 | $K_{\frac{1}{2}}(at)$ | $\dfrac{\pi}{[2a(s+a)]^{\frac{1}{2}}}$ | Re $s > -$ Re |
| | 4 | $tK_1(at)$ | $\dfrac{s}{a(s^2-a^2)}-\dfrac{a\log\frac{s+(s^2-a^2)^{\frac{1}{2}}}{a}}{(s^2-a^2)^{\frac{3}{2}}}$ | Re $s > -$ Re |
| | 5 | $K_\nu(at)$ | $\dfrac{\pi\operatorname{cosec}(\nu\pi)[\{s+(s^2-a^2)^{\frac{1}{2}}\}^\nu-\{s-(s^2-a^2)^{\frac{1}{2}}\}^\nu]}{2a^\nu(s^2-a^2)^{\frac{1}{2}}}$ | $\lvert$Re $\nu\rvert < 1$<br>Re $s > -$ Re |
| 13.2 | 1 | $\frac{1}{t^{\frac{1}{2}}}K_\nu(t)$ | $(\frac{\pi}{2})^{\frac{1}{2}}\dfrac{\pi}{\cos(\nu\pi)}P_{\nu-\frac{1}{2}}(s)$ | $\lvert$Re $\nu\rvert < \frac{1}{2}$<br>Re $s > -1$ |

| | | f(t) | g(s) | |
|---|---|---|---|---|
| 13.2 (Contd.) | 2 | $t^{\mu}K_{\nu}(at)$ | $\left(\frac{\pi}{2a}\right)^{\frac{1}{2}} \frac{\Gamma(\mu-\nu+1)\Gamma(\mu+\nu+1)}{(s^2-a^2)^{\frac{\mu}{2}+\frac{1}{4}}} P^{-\mu-\frac{1}{2}}_{\nu-\frac{1}{2}}\left(\frac{s}{a}\right)$ $= \frac{\sin(\mu\pi)\Gamma(\mu-\nu+1)}{\sin[(u+\nu)\pi](s^2-a^2)^{\frac{\mu+1}{2}}} Q^{\nu}_{\mu}\left[\frac{s}{(s^2-a^2)^{\frac{1}{2}}}\right]$ | $\mathrm{Re}(\mu+\nu) > -1$ $\mathrm{Re}(\mu-\nu) > -1$ $\mathrm{Re}\, s > -\mathrm{Re}\, a$ |
| | 3 | $K_0(at^{\frac{1}{2}})$ | $-\frac{e^{\frac{a^2}{4s}}}{2s} \mathrm{Ei}\left(-\frac{a^2}{4s}\right)$ | $\mathrm{Re}\, s > o$ |
| | 4 | $\frac{1}{t^{\frac{1}{2}}} K_0(at^{\frac{1}{2}})$ | $\frac{\pi^{\frac{1}{2}}}{2s^{\frac{1}{2}}} e^{\frac{a^2}{8s}} K_0\left(\frac{a^2}{8s}\right)$ | $\mathrm{Re}\, s > o$ |
| | 5 | $\frac{1}{t^{\frac{1}{2}}} K_{\frac{1}{3}}\left(\frac{2}{t^{\frac{1}{2}}}\right)$ | $\frac{\pi}{3^{\frac{1}{2}} s^{\frac{2}{3}}} e^{-3s^{\frac{1}{3}}}$ | $\mathrm{Re}\, s > o$ |
| | 6 | $\frac{1}{t^{\frac{3}{2}}} K_{\frac{1}{3}}\left(\frac{2}{t^{\frac{1}{2}}}\right)$ | $\frac{\pi}{3^{\frac{1}{2}}} e^{-3s^{\frac{1}{3}}}$ | $\mathrm{Re}\, s > o$ |
| | 7 | $\frac{1}{t} K_{\frac{2}{3}}\left(\frac{2}{t^{\frac{1}{2}}}\right)$ | $\frac{\pi}{3^{\frac{1}{2}} s^{\frac{1}{3}}} e^{-3s^{\frac{1}{3}}}$ | $\mathrm{Re}\, s > o$ |
| | 8 | $K_1(at^{\frac{1}{2}})$ | $\frac{a\pi^{\frac{1}{2}}}{8s^{\frac{3}{2}}} e^{\frac{a^2}{8s}} \left[K_1\left(\frac{a^2}{8s}\right) - K_0\left(\frac{a^2}{8s}\right)\right]$ | $\mathrm{Re}\, s > o$ |
| | 9 | $\frac{1}{t^{\frac{1}{2}}} K_{\nu}(at^{\frac{1}{2}})$ | $\frac{\pi^{\frac{1}{2}}}{2s^{\frac{1}{2}}} \sec\frac{\nu\pi}{2} e^{\frac{a^2}{8s}} K_{\frac{\nu}{2}}\left(\frac{a^2}{8s}\right)$ | $\lvert\mathrm{Re}\, \nu\rvert < 1$ $\mathrm{Re}\, s > o$ |
| | 10 | $t^{\mu}K_{\nu}(at^{\frac{1}{2}})$ | $\frac{\Gamma(\mu+\frac{\nu}{2}+1)\Gamma(\mu-\frac{\nu}{2}+1)}{as^{\mu+\frac{1}{2}}} e^{\frac{a^2}{8s}} \cdot$ $\cdot\, W_{-\mu-\frac{1}{2},\frac{\nu}{2}}\left(\frac{a^2}{4s}\right)$ | $\mathrm{Re}(\mu \pm\frac{\nu}{2}) > -1$ $\mathrm{Re}\, s > o$ |
| | 11 | $t^{\frac{\nu}{2}} K_{\nu}(at^{\frac{1}{2}})$ | $\frac{a^{\nu}\Gamma(\nu+1)}{(2s)^{\nu+1}} e^{\frac{a^2}{4s}} \Gamma\left(-\nu, \frac{a^2}{4s}\right)$ | $\mathrm{Re}\, \nu > -1$ $\mathrm{Re}\, s > o$ |

| | | f(t) | g(s) | |
|---|---|---|---|---|
| 13.2 (Contd.) | 12 | $\frac{t^{\mu-1}}{(t+b)^{\mu}} K_{\nu}[a(t^2+bt)^{\frac{1}{2}}]$ | $\frac{\Gamma(\mu+\frac{\nu}{2})\Gamma(\mu-\frac{\nu}{2})}{ab} e^{\frac{bs}{2}} W_{\frac{1}{2}-\mu, \frac{\nu}{2}}\left[\frac{a^2 b}{2[s+(s^2-a^2)^{\frac{1}{2}}]}\right] \cdot W_{\frac{1}{2}-\mu, \frac{\nu}{2}}\left[\frac{b[s+(s^2-a^2)^{\frac{1}{2}}]}{2}\right]$ | $Re(\mu \pm \frac{\nu}{2}) > 0$ <br> $\lvert\arg b\rvert < \pi$ <br> $Re\, s > \lvert Re\, a\rvert$ |
| 13.3 | 1 | $\frac{1}{t} e^{-\frac{a}{t}} K_{\nu}(bt)$ | $2 K_{\nu}\left[[2as+2a(s^2-a^2)^{\frac{1}{2}}]^{\frac{1}{2}}\right] K_{\nu}\left[\frac{1}{a}[bs-b(s^2-a^2)^{\frac{1}{2}}]^{\frac{1}{2}}\right]$ | $Re\, a > 0$ <br> $Re\, s > -Re\, b$ |
| | 2 | $\frac{1}{t} e^{-\frac{a+b}{2t}} K_{\nu}(\frac{a-b}{2t})$ | $2 K_{\nu}[(a^{\frac{1}{2}}+b^{\frac{1}{2}}) s^{\frac{1}{2}}] K_{\nu}[(a^{\frac{1}{2}}-b^{\frac{1}{2}}) s^{\frac{1}{2}}]$ | $Re\, a > Re\, b >$ [illegible] <br> $Re\, s > 0$ |
| 13.3.1 | 1 | $\frac{1}{t} e^{t-\frac{1}{2t}} K_{\nu}(t)$ | $K_{\nu}[(\frac{s}{2})^{\frac{1}{2}}+(\frac{s}{2}-1)^{\frac{1}{2}}] K_{\nu}[(\frac{s}{2})^{\frac{1}{2}}-(\frac{s}{2}-1)^{\frac{1}{2}}]$ | $Re\, s > 2$ |
| 13.3.2 | 1 | $\frac{1}{t^{\frac{1}{2}}} e^{\frac{a}{t}} K_0(\frac{a}{t})$ | $\frac{\pi^{\frac{3}{2}}}{2s^{\frac{1}{2}}}\left[\mathbf{H}_0[(8as)^{\frac{1}{2}}] - Y_0[(8as)^{\frac{1}{2}}]\right]$ | $Re\, s > 0$ |
| | 2 | $\frac{1}{t^{\frac{1}{2}}} e^{-\frac{a}{t}} K_{\nu}(\frac{a}{t})$ | $\frac{2\pi^{\frac{1}{2}}}{s^{\frac{1}{2}}} K_{2\nu}[(8as)^{\frac{1}{2}}]$ | $Re\, a > 0$ <br> $Re\, s > 0$ |
| | 3 | $\frac{e^{\frac{a}{t}}}{t^{\frac{3}{2}}}[K_1(\frac{a}{t}) - K_0(\frac{a}{t})]$ | $\frac{2^{\frac{1}{2}}\pi^{\frac{3}{2}}}{a^{\frac{1}{2}}}\left[Y_{-1}[(8as)^{\frac{1}{2}}] - \mathbf{H}_{-1}[(8as)^{\frac{1}{2}}]\right]$ | $Re\, s > 0$ |
| 13.7 | 1 | $K_0(2a \sinh \frac{t}{2})$ | $\frac{\pi}{2} Y_s(a) \frac{\partial J_s(a)}{\partial s} - \frac{\pi}{2} J_s(a) \frac{\partial Y_s(a)}{\partial s}$ | $Re\, a > 0$ <br> $Re\, s > -\infty$ |
| | 2 | $\cosh t\, K_0(a \sinh \frac{t}{2})$ | $\frac{\pi}{2} Y'_s(a) \frac{\partial J'_s(a)}{\partial s} - \frac{\pi}{2} J'_s(a) \frac{\partial Y'_s(a)}{\partial s} - \frac{\pi}{2}\frac{s^2}{a^2}\left[J_s(a)\frac{\partial Y_s(a)}{\partial s} - Y_s(a)\frac{\partial J_s(a)}{\partial s}\right]$ <br> where $J'_s = \frac{dJ_s}{da}$ | $Re\, a > 0$ <br> $Re\, s > -\infty$ |
| | 3 | $K_{\nu}[2a \sinh \frac{t}{2}]$ | $\frac{\pi^2 \operatorname{cosec}(\nu\pi)}{2}\left[J_{\frac{\nu}{2}-s}(a) Y_{-\frac{\nu}{2}-s}(a) - J_{-\frac{\nu}{2}-s}(a) Y_{\frac{\nu}{2}-s}(a)\right]$ | $Re\, a > 0$ <br> $\lvert Re\, \nu\rvert < 1$ <br> $Re\, s > -\infty$ |

| | | f(t) | g(s) | |
|---|---|---|---|---|
| 13.7 (Contd.) | 4 | $\operatorname{cosech}\frac{t}{2}\, K_\nu[a \operatorname{cosech}\frac{t}{2}]$ | $a^{-1}\,\Gamma(s+\frac{\nu}{2}+\frac{1}{2})\,\Gamma(s-\frac{\nu}{2}+\frac{1}{2})\, W_{-s,\frac{\nu}{2}}(ia)\,.$ $\cdot\, W_{-s,\frac{\nu}{2}}(-ia)$ | Re a > o; $\operatorname{Re}(s\pm\frac{\nu}{2}) > -1$ |
| 13.7.3 | 1 | $\operatorname{cosech}\frac{t}{2}\exp\left(-\frac{ae^t+b}{e^t-1}\right) K_\nu\left[\frac{a^{\frac{1}{2}}b^{\frac{1}{2}}}{\sinh\frac{t}{2}}\right]$ | $\frac{1}{(ab)^{\frac{1}{2}}}\Gamma(s+\frac{\nu}{2}+\frac{1}{2})\,\Gamma(s-\frac{\nu}{2}+\frac{1}{2})\, e^{\frac{b-a}{2}}\, W_{-s,\frac{\nu}{2}}(a)\,.$ $\cdot\, W_{-s,\frac{\nu}{2}}(b)$ | Re a > o; Re b > o; $\operatorname{Re}(s\pm\frac{\nu}{2}) > -\frac{1}{2}$ |
| | 2 | $\operatorname{cosech} t\; e^{(a+b)\coth t} K_\nu[2a^{\frac{1}{2}}b^{\frac{1}{2}}\operatorname{cosech} t]$ | $\frac{\Gamma(\frac{1+\nu+s}{2})\,\Gamma(\frac{1-\nu+s}{2})}{2a^{\frac{1}{2}}b^{\frac{1}{2}}}\, W_{-\frac{s}{2},\frac{\nu}{2}}(2a)\,.$ $\cdot\, W_{\frac{s}{2},\frac{\nu}{2}}(2b)$ | Re a > o; Re b > o; $\operatorname{Re}(s\pm\nu) > -1$ |
| 13.10.2 | 1 | $\frac{1}{t^{\frac{1}{2}}} K_0(at^{\frac{1}{2}}) + \frac{\pi}{2t^{\frac{1}{2}}} Y_0(at^{\frac{1}{2}})$ | $(\frac{\pi}{s})^{\frac{1}{2}}\sinh\frac{a^2}{8s}\, K_0\left(\frac{a^2}{8s}\right)$ | Re s > o |
| | 2 | $\frac{1}{t^{\frac{1}{2}}} K_0(at^{\frac{1}{2}}) - \frac{\pi}{2t^{\frac{1}{2}}} Y_0(at^{\frac{1}{2}})$ | $(\frac{\pi}{s})^{\frac{1}{2}}\cosh\frac{a^2}{8s}\, K_0\left(\frac{a^2}{8s}\right)$ | Re s > o |
| | 3 | $\frac{1}{t^{\frac{1}{2}}} K_\nu(at^{\frac{1}{2}})\Big\{\sin[(\frac{\nu}{2}-\frac{1}{4})\pi]\, J_\nu(at^{\frac{1}{2}})$ $+\cos[(\frac{\nu}{2}-\frac{1}{4})\pi]\, Y_\nu(at^{\frac{1}{2}})\Big\}$ | $-\frac{\Gamma(\frac{1}{4}+\frac{\nu}{2})\,\Gamma(\frac{1}{4}-\frac{\nu}{2})}{(2\pi)^{\frac{1}{2}}a^2}\, s^{\frac{1}{2}}\, W_{\frac{1}{4},\frac{\nu}{2}}(i\frac{a^2}{2s})\,.$ $\cdot\, W_{\frac{1}{4},\frac{\nu}{2}}(-i\frac{a^2}{2s})$ | $\lvert\operatorname{Re}\nu\rvert < \frac{1}{2}$; Re s > o |
| 13.12 | 1 | $I_0(at)\log a + K_0(at)$ | $\frac{\log[s+(s^2-a^2)^{\frac{1}{2}}]}{(s^2-a^2)^{\frac{1}{2}}}$ | Re s > \|Re a\| |
| 13.12.2 | 1 | $t^\nu K_\nu(at^{\frac{1}{2}})\, I_\nu(at^{\frac{1}{2}})$ | $\frac{\Gamma(\nu+\frac{1}{2})\, a^{\nu-1}}{2\, s^{\frac{3\nu+1}{2}}}\, e^{\frac{a^2}{2s}}\, W_{-\frac{\nu}{2},\frac{\nu}{2}}(\frac{a^2}{s})$ | $\operatorname{Re}\nu > -\frac{1}{2}$ |
| 13.12.7 | 1 | $t[I_0(at)\log a + K_0(at)] + \frac{\sinh(at)}{a}$ | $\frac{s\log[s+(s^2-a^2)^{\frac{1}{2}}]}{(s^2-a^2)^{\frac{3}{2}}}$ | Re s > \|Re a\| |
| | 2 | $t[I_1(at)\log a - K_1(at)] + \frac{\cosh(at)}{a}$ | $\frac{a\log[s+(s^2-a^2)^{\frac{1}{2}}]}{(s^2-a^2)^{\frac{3}{2}}}$ | Re s > \|Re a\| |

| | | f(t) | g(s) | |
|---|---|---|---|---|
| 15 | 1 | $\theta_1(\frac{\nu}{2a} \mid \frac{t}{a^2})$ | $-\frac{a}{s^{\frac{1}{2}}}\sinh(\nu s^{\frac{1}{2}})\,\mathrm{sech}(as^{\frac{1}{2}})$ | $-a \leqslant \nu \leqslant a$<br>Re s > o |
| | 2 | $\theta_2(n \mid at)$ | $(-1)^n \frac{\tanh[(\frac{s}{a})^{\frac{1}{2}}]}{(as)^{\frac{1}{2}}}$ | n an integer<br>Re s > o |
| | 3 | $\theta_2(\frac{1}{2}+\frac{\nu}{2a} \mid \frac{t}{a^2})$ | $-\frac{a}{s^{\frac{1}{2}}}\sinh(\nu s^{\frac{1}{2}})\,\mathrm{sech}(as^{\frac{1}{2}})$ | $-a \leqslant \nu \leqslant a$<br>Re s > o |
| | 4 | $\theta_3(n \mid at)$ | $\frac{\coth[(\frac{s}{a})^{\frac{1}{2}}]}{(as)^{\frac{1}{2}}}$ | n an integer<br>Re s > o |
| | 5 | $\theta_3(\nu \mid t)$ | $\frac{\cosh[(2\nu-1)s^{\frac{1}{2}}]}{s^{\frac{1}{2}}\sinh s^{\frac{1}{2}}}$ | $o \leqslant \nu \leqslant 1$<br>Re s > o |
| | 6 | $\theta_3(\mu \mid \frac{t}{a^2}) - \theta_3(\nu \mid \frac{t}{a^2})$ | $\frac{\sinh[(a-\nu+\mu)s^{\frac{1}{2}}]\sinh[(\mu+\nu)s^{\frac{1}{2}}]}{s^{\frac{1}{2}}\sinh(as^{\frac{1}{2}})}$<br>$o \leqslant \mu+\nu \leqslant \nu-\mu \leqslant a$<br>$\frac{\sinh[(a-\nu-\mu)s^{\frac{1}{2}}]\sinh[(\nu-\mu)s^{\frac{1}{2}}]}{s^{\frac{1}{2}}\sinh(as^{\frac{1}{2}})}$<br>$o \leqslant \nu-\mu \leqslant \mu+\nu \leqslant a$ | Re s > o |
| | 7 | $\theta_4(n \mid at)$ | $\frac{\mathrm{cosech}[(\frac{s}{a})^{\frac{1}{2}}]}{(as)^{\frac{1}{2}}}$ | n an integer<br>Re s > o |
| | 8 | $\theta_4(\frac{1}{2} \mid t)$ | $\frac{\coth s^{\frac{1}{2}}}{s^{\frac{1}{2}}}$ | Re s > o |
| | 9 | $\theta_4(\frac{\nu}{2a} \mid \frac{t}{a^2})$ | $\frac{a}{s^{\frac{1}{2}}}\cosh(\nu s^{\frac{1}{2}})\,\mathrm{cosech}(as^{\frac{1}{2}})$ | $-a \leqslant \nu \leqslant a$<br>Re s > o |
| | 10 | $\hat{\theta}_1(\frac{\nu}{2a} \mid \frac{t}{a^2})$ | $-\frac{a}{s^{\frac{1}{2}}}\cosh(\nu s^{\frac{1}{2}})\,\mathrm{sech}(as^{\frac{1}{2}})$ | $-a \leqslant \nu \leqslant a$<br>Re s > o |
| | 11 | $\hat{\theta}_2(\frac{1}{2} \mid at)$ | $\frac{\mathrm{sech}[(\frac{s}{a})^{\frac{1}{2}}]}{(as)^{\frac{1}{2}}}$ | Re s > o |

| | | f(t) | g(s) | |
|---|---|---|---|---|
| 15 (Contd.) | 12 | $\hat{\theta}_2(\nu\|t)$ | $\frac{1}{s^{\frac{1}{2}}}\cosh[(2\nu-1)s^{\frac{1}{2}}]\operatorname{sech} s^{\frac{1}{2}}$ | $0 \leqslant \nu \leqslant 1$<br>Re s > o |
| | 13 | $\hat{\theta}_3(\nu\|t)$ | $-\frac{1}{s^{\frac{1}{2}}}\sinh[(2\nu-1)s^{\frac{1}{2}}]\operatorname{cosech} s^{\frac{1}{2}}$ | $0 \leqslant \nu \leqslant 1$<br>Re s > o |
| | 14 | $\hat{\theta}_4\left(\frac{\nu}{2a}\middle\|\frac{t}{a^2}\right)$ | $-\frac{1}{s^{\frac{1}{2}}}\sinh(\nu s^{\frac{1}{2}})\operatorname{cosech}(as^{\frac{1}{2}})$ | $-a \leqslant \nu \leqslant a$<br>Re s > o |
| | 15 | $\left[\frac{\partial}{\partial\nu}\theta_1\left(\frac{\nu}{2}\middle\|at\right)\right]_{\nu=0}$ | $-\frac{1}{a}\operatorname{sech}\left[\left(\frac{s}{a}\right)^{\frac{1}{2}}\right]$ | Re s > o |
| | 16 | $\frac{\partial}{\partial\nu}\theta_1\left(\frac{\nu}{2a}\middle\|\frac{t}{a^2}\right)$ | $-a\cosh(\nu s^{\frac{1}{2}})\operatorname{sech}(as^{\frac{1}{2}})$ | $-a < \nu < a$<br>Re s > o |
| | 17 | $\frac{\partial}{\partial\nu}\theta_2\left(\frac{1}{2}+\frac{\nu}{2a}\middle\|\frac{t}{a^2}\right)$ | $-a\cosh(\nu s^{\frac{1}{2}})\operatorname{sech}(as^{\frac{1}{2}})$ | $-a < \nu < a$<br>Re s > o |
| | 18 | $\frac{\partial}{\partial\nu}\theta_2\left(\frac{\nu}{2a}\middle\|\frac{t}{a^2}\right)$ | $-a\cosh[(a-\nu)s^{\frac{1}{2}}]\operatorname{sech}(as^{\frac{1}{2}})$ | $0 < \nu < 2a$<br>Re s > o |
| | 19 | $\frac{\partial}{\partial\nu}\theta_3\left(\frac{\nu}{2a}\middle\|\frac{t}{a^2}\right)$ | $-a\sinh[(a-\nu)s^{\frac{1}{2}}]\operatorname{cosech}(as^{\frac{1}{2}})$ | $0 < \nu < 2a$<br>Re s > o |
| | 20 | $\frac{\partial}{\partial\nu}\theta_4\left(\frac{\nu}{2a}\middle\|\frac{t}{a^2}\right)$ | $a\sinh(\nu s^{\frac{1}{2}})\operatorname{cosech}(as^{\frac{1}{2}})$ | $-a < \nu < a$<br>Re s > o |
| | 21 | $\frac{\partial}{\partial\nu}\hat{\theta}_1\left(\frac{\nu}{2a}\middle\|\frac{t}{a^2}\right)$ | $-a\sinh(\nu s^{\frac{1}{2}})\operatorname{sech}(as^{\frac{1}{2}})$ | $-a < \nu < a$<br>Re s > o |
| | 22 | $\frac{\partial}{\partial\nu}\hat{\theta}_2\left(\frac{\nu}{2}\middle\|t\right)$ | $\sinh[(\nu-1)s^{\frac{1}{2}}]\cosh s^{\frac{1}{2}}$ | $0 < \nu < 2$<br>Re s > o |
| | 23 | $\frac{\partial}{\partial\nu}\hat{\theta}_3\left(\frac{\nu}{2}\middle\|t\right)$ | $\cosh[(\nu-1)s^{\frac{1}{2}}]\operatorname{cosech} s^{\frac{1}{2}}$ | $0 < \nu < 2$<br>Re s > o |
| | 24 | $\frac{\partial}{\partial\nu}\hat{\theta}_4\left(\frac{\nu}{2a}\middle\|\frac{t}{a^2}\right)$ | $-a\cosh(\nu s^{\frac{1}{2}})\operatorname{cosech}(as^{\frac{1}{2}})$ | $-a \leqslant \nu \leqslant a$<br>Re s > o |

| | | f(t) | g(s) | |
|---|---|---|---|---|
| 15 (Contd.) | 25 | $\left[\frac{\partial}{\partial \nu} \hat{\theta}_4 \left(\frac{\nu}{2a}\middle|\frac{t}{a^2}\right)\right]_{\nu=o}$ | $-a \operatorname{cosech}(as^{\frac{1}{2}})$ | Re s > o |
| | 26 | $\int_o^1 \hat{\theta}_2(\frac{u}{2}\|at)\,du$ | $\frac{1}{s} \tanh[(\frac{s}{a})^{\frac{1}{2}}]$ | Re s > o |
| | 27 | $\int_1^a \theta_3(\frac{u}{2}\|t)\,du$ | $\frac{1}{s} \sinh[(a-1)s^{\frac{1}{2}}] \operatorname{cosech} s^{\frac{1}{2}}$ | o ≤ a ≤ 2<br>Re s > o |
| | 28 | $\int_o^a \hat{\theta}_4(\frac{u}{2}\|t)\,du + \int_o^t \left[\frac{\partial}{\partial a}\hat{\theta}_4(\frac{a}{2}\|u)\right]_{a=o} du$ | $\frac{1}{s} \cosh(as^{\frac{1}{2}}) \operatorname{cosech} s^{\frac{1}{2}}$ | − 1 < a < 1<br>Re s > o |
| | 29 | $\int_a^1 \hat{\theta}_3(\frac{u}{2}\|t)\,du - \int_o^t \left[\frac{\partial}{\partial a}\theta_4(\frac{a}{2}\|u)\right]_{a=o} du$ | $\frac{1}{s} \cosh[(a-1)s^{\frac{1}{2}}] \operatorname{cosech} s^{\frac{1}{2}}$ | o < a < 2<br>Re s > o |
| | 30 | $\int_o^a \theta_4(\frac{u}{2}\|t)\,du$ | $-\frac{1}{s} \sinh(as^{\frac{1}{2}}) \operatorname{cosech} s^{\frac{1}{2}}$ | − 1 < a < 1<br>Re s > o |
| | 31 | $\int_o^a \theta_2(\frac{u}{2}\|t)\,du$ | $\frac{1}{s} - \frac{1}{s} \cosh[(a-1)s^{\frac{1}{2}}] \operatorname{sech} s^{\frac{1}{2}}$ | o < a < 2<br>Re s > o |
| | 32 | $\int_1^a \hat{\theta}_2(\frac{u}{2}\|t)\,du$ | $\frac{1}{s} \sinh[(a-1)s^{\frac{1}{2}}] \operatorname{sech} s^{\frac{1}{2}}$ | o ≤ a ≤ 2<br>Re s > o |
| | 33 | $\int_1^a \theta_1(\frac{u}{2}\|t)\,du$ | $\frac{\cosh(as^{\frac{1}{2}}) \operatorname{sech}(s^{\frac{1}{2}}) - 1}{s}$ | − 1 ≤ a ≤ 1<br>Re s > o |
| | 34 | $\int_o^a \hat{\theta}_1(\frac{u}{2}\|t)\,du$ | $\frac{1}{s} \sinh(as^{\frac{1}{2}}) \operatorname{sech} s^{\frac{1}{2}}$ | − 1 ≤ a ≤ 1<br>Re s > o |
| | 35 | $\int_o^1 \theta_1(\frac{u}{2}\|t)\,du$ | $\frac{1}{s} - \frac{\operatorname{sech} s^{\frac{1}{2}}}{s}$ | Re s > o |
| | 36 | $\int_o^1 \hat{\theta}_2(\frac{u}{2}\|t)\,du$ | $\frac{\tanh s^{\frac{1}{2}}}{s}$ | Re s > o |

| | | f(t) | g(s) | |
|---|---|---|---|---|
| 15.3 | 1 | $e^{at}\hat{\theta}_3(a^{\frac{1}{2}}t\mid t)$ | $\frac{1}{2s^{\frac{1}{2}}}[\tanh(s^{\frac{1}{2}}+a^{\frac{1}{2}})-\tanh(s^{\frac{1}{2}}-a^{\frac{1}{2}})+2]$ | Re s > o |
| | 2 | $e^{at}\theta_3(a^{\frac{1}{2}}t\mid t)$ | $\frac{1}{2s^{\frac{1}{2}}}[\tanh(s^{\frac{1}{2}}+a^{\frac{1}{2}})+\tanh(s^{\frac{1}{2}}-a^{\frac{1}{2}})]$ | Re s > o |
| 15.3.2 | 1 | $e^{a^2 t}[\theta_3(at\mid t)+\hat{\theta}_3(at\mid t)]-\frac{1}{(\pi t)^{\frac{1}{2}}}$ | $\frac{\tanh(s^{\frac{1}{2}}+a)}{s^{\frac{1}{2}}}$ | Re s > o |
| 16 | 1 | $\mathrm{Erf}\left(\frac{t}{a}\right)$ | $\frac{1}{s}e^{\frac{a^2s^2}{4}}\mathrm{Erfc}\left(\frac{as}{2}\right)$ | $\lvert\arg a\rvert<\frac{\pi}{4}$<br>Re s > o |
| | 2 | $\mathrm{Erfc}\left(\frac{t}{a}\right)$ | $\frac{1-e^{\frac{a^2s^2}{4}}\mathrm{Erfc}\left(\frac{as}{2}\right)}{s}$ | $\lvert\arg a\rvert<\frac{\pi}{4}$<br>Re s > o |
| 16.2 | 1 | $\mathrm{Erf}(a^{\frac{1}{2}}t^{\frac{1}{2}})$ | $\frac{a^{\frac{1}{2}}}{s(s+a)^{\frac{1}{2}}}$ | Re s > Max o, - Re a |
| | 2 | $\mathrm{Erfc}(a^{\frac{1}{2}}t^{\frac{1}{2}})$ | $\frac{(s+a)^{\frac{1}{2}}-a^{\frac{1}{2}}}{s(s+a)^{\frac{1}{2}}}$ | Re s > - Re a |
| | 3 | $\mathrm{Erf}\left(\frac{a^{\frac{1}{2}}}{2t^{\frac{1}{2}}}\right)$ | $\frac{1-e^{-a^{\frac{1}{2}}s^{\frac{1}{2}}}}{s}$ | Re a > o<br>Re s > o |
| | 4 | $\mathrm{Erfc}\left(\frac{a^{\frac{1}{2}}}{2t^{\frac{1}{2}}}\right)$ | $\frac{1}{s}e^{-a^{\frac{1}{2}}s^{\frac{1}{2}}}$ | Re a > o<br>Re s > o |
| | 5 | $e^{-ab}\mathrm{Erfc}\left(\frac{a}{2t^{\frac{1}{2}}}-bt^{\frac{1}{2}}\right)+e^{ab}\mathrm{Erfc}\left(\frac{a}{2t^{\frac{1}{2}}}+bt^{\frac{1}{2}}\right)$ | $\frac{2e^{-a(s+b^2)^{\frac{1}{2}}}}{s}$ | Re s > o |
| 16.3.1 | 1 | $e^{-a^2t^2}\mathrm{Erf}(iat)$ | $\frac{\pi^{\frac{1}{2}}e^{\frac{s^2}{4a^2}}}{2ai}\mathrm{Ei}\left(-\frac{s^2}{4a^2}\right)$ | $\lvert\arg a\rvert<\frac{\pi}{4}$<br>Re s > o |
| | 2 | $e^{-a^2t^2}\mathrm{Erfc}(iat)$ | $\frac{\pi^{\frac{1}{2}}}{2a}e^{\frac{s^2}{4a^2}}\left[\mathrm{Erfc}\left(\frac{s}{2a}\right)+\frac{i}{\pi}\mathrm{Ei}\left(-\frac{s^2}{4a^2}\right)\right]$ | $\lvert\arg a\rvert<\frac{\pi}{4}$<br>Re s > o |

| | | f(t) | g(s) | |
|---|---|---|---|---|
| 16.3.1 (Contd.) | 3 | $e^{at}[\mathrm{Erf}(\frac{t}{2}+a)-\mathrm{Erf}(a)]$ | $e^{s^2-a^2}\frac{\mathrm{Erfc}(s)}{s-a}$ | Re s > Re a |
| | 4 | $e^{at}[\mathrm{Erf}(at+\frac{1}{2})-\mathrm{Erf}(\frac{1}{2})]$ | $\frac{a\,e^{\frac{s^2}{4a^2}-\frac{1}{4}}\mathrm{Erfc}(\frac{s}{2a})}{s-a}$ | Re s > Re a |
| 16.3.2 | 1 | $e^{-at}\mathrm{Erf}(bt^{\frac{1}{2}})$ | $\frac{b}{(s+a)[s+a+b^2]^{\frac{1}{2}}}$ | Re s > Max − Re a, − Re(a+b²) |
| | 2 | $e^{at}\mathrm{Erf}(a^{\frac{1}{2}}t^{\frac{1}{2}})$ | $\frac{a^{\frac{1}{2}}}{s^{\frac{1}{2}}(s-a)}$ | Re s > Max o, Re a |
| | 3 | $e^{a^2t}\mathrm{Erfc}(a\,t^{\frac{1}{2}})$ | $\frac{1}{s^{\frac{1}{2}}(s^{\frac{1}{2}}+a)}$ | Re s > o if Re a ⩾ o<br>Re s > Max o, Re a² if Re a < o |
| | 4 | $1-e^{a^2t}\mathrm{Erfc}(at^{\frac{1}{2}})$ | $\frac{a}{s(s^{\frac{1}{2}}+a)}$ | Re s > o if Re a ⩾ o<br>Re s > Max o, Re a² if Re a < o |
| | 5 | $2e^{a^2t}\mathrm{Erfc}(at^{\frac{1}{2}})-1$ | $\frac{1}{s}\left(\frac{s^{\frac{1}{2}}-a}{s^{\frac{1}{2}}+a}\right)$ | Re s > o if Re a ⩾ o<br>Re s > Max o, Re a² if Re a < o |
| | 6 | $t^{\frac{1}{2}}-\pi^{\frac{1}{2}}\,at\,e^{a^2t}\mathrm{Erfc}(at^{\frac{1}{2}})$ | $\frac{\pi^{\frac{1}{2}}}{2s^{\frac{1}{2}}(a+s^{\frac{1}{2}})^2}$ | Re s > o if Re a ⩾ o<br>Re s > Max o, Re a² if Re a < o |
| | 7 | $\frac{1}{t^{\frac{1}{2}}}-\pi^{\frac{1}{2}}\,ae^{a^2t}\mathrm{Erfc}(at^{\frac{1}{2}})$ | $\frac{\pi^{\frac{1}{2}}}{s^{\frac{1}{2}}+a}$ | Re s > o if Re a ⩾ o<br>Re s > Max o, Re a² if Re a < o |
| | 8 | $\frac{e^{-at}}{t^{\frac{1}{2}}}+(\pi a)^{\frac{1}{2}}\mathrm{Erf}[(at)^{\frac{1}{2}}]$ | $\frac{[\pi(s+a)]^{\frac{1}{2}}}{s}$ | Re s > Max o, − Re a |
| | 9 | $\frac{e^{-at}}{t^{\frac{1}{2}}}+\pi^{\frac{1}{2}}(a-b)^{\frac{1}{2}}e^{-bt}\mathrm{Erf}[(a-b)^{\frac{1}{2}}t^{\frac{1}{2}}]$ | $\frac{[\pi(s+a)]^{\frac{1}{2}}}{s+b}$ | Re s > Max − Re a, − Re b |
| | 10 | $t^{\frac{1}{2}}e^{-\frac{a}{t}}-(\pi a)^{\frac{1}{2}}\mathrm{Erfc}(\frac{a}{t})^{\frac{1}{2}}$ | $\frac{\pi^{\frac{1}{2}}}{2}\,\frac{e^{-2a^{\frac{1}{2}}s^{\frac{1}{2}}}}{s^{\frac{3}{2}}}$ | Re a ⩾ o<br>Re s > o |

| | | f(t) | g(s) | |
|---|---|---|---|---|
| 16.3.2 (Contd.) | 11 | $t^{\nu} e^{\frac{a^2}{t}} \operatorname{Erfc}(\frac{a}{t^{\frac{1}{2}}})$ | $a^{\nu+1} \pi \sec[(\nu+1)\pi] s^{-\frac{\nu+1}{2}} \cdot [\mathbf{H}_{-\nu-1}(2as^{\frac{1}{2}}) - Y_{-\nu-1}(2as^{\frac{1}{2}})]$ | $\operatorname{Re} \nu > -\frac{3}{2}$<br>$\operatorname{Re} s > 0$ |
| | 12 | $t^{\nu} e^{\frac{a^2}{t}} \operatorname{Erf}(\frac{ia}{t^{\frac{1}{2}}})$ | $-i\pi a^{\nu+1} \sec[(\nu+1)\pi] s^{-\frac{\nu+1}{2}} \cdot [\mathbf{L}_{-\nu-1}(2as^{\frac{1}{2}}) - I_{\nu+1}(2as^{\frac{1}{2}})]$ | $\operatorname{Re} \nu > -\frac{3}{2}$<br>$\operatorname{Re} s > 0$ |
| | 13 | $e^{-b^2 t}\left[e^{-iab} \operatorname{Erfc}\left(\frac{a}{2t^{\frac{1}{2}}} - ib\,t^{\frac{1}{2}}\right) + e^{iab} \operatorname{Erfc}\left(\frac{a}{2t^{\frac{1}{2}}} + ib\,t^{\frac{1}{2}}\right)\right]$ | $\frac{2e^{-as^{\frac{1}{2}}}}{s+b^2}$ | $\operatorname{Re} a^2 \geq 0$<br>$\operatorname{Re} s > -\operatorname{Re} b^2$ |
| | 14 | $e^{a^2 t} \operatorname{Erfc}\left(at^{\frac{1}{2}} + \frac{b}{t^{\frac{1}{2}}}\right)$ | $\frac{e^{-2b(s^{\frac{1}{2}}+a)}}{s^{\frac{1}{2}}(s^{\frac{1}{2}}+a)}$ | $\operatorname{Re} b^2 \geq 0$<br>$\operatorname{Re} s > 0$ if $\operatorname{Re} a \geq 0$<br>$\operatorname{Re} s > \operatorname{Max} 0, \operatorname{Re} a^2$ if $\operatorname{Re} a < 0$ |
| 16.3.2.1 | 1 | $(t+2a) \operatorname{Erfc}\left[\left(\frac{a}{t}\right)^{\frac{1}{2}}\right] - 2\left(\frac{at}{\pi}\right)^{\frac{1}{2}} e^{-\frac{a}{t}}$ | $\frac{e^{-2a^{\frac{1}{2}}s^{\frac{1}{2}}}}{s^2}$ | $\operatorname{Re} a \geq 0$<br>$\operatorname{Re} s > 0$ |
| | 2 | $1 + (2a^2 t - 1) e^{a^2 t} \operatorname{Erfc}(at^{\frac{1}{2}}) - \frac{2a}{\pi^{\frac{1}{2}}} t^{\frac{1}{2}}$ | $\frac{a^2}{s(a+s^{\frac{1}{2}})^2}$ | $\operatorname{Re} s > 0$ if $\operatorname{Re} a \geq 0$<br>$\operatorname{Re} s > \operatorname{Max} 0, \operatorname{Re} a^2$ if $\operatorname{Re} a < 0$ |
| | 3 | $(2a^2 t + 1) e^{a^2 t} \operatorname{Erfc}(at^{\frac{1}{2}}) - 2a\left(\frac{t}{\pi}\right)^{\frac{1}{2}}$ | $\frac{1}{(a+s^{\frac{1}{2}})^2}$ | $\operatorname{Re} s > 0$ if $\operatorname{Re} a \geq 0$<br>$\operatorname{Re} s > \operatorname{Max} 0, \operatorname{Re} a^2$ if $\operatorname{Re} a < 0$ |
| | 4 | $(2a^2 t+2) t^{\frac{1}{2}} - a\pi^{\frac{1}{2}} t(2a^2 t+3) e^{a^2 t} \operatorname{Erfc}(at^{\frac{1}{2}})$ | $\frac{1}{(a+s^{\frac{1}{2}})^3}$ | $\operatorname{Re} s > 0$ if $\operatorname{Re} a \geq 0$<br>$\operatorname{Re} s > \operatorname{Max} 0, \operatorname{Re} a^2$ if $\operatorname{Re} a < 0$ |
| | 5 | $t(2at^2+1) e^{a^2 t} \operatorname{Erfc}(at^{\frac{1}{2}}) - \frac{2a}{\pi^{\frac{1}{2}}} t^{\frac{3}{2}}$ | $\frac{1}{s^{\frac{1}{2}}(a+s^{\frac{1}{2}})^3}$ | $\operatorname{Re} s > 0$ if $\operatorname{Re} a \geq 0$<br>$\operatorname{Re} s > \operatorname{Max} 0, \operatorname{Re} a^2$ if $\operatorname{Re} a < 0$ |
| | 6 | $(2a^4 t^2 + 5a^2 t + 1) e^{a^2 t} \operatorname{Erfc}(at^{\frac{1}{2}}) - \frac{2}{\pi^{\frac{1}{2}}} at^{\frac{1}{2}}(a^2 t + 2)$ | $\frac{s^{\frac{1}{2}}}{(a+s^{\frac{1}{2}})^3}$ | $\operatorname{Re} s > 0$ if $\operatorname{Re} a \geq 0$<br>$\operatorname{Re} s > \operatorname{Max} 0, \operatorname{Re} a^2$ if $\operatorname{Re} a < 0$ |

| | | f(t) | g(s) | |
|---|---|---|---|---|
| 16.3.2.1 (Contd.) | 7 | $1-(2a^4t^2-a^2t+1)e^{a^2t}\mathrm{Erfc}(at^{\frac{1}{2}})+2(a^3t-a)\dfrac{t^{\frac{1}{2}}}{\pi^{\frac{1}{2}}}$ | $\dfrac{a^3}{s(a+s^{\frac{1}{2}})^3}$ | Re s > o if Re a ⩾ o<br>Re s > Max o, Re $a^2$ if Re a < o |
| | 8 | $t\left(\dfrac{4a^4}{3}t^2+4a^2t+1\right)e^{a^2t}\mathrm{Erfc}(at^{\frac{1}{2}})-\dfrac{2a^3}{3\pi^{\frac{1}{2}}}t^{\frac{5}{2}}(2a^2t+5)$ | $\dfrac{1}{(a+s^{\frac{1}{2}})^4}$ | Re s > o if Re a ⩾ o<br>Re s > Max o, Re $a^2$ if Re a < o |
| | 9 | $1-2(8a^4t^2+8a^2t+1)e^{a^2t}\mathrm{Erfc}(at^{\frac{1}{2}})+8a(2a^2t+1)(\frac{t}{\pi})^{\frac{1}{2}}$ | $\dfrac{1}{s}\left(\dfrac{a-s^{\frac{1}{2}}}{a+s^{\frac{1}{2}}}\right)^3$ | Re s > o if Re a ⩾ o<br>Re s > Max o, Re $a^2$ if Re a < o |
| | 10 | $\mathrm{Erfc}\left(\dfrac{a}{t^{\frac{1}{2}}}\right)-e^{2ab+b^2t}\mathrm{Erfc}\left(\dfrac{a}{t^{\frac{1}{2}}}+bt^{\frac{1}{2}}\right)$ | $\dfrac{b\,e^{-2as^{\frac{1}{2}}}}{s(s^{\frac{1}{2}}+b)}$ | Re s > o if Re b ⩾ o<br>Re s > Max o, Re $b^2$ if Re b < o<br>Re $a^2$ ⩾ o |
| | 11 | $\dfrac{1}{t^{\frac{1}{2}}}e^{-\frac{a^2}{4t}}-\pi^{\frac{1}{2}}be^{ab+b^2t}\mathrm{Erfc}\left(\dfrac{a}{2t^{\frac{1}{2}}}+bt^{\frac{1}{2}}\right)$ | $\dfrac{\pi^{\frac{1}{2}}e^{-as^{\frac{1}{2}}}}{s^{\frac{1}{2}}+b}$ | Re s > o if Re b ⩾ o<br>Re s > Max o, Re $b^2$ if Re b < o<br>Re $a^2$ ⩾ o |
| | 12 | $\dfrac{2t^{\frac{1}{2}}}{\pi^{\frac{1}{2}}}e^{-\frac{a^2}{4t}}-(2bt+a)e^{ab+b^2t}\,\cdot$<br>$\cdot\ \mathrm{Erfc}\left(\dfrac{a}{2t^{\frac{1}{2}}}+bt^{\frac{1}{2}}\right)$ | $\dfrac{e^{-as^{\frac{1}{2}}}}{s^{\frac{1}{2}}(b+s^{\frac{1}{2}})^2}$ | Re s > o if Re b ⩾ o<br>Re s > Max o, Re $b^2$ if Re b < o |
| | 13 | $\mathrm{Erfc}\left(\dfrac{a}{2t^{\frac{1}{2}}}\right)-\dfrac{2bt^{\frac{1}{2}}}{\pi^{\frac{1}{2}}}e^{-\frac{a^2}{4t}}$<br>$+(2b^2t+ab-1)e^{ab+b^2t}\mathrm{Erfc}\left(\dfrac{a}{2t^{\frac{1}{2}}}+bt^{\frac{1}{2}}\right)$ | $\dfrac{b^2e^{-as^{\frac{1}{2}}}}{s(b+s^{\frac{1}{2}})^2}$ | Re s > o if Re b ⩾ o<br>Re s > Max o, Re $b^2$ if Re b < o |
| | 14 | $(2bt^2+ab+1)e^{ab+b^2t}\mathrm{Erfc}\left(\dfrac{a}{2t^{\frac{1}{2}}}+bt^{\frac{1}{2}}\right)-\dfrac{2bt^{\frac{1}{2}}}{\pi^{\frac{1}{2}}}e^{-\frac{a^2}{4t}}$ | $\dfrac{e^{-as^{\frac{1}{2}}}}{(b+s^{\frac{1}{2}})^2}$ | Re s > o if Re b ⩾ o<br>Re s > Max o, Re $b^2$ if Re b < o |
| 17 | 1 | $C(at)$ | $\dfrac{a^{\frac{1}{2}}[(s^2+a^2)^{\frac{1}{2}}+s]^{\frac{1}{2}}}{2s(s^2+a^2)^{\frac{1}{2}}}$ | Re s > o |
| | 2 | $S(at)$ | $\dfrac{a^{\frac{1}{2}}[(s^2+a^2)^{\frac{1}{2}}-s]^{\frac{1}{2}}}{2s(s^2+a^2)^{\frac{1}{2}}}$ | Re s > o |
| | 3 | $tS(at)$ | $\dfrac{a^{\frac{1}{2}}[(s^2+a^2)^{\frac{1}{2}}-s]^{\frac{1}{2}}}{2s^2(s^2+a^2)^{\frac{1}{2}}}\left[\dfrac{s}{2(s^2+a^2)^{\frac{1}{2}}}+\dfrac{s^2}{s^2+a^2}+1\right]$ | Re s > o |

| | | f(t) | g(s) | |
|---|---|---|---|---|
| 17.1 | 1 | $C(at^2)$ | $\frac{1}{s}\left[\cos\frac{s^2}{4a}\left\{\frac{1}{2}-S\left(\frac{s^2}{4a}\right)\right\}-\sin\frac{s^2}{4a}\left\{\frac{1}{2}-C\left(\frac{s^2}{4a}\right)\right\}\right]$ | Re s > o |
| | 2 | $S(at^2)$ | $\frac{1}{s}\left[\cos\frac{s^2}{4a}\left\{\frac{1}{2}-C\left(\frac{s^2}{4a}\right)\right\}+\sin\frac{s^2}{4a}\left\{\frac{1}{2}-S\left(\frac{s^2}{4a}\right)\right\}\right]$ | Re s > o |
| 18 | 1 | $Si(at)$ | $\frac{1}{s}\cot^{-1}\frac{s}{a}$ | Re s > o |
| | 2 | $Ci(at)$ | $-\frac{1}{2s}\log\left(1+\frac{s^2}{a^2}\right)$ | Re s > o |
| | 3 | $ci(at)$ | $\frac{1}{2s}\log\left(1+\frac{s^2}{a^2}\right)$ | Re s > o |
| | 4 | $si(at)$ | $-\frac{1}{s}\tan^{-1}\frac{s}{a}$ | Re s > \|Im a\| |
| 18.1 | 1 | $Si(at^2)$ | $\frac{\pi}{s}\left\{\left[\frac{1}{2}-C\left(\frac{s^2}{4a}\right)\right]^2+\left[\frac{1}{2}-S\left(\frac{s^2}{4a}\right)\right]^2\right\}$ | Re s > o |
| 18.5 | 1 | $\sin(at)\,ci(bt)$ | $-b\,\frac{s\tan^{-1}\frac{2as}{s^2+b^2-a^2}-\frac{a}{2}\log\frac{(s^2+b^2-a^2)^2+4a^2s^2}{b^2}}{2(s^2+a^2)}$ | b ≠ o<br>Re s > \|Im a\| |
| | 2 | $\cos(at)\,si(bt)$ | $-b\,\frac{s\tan^{-1}\frac{2bs}{b^2-a^2-s^2}+\frac{a}{2}\log\frac{(b+a)^2+s^2}{(b-a)^2+s^2}}{2(s^2+a^2)}$ | b ≠ o<br>Re s > \|Im a\| |
| | 3 | $\cos t\,ci(t)$ | $\frac{\tan^{-1}\frac{2}{s}+\frac{s}{2}\log[s^2(s^2+4)]}{2(s^2+1)}$ | Re s > o |
| | 4 | $\sin t\,si(t)+\cos t\,ci(t)$ | $\frac{\frac{s}{2}\log(s^2+4)+\tan^{-1}\frac{2}{s}}{s^2+1}$ | Re s > o |
| | 5 | $\sin t\,ci(t)-\cos t\,si(t)$ | $\frac{\frac{1}{2}\log(s^2+4)-s\tan^{-1}\frac{2}{s}}{s^2+1}$ | Re s > o |
| | 6 | $\cos t\,si(t)+\sin t\,ci(t)$ | $\frac{\log s}{s^2+1}$ | Re s > o |

| | | f(t) | g(s) | |
|---|---|---|---|---|
| 18.5 (Contd.) | 7 | $\sin t\,\mathrm{si}(t) - \cos t\,\mathrm{ci}(t)$ | $-\frac{s \log s}{s^2+1}$ | Re s > o |
| | 8 | $\sin(at)\mathrm{Si}(at) + \cos(at)\mathrm{Ci}(at)$ | $-\frac{s \log \frac{s}{a}}{s^2+a^2}$ | Re s > o |
| | 9 | $\cos(at)\mathrm{Si}(at) - \sin(at)\mathrm{Ci}(at)$ | $\frac{a \log \frac{s}{a}}{s^2+a^2}$ | Re s > o |
| | 10 | $\cos(at)\mathrm{Si}(at) + \sin(at)[\log a - \mathrm{Ci}(at)]$ | $\frac{a \log s}{s^2+a^2}$ | Re s > o |
| | 11 | $\cos(at)[\log a - \mathrm{Ci}(at)] - \sin(at)\mathrm{Si}(at)$ | $\frac{s \log s}{s^2+a^2}$ | Re s > o |
| | 12 | $t[\log a + \frac{\sin(at)}{at} + \mathrm{ci}(at)]$ | $\frac{\log(s^2+a^2)}{2s^2}$ | Re a > o<br>Re s > $\lvert$Im a$\rvert$ |
| 18.5.4 | 1 | $\sin(at)[\log \frac{2a}{\gamma t} - \mathrm{Ci}(2at)] + \cos(at)\mathrm{Si}(at)$ | $\frac{a \log(s^2+a^2)}{s^2+a^2}$ | Re s > $\lvert$Im a$\rvert$ |
| | 2 | $\cos(at)[\log \frac{2a}{\gamma t} - \mathrm{Ci}(2at)] - \sin(at)\mathrm{Si}(2at)$ | $\frac{s \log(s^2+a^2)}{s^2+a^2}$ | Re s > $\lvert$Im a$\rvert$ |
| 19 | 1 | $\mathrm{Ei}(-at)$ | $-\frac{1}{s}\log(\frac{s}{a}+1)$ | $\lvert\arg a\rvert < \pi$<br>Re s > o |
| | 2 | $\overline{\mathrm{Ei}}(at)$ | $-\frac{1}{s}\log(\frac{s}{a}-1)$ | Re a > o<br>Re s > Re a |
| 19.2 | 1 | $\frac{1}{t^{\frac{1}{2}}}\mathrm{Ei}(-at)$ | $-2(\frac{\pi}{s})^{\frac{1}{2}}\log[(\frac{s}{a})^{\frac{1}{2}} + (\frac{s}{a}+1)^{\frac{1}{2}}]$ | $\lvert\arg a\rvert < \pi$<br>Re s > o |
| 19.3 | 1 | $e^{-bt}[\log a - \mathrm{Ei}(-at)]$ | $\frac{\log(s+a+b)}{s+b}$ | $\lvert\arg a\rvert < \pi$<br>Re s > − Re b |
| 19.3.2 | 1 | $\frac{1}{t^{\frac{1}{2}}}e^{-bt}[\log a - \mathrm{Ei}(-at)]$ | $\frac{2\pi^{\frac{1}{2}}\log[(s+a+b)^{\frac{1}{2}} + (s+b)^{\frac{1}{2}}]}{(s+b)^{\frac{1}{2}}}$ | $\lvert\arg a\rvert < \pi$<br>Re s > − Re b |

| | | f(t) | g(s) | |
|---|---|---|---|---|
| 19.5 | 1 | $\sin t\,\overline{Ei}(t)$ | $\dfrac{s\tan^{-1}\frac{1}{s-1}-\frac{1}{2}\log(s^2-2s+2)}{s^2+1}$ | Re s > 1 |
| | 2 | $\cos t\,\overline{Ei}(t)$ | $-\dfrac{\tan^{-1}\frac{1}{s-1}+\frac{s}{2}\log(s^2-2s+2)}{s^2+1}$ | Re s > 1 |
| | 3 | $\sin(at)Ei(-t)$ | $\dfrac{s\tan^{-1}\frac{a}{s+1}-\frac{a}{2}\log[(s+1)^2+a^2]}{s^2+a^2}$ | Re s > \|Im a\| |
| | 4 | $\cos(at)Ei(-t)$ | $-\dfrac{a\tan^{-1}\frac{a}{s+1}+\frac{s}{2}\log[(s+1)^2+a^2]}{s^2+a^2}$ | Re s > \|Im a\| |
| 19.12.3 | 1 | $e^{t}I_0(bt)Ei(-t)$ | $-\dfrac{2\log\dfrac{[(s+b)^{\frac{1}{2}}+1][(s-b)^{\frac{1}{2}}+1]+(s+b-1)^{\frac{1}{2}}(s-b-1)^{\frac{1}{2}}}{[(s+b)^{\frac{1}{2}}+1][(s-b)^{\frac{1}{2}}+1]-(s+b-1)^{\frac{1}{2}}(s-b-1)^{\frac{1}{2}}}}{(s+b-1)^{\frac{1}{2}}(s-b-1)^{\frac{1}{2}}}$ | Re s > 1+\|Re b\| |
| 20.3 | 1 | $li(e^{at})$ | $-\frac{1}{s}\log(\frac{s}{a}-1)$ | Re s > Re a |
| | 2 | $li(e^{-at})$ | $-\frac{1}{s}\log(\frac{s}{a}+1)$ | Re s > o |
| 21 | 1 | $\Gamma(\nu,at)$ | $\frac{\Gamma(\nu)}{s}[1-(1+\frac{s}{a})^{-\nu}]$ | Re ν > o<br>Re s > − Re a |
| | 2 | $\Gamma(\nu,\frac{a}{t})$ | $2a^{\frac{\nu}{2}}s^{\frac{\nu}{2}-1}K_\nu(2a^{\frac{1}{2}}s^{\frac{1}{2}})$ | \|arg a\| < $\frac{\pi}{2}$<br>Re s > o |
| 21.1 | 1 | $\gamma(\frac{1}{4},\frac{t^2}{a})$ | $a^{\frac{1}{4}}s^{-\frac{1}{2}}e^{\frac{as^2}{8}}K_{\frac{1}{4}}(\frac{as^2}{8})$ | Re a > o<br>Re s > o |
| | 2 | $\gamma\left(\nu,\frac{t^2}{2a^2}\right)$ | $\frac{\Gamma(2\nu)}{2^{\nu+1}s}e^{\frac{a^2s^2}{4}}D_{-2\nu}(as)$ | Re ν > o<br>\|arg a\| < $\frac{\pi}{4}$<br>Re s > o |
| 21.2 | 1 | $\binom{t}{n}t^{\nu-1}$ | $\frac{\Gamma(\nu)}{s^\nu}\Phi_n(\nu,\frac{1}{s})$ | Re ν > o<br>Re s > o |

where

$$\sum_{n=0}^{\infty}x^n\,\Phi_n(\nu,\tfrac{1}{s})=[1-\tfrac{1}{s}\log(x+1)]^{-\nu}$$

| | | f(t) | g(s) | |
|---|---|---|---|---|
| 21.3 | 1 | $e^{bt}\gamma(\nu,at)$ | $\dfrac{\Gamma(\nu)a^{\nu}}{(s-b)(s+a-b)^{\nu}}$ | $\mathrm{Re}\,\nu>0$<br>$\mathrm{Re}\,s>\mathrm{Re}\,b,\ \mathrm{Re}(b-a)$ |
| | 2 | $e^{at}\Gamma(\nu,at)$ | $\Gamma(\nu)\dfrac{1-(\frac{a}{s})^{\nu}}{s-a}$ | $\mathrm{Re}\,\nu>0$<br>$\mathrm{Re}\,s>0$ |
| | 3 | $\psi(e^{t})$ | $-\dfrac{\zeta'(s)}{s\zeta(s)}$ | $\mathrm{Re}\,s>1$ |
| 21.3.1 | 1 | $e^{-\frac{t^2}{a}}\gamma(\nu,\frac{e^{i\pi}t^2}{a})$ | $\dfrac{\Gamma(2\nu)}{2^{2\nu}}a^{\frac{1}{2}}e^{\frac{as^2}{4}+\nu\pi i}\Gamma(\frac{1}{2}-\nu,\frac{as^2}{4})$ | $\lvert\arg a\rvert<\frac{\pi}{2}$<br>$\mathrm{Re}\,\nu>0$<br>$\mathrm{Re}\,s>0$ |
| | 2 | $\int_0^\infty \dfrac{t^{u-1}}{\Gamma(u)}du$ | $\dfrac{1}{\log s}$ | $\mathrm{Re}\,s>1$ |
| | 3 | $\sum_{n=1}^{\infty} n\int_{(2n-1)a}^{(2n+1)a}\dfrac{t^{u-1}}{\Gamma(u)}du$ | $\dfrac{s^{a}}{(s^{2a}-1)\log s}$ | $\mathrm{Re}\,a>0$<br>$\mathrm{Re}\,s>1$ |
| | 4 | $\sum_{n=1}^{\infty}\int_{(4n-3)a}^{(4n-1)a}\dfrac{t^{u-1}}{\Gamma(u)}du$ | $\dfrac{s^{a}}{(s^{2a}+1)\log s}$ | $\mathrm{Re}\,a>0$<br>$\mathrm{Re}\,s>1$ |
| | 5 | $\sum_{n=1}^{\infty}(2n-1)\int_{(n-1)a}^{na}\dfrac{t^{u-1}}{\Gamma(u)}du$ | $\dfrac{s^{a}+1}{(s^{a}-1)\log s}$ | $\mathrm{Re}\,a>0$<br>$\mathrm{Re}\,s>1$ |
| | 6 | $\sum_{n=1}^{\infty}\left[\int_{(8n-7)a}^{(8n-5)a}\dfrac{t^{u-1}}{\Gamma(u)}du-\int_{(8n-3)a}^{(8n-1)a}\dfrac{t^{u-1}}{\Gamma(u)}du\right]$ | $\dfrac{s^{a}(s^{2a}-1)}{(s^{4a}+1)\log s}$ | $\mathrm{Re}\,a>0$<br>$\mathrm{Re}\,s>1$ |
| | 7 | $\sum_{n=1}^{\infty}\left[\int_{(2n-2)a}^{(2n-1)a}\dfrac{t^{u-1}}{\Gamma(u)}du-\int_{(2n-1)a}^{2na}\dfrac{t^{u-1}}{\Gamma(u)}du\right]$ | $\dfrac{s^{a}-1}{(s^{a}+1)\log s}$ | $\mathrm{Re}\,a>0$<br>$\mathrm{Re}\,s>1$ |
| | 8 | $\int_a^\infty \dfrac{t^{u-1}}{\Gamma(u)}du$ | $\dfrac{1}{s^{a}\log s}$ | $\mathrm{Re}\,a\geqslant 0$<br>$\mathrm{Re}\,s>1$ |

| | | f(t) | g(s) | |
|---|---|---|---|---|
| 21.3.2 | 1 | $t^{\mu} e^{\frac{a}{t}} \Gamma(\nu, \frac{a}{t})$ | $2^{3+\mu-2\nu} \Gamma(2+\mu-\nu) (\frac{a}{s})^{\frac{\mu+1}{2}} S_{2\nu-\mu-2,\mu+1}(2a^{\frac{1}{2}} s^{\frac{1}{2}})$ | $\mathrm{Re}(\nu-\mu) < 2$<br>$\lvert \arg a \rvert < \pi$<br>$\mathrm{Re}\, s > 0$ |
| 21.3.2.1 | 1 | $\int_0^2 \frac{t^{u-1}\, du}{\Gamma(u) u^{\frac{1}{2}} (2-u)^{\frac{1}{2}}}$ | $\frac{\pi}{s} I_0(\log s)$ | $\mathrm{Re}\, s > -\infty$ |
| 23.1 | 1 | $\frac{P_{\nu}\left[\frac{2}{(1+at)^2} - 1\right]}{1+at}$ | $\frac{1}{s} e^{\frac{s}{a}} W_{\nu+\frac{1}{2},0}(\frac{s}{a}) W_{-\nu-\frac{1}{2},0}(\frac{s}{a})$ | $\mathrm{Re}\, s > 0$ |
| 23.2 | 1 | $t^{\frac{1}{2}} P_{\nu}^{\frac{1}{4}}[(1+a^2t^2)^{\frac{1}{2}}] P_{\nu}^{-\frac{1}{4}}[(1+a^2t^2)^{\frac{1}{2}}]$ | $\frac{\pi^{\frac{1}{2}}}{2^{\frac{3}{2}} a s^{\frac{1}{2}}} H_{\nu+\frac{1}{2}}^{(1)}(\frac{s}{2a}) H_{\nu+\frac{1}{2}}^{(2)}(\frac{s}{2a})$ | $\mathrm{Re}\, s > 0$ |
| | 2 | $\frac{P_{\nu}^{\mu}[(1+at)^{\frac{1}{2}}]}{t^{\frac{\mu}{2}} (1+at)^{\frac{1}{2}}}$ | $2^{\mu} a^{-\frac{1}{4}} s^{\frac{\mu}{2}-\frac{3}{4}} e^{\frac{s}{2a}} W_{\frac{\mu}{2}-\frac{1}{4},\frac{\nu}{2}+\frac{1}{4}}(\frac{s}{a})$ | $\mathrm{Re}\, \mu < 1$<br>$\mathrm{Re}\, s > 0$ |
| | 3 | $\frac{1}{t^{\frac{\mu}{2}}} P_{\nu}^{\mu}[(1+at)^{\frac{1}{2}}]$ | $2^{\mu} a^{\frac{1}{4}} s^{\frac{\mu}{2}-\frac{5}{4}} e^{\frac{s}{2a}} W_{\frac{\mu}{2}+\frac{1}{4},\frac{\nu}{2}+\frac{1}{4}}(\frac{s}{a})$ | $\mathrm{Re}\, \mu < 1$<br>$\mathrm{Re}\, s > 0$ |
| | 4 | $\frac{(b+t)^{\frac{\nu}{2}} (-1 - \frac{a+b}{t})^{\frac{\mu}{2}}}{(a+t)^{\frac{\nu}{2}+\frac{1}{2}}} P_{\nu}^{\mu}\left[\left\{\frac{ab}{(a+t)(b+t)}\right\}^{\frac{1}{2}}\right]$ | $\left(\frac{2}{s}\right)^{\frac{1}{2}} c^{\frac{a+b}{2}s} D_{\mu-\nu-1}\left[(2as)^{\frac{1}{2}}\right] D_{\mu+\nu}\left[(2bs)^{\frac{1}{2}}\right]$ | $\lvert \arg a \rvert < \pi$<br>$\lvert \arg b \rvert < \pi$<br>$\mathrm{Re}\, \mu < 1$<br>$\lvert \arg(as) \rvert < \pi$<br>$\lvert \arg(bs) \rvert < \pi$<br>$\mathrm{Re}\, s > 0$ |
| 23.2.1 | 1 | $\frac{P_{\nu}^{\mu}(1 + \frac{t}{a})}{(t^2+2at)^{\frac{\mu}{2}}}$ | $\left(\frac{2a}{\pi}\right)^{\frac{1}{2}} s^{\mu-\frac{1}{2}} e^{as} K_{\nu+\frac{1}{2}}(as)$ | $\mathrm{Re}\, \mu < 1$<br>$\lvert \arg a \rvert < \pi$<br>$\mathrm{Re}\, s > 0$ |
| | 2 | $(1 + \frac{2a}{t})^{\frac{\nu}{2}} P_{\mu}^{\nu}(1 + \frac{t}{a})$ | $\frac{1}{s} e^{as} W_{\nu,\mu+\frac{1}{2}}(2as)$ | $\lvert \arg a \rvert < \pi$<br>$\mathrm{Re}\, \nu < 1$<br>$\mathrm{Re}\, s > 0$ |
| | 3 | $t^{b+\frac{\mu}{2}-1} (at+1)^{\frac{\mu}{2}} P_{\nu}^{-\mu}(1+at)$ | $-\frac{\sin(\nu\pi)}{\pi} a^{\frac{\mu}{2}} \frac{E(-\nu, \nu+1, b+\mu : \mu+1 : \frac{2s}{a})}{s^{b+\mu}}$ | $\mathrm{Re}(b+\mu) > 0$<br>$\mathrm{Re}\, s > 0$ |

| | | f(t) | g(s) | |
|---|---|---|---|---|
| 23.2.1 (Contd.) | 4 | $t^{b-\frac{\mu}{2}-1}(at+2)^{-\frac{\mu}{2}}P_{\nu}^{-\mu}(1+at)$ | $\dfrac{a^{\frac{\mu}{2}}E(\mu+\nu+1,\mu-\nu,b:\mu+1:\frac{2s}{a})}{2^{\mu}s^{b}\Gamma(\mu+\nu+1)\Gamma(\mu-\nu)}$ | Re b > o<br>Re s > o |
| | 5 | $t^{a+\frac{\mu}{2}-1}(t+2)^{\frac{\mu}{2}}Q_{\nu}^{\mu}(1+t)$ | $\dfrac{\Gamma(\nu+\mu+1)}{\Gamma(\nu-\mu+1)}\left\{\dfrac{\sin(\nu\pi)}{2s^{a+\mu}\sin(\mu\pi)}E(-\nu,\nu+1,a+\mu:\mu+1:2s) - \dfrac{\sin[(\mu+\nu)\pi]}{2^{1-\mu}s^{a}\sin(\mu\pi)}E(\nu-\mu+1,-\nu-\mu,a:1-\mu:2s)\right\}$ | Re a > o<br>Re(a+μ) > o<br>Re s > o |
| | 6 | $t^{a-\frac{\mu}{2}-1}(t+2)^{\frac{\mu}{2}}Q_{\nu}^{\mu}(1+t)$ | $-\dfrac{\sin(\nu\pi)}{2s^{a-\mu}\sin(\mu\pi)}E(-\nu,\nu+1,a-\mu:1-\mu:2s) - \dfrac{\sin[(\mu-\nu)\pi]}{2^{1+\mu}s^{a}\sin(\mu\pi)}E(\mu+\nu+1,\mu-\nu,a:1+\mu:2s)$ | Re a > o<br>Re(a-μ) > o<br>Re s > o |
| | 7 | $[(a+t)(b+t)]^{\frac{\nu}{2}}P_{\nu}[\frac{2(a+t)(b+t)}{ab}-1]$ | $\frac{1}{\pi}(ab)^{\frac{\nu+1}{2}}e^{\frac{a+b}{2}s}K_{\nu+\frac{1}{2}}(\frac{as}{2})K_{\nu+\frac{1}{2}}(\frac{bs}{2})$ | \|arg a\| < π<br>\|arg b\| < π<br>\|arg as\| < π<br>\|arg bs\| < π |
| 23.3 | 1 | $\dfrac{(1-a^2+a^2e^{-t})^{\mu}}{(1-e^{-t})^{\frac{1}{2}}}\left\{P_{2\nu}^{2\mu}\left[a(1-e^{-t})^{\frac{1}{2}}\right] + P_{2\nu}^{2\mu}\left[-a(1-e^{-t})^{\frac{1}{2}}\right]\right\}$ | $\dfrac{2^{2\mu+1}\pi\Gamma(s)\,{}_2F_1[-\mu-\nu,\frac{1}{2}-\mu+\nu;s+\frac{1}{2};a^2]}{\Gamma(\frac{1}{2}-\mu-\nu)\Gamma(1-\mu+\nu)\Gamma(s+\frac{1}{2})}$ | \|a\| < 1<br>Re s > o |
| | 2 | $(1-a^2+a^2e^{-t})^{\mu}\left\{P_{2\nu}^{2\mu}\left[a(1-e^{-t})^{\frac{1}{2}}\right] - P_{2\nu}^{2\mu}\left[-a(1-e^{-t})^{\frac{1}{2}}\right]\right\}$ | $\dfrac{-2^{2\mu+1}\pi a\Gamma(s)\,{}_2F_1[\frac{1}{2}-\mu-\nu,\nu-\mu+1;s+\frac{3}{2};a^2]}{\Gamma(\frac{1}{2}-\mu+\nu)\Gamma(-\mu-\nu)\Gamma(s+\frac{3}{2})}$ | \|a\| < 1<br>Re s > o |
| | 3 | $\left[(e^{t}-1)\left(\frac{ae^{t}}{a-2}-1\right)\right]^{\frac{\mu}{2}}P_{\nu}^{-\mu}(ae^{t}-a+1)$ | $\dfrac{\Gamma(s-\mu+\nu+1)\Gamma(s-\nu-\mu)}{\Gamma(s+1)}\left(\dfrac{a}{a-2}\right)^{\frac{s}{2}}P_{\nu}^{\mu-s}(a-1)$ | Re a > o<br>Reμ > - 1<br>Re s > Max Re(μ-ν)-1, Re(μ+ν) |

| | | f(t) | g(s) | |
|---|---|---|---|---|
| 23.3 (Contd.) | 4 | $(1-e^{-2t})^{\frac{\mu}{2}} P_\nu^{-\mu}(e^t)$ | $\dfrac{2^{s-1}\,\Gamma(\frac{s+\nu+1}{2})\,\Gamma(\frac{s-\nu}{2})}{\pi^{\frac{1}{2}}\,\Gamma(s+\mu+1)}$ | Re s>Max Re $\nu$, (−1−Re$\nu$) <br> Re $\mu$ > − 1 |
| 23.7 | 1 | $\sinh^{2\mu}(\frac{t}{2}) P_{2n}^{-2\mu}(\cosh\frac{t}{2})$ | $\dfrac{\Gamma(2\mu+\frac{1}{2})\Gamma(s-n-\mu)\Gamma(s+n-\mu+\frac{1}{2})}{4^{\mu}\pi^{\frac{1}{2}}\Gamma(s+n+\mu+1)\Gamma(s-n+\mu+\frac{1}{2})}$ | Re $\mu$ > $-\frac{1}{4}$ <br> n = 0,1,2,... <br> Re s > n + Re $\mu$ |
| 24 | 1 | $\ker t + i \,\mathrm{kei}\, t + \frac{\pi}{4} \mathrm{ber}\, t + i\frac{\pi}{4} \mathrm{bei}\, t$ | $\dfrac{\log[s+(s^2-i)^{\frac{1}{2}}]}{(s^2-i)^{\frac{1}{2}}}$ | Re s > $2^{-\frac{1}{2}}$ |
| | 2 | $t[\ker(at) + i\,\mathrm{kei}(at)]$ | $\dfrac{s\log\dfrac{i^{-\frac{1}{2}}[s+(s^2-ia^2)^{\frac{1}{2}}]}{a}}{(s^2-ia^2)^{\frac{3}{2}}} - \dfrac{1}{s^2-ia^2}$ | Re$(s \pm ai^{\frac{1}{2}}) > 0$ |
| | 3 | ber(at) | $\left[\dfrac{1}{2(s^4+a^4)^{\frac{1}{2}}} + \dfrac{s^2}{2(s^4+a^4)}\right]^{\frac{1}{2}}$ | Re s > $\dfrac{\lvert\mathrm{Re}\, a\rvert + \lvert\mathrm{Im}\, a\rvert}{2^{\frac{1}{2}}}$ |
| | 4 | bei(at) | $\left[\dfrac{1}{2(s^4+a^4)^{\frac{1}{2}}} - \dfrac{s^2}{2(s^4+a^4)}\right]^{\frac{1}{2}}$ | Re s > $\dfrac{\lvert\mathrm{Re}\, a\rvert + \lvert\mathrm{Im}\, a\rvert}{2^{\frac{1}{2}}}$ |
| | 5 | ber(at) * bei(at) | $\dfrac{a^3}{2(s^4+a^4)}$ | Re s > $\dfrac{\lvert\mathrm{Re}\, a\rvert + \lvert\mathrm{Im}\, a\rvert}{2^{\frac{1}{2}}}$ |
| | 6 | $t[\ker_1(at) + i\,\mathrm{kei}_1(at)]$ | $\dfrac{s}{ai^{\frac{1}{2}}(s^2-ia^2)} - \dfrac{ai^{\frac{1}{2}}}{(s^2-ia^2)^{\frac{3}{2}}} \log\dfrac{s+(s^2-ia^2)^{\frac{1}{2}}}{ai^{\frac{1}{2}}}$ | Re$(s \pm ai^{\frac{1}{2}}) > 0$ |
| | 7 | $\ker_\nu(at) + i\,\mathrm{kei}_\nu(at)$ | $\dfrac{\pi\,\mathrm{cosec}(\nu\pi)}{2(s^2-ia^2)^{\frac{1}{2}} a^{\nu} e^{\frac{i\pi\nu}{4}}}\left\{[s+(s^2-ia)^{\frac{1}{2}}]^{\nu} - [s-(s^2-ia^2)^{\frac{1}{2}}]^{\nu}\right\}$ | $\lvert\mathrm{Re}\,\nu\rvert < 1$ <br> Re s > $\dfrac{\lvert\mathrm{Re}\, a\rvert}{2^{\frac{1}{2}}}$ |
| | 8 | $\mathrm{ber}_\nu(at) + i\,\mathrm{bei}_\nu(at)$ | $\dfrac{a^{\nu} e^{\frac{3i\pi\nu}{4}}}{(s^2-ia^2)^{\frac{1}{2}}[s+(s^2-ia^2)^{\frac{1}{2}}]^{\nu}}$ | Re $\nu$ > − 1 <br> Re s > $\dfrac{\lvert\mathrm{Re}\, a\rvert}{2^{\frac{1}{2}}}$ |

| | | f(t) | g(s) | |
|---|---|---|---|---|
| 24.2 | 1 | $\mathrm{ber}(at^{\frac{1}{2}})$ | $\frac{1}{s}\cos\frac{a^2}{4s}$ | Re s > 0 |
| | 2 | $\mathrm{bei}(at^{\frac{1}{2}})$ | $\frac{1}{s}\sin\frac{a^2}{4s}$ | Re s > 0 |
| | 3 | $t^{\frac{\nu}{2}}\,\mathrm{ber}_\nu(at^{\frac{1}{2}})$ | $\frac{a^\nu}{2^\nu s^{\nu+1}}\cos\left(\frac{a^2+3\nu\pi s}{4s}\right)$ | Re ν > − 1<br>Re s > 0 |
| | 4 | $t^{\frac{\nu}{2}}\,\mathrm{bei}_\nu(at^{\frac{1}{2}})$ | $\frac{a^\nu}{2^\nu s^{\nu+1}}\sin\left(\frac{a^2+3\nu\pi s}{4s}\right)$ | Re ν > − 1<br>Re s > 0 |
| | 5 | $V_\nu^{(b)}(at^{\frac{1}{2}})$ | $\frac{16s}{a^4}\,I_\nu(\frac{a^2}{2s})$ | Re ν > 0<br>Re s > 0 |
| | 6 | $t^{\frac{1}{2}}\,W_\nu^{(b)}(at^{\frac{1}{2}})$ | $\frac{a}{2s^2}\,I_\nu(\frac{a^2}{2s})$ | Re ν > − 2<br>Re s > 0 |
| | 7 | $X_\nu^{(b)}(at^{\frac{1}{2}})$ | $s^{-1}\,I_\nu(\frac{a^2}{2s})$ | Re ν > − 1<br>Re s > 0 |
| | 8 | $\frac{1}{t^{\frac{1}{2}}}\,Z_\nu^{(b)}(at^{\frac{1}{2}})$ | $\frac{2}{a}\,I_\nu(\frac{a^2}{2s})$ | Re ν > 0<br>Re s > 0 |
| | 9 | $t^{\frac{\nu}{2}}\,[\cos\frac{3\pi\nu}{4}\,\mathrm{bei}_\nu(at^{\frac{1}{2}}) - \sin\frac{3\pi\nu}{4}\,\mathrm{ber}_\nu(at^{\frac{1}{2}})]$ | $(\frac{a}{2})^\nu s^{-\nu-1}\sin\frac{a^2}{4s}$ | Re ν > − 2<br>Re s > 0 |
| | 10 | $t^{\frac{\nu}{2}}\,[\cos\frac{3\pi\nu}{4}\mathrm{ber}_\nu(at^{\frac{1}{2}}) + \sin\frac{3\pi\nu}{4}\,\mathrm{bei}_\nu(at^{\frac{1}{2}})]$ | $(\frac{a}{2})^\nu s^{-\nu-1}\cos\frac{a^2}{4s}$ | Re ν > − 1<br>Re s > 0 |
| | 11 | $\frac{d^n}{dt^n}\,X_\nu^{(b)}(2t^{\frac{1}{2}})$ | $s^{n-1}\,I_\nu(\frac{2}{s})$ | Re ν > n − 1<br>n = 0,1,2,...<br>Re s > 0 |
| 24.12 | 1 | $\mathrm{ker}(at) + i\,\mathrm{kei}(at) + \frac{\pi}{4}\,\mathrm{ber}(at) + i\frac{\pi}{4}\,\mathrm{bei}(at) + \log a\,.\,I_0(ai^{\frac{1}{2}}t)$ | $\frac{\log[s+(s^2-ia^2)^{\frac{1}{2}}]}{(s^2-ia^2)^{\frac{1}{2}}}$ | $\mathrm{Re}\,s > \frac{\lvert\mathrm{Re}\,a\rvert+\lvert\mathrm{Im}\,a\rvert}{2^{\frac{1}{2}}}$ |

| | | f(t) | g(s) | |
|---|---|---|---|---|
| 25 | 1 | $H_0(at)$ | $\dfrac{2\log\left[\dfrac{(s^2+a^2)^{\frac{1}{2}}}{s}+\dfrac{a}{s}\right]}{\pi(s^2+a^2)^{\frac{1}{2}}} = \dfrac{2\sinh^{-1}\dfrac{a}{s}}{\pi(s^2+a^2)^{\frac{1}{2}}}$ | Re $s > \lvert \text{Im } a \rvert$ |
| | 2 | $H_{\frac{1}{2}}(at)$ | $\left(\dfrac{2}{as}\right)^{\frac{1}{2}} - \dfrac{[s+(s^2+a^2)^{\frac{1}{2}}]^{\frac{1}{2}}}{a^{\frac{1}{2}}(s^2+a^2)^{\frac{1}{2}}}$ | Re $a > 0$<br>Re $s > \lvert \text{Im } a \rvert$ |
| | 3 | $H_1(at)$ | $\dfrac{2}{\pi}\left[\dfrac{1}{s} - \dfrac{s}{a(s^2+a^2)^{\frac{1}{2}}}\log\dfrac{(s^2+a^2)^{\frac{1}{2}}+a}{s}\right]$ | Re $s > \lvert \text{Im } a \rvert$ |
| | 4 | $\dfrac{1}{t}H_1(at)$ | $\dfrac{2}{\pi}\left[-1 + \dfrac{(s^2+a^2)^{\frac{1}{2}}}{a}\log\dfrac{(s^2+a^2)^{\frac{1}{2}}+a}{s}\right]$ | Re $s > \lvert \text{Im } a \rvert$ |
| | 5 | $H_2(at)$ | $\dfrac{2}{\pi}\left[-\dfrac{2}{a} + \dfrac{a}{3s^2} + \dfrac{a^2+2s^2}{a^2(s^2+a^2)^{\frac{1}{2}}}\log\dfrac{(s^2+a^2)^{\frac{1}{2}}+a}{s}\right]$ | Re $s > \lvert \text{Im } a \rvert$ |
| | 6 | $\dfrac{1}{t}H_2(at)$ | $\dfrac{2}{\pi}\left[\dfrac{s}{a} + \dfrac{a}{3s} - \dfrac{(s^2+a^2)^{\frac{1}{2}}}{a}\log\dfrac{(s^2+a^2)^{\frac{1}{2}}+a}{s}\right]$ | Re $s > \lvert \text{Im } a \rvert$ |
| | 7 | $H_3(at)$ | $\dfrac{2}{\pi}\left[\dfrac{1}{3s} + \dfrac{4s}{a^2} + \dfrac{2a^2}{15s^3}\right] - \dfrac{6a^2s+8s^3}{\pi a^3(s^2+a^2)^{\frac{1}{2}}}\log\dfrac{(s^2+a^2)^{\frac{1}{2}}+a}{s}$ | Re $s > \lvert \text{Im } a \rvert$ |
| | 8 | $\dfrac{1}{t}H_3(at)$ | $\dfrac{2}{\pi}\left[\dfrac{a^2}{15s^2} - \dfrac{4s^2}{3a^2} - \dfrac{7}{9} + \dfrac{(4s^2+a^2)(s^2+a^2)^{\frac{1}{2}}}{3a^3}\log\dfrac{(s^2+a^2)^{\frac{1}{2}}+a}{s}\right]$ | Re $s > \lvert \text{Im } a \rvert$ |
| | 9 | $H_{-n-\frac{1}{2}}(at)$ | $\dfrac{(-1)^n[(s^2+a^2)^{\frac{1}{2}}-s]^{n+\frac{1}{2}}}{a^{n+\frac{1}{2}}(s^2+a^2)^{\frac{1}{2}}}$ | $n=0,1,2,\ldots$<br>Re $s > \lvert \text{Im } a \rvert$ |
| | 10 | $L_0(at)$ | $\dfrac{2}{\pi(s^2-a^2)^{\frac{1}{2}}}\sin^{-1}\dfrac{a}{s}$ | Re $s > \lvert \text{Re } a \rvert$ |
| | 11 | $L_{\frac{1}{2}}(at)$ | $\dfrac{[s+(s^2-a^2)^{\frac{1}{2}}]^{\frac{1}{2}}}{a^{\frac{1}{2}}(s^2-a^2)^{\frac{1}{2}}} - \left(\dfrac{2}{as}\right)^{\frac{1}{2}}$ | Re $s > \lvert \text{Re } a \rvert$ |

| | | f(t) | g(s) | |
|---|---|---|---|---|
| 25 (Contd.) | 12 | $L_1(at)$ | $\frac{2}{\pi s}\left[\frac{s^2}{a(s^2-a^2)^{\frac{1}{2}}}\sin^{-1}\frac{a}{s}-1\right]$ | Re s > \|Re a\| |
| | 13 | $\frac{1}{t}L_1(at)$ | $\frac{2}{\pi}\left[1-\frac{(s^2-a^2)^{\frac{1}{2}}}{a}\sin^{-1}\frac{a}{s}\right]$ | Re s > \|Re a\| |
| | 14 | $L_2(at)$ | $\frac{2}{a\pi}\left[\frac{2s^2-a^2}{a(s^2-a^2)^{\frac{1}{2}}}\sin^{-1}\frac{a}{s}-2-\frac{a^2}{3s^2}\right]$ | Re s > \|Re a\| |
| | 15 | $\frac{1}{t}L_2(at)$ | $\frac{2}{\pi}\left[\frac{s}{a}-\frac{a}{3s}-\frac{s(s^2-a^2)^{\frac{1}{2}}}{a^2}\sin^{-1}\frac{a}{s}\right]$ | Re s > \|Re a\| |
| | 16 | $L_3(at)$ | $\frac{2}{\pi}\left[\frac{1}{3s}-\frac{4s}{a^2}-\frac{2a^2}{15s^3}+\frac{4s^3-3as}{a^3(s^2-a^2)^{\frac{1}{2}}}\sin^{-1}\frac{a}{s}\right]$ | Re s > \|Re a\| |
| | 17 | $\frac{1}{t}L_3(at)$ | $\frac{2}{\pi}\left[\frac{4s^2}{3a^2}-\frac{7}{9}-\frac{a^2}{15s^2}-\frac{(4s^2-a^2)(s^2-a^2)^{\frac{1}{2}}}{3a^3}\sin^{-1}\frac{a}{s}\right]$ | Re s > \|Re a\| |
| | 18 | $L_{-n-\frac{1}{2}}(at)$ | $\frac{[s-(s^2-a^2)^{\frac{1}{2}}]^{n+\frac{1}{2}}}{a^{n+\frac{1}{2}}(s^2-a^2)^{\frac{1}{2}}}$ | n = 0,1,2,... Re s > \|Re a\| |
| 25.2 | 1 | $t^{\frac{1}{2}}H_{\frac{1}{2}}(at)$ | $\frac{(\frac{2}{\pi})^{\frac{1}{2}}a^{\frac{3}{2}}}{s(s^2+a^2)}$ | Re s > \|Im a\| |
| | 2 | $t^{\frac{1}{2}}H_{-\frac{1}{2}}(at)$ | $\frac{(2a)^{\frac{1}{2}}}{\pi^{\frac{1}{2}}(s^2+a^2)}$ | Re s > \|Im a\| |
| | 3 | $\frac{1}{t^{\frac{1}{2}}}H_{\frac{1}{2}}(at)$ | $\frac{\log(1+\frac{a^2}{s^2})}{(2\pi a)^{\frac{1}{2}}}$ | Re s > \|Im a\| |
| | 4 | $\frac{1}{t^{\frac{1}{2}}}H_{-\frac{1}{2}}(at)$ | $(\frac{2}{\pi a})^{\frac{1}{2}}\tan^{-1}\frac{a}{s}$ | Re s > \|Im a\| |
| | 5 | $t^{\frac{1}{2}}H_{\frac{3}{2}}(at)$ | $(\frac{2a}{\pi})^{\frac{1}{2}}\left[\frac{1}{2s^2}-\frac{1}{s^2+a^2}+\frac{\log(1+\frac{a^2}{s^2})}{2a^2}\right]$ | Re s > \|Im a\| |
| | 6 | $t^{\frac{1}{2}}H_{-\frac{3}{2}}(at)$ | $(\frac{2}{a\pi})^{\frac{1}{2}}\left[\frac{s}{s^2+a^2}-\frac{1}{a}\tan^{-1}\frac{a}{s}\right]$ | Re s > \|Im a\| |

| | | f(t) | g(s) | |
|---|---|---|---|---|
| 25.2 (Contd.) | 7 | $\frac{1}{t^{\frac{1}{2}}} \mathbf{H}_{\frac{3}{2}}(at)$ | $\frac{1}{(2\pi a)^{\frac{1}{2}}}\left[\frac{a}{s} - \frac{s}{a}\log\left(1+\frac{a^2}{s^2}\right)\right]$ | Re s > \|Im a\| |
| | 8 | $t^{\frac{3}{2}}\mathbf{H}_{\frac{3}{2}}(at)$ | $(\frac{2}{\pi})^{\frac{1}{2}} a^{\frac{5}{2}} \frac{(3s^2+a^2)}{s^3(s^2+a^2)^2}$ | Re s > \|Im a\| |
| | 9 | $\frac{\mathbf{H}_\nu(t)}{t^{\frac{1}{2}}}$ | $(\frac{2}{\pi})^{\frac{1}{2}} \int_0^{\frac{\pi}{2}} \frac{\sin u\, du}{(s^2+\sin^2 u)^{\frac{1}{2}}[s+(s^2+\sin^2 u)^{\frac{1}{2}}]^{\nu+\frac{1}{2}}}$ | Re $\nu > -\frac{3}{2}$<br>Re s > o |
| | 10 | $t^{\frac{1}{2}}\mathbf{L}_{\frac{1}{2}}(at)$ | $\frac{(\frac{2}{\pi})^{\frac{1}{2}} a^{\frac{3}{2}}}{s(s^2-a^2)}$ | Re s > \|Re a\| |
| | 11 | $t^{\frac{1}{2}}\mathbf{L}_{-\frac{1}{2}}(at)$ | $\frac{(2a)^{\frac{1}{2}}}{\pi^{\frac{1}{2}}(s^2-a^2)}$ | Re s > \|Re a\| |
| | 12 | $\frac{1}{t^{\frac{1}{2}}} \mathbf{L}_{\frac{1}{2}}(at)$ | $-\frac{1}{(2\pi a)^{\frac{1}{2}}}\log(1-\frac{a^2}{s^2})$ | Re s > \|Re a\| |
| | 13 | $\frac{1}{t^{\frac{1}{2}}} \mathbf{L}_{-\frac{1}{2}}(at)$ | $(\frac{2}{a\pi})^{\frac{1}{2}} \coth^{-1} \frac{s}{a}$ | Re s > \|Re a\| |
| | 14 | $t^{\frac{1}{2}}\mathbf{L}_{\frac{3}{2}}(at)$ | $(\frac{2a}{\pi})^{\frac{1}{2}}\left[\frac{1}{s^2-a^2} - \frac{1}{2s^2} - \frac{1}{2a^2}\log(1-\frac{a^2}{s^2})\right]$ | Re s > \|Re a\| |
| | 15 | $t^{\frac{1}{2}}\mathbf{L}_{-\frac{3}{2}}(at)$ | $(\frac{2}{\pi a})^{\frac{1}{2}}\left[\frac{s}{s^2-a^2} - \frac{1}{a}\coth^{-1}\frac{s}{a}\right]$ | Re s > \|Re a\| |
| | 16 | $\frac{1}{t^{\frac{1}{2}}} \mathbf{L}_{\frac{3}{2}}(at)$ | $\frac{1}{(2\pi a)^{\frac{1}{2}}}\left[\frac{s}{a}\log(1-\frac{a^2}{s^2}) - \frac{a}{s}\right]$ | Re s > \|Re a\| |
| | 17 | $t^{\frac{3}{2}}\mathbf{L}_{\frac{3}{2}}(at)$ | $(\frac{2}{\pi})^{\frac{1}{2}} a^{\frac{5}{2}} \frac{(3s^2-a^2)}{s^2(s^2-a^2)^2}$ | Re s > \|Re a\| |
| | 18 | $\frac{\mathbf{L}_\nu(t)}{t^{\frac{1}{2}}}$ | $(\frac{2}{\pi})^{\frac{1}{2}} \int_0^{\frac{\pi}{2}} \frac{\sin u\, du}{(s^2-\sin^2 u)^{\frac{1}{2}}[s+(s^2-\sin^2 u)^{\frac{1}{2}}]^{\nu+\frac{1}{2}}}$ | Re $\nu > -\frac{3}{2}$<br>Re s > 1 |
| | 19 | $t^\nu \mathbf{L}_\nu(at)$ | $\frac{(2a)^\nu \Gamma(\nu+\frac{1}{2})}{\pi^{\frac{1}{2}}(s^2-a^2)^{\nu+\frac{1}{2}}} - \frac{\Gamma(2\nu+1)2^{\frac{1}{2}}a^\nu(a^2-s^2)^{\frac{\nu}{2}+\frac{1}{4}}}{\pi^{\frac{1}{2}}s^{\nu+\frac{1}{2}}} P^{-\nu-\frac{1}{2}}_{-\nu-\frac{1}{2}}\left(\frac{a}{s}\right)$ | Re $\nu > -\frac{1}{2}$<br>Re s > \|Re a\| |

| | | f(t) | g(s) | |
|---|---|---|---|---|
| 25.2 (Contd.) | 20 | $t^{\frac{\nu}{2}} L_{\nu}(at^{\frac{1}{2}})$ | $(\frac{a}{2})^{\nu} \frac{e^{\frac{a^2}{4s}}}{s^{\nu+1}} \mathrm{Erf}(\frac{a}{2s^{\frac{1}{2}}})$ | $\mathrm{Re}\,\nu > -\frac{3}{2}$ <br> $\mathrm{Re}\, s > 0$ |
| | 21 | $t^{\frac{\nu}{2}} L_{-\nu}(at^{\frac{1}{2}})$ | $\frac{a^{\nu}}{2^{\nu}\Gamma(\frac{1}{2}-\nu)s^{\nu+1}} e^{\frac{a^2}{4s}} \gamma(\frac{1}{2}-\nu, \frac{a^2}{4s})$ | $\mathrm{Re}\, s > 0$ |
| 25.5 | 1 | $t^{\frac{1}{2}} \int_0^{\frac{\pi}{2}} H_{\nu}(t\sin\theta) \sin^{1-\nu}\theta \, d\theta$ | $(\frac{\pi}{2})^{\frac{1}{2}} \left\{ \frac{1}{2^{\nu-\frac{1}{2}} s^{\nu+\frac{1}{2}}} - \frac{[s+(s^2+1)^{\frac{1}{2}}]^{\frac{1}{2}-\nu}}{(s^2+1)^{\frac{1}{2}}} \right\}$ | $\mathrm{Re}\, s > 1$ |
| | 2 | $t^{\frac{1}{2}} \int_0^{\frac{\pi}{2}} L_{\nu}(t\sin\theta) \sin^{1-\nu}\theta \, d\theta$ | $(\frac{\pi}{2})^{\frac{1}{2}} \left\{ \frac{[(s^2-1)^{\frac{1}{2}}+s]^{\frac{1}{2}-\nu}}{(s^2-1)^{\frac{1}{2}}} - \frac{1}{2^{\nu-\frac{1}{2}} s^{\nu+\frac{1}{2}}} \right\}$ | $\mathrm{Re}\, s > 1$ |
| 25.10 | 1 | $t[J_1(at)H_0(at) - J_0(at)H_1(at)]$ | $\frac{2a^2}{\pi s(s^2+a^2)^{\frac{3}{2}}}$ | $\mathrm{Re}\, s > \lvert \mathrm{Im}\, a \rvert$ |
| | 2 | $t[J_{\nu}(at)H'_{\nu}(at) - J'_{\nu}(at)H_{\nu}(at)]$ | $\frac{2a^{2\nu}}{\pi s(s^2+a^2)^{\nu+\frac{1}{2}}}$ | $\mathrm{Re}\,\nu > -1$ <br> $\mathrm{Re}\, s > \lvert \mathrm{Im}\, a \rvert$ |
| | 3 | $H_0(t) - Y_0(t)$ | $\frac{2}{\pi(s^2+1)^{\frac{1}{2}}} \log \frac{[s+(s^2+1)^{\frac{1}{2}}][1+(s^2+1)^{\frac{1}{2}}]}{s}$ | $\mathrm{Re}\, s > 1$ |
| 25.12 | 1 | $t[I_1(at)L_0(at) - I_0(at)L_1(at)]$ | $\frac{2a^2}{\pi s(s^2-a^2)^{\frac{3}{2}}}$ | $\mathrm{Re}\, s > \lvert \mathrm{Re}\, a \rvert$ |
| | 2 | $t[I_{\nu}(at)L'_{\nu}(at) - I'_{\nu}(at)L_{\nu}(at)]$ | $\frac{2a^{2\nu}}{\pi s(s^2-a^2)^{\nu+\frac{1}{2}}}$ | $\mathrm{Re}\,\nu > -1$ <br> $\mathrm{Re}\, s > \lvert \mathrm{Re}\, a \rvert$ |
| 25.12.2 | 1 | $t^{\frac{\nu}{2}} [I_{\nu}(at^{\frac{1}{2}}) - L_{\nu}(at^{\frac{1}{2}})]$ | $(\frac{a}{2})^{\nu} s^{-\nu-1} e^{\frac{a^2}{4s}} \mathrm{Erfc}\left(\frac{a}{2s^{\frac{1}{2}}}\right)$ | $\mathrm{Re}\,\nu > -1$ <br> $\mathrm{Re}\, s > 0$ |
| | 2 | $t^{\frac{\nu}{2}} [I_{\nu}(at^{\frac{1}{2}}) - L_{-\nu}(at^{\frac{1}{2}})]$ | $\frac{2^{\nu} e^{\frac{a^2}{4s}} \Gamma(\frac{1}{2}-\nu, \frac{a^2}{4s})}{\Gamma(\frac{1}{2}-\nu) a^{\nu} s^{\nu+1}}$ | $\mathrm{Re}\,\nu > -1$ <br> $\mathrm{Re}\, s > 0$ |
| | 3 | $t^{\nu} [I_{\nu}(at) - L_{\nu}(at)]$ | $\frac{2^{\frac{1}{2}} a^{\nu} \Gamma(2\nu+1)}{s^{\nu+\frac{1}{2}}(a^2-s^2)^{\frac{\nu}{2}+\frac{1}{4}}} P^{-\nu-\frac{1}{2}}_{-\nu-\frac{1}{2}}(\frac{a}{s})$ | $\mathrm{Re}\,\nu > -\frac{1}{2}$ <br> $\mathrm{Re}\, s > \lvert \mathrm{Re}\, a \rvert$ |

| | | f(t) | g(s) | |
|---|---|---|---|---|
| 25.12.2 (Contd.) | 4 | $t^{\nu+1}[I_\nu(at)-L_\nu(at)]$ | $\frac{2^{\frac12}\Gamma(2\nu+3)}{\pi^{\frac12}a^{\nu+2}s^{\nu+\frac12}(a^2-s^2)^{\frac{\nu}{2}+\frac34}}P^{-\nu-\frac32}_{-\nu-\frac32}(\frac{a}{s})$ | Re $\nu > -1$<br>Re $s > \lvert$Re $a\rvert$ |
| 27.2 | 1 | $\frac{1}{t^{\frac12}}D_{2n}(at^{\frac12})$ | $\frac{\Gamma(n+\frac12)(\frac{a^2}{2}-2s)^n}{(s+\frac{a^2}{4})^{n+\frac12}}$ | $n=0,1,2,\ldots$<br>Re $s > -$ Re $\frac{a^2}{4}$ |
| | 2 | $D_{2n+1}(at^{\frac12})$ | $\frac{a(-2)^n\Gamma(n+\frac32)(s-\frac{a^2}{4})^n}{(s+\frac{a^2}{4})^{n+\frac32}}$ | $n=0,1,2,\ldots$<br>Re $s > -$ Re $\frac{a^2}{4}$ |
| | 3 | $\frac{D_n[(2t)^{\frac12}]D_n[i(2t)^{\frac12}]}{t^{\frac12}}$ | $\frac{\pi^{\frac12}i^n n!P_n(\frac1s)}{s^{\frac12}}$ | $n=0,1,2,3,\ldots$<br>Re $s > 0$ |
| | 4 | $\frac{D_n[2(at)^{\frac12}]D_n[2(bt)^{\frac12}]}{t^{\frac12}}$ | $\frac{n!\pi^{\frac12}}{(s+a+b)^{\frac12}}\left(\frac{a+b-s}{a+b+s}\right)^{\frac n2}P_n\left[2\left\{\frac{ab}{(a+b)^2-s^2}\right\}^{\frac12}\right]$ | $n=0,1,2,\ldots$<br>Re $s > -$ Re$(a+b)$ |
| | 5 | $\frac{D_n(2t^{\frac12}\cos a)D_n(2t^{\frac12}\sin a)}{t^{\frac12}}$ | $2^n n!\pi^{\frac12}\frac{(1-s)^{\frac n2}}{(1+s)^{\frac{n+1}{2}}}\sum_{r=0}^{m}\frac{(-1)^r(2n-2r)!\ \sin^{n-2r}(2a)}{r!(n-r)!(n-2r)!(1-s^2)^{\frac n2-r}}$ | $n=0,1,2,\ldots$<br>$m=\frac n2$ if m is even<br>$m=\frac{n-1}{2}$ if m is odd<br>Re $s > 1$ |
| | 6 | $[D_{-n-1}(-iat^{\frac12})]^2-[D_{-n-1}(iat^{\frac12})]^2$ | $\frac{2^{\frac12}a\pi i(s-\frac{a^2}{2})^n}{n!s^{\frac12}(s+\frac{a^2}{2})^{n+1}}$ | $n=0,1,2,\ldots$<br>Re $s > 0$ |
| | 7 | $D_\nu(-at^{\frac12})-D_\nu(at^{\frac12})$ | $\frac{2^{\frac{\nu+1}{2}}\pi a(s-\frac{a^2}{4})^{\frac{\nu-1}{2}}}{\Gamma(-\frac{\nu}{2})(s+\frac{a^2}{4})^{\frac{\nu}{2}+1}}$ | Re $s > \lvert$Re $\frac{a^2}{4}\rvert$ |
| | 8 | $\frac{1}{t^{\frac12}}[D_\nu(at^{\frac12})+D_\nu(-at^{\frac12})]$ | $\frac{2^{\frac{\nu}{2}+1}\pi(s-\frac{a^2}{4})^{\frac{\nu}{2}}}{\Gamma(\frac{1-\nu}{2})(s+\frac{a^2}{4})^{\frac{\nu+1}{2}}}$ | Re $s > \lvert$Re $\frac{a^2}{4}\rvert$ |
| 27.3 | 1 | $\frac{e^{\frac t2}}{(e^t-1)^{\nu+\frac12}}\exp\left[-\frac{a^2e^{-t}}{4(1-e^{-t})}\right]D_{2\nu}\left[\frac{a}{(1-e^{-t})^{\frac12}}\right]$ | $2^{s+\nu}\Gamma(s+\nu)D_{-2s}(a)$ | $\lvert\arg a\rvert < \frac{\pi}{4}$<br>Re $s > -$ Re $\nu$ |

| | | f(t) | g(s) | |
|---|---|---|---|---|
| 27.3.1 | 1 | $e^{-\frac{at^2}{4}}[D_{2\nu}(-at)-D_{2\nu}(at)]$ | $(2\pi)^{\frac{1}{2}}\frac{s^{2\nu}}{a^{2\nu+1}}e^{\frac{s^2}{2a^2}}\frac{\Gamma(-\nu,\frac{s^2}{2a^2})}{\Gamma(-\nu)}$ | Re s > o |
| 27.3.2 | 1 | $\frac{e^{at}D_\nu(bt^{\frac{1}{2}})}{t^{\frac{\nu+1}{2}}}$ | $\frac{2^{\frac{\nu}{2}}\pi^{\frac{1}{2}}[(s+\frac{b^2}{4}-a)^{\frac{1}{2}}+(\frac{b^2}{2})^{\frac{1}{2}}]^\nu}{(s+\frac{b^2}{4}-a)^{\frac{1}{2}}}$ | Re $\nu$ < 1<br>Re s > Re $(a-\frac{b^2}{4})$ |
| | 2 | $\frac{e^{\frac{a^2t}{4}}D_\nu(at^{\frac{1}{2}})}{t^{\frac{\nu+1}{2}}}$ | $(\frac{\pi}{s})^{\frac{1}{2}}(a+2^{\frac{1}{2}}s^{\frac{1}{2}})^\nu$ | Re $\nu$ < 1<br>Re s > o if Re a $\geq$ o<br>Re s > Max o, $\frac{1}{2}$ Re $a^2$ if Re a < o |
| | 3 | $t^{\frac{\nu-1}{2}}e^{-\frac{a^2t}{4}}D_{-\nu}(at^{\frac{1}{2}})$ | $\frac{\pi^{\frac{1}{2}}[(2s+a^2)^{\frac{1}{2}}-a]^\nu}{(2s)^\nu(s+\frac{a^2}{2})^{\frac{1}{2}}}$ | Re $\nu$ > - 1<br>Re s > - $\frac{1}{2}$ Re $a^2$ |
| | 4 | $\frac{e^{at}D_\nu(bt^{\frac{1}{2}})}{t^{\frac{\nu+3}{2}}}$ | $-\frac{2^{\frac{\nu}{2}+1}\pi^{\frac{1}{2}}}{\nu+1}[(s+\frac{b^2}{4}-a)^{\frac{1}{2}}+(\frac{b^2}{2})^{\frac{1}{2}}]^{\nu+1}$ | Re $\nu$ < - 1<br>Re s > Re$(a-\frac{b^2}{4})$ |
| | 5 | $\frac{e^{\frac{a^2t}{4}}D_\nu(at^{\frac{1}{2}})}{t^{\frac{\nu+3}{2}}}$ | $\frac{(2\pi)^{\frac{1}{2}}}{\nu+1}(a+2^{\frac{1}{2}}s^{\frac{1}{2}})^{\nu+1}$ | Re $\nu$ < - 1<br>Re s > o if Re a $\geq$ o<br>Re s > Max o, $\frac{1}{2}$ Re $a^2$ if Re a < o |
| | 6 | $t^{\frac{\nu-3}{2}}e^{-\frac{a^2t}{4}}D_{-\nu}(at^{\frac{1}{2}})$ | $\frac{\pi^{\frac{1}{2}}[(2s+a^2)^{\frac{1}{2}}-a]^{\nu-1}}{(\nu-1)2^{\nu-\frac{3}{2}}s^{\nu-1}}$ | Re $\nu$ > 1<br>Re s > - $\frac{1}{2}$ Re $a^2$ |
| | 7 | $t^{\nu-1}e^{\frac{a^2t}{4}}D_{2\mu-1}(at^{\frac{1}{2}})$ | $\frac{(2\pi)^{\frac{1}{2}}\Gamma(2\nu)}{2^\nu}\frac{(s-\frac{a^2}{2})^{\frac{\mu-\nu}{2}}}{s^{\frac{\mu+\nu}{2}}}P^{\mu-\nu}_{\mu+\nu-1}\left(\frac{a}{2^{\frac{1}{2}}s^{\frac{1}{2}}}\right)$ | Re $\nu$ > o<br>Re$(\nu-\mu)$ > - 1<br>Re s > o |
| | 8 | $\frac{1}{t^\nu}e^{-\frac{a^2}{4t}}D_{2\nu-1}\left(\frac{a}{t^{\frac{1}{2}}}\right)$ | $2^{\nu-\frac{1}{2}}\pi^{\frac{1}{2}}s^{\nu-1}e^{-2^{\frac{1}{2}}as^{\frac{1}{2}}}$ | Re $a^2$ > o<br>Re s > o |
| | 9 | $t^{\nu-1}e^{\frac{a^2t}{4}}D_{2\nu+2n-1}(at^{\frac{1}{2}})$ | $\frac{\pi^{\frac{1}{2}}\Gamma(2n+2\nu)}{2^{2n-\frac{1}{2}+\nu}n!}\frac{(a^2-2s)^n}{s^{n+\nu}}$<br>$\cdot\, {}_2F_1[n+\nu,\frac{1}{2}-\nu;n+1;1-\frac{a^2}{2s}]$ | n = 0,1,2,...<br>Re $\nu$ > o<br>Re s > o |

| | | f(t) | g(s) | |
|---|---|---|---|---|
| 27.3.2 (Contd.) | 10 | $e^{at}[D_\nu(-bt^{\frac{1}{2}})-D_\nu(bt^{\frac{1}{2}})]$ | $\dfrac{2^{\frac{\nu+1}{2}}\pi b(s-a-\frac{b^2}{4})^{\frac{\nu-1}{2}}}{\Gamma(-\frac{\nu}{2})(s-a+\frac{b^2}{4})^{\frac{\nu}{2}+1}}$ | $\mathrm{Re}\, s > \mathrm{Re}(a-\frac{b^2}{4})$ |
| | 11 | $\frac{1}{t^{\frac{1}{2}}}e^{\frac{(a+b)t}{2}}D_{2n}[(2at)^{\frac{1}{2}}]D_{2m}[(2at)^{\frac{1}{2}}]$ | $\dfrac{\pi^{\frac{1}{2}}(2m+2n)!}{(-2)^{m+n}(m+n)!}\dfrac{(s-a)^n(s-b)^m}{s^{m+n+\frac{1}{2}}}$ $\cdot\, {}_2F_1[-m,-n;m-n+\frac{1}{2};\ \frac{s(s-a-b)}{(s-a)(s-b)}]$ | $m,n=0,1,2,\ldots$ $\mathrm{Re}\, s > \frac{1}{2}\mathrm{Re}(b-a)$ |
| | 12 | $\frac{1}{t^{\frac{1}{2}}}e^{\frac{(a+b)t}{2}}D_{2n+1}[(2at)^{\frac{1}{2}}]D_{2m+1}[(2at)^{\frac{1}{2}}]$ | $\dfrac{(\pi ab)^{\frac{1}{2}}(2m+2n+2)!}{2^{m+n+1}(m+n+1)!}\dfrac{(s-a)^n(s-b)^m}{s^{m+n+\frac{3}{2}}}$ ${}_2F_1[-m,-n;-m-n-\frac{1}{2};\ \frac{s(s-a-b)}{(s-a)(s-b)}]$ | $m,n=0,1,2,\ldots$ $\mathrm{Re}\, s > \frac{1}{2}\mathrm{Re}(b-a)$ |
| | 13 | $\frac{1}{t^{\frac{1}{2}}}e^{at}[D_\nu(-bt^{\frac{1}{2}})+D_\nu(bt^{\frac{1}{2}})]$ | $\dfrac{2^{\frac{\nu}{2}+1}\pi(s-a-\frac{b^2}{4})^{\frac{\nu}{2}}}{\Gamma(\frac{1-\nu}{2})(s-a+\frac{b^2}{4})^{\frac{\nu+1}{2}}}$ | $\mathrm{Re}\, s > \mathrm{Re}(a-\frac{b^2}{4})$ |
| 27.3.2.1 | 1 | $t^\nu e^{\frac{a^2t^2}{4}}D_{-\mu}(at)$ | $\dfrac{\Gamma(\nu+1)}{\Gamma(\mu)}\int_0^\infty u^{\mu-1}(s+au)^{-\nu-1}e^{-\frac{u^2}{2}}du$ $=\dfrac{s^{\mu-\nu-1}}{a^\mu}\sum_{r=0}^\infty(r!)^{-1}(\mu)_{2r}\Gamma(\nu-2r-\mu+1)\left(-\dfrac{s^2}{2a^2}\right)^r$ | $\mathrm{Re}\,\nu > -1$ $\mathrm{Re}\, s > 0$ |
| 28.2.1 | 1 | $t^{\frac{1}{2}}s_{\mu,\frac{1}{4}}(at^2)$ | $\dfrac{\Gamma(2\mu+\frac{3}{2})s^{\frac{1}{2}}}{a\,2^{2\mu+2}}S_{-\mu-1,\frac{1}{4}}\left(\dfrac{s^2}{4a}\right)$ | $\mathrm{Re}\,\mu > -\frac{3}{4}$ $\mathrm{Re}\, s > 0$ |
| 29 | 1 | $Ji_0(at)$ | $\dfrac{\sinh^{-1}(\frac{s}{a})}{s}$ $=\dfrac{1}{s}\log\left[\dfrac{s+(s^2+a^2)^{\frac{1}{2}}}{a}\right]$ | $\mathrm{Re}\, s > 0$ |
| | 2 | $Ji_\nu(at)$ | $\dfrac{1}{\nu s}\left\{1-\left[\dfrac{(s^2+a^2)^{\frac{1}{2}}-s}{a}\right]^\nu\right\}$ | $\mathrm{Re}\,\nu > 0$ $\mathrm{Re}\, s > 0$ |
| | 3 | $Ji_0(at^{\frac{1}{2}})$ | $\dfrac{Ei(-\frac{a^2}{4s})}{2s}$ | $\mathrm{Re}\, s > 0$ |

| | | f(t) | g(s) | |
|---|---|---|---|---|
| 29 (Contd.) | 4 | $Yi_0(at)$ | $\dfrac{[\sinh^{-1}(\frac{s}{a})]^2}{s} = \dfrac{1}{s}\log^2\left[\dfrac{s+(s^2+a^2)^{\frac{1}{2}}}{a}\right]$ | Re s > o |
| | 5 | $Yi_\nu(at)$ | $\dfrac{1+\cos(\nu\pi)}{s\nu\sin(\nu\pi)} - \dfrac{[(s^2+a^2)^{\frac{1}{2}}+s]^\nu + [(s^2+a^2)^{\frac{1}{2}}-s]^\nu\cos(\nu\pi)}{\nu a^\nu s\sin(\nu\pi)}$ | \|Re ν\| < 1<br>Re s > \|Im a\| |
| | 6 | $Ii_0(at)$ | $\dfrac{1}{s}\left\{\log\left[\dfrac{s+(s^2-a^2)^{\frac{1}{2}}}{a}\right] - \dfrac{\pi i}{2}\right\}$ | Re s > \|Re a\| |
| | 7 | $Ki_0(t)$ | $\dfrac{(\cosh^{-1}s)^2}{2s} + \dfrac{\pi^2}{8s} = \dfrac{\log^2[s+(s^2-1)^{\frac{1}{2}}]}{2s} + \dfrac{\pi^2}{8s}$ | Re s > o |
| | 8 | $Ki_\nu(at)$ | $\dfrac{\pi\,\mathrm{cosec}(\nu\pi)}{\nu s}\left\{\dfrac{[s+(s^2-a^2)^{\frac{1}{2}}]^\nu + [s-(s^2-a^2)^{\frac{1}{2}}]^\nu}{2a^\nu} - \cos\dfrac{\nu\pi}{2}\right\}$ | \|Re ν\| < 1<br>Re s > \|Re a\| |
| | 9 | $\pi Yi_0(at) - 2\log a\, Ji_0(at)$ | $\dfrac{\log^2 a - \log^2[s+(s^2+a^2)^{\frac{1}{2}}]}{s}$ | Re s > \|Im a\| |
| | 10 | $Ki_0(at) + \log a\, Ii_0(at)$ | $\dfrac{\log^2[s+(s^2-a^2)^{\frac{1}{2}}] - \log^2 a - i\pi\log a + \frac{\pi^2}{4}}{2s}$ | Re s > \|Re a\| |
| 30 | 1 | ${}_0F_1[\;;n+1;t]$ | $\dfrac{{}_1F_1[1;n+1;\frac{1}{s}]}{s}$ | n = 0,1,2,...<br>Re s > o |
| | 2 | ${}_1F_1[\nu;1;at]$ | $\dfrac{s^{\nu-1}}{(s-a)^\nu}$ | Re s > Max o, Re a |
| | 3 | $k_0(at)$ | $\dfrac{1}{s+a}$ | Re s > − Re a |
| | 4 | $k_{2n+2}(at)$ | $\dfrac{2a(a-s)^n}{(a+s)^{n+2}}$ | n = 0,1,2,...<br>Re s > − Re a |

| | | f(t) | g(s) | |
|---|---|---|---|---|
| 30 (Contd.) | 5 | $k_{2\nu}(at)$ | $\frac{\sin(\nu\pi)}{2\pi\nu(1-\nu)a}\ {}_2F_1[1,2;2-\nu;\ \frac{a-s}{2a}]$ | Re s > 0 |
| | 6 | $\frac{1}{t}\,k_{2m+2}(at)k_{2n+2}(at)$ | $4a^2\ \frac{(-s)^{m+n}}{(s+2a)^{m+n+2}}\ {}_2F_1\left[-m,-n;2;\ \frac{4a^2}{s^2}\right]$ | m, n = 0, 1, 2, ... <br> Re s > − 2 Re a |
| | 7 | $\frac{1}{t}\,W_{0,\nu}(at)$ | $\frac{a\pi}{2s}\ \sec(\nu\pi)P_{\nu-\frac{1}{2}}(\frac{2s}{a})$ | $\frac{1}{2}<$ Re $\nu<\frac{3}{2}$ <br> Re s > 0 |
| 30.2 | 1 | $t^{n-\frac{1}{2}}\,k_{2n+2}(at)$ | $(\frac{\pi}{a})^{\frac{1}{2}}\ \frac{(2n)!}{(n+1)!\,2^{2n+\frac{1}{2}}}\left(-\frac{1}{s+a}\right)^{n+1}P^1_{2n+1}\left[\left(\frac{s-a}{s+a}\right)^{\frac{1}{2}}\right]$ | n = 0, 1, 2, ... <br> Re s > 0 |
| | 2 | $t^b\prod_{r=1}^{n}k_{2m_r+2}(a_rt)$ | $(-1)^m2^n\left(\prod_{r=1}^{n}a_r\right)(s+a)^{-b-1-n}\,\Gamma(b+1+n)$ <br> $\cdot\ F_A\left(b+1+n;-m_1,\dots,-m_n;2,\dots,2;\ \frac{2a_1}{s+a},\dots,\frac{2a_n}{s+a}\right)$ <br> $m=\sum_{r=1}^{n}m_r\quad a=\sum_{r=1}^{n}a_r$ | Re(b+n) > − 1 <br> n = 1, 2, 3, ... <br> $m_i$ = 1, 2, 3, ... <br> Re s > 0 |
| | 3 | $t^bM_{\mu,\nu}(at)$ | $\frac{a^{\nu+\frac{1}{2}}\,\Gamma(b+\nu+\frac{3}{2})}{(s+\frac{a}{2})^{b+\nu+\frac{3}{2}}}$ <br> $\cdot\ {}_2F_1[b+\nu+\frac{3}{2},\nu-\mu+\frac{1}{2};2\nu+1;\ \frac{a}{s+\frac{a}{2}}]$ | Re(b+ν) > $-\frac{3}{2}$ <br> Re s > $\frac{1}{2}$ \|Re a\| |
| | 4 | $t^{\nu-\frac{1}{2}}\,M_{\mu,\nu}(at)$ | $a^{\nu+\frac{1}{2}}\,\Gamma(2\nu+1)\ \frac{(s-\frac{a}{2})^{\mu-\nu-\frac{1}{2}}}{(s+\frac{a}{2})^{\mu+\nu+\frac{1}{2}}}$ | Re ν > $-\frac{1}{2}$ <br> Re s > $\frac{1}{2}$ \|Re a\| |
| | 5 | $t^b\prod_{r=1}^{n}M_{\mu_r,\nu_r-\frac{1}{2}}(a_rt)$ | $\frac{\prod_{r=1}^{n}a_r^{\nu_r}\,\Gamma(b+1+U)}{(s+a)^{b+1+U}}$ <br> $\cdot\ F_A\left(b+1+U;\nu_1-\mu_1,\dots,\nu_n-\mu_n;2\nu_1,\dots,2\nu_n;\ \frac{a_1}{s+a},\dots,\frac{a_n}{s+a}\right)$ <br> $U=\sum_{r=1}^{n}\nu_r\qquad a=\frac{1}{2}\sum_{r=1}^{n}a_r$ | Re(b+U) > − 1 <br> n = 1, 2, 3, ... <br> Re$(s\pm\frac{a_1}{2}\pm\dots\pm\frac{a_n}{2})>0$ |

| | | f(t) | g(s) | |
|---|---|---|---|---|
| 30.2 (Contd.) | 6 | $t^{\nu-\frac{1}{2}} W_{\mu,\nu}(at)$ | $\dfrac{\Gamma(\mu+\nu+\frac{1}{2}) a^{\nu+\frac{1}{2}} (\frac{a}{2}-s)^{\mu-\nu-\frac{1}{2}}}{(\frac{a}{2}+s)^{\mu+\nu+\frac{1}{2}}}$ | $\mathrm{Re}\,\nu > -\frac{1}{2}$<br>$\mathrm{Re}\,s > \frac{1}{2}\,\lvert\mathrm{Re}\,a\rvert$ |
| | 7 | $t^{b}\, W_{\mu,\nu}(at)$ | $\dfrac{\Gamma(b+\nu+\frac{3}{2})\,\Gamma(b-\nu+\frac{3}{2})}{a^{b+1}\Gamma(b-\mu+2)}$<br>$\cdot\,{}_2F_1[b+\nu+\frac{3}{2}, b-\nu+\frac{3}{2}; b-\mu+2; \frac{1}{2}-\frac{s}{a}]$ | $\mathrm{Re}(b+\nu) > -\frac{3}{2}$<br>$\mathrm{Re}(b-\nu) > -\frac{3}{2}$<br>$\mathrm{Re}\,s > -\frac{1}{2}\,\mathrm{Re}\,a$ |
| | 8 | $t^{c-1}\,{}_1F_1[a;c;bt]$ | $\Gamma(c)\,s^{a-c}(s-b)^{-a}$ | $\mathrm{Re}\,c > 0$<br>$\mathrm{Re}\,b > 0$<br>$\mathrm{Re}\,s > 0$ |
| | 9 | $t^{d}\,\Phi_1(a,b,c;x,yt)$ | $\dfrac{\Gamma(d+1)}{s^{d+1}} F_1(a,b,d+1,c;x,\frac{y}{s})$ | $\mathrm{Re}\,d > -1$<br>$\mathrm{Re}\,s > \mathrm{Max}\; 0, \mathrm{Re}\,y$ |
| | 10 | $t^{c-1}\Phi_2(a,b,c;xt,yt)$ | $\dfrac{\Gamma(c)}{s^{c}(1-\frac{x}{s})^{a}(1-\frac{y}{s})^{b}}$ | $\mathrm{Re}\,c > 0$<br>$\mathrm{Re}\,s > \mathrm{Max}\; 0, \mathrm{Re}\,x, \mathrm{Re}\,y$ |
| | 11 | $t^{c-1}\Phi_2(a_1,\ldots,a_n;c;b_1 t,\ldots,b_n t)$ | $\dfrac{\Gamma(c)}{s^{c}}\left(1-\dfrac{b_1}{s}\right)^{-a_1}\cdots\left(1-\dfrac{b_n}{s}\right)^{-a_n}$ | $\mathrm{Re}\,c > 0$<br>$\mathrm{Re}\,s > \mathrm{Max}\; 0, \mathrm{Re}\,b_j\,(j=1,\ldots,n)$ |
| | 12 | $t^{d}\,\Phi_2(a,b,c;xt,y)$ | $\dfrac{\Gamma(d+1)}{s^{d+1}}\,\Xi_1(a,b,d+1,c;\frac{x}{s},y)$ | $\mathrm{Re}\,d > -1$<br>$\mathrm{Re}\,s > \mathrm{Max}\; 0, \mathrm{Re}\,x$ |
| | 13 | $t^{d}\,\Phi_2(a,b,c;xt,yt)$ | $\dfrac{\Gamma(d+1)}{s^{d+1}}\,F_1(d+1,a,b,c;\frac{x}{s},\frac{y}{s})$ | $\mathrm{Re}\,d > -1$<br>$\mathrm{Re}\,s > \mathrm{Max}\; 0, \mathrm{Re}\,x, \mathrm{Re}\,y$ |
| | 14 | $t^{a}\,\Phi_3(b,c;xt,y)$ | $\dfrac{\Gamma(a+1)}{s^{a+1}}\,\Xi_2(a+1,b,c;\frac{x}{s},y)$ | $\mathrm{Re}\,a > -1$<br>$\mathrm{Re}\,s > \mathrm{Max}\; 0, \mathrm{Re}\,x$ |
| | 15 | $t^{a}\,\Phi_3(b,c;x,yt)$ | $\dfrac{\Gamma(a+1)}{s^{a+1}}\,\Phi_2(b,a+1,c;x,\frac{y}{s})$ | $\mathrm{Re}\,a > -1$<br>$\mathrm{Re}\,s > \mathrm{Max}\; 0, \mathrm{Re}\,y$ |
| | 16 | $t^{c-1}\Phi_3(b,c;xt,yt)$ | $\dfrac{\Gamma(c)\,e^{\frac{y}{s}}}{s^{c}(1-\frac{x}{s})^{b}}$ | $\mathrm{Re}\,c > 0$<br>$\mathrm{Re}\,s > \mathrm{Max}\; 0, \mathrm{Re}\,x$ |

| | | f(t) | g(s) | |
|---|---|---|---|---|
| 0.2 (contd.) | 17 | $t^{a}\,\Phi_3(b,c;xt,yt)$ | $\frac{\Gamma(a+1)}{s^{a+1}}\,\Phi_1(a+1,b,c;\frac{x}{s},\frac{y}{s})$ | Re a > − 1<br>Re s > Max o, Re x |
| | 18 | $t^{\nu}\,\Xi_1(a,b,c,d;x,yt)$ | $\frac{\Gamma(\nu+1)}{s^{\nu+1}}\,F_3(a,b,c,\nu+1;d;x,\frac{y}{s})$ | Re ν > − 1<br>Re s > Max o, Re y |
| | 19 | $t^{d}\,\Xi_2(a,b,c;x,yt)$ | $\frac{\Gamma(d+1)}{s^{d+1}}\,\Xi_1(a,d+1,b,c;x,\frac{y}{s})$ | Re d > − 1<br>Re s > Max o, Re y |
| | 20 | $t^{\nu}\,\Psi_1(a,b,c,d;x,yt)$ | $\frac{\Gamma(\nu+1)}{s^{\nu+1}}\,F_2(a,b,\nu+1,c,d;x,\frac{y}{s})$ | Re ν > − 1<br>Re s > Max o, Re y |
| | 21 | $t^{d}\,\Psi_2(a,b,c;xt,y)$ | $\frac{\Gamma(d+1)}{s^{d+1}}\,\psi_1(a,d+1,b,c;\frac{x}{s},y)$ | Re d > − 1<br>Re s > Max o, Re x |
| | 22 | $t^{d}\,\Psi_2(a,b,c;xt,yt)$ | $\frac{\Gamma(d+1)}{s^{d+1}}\,F_4(d+1,a,b,c;\frac{x}{s},\frac{y}{s})$ | Re d > − 1<br>Re s > Max o, Re x, Re y |
| 0.2.1 | 1 | $t^{a}\,\Phi_3(b,c;x,yt^2)$ | $\frac{\Gamma(a+1)}{s^{a+1}}\;{}_1\left(\frac{a+1}{2},b,\frac{a}{2}+1,c;\frac{4y}{s^2},x\right)$ | Re a > $\frac{1}{2}$<br>Re s > 2\|Re $y^{\frac{1}{2}}$\| |
| | 2 | $t^{d}\,\Xi_2(a,b,c;x,yt^2)$ | $\frac{\Gamma(d+1)}{s^{d+1}}\,F_3\left(a,\frac{d+1}{2},b,\frac{d}{2}+1,c;x,\frac{4y}{s^2}\right)$ | Re d > $\frac{1}{2}$<br>Re s > 2\|Re $y^{\frac{1}{2}}$\| |
| 0.3 | 1 | $\frac{e^{(a+b)t}}{t}\,k_{2m+2}(at)\,k_{2n+2}(bt)$ | $4ab\,\frac{(-1)^{m+n}(m+n+1)!}{(m+1)!(n+1)!}\,\frac{(s-2a)^{m}(s-2b)^{n}}{s^{m+n+2}}$<br>$\cdot\,{}_2F_1\left[-m,-n;-m-n-1;\ \frac{s(s-2a-2b)}{(s-2a)(s-2b)}\right]$ | m,n = 0,1,2,...<br>Re s > o |
| | 2 | $e^{\frac{at}{2}}\,M_{\mu,\nu}(at)$ | $\frac{a^{\nu+\frac{1}{2}}\Gamma(\nu+\frac{3}{2})}{s^{\nu+\frac{3}{2}}}\,{}_2F_1[\nu+\frac{3}{2},\nu-\mu+\frac{1}{2};2\nu+1;\frac{a}{s}]$ | Re ν > − $\frac{3}{2}$<br>Re s > $\frac{1}{2}$\|Re a\| |
| | 3 | $(e^{t}-1)^{\nu-\frac{1}{2}}\exp(-\frac{a}{2}e^{t})$<br>$\cdot\,M_{\mu,\nu}(ae^{t}-a)$ | $\frac{\Gamma(2\nu+1)\,\Gamma(\frac{1}{2}+\mu-\nu+s)}{\Gamma(s+1)}\,W_{-\mu-\frac{s}{2},\,\nu-\frac{s}{2}}(a)$ | Re ν > − $\frac{1}{2}$<br>Re s > Re(ν−μ) − $\frac{1}{2}$ |
| | 4 | $\frac{1}{t}\,e^{-\frac{a}{2t}}\,W_{\frac{1}{2},\nu}(\frac{a}{t})$ | $\frac{2}{\pi^{\frac{1}{2}}}\,(2as)^{\frac{1}{2}}K_{\nu+\frac{1}{2}}(a^{\frac{1}{2}}s^{\frac{1}{2}})\,K_{\nu-\frac{1}{2}}(a^{\frac{1}{2}}s^{\frac{1}{2}})$ | Re a > o<br>Re s > o |

| | | f(t) | g(s) | |
|---|---|---|---|---|
| 30.3 (Contd.) | 5 | $\frac{e^{\frac{a}{2t}}}{t} W_{-\frac{1}{2},\mu}(\frac{a}{t})$ | $\frac{(a\pi^3 s)^{\frac{1}{2}}}{4\mu}\left[H^{(1)}_{\mu+\frac{1}{2}}(a^{\frac{1}{2}}s^{\frac{1}{2}})H^{(2)}_{\mu-\frac{1}{2}}(a^{\frac{1}{2}}s^{\frac{1}{2}}) + H^{(1)}_{\mu-\frac{1}{2}}(a^{\frac{1}{2}}s^{\frac{1}{2}})H^{(2)}_{\mu+\frac{1}{2}}(a^{\frac{1}{2}}s^{\frac{1}{2}})\right]$ | $\lvert \arg a \rvert < \pi$<br>Re $s > 0$ |
| | 6 | $\frac{e^t}{(e^t-1)^{\mu+1}} \exp\left[-\frac{a}{2(e^t-1)}\right] W_{\mu,\nu}\left(\frac{a}{e^t-1}\right)$ | $\frac{1}{a}\Gamma(\mu+s)\, W_{-s,\nu}(a)$ | Re $a > 0$<br>Re $s > -$ Re $\mu$ |
| | 7 | $(1-e^{-t})^{-\mu} \exp\left[-\frac{a}{2(e^t-1)}\right] W_{\mu,\nu}\left[\frac{a}{e^t-1}\right]$ | $\frac{\Gamma(\frac{1}{2}+\nu+s)\Gamma(\frac{1}{2}-\nu+s)}{\Gamma(1-\mu+s)} e^{\frac{a}{2}} W_{-s,\nu}(a)$ | Re $a > 0$<br>$\mathrm{Re}(\frac{1}{2} \pm \nu+s) > 0$ |
| 30.3.1 | 1 | $e^{-at^2} k_{2n}(at^2)$ | $(-1)^{n-1} \frac{s^{n-\frac{3}{2}} e^{\frac{s^2}{16a}}}{2^{\frac{3n}{2}+\frac{1}{4}} a^{\frac{n}{2}-\frac{1}{4}}} W_{-\frac{3}{4}-\frac{n}{2},\frac{1}{4}-\frac{n}{2}}\left(\frac{s^2}{8a}\right)$ | $n = 0,1,2,\ldots$<br>Re $s > -\infty$ |
| 30.3.2 | 1 | $t^{-\frac{1}{2}} e^{-at^{\frac{1}{2}}} k_{2n}(at^{\frac{1}{2}})$ | $\frac{e^{\frac{a^2}{2s}}}{a} \sum_{r=0}^{n-1} (-1)^r \binom{n-1}{r} \left(\frac{2a^2}{s}\right)^{\frac{n+1-r}{2}} \cdot D_{-n+r-1}\left(\frac{2^{\frac{1}{2}}a}{s^{\frac{1}{2}}}\right)$ | $n = 1,2,3,\ldots$<br>Re $s > 0$ |
| | 2 | $t^{\mu-1} e^{at}\, {}_1F_1[\nu;\mu;bt]$ | $\Gamma(\mu)\, \frac{(s-a)^{\nu-\mu}}{(s-a-b)^{\nu}}$ | Re $\mu > 0$<br>Re $s >$ Max Re$(a+b)$, Re a |
| | 3 | $\frac{t^{c-1} e^{-t}}{(1-b)^{2a}}\, {}_1F_1[a;c;-\frac{4bt}{(1-b)^2}]$ | $\frac{\Gamma(c)}{(s+1)^c}\left(1-2\,\frac{s-1}{s+1}\, b+b^2\right)^{-a}$ | Re $c > 0$<br>Re $s >$ Max $-1$, $-$Re $\left(\frac{1+b}{1-b}\right)$ |
| | 4 | $\frac{e^{-\frac{at}{2}} M_{\mu,\frac{1}{4}}(at)}{t^{\frac{1}{4}}}$ | $\frac{a^{\frac{3}{4}} \pi^{\frac{1}{2}} s^{\mu-\frac{3}{4}}}{2(s+a)^{\mu+\frac{1}{4}}}$ | Re $s >$ Max $0$, $-$ Re a |
| | 5 | $\frac{e^{-\frac{at}{2}} M_{\mu,-\frac{1}{4}}(at)}{t^{\frac{3}{4}}}$ | $\frac{a^{\frac{1}{4}}\pi^{\frac{1}{2}} s^{\mu-\frac{1}{4}}}{(s+a)^{\mu+\frac{1}{4}}}$ | Re $s >$ Max $0$, $-$ Re a |
| | 6 | $\frac{e^{\frac{at}{2}} M_{-\frac{1}{4},\frac{n}{2}+\frac{1}{4}}(at)}{t^{\frac{5}{4}}}$ | $\frac{4a^{\frac{1}{4}}\Gamma(n+\frac{3}{2})}{n\Gamma(\frac{n}{2})} Q_n[(\frac{s}{a})^{\frac{1}{2}}]$ | $n = 1,2,3,\ldots$<br>Re $s > \lvert$Re a$\rvert$ |

| | | f(t) | g(s) | |
|---|---|---|---|---|
| 30.3.2 (Contd.) | 7 | $t^{\nu-\frac{1}{2}} e^{at} M_{\mu,\nu}(bt)$ | $\dfrac{b^{\nu+\frac{1}{2}}\Gamma(2\nu+1)(s-a-\frac{b}{2})^{\mu-\nu-\frac{1}{2}}}{(s-a+\frac{b}{2})^{\mu+\nu+\frac{1}{2}}}$ | $\operatorname{Re}\nu > -\frac{1}{2}$<br>$\operatorname{Re} s > \operatorname{Re}(a \pm \frac{b}{2})$ |
| | 8 | $t^{\nu-\frac{1}{2}} e^{\frac{at}{2}} M_{n+\nu+\frac{1}{2},\nu}(at)$ | $\dfrac{a^{\nu+\frac{1}{2}}\Gamma(2\nu+1)(s-a)^{n}}{s^{n+2\nu+1}}$ | $\operatorname{Re}\nu > -\frac{1}{2}$<br>$\operatorname{Re} s > 0$ |
| | 9 | $t^{\frac{a}{2}} e^{\frac{at}{2}} M_{\mu,\nu}(at)$ | $\dfrac{a^{\nu+\frac{1}{2}}\Gamma(\frac{a}{2}+\nu+\frac{3}{2})}{s^{\frac{a}{2}+\nu+\frac{3}{2}}}\ {}_2F_1\left[\frac{a}{2}+\nu+\frac{3}{2}, \nu-\mu+\frac{1}{2}; 2\nu+1; \frac{a}{s}\right]$ | $\operatorname{Re}(\frac{a}{2}+\nu) > -\frac{3}{2}$<br>$\operatorname{Re} s > \frac{1}{2}\lvert\operatorname{Re} a\rvert$ |
| | 10 | $\dfrac{1}{t^{\nu}} e^{\frac{a^2}{2t}} W_{\nu,\nu}(\frac{a^2}{t})$ | $\dfrac{a\pi^{\frac{1}{2}}\Gamma(2\nu+\frac{1}{2})}{s^{\nu+\frac{1}{2}}}[\mathbf{H}_{2\nu}(2as^{\frac{1}{2}})-Y_{2\nu}(2as^{\frac{1}{2}})]$ | $\operatorname{Re} s > 0$ |
| | 11 | $t^{3\nu-\frac{1}{2}} e^{\frac{a}{2t}} W_{\nu,\nu}(\frac{a}{t})$ | $\dfrac{\Gamma(2\nu+\frac{1}{2})a^{\nu+\frac{1}{2}}}{2s^{2\nu}} H^{(1)}_{2\nu}(a^{\frac{1}{2}}s^{\frac{1}{2}}) H^{(2)}_{2\nu}(a^{\frac{1}{2}}s^{\frac{1}{2}})$ | $\lvert\arg a\rvert < \pi$<br>$\operatorname{Re}\nu > -\frac{1}{4}$<br>$\operatorname{Re} s > 0$ |
| | 12 | $\dfrac{e^{-\frac{a}{2t}}}{t^{3\nu+\frac{1}{2}}} W_{\nu,\nu}(\frac{a}{t})$ | $\dfrac{2s^{2\nu}}{\pi^{\frac{1}{2}}a^{\nu-\frac{1}{2}}}[K_{2\nu}(a^{\frac{1}{2}}s^{\frac{1}{2}})]^2$ | $\operatorname{Re} a > 0$<br>$\operatorname{Re} s > 0$ |
| | 13 | $t^{\mu} e^{\frac{a}{2t}} W_{\mu,\nu}(\frac{a}{t})$ | $\dfrac{a^{\frac{1}{2}}}{2^{2\mu-1}s^{\mu+\frac{1}{2}}} S_{2\mu,2\nu}(2a^{\frac{1}{2}}s^{\frac{1}{2}})$ | $\lvert\arg a\rvert < \pi$<br>$\operatorname{Re}(\mu\pm\nu) > -\frac{1}{2}$<br>$\operatorname{Re} s > 0$ |
| | 14 | $\dfrac{1}{t^{\mu}} e^{-\frac{a}{2t}} W_{\mu,\nu}(\frac{a}{t})$ | $2a^{\frac{1}{2}}s^{\mu-\frac{1}{2}} K_{2\nu}(2a^{\frac{1}{2}}s^{\frac{1}{2}})$ | $\operatorname{Re} a > 0$<br>$\operatorname{Re} s > 0$ |
| | 15 | $t^{b} e^{-\frac{at}{2}} W_{\mu,\nu}(at)$ | $a^{1-b}\,{}_2F_1[b+\nu+\frac{3}{2}, b-\nu+\frac{3}{2}; b-\mu+2; -\frac{s}{a}]$ | $\operatorname{Re} s > -\frac{1}{2}\operatorname{Re} a$ |
| 30.3.2.1 | 1 | $t^{2\nu-1} e^{-\frac{t^2}{2a}} M_{-3\nu,\nu}(\frac{t^2}{a})$ | $\dfrac{\Gamma(4\nu+1)}{2\pi^{\frac{1}{2}}a^{\nu}s^{4\nu}} e^{\frac{as^2}{8}} K_{2\nu}(\frac{as^2}{8})$ | $\operatorname{Re} a > 0$<br>$\operatorname{Re}\nu > -\frac{1}{4}$<br>$\operatorname{Re} s > 0$ |
| | 2 | $t^{2\nu-1} e^{-\frac{t^2}{2a}} M_{\mu,\nu}(\frac{t^2}{a})$ | $\dfrac{\Gamma(4\nu+1)a^{\frac{\mu+\nu-1}{2}} s^{\mu-\nu-1}}{2^{\mu+3\nu}} e^{\frac{as^2}{8}} \cdot W_{-\frac{\mu+3\nu}{2},\frac{\mu-\nu}{2}}\left(\frac{as^2}{4}\right)$ | $\operatorname{Re} a > 0$<br>$\operatorname{Re}\nu > -\frac{1}{4}$<br>$\operatorname{Re} s > 0$ |

| | | f(t) | g(s) | |
|---|---|---|---|---|
| 31.2 | 1 | $t^{a-1}{}_2F_1[-n,n+b;a;t]$ | $\frac{\Gamma(a)}{s^a} A_n(b,\frac{1}{s})$ | $n=0,1,2,\ldots$ Re $s>0$ |
| | 2 | $t^{\nu-1}{}_2F_1[1,\frac{1}{2};\nu;-\frac{t}{a}]$ | $(\pi a)^{\frac{1}{2}}\Gamma(\nu)s^{-\nu+\frac{1}{2}}e^{as}\mathrm{Erfc}[(as)^{\frac{1}{2}}]$ | Re $\nu>0$ $\lvert\arg a\rvert<\pi$ Re $s>0$ |
| | 3 | $t^{c-1}{}_2F_1[a,b;c;-ht]$ | $\Gamma(c)s^{-c}(\frac{s}{h})^{\frac{a+b-1}{2}}e^{\frac{s}{2h}}W_{\frac{1-a-b}{2},\frac{a-b}{2}}\left(\frac{s}{2h}\right)$ | Re $c>0$ $\lvert\arg h\rvert<\pi$ Re $s>0$ |
| | 4 | $t^{\nu}{}_2F_1[a,b;c;-ht]$ | $\frac{\Gamma(c)}{\Gamma(a)\Gamma(b)}s^{-\nu-1}E(a,b,\nu+1:c:\frac{s}{h})$ | Re $\nu>-1$ $\lvert\arg h\rvert<\pi$ Re $s>0$ |
| 31.2.1 | 1 | $t^{\nu}(1+ht)^{a+b-c}{}_2F_1[a,b;c;-ht]$ | $\frac{\Gamma(c)}{\Gamma(c-a)\Gamma(c-b)s^{\nu+1}}E[c-a,c-b,\nu+1:c:\frac{s}{h})$ | Re $\nu>-1$ $\lvert\arg h\rvert<\pi$ Re $s>0$ |
| | 2 | $\frac{{}_2F_1\left[\nu,\nu;1;\frac{t(a+b+t)}{(a+t)(b+t)}\right]}{[(a+t)(b+t)]^{\nu}}$ | $\frac{e^{\frac{a+b}{2}s}K_{\nu-\frac{1}{2}}\left(\frac{as}{2}\right)K_{\nu-\frac{1}{2}}\left(\frac{bs}{2}\right)}{\pi(ab)^{\nu-\frac{1}{2}}}$ | $\lvert\arg a\rvert<\pi$ $\lvert\arg b\rvert<\pi$ $\lvert\arg as\rvert<\pi$ $\lvert\arg bs\rvert<\pi$ Re $s>0$ |
| | 3 | $\frac{\left(1+\frac{a}{t}\right)^{\mu}\left(1+\frac{b}{t}\right)^{\nu}}{t^{\frac{1}{2}}}{}_2F_1\left[-\mu,-\nu;\frac{1}{2}-\mu-\nu;\frac{t(a+b+t)}{(a+t)(b+t)}\right]$ | $\frac{\Gamma(\frac{1}{2}-\mu-\nu)e^{\frac{a+b}{2}s}}{2^{\mu+\nu}s^{\frac{1}{2}}}D_{2\mu}\left[(2as)^{\frac{1}{2}}\right]\cdot D_{2\nu}\left[(2bs)^{\frac{1}{2}}\right]$ | $\lvert\arg a\rvert<\pi$ $\lvert\arg b\rvert<\pi$ Re$(\mu+\nu)<1$ $\lvert\arg as\rvert<\pi$ $\lvert\arg bs\rvert<\pi$ Re $s>0$ |
| | 4 | $\frac{t^{c-1}}{(a+t)^{\mu}(b+t)^{\nu}}{}_2F_1[\mu,\nu;c;\frac{t(a+b+t)}{(a+t)(b+t)}]$ | $\Gamma(c)(ab)^{\frac{c-\mu-\nu-1}{2}}\frac{1}{s}e^{\frac{a+b}{2}s}\cdot W_{\frac{-\mu+\nu-c+1}{2},\frac{\mu+\nu-c}{2}}(as)\cdot W_{\frac{\mu-\nu-c+1}{2},\frac{\mu+\nu-c}{2}}(bs)$ | $\lvert\arg a\rvert<\pi$ $\lvert\arg b\rvert<\pi$ Re $c>0$ $\lvert\arg as\rvert<\pi$ $\lvert\arg bs\rvert<\pi$ Re $s>0$ |
| 31.3 | 1 | $(1-e^{-t})^{\nu}{}_2F_1[-n,\nu+b+n;b;e^{-t}]$ | $\frac{B(s,\nu+n+1)B(s,b+n-s)}{B(s,b-s)}$ | Re $\nu>-1$ Re $s>0$ |

| | | f(t) | g(s) | |
|---|---|---|---|---|
| 1.3 (Contd.) | 2 | $(1-e^{-t})^{\nu}{}_2F_1[a,b;c;he^{-t}]$ | $B(s,\nu+1)\,{}_3F_2\left[\begin{matrix}a,b,s;\\c,s+\nu+1;\end{matrix}\,h\right]$ | Re $\nu > -1$<br>$\lvert\arg(1-h)\rvert < \pi$<br>Re $s > 0$ |
| | 3 | $(1-e^{-t})^{c-1}{}_2F_1[a,b;c;h(1-e^{-t})]$ | $B(s,c)\,{}_2F_1[a,b;s+c;h]$ | Re $c > 0$<br>$\lvert\arg(1-h)\rvert < \pi$<br>Re $s > 0$ |
| | 4 | $(1-e^{-t})^{c-1}{}_2F_1[a,b;c;1-e^{-t}]$ | $\frac{\Gamma(s)\Gamma(c-a-b+s)\Gamma(c)}{\Gamma(c-a+s)\Gamma(c-b+s)}$ | Re $c > 0$<br>Re $s >$ Max $0$, Re$(a+b-c)$ |
| | 5 | $e^{-at}(1-e^{-t})^{b-a-n-1}{}_2F_1[-n,b-c-n;b-a-n;1-e^{-t}]$ | $\frac{\Gamma(b-a-n)\Gamma(s+a)(s+c)_n}{\Gamma(s+b)}$ | Re$(b-a) > n$<br>$n = 0,1,2,\ldots$<br>Re $s > -$ Re $a$ |
| | 6 | $e^{-ht}(1-e^{-t})^{c-1}{}_2F_1[a,b;c;1-e^{-t}]$ | $\frac{\Gamma(c)\Gamma(s+h)\Gamma(s+c+h-b-a)}{\Gamma(s+c+h-a)\Gamma(s+c+h-b)}$ | Re $c > 0$<br>Re $s >$ Max $-$ Re $h$, Re$(a+b-c-h)$ |
| | 7 | $(1-e^{-t})^{\nu}{}_2F_1[a,b;c;h(1-e^{-t})]$ | $B(s,\nu+1)\,{}_3F_2\left[\begin{matrix}a,b,\nu+1;\\c,s+\nu+1;\end{matrix}\,h\right]$ | Re $\nu > -1$<br>$\lvert\arg(1-h)\rvert < \pi$<br>Re $s > 0$ |
| | 1 | ${}_0F_2\left[\begin{matrix};\\\frac{1}{2},1;\end{matrix}\,-t\right]$ | $\frac{1}{s}\cos\frac{2}{s^{\frac{1}{2}}}$ | Re $s > 0$ |
| | 2 | ${}_pF_q\left[\begin{matrix}(a);\\(b);\end{matrix}\,ct\right]$ | $\frac{1}{s}\,{}_{p+1}F_q\left[\begin{matrix}(a),1;\\(b);\end{matrix}\,\frac{c}{s}\right]$ | $q \geq p$<br>Re $s > \lvert$Re $c\rvert$ |
| | 3 | $t^{\mu}{}_0F_2\left[\begin{matrix};\\\mu+1,\frac{3}{2};\end{matrix}\,-t\right]$ | $\frac{\Gamma(\mu+1)\sin\frac{2}{s^{\frac{1}{2}}}}{2s^{\mu+\frac{1}{2}}}$ | Re $\mu > -1$<br>Re $s > 0$ |
| | 4 | ${}_2F_2\left[\begin{matrix}-n,n+1;\\1,1;\end{matrix}\,ct\right]$ | $sP_n(1-\frac{2c}{s})$ | $n = 0,1,2,\ldots$<br>Re $s > 0$ |
| | 5 | ${}_pF_{q+1}\left[\begin{matrix}(a);\\(b),1;\end{matrix}\,ct\right]$ | $\frac{1}{s}\,{}_pF_q\left[\begin{matrix}(a);\\(b);\end{matrix}\,\frac{c}{s}\right]$ | $q \geq p-1$<br>Re $s > \lvert$Re $c\rvert$ |

| | | f(t) | g(s) | |
|---|---|---|---|---|
| 32 (Contd.) | 6 | $\sum_{i,-i} \frac{1}{i} E\left(a, a+\frac{1}{m}, \ldots, a+\frac{m-1}{m} :: \frac{b e^{i\pi}}{m^m t}\right)$ | $\frac{(2\pi)^{\frac{1+m}{2}}}{m^{\frac{1}{2}+ma}} b^a s^{a-1} e^{-b^{\frac{1}{m}} s^{\frac{1}{m}}}$ | Re a > 0<br>Re b > 0<br>m = 2,3,4,...<br>Re s > 0 |
| | | $\sum_{i,-i}$ denotes that in the expression following the Σ sign i is to be replaced by -i and the two expressions are to be added. | | |
| | 7 | $\sum_{i,-i} \frac{1}{i} E\left[\Delta(n;n\nu), \Delta(n;-n\nu) : \Delta(n;\tfrac{1}{2}) : \frac{a e^{i\pi}}{n^n t}\right]$ | $2^{\frac{n+1}{2}} \pi^{\frac{n}{2}} s^{-1} e^{-\frac{1}{2} a^{\frac{1}{n}} s^{\frac{1}{n}}} K_{n\nu}\left(\frac{a^{\frac{1}{n}} s^{\frac{1}{n}}}{2}\right)$ | n = 2,3,4,...<br>Re a > 0<br>Re s > 0 |
| | | $\Delta(n;\alpha)$ represents the set of parameters $\frac{\alpha}{n}, \frac{\alpha+1}{n}, \ldots, \frac{\alpha+n-1}{n}$<br>For defitition of $\sum_{i,-i}$ see preceding entry. | | |
| 32.1 | 1 | ${}_0F_2\left[\begin{matrix} ; \\ 1, \frac{2}{3} ; \end{matrix} - a^3 t^3\right]$ | $\frac{1}{(s^3+27a^3)^{\frac{1}{3}}}$ | Re s > Max − 3 Re a, $\frac{3 \text{ Re } a + 3^{\frac{3}{2}} \lvert \text{Im } a \rvert}{2}$ |
| | 2 | ${}_0F_n\left[\begin{matrix} ; \\ \frac{1}{n}, \frac{2}{n}, \ldots, \frac{n-1}{n}, 1 ; \end{matrix} \left(\frac{t}{n}\right)^n\right]$ | $\frac{1}{s} e^{s^{-n}}$ | n = 1,2,3,...<br>Re s > 0 |
| | 3 | ${}_pF_q\left[\begin{matrix} (a) ; \\ (b) ; \end{matrix} (ct)^2\right]$ | $\frac{1}{s}\, {}_{p+2}F_q\left[\begin{matrix} (a), 1, \frac{1}{2} ; \\ (b) ; \end{matrix} \frac{4c^2}{s^2}\right]$ | q ≥ p + 1<br>Re s > 2\|Re c\| |
| 32.2 | 1 | $t^{\frac{1}{2}}\, {}_0F_2\left[\begin{matrix} ; \\ \frac{3}{2}, \frac{3}{2} ; \end{matrix} - t\right]$ | $\frac{\pi^{\frac{1}{2}} \sin \frac{2}{s^{\frac{1}{2}}}}{4s}$ | Re s > 0 |
| | 2 | $t^b\, {}_0F_2\left[\begin{matrix} ; \\ b+1, \frac{3}{2} ; \end{matrix} - \frac{t}{a}\right]$ | $\frac{a^{\frac{1}{2}} \Gamma(b+1) \sin \frac{2}{a^{\frac{1}{2}} s^{\frac{1}{2}}}}{2 s^{b+\frac{1}{2}}}$ | Re b > − 1<br>Re s > 0 |
| | 3 | $t^b\, {}_0F_2\left[\begin{matrix} ; \\ b+1, \frac{1}{2} ; \end{matrix} - \frac{t}{a}\right]$ | $\frac{\Gamma(b+1) \cos \frac{2}{a^{\frac{1}{2}} s^{\frac{1}{2}}}}{s^{b+1}}$ | Re b > − 1<br>Re s > 0 |
| | 4 | $t^{\mu-1}\, {}_0F_2\left[\begin{matrix} ; \\ \mu, \nu ; \end{matrix} - at\right]$ | $\frac{\Gamma(\mu)\Gamma(\nu)}{a^{\frac{\nu-1}{2}} s^{\mu-\frac{\nu-1}{2}}} J_{\nu-1}\left(\frac{2a^{\frac{1}{2}}}{s^{\frac{1}{2}}}\right)$ | Re μ > 0<br>Re s > 0 |

| | | f(t) | g(s) | |
|---|---|---|---|---|
| 32.2 (Contd.) | 5 | $t^{\mu-1}{}_1F_2\left[\begin{matrix}1; \\ \mu,\nu;\end{matrix}\ at\right]$ | $\frac{(\nu-1)\Gamma(\mu)}{a^{\nu-1}} s^{\nu-\mu-1} e^{\frac{a}{s}} \gamma(\nu-1, \frac{a}{s})$ | Re $\nu > 1$<br>Re$(\nu-\mu) > 1$<br>Re $s > 0$ |
| | 6 | $t^{\nu-1}{}_1F_2\left[\begin{matrix}-n; \\ \mu,\nu;\end{matrix}\ at\right]$ | $\frac{n!\Gamma(\nu)}{\mu_n s^{\nu}} L_n^{\mu-1}(\frac{a}{s})$ | Re $\nu > 0$<br>$n = 0,1,2,...$<br>Re $s > 0$ |
| | 7 | $t^{\mu-1}{}_1F_2\left[\begin{matrix}\frac{\nu}{2}; \\ \nu,\mu;\end{matrix}\ at\right]$ | $\frac{2^{\nu-1}\Gamma(\frac{\nu+1}{2})\Gamma(\mu)}{a^{\frac{\nu-1}{2}} s^{\mu-\frac{\nu}{2}+\frac{1}{2}}} e^{\frac{a}{2s}} I_{\nu-\frac{1}{2}}(\frac{a}{2s})$ | Re $\mu > 0$<br>Re $s > 0$ |
| | 8 | $t^{a-1}{}_2F_2\left[\begin{matrix}-n,n; \\ a,\frac{1}{2};\end{matrix}\ t\right]$ | $\frac{\Gamma(a)}{s^a}\cos[2n \sin^{-1}(\frac{1}{s^{\frac{1}{2}}})]$ | $n = 0,1,2,...$<br>Re $a > 0$<br>Re $s > 0$ |
| | 9 | $t^{a-1}{}_2F_2\left[\begin{matrix}-n,n+1; \\ 1, \quad a;\end{matrix}\ t\right]$ | $\frac{\Gamma(a)}{s^a} P_n(1-\frac{2}{s})$ | Re $a > 0$<br>Re $s > 0$ |
| | 10 | $t^{a-1}{}_2F_2\left[\begin{matrix}-n,n+1; \\ a, \frac{3}{2};\end{matrix}\ t\right]$ | $\frac{\Gamma(a)}{(2n+1)s^a}\sin[(2n+1)\sin^{-1}(\frac{1}{s^{\frac{1}{2}}})]$ | $n = 0,1,2,...$<br>Re $a > 0$<br>Re $s > 0$ |
| | 11 | $t^{a-1}{}_2F_2\left[\begin{matrix}-n,a+n; \\ a, \quad b;\end{matrix}\ t\right]$ | $\frac{\Gamma(a)}{s^a}{}_2F_1[-n,a+n;b;\frac{1}{s}]$ | Re $a > 0$<br>$n = 0,1,2,...$<br>Re $s > 0$ |
| | 12 | $t^{a-1}{}_2F_2\left[\begin{matrix}-n,n+2\nu; \\ \nu+\frac{1}{2}, \ a;\end{matrix}\ t\right]$ | $n B(n,2\nu)\frac{\Gamma(a)}{s^a} C_n^{\nu}(1-\frac{2}{s})$ | Re $a > 0$<br>$n = 0,1,2,...$<br>Re $s > 0$ |
| | 13 | $t^{\mu-1}{}_2F_2\left[\begin{matrix}\nu,\nu+\frac{1}{2}; \\ 2\nu+\frac{1}{2}, \ \mu;\end{matrix}\ at\right]$ | $\frac{2^{2\nu}\Gamma(2\nu+\frac{1}{2})\Gamma(\mu)}{a^{\nu}\pi^{\frac{1}{2}}\Gamma(2\nu)s^{\mu-\nu}} Q_{2\nu-1}\left[\left(\frac{s}{a}\right)^{\frac{1}{2}}\right]$ | Re $\mu > 0$<br>Re $s > 0$ |
| | 14 | $t^{b_q-1}{}_pF_q\left[\begin{matrix}a_1,\dots,a_p; \\ b_1,\dots,b_q;\end{matrix}\ kt\right]$ | $\frac{\Gamma(b_q)}{s^{b_q}}{}_pF_{q-1}\left[\begin{matrix}a_1,\dots,a_p; \\ b_1,\dots,b_{q-1};\end{matrix}\ \frac{k}{s}\right]$ | $p \leq q$<br>Re $b_q > 0$<br>Re $s > 0$ if $p < q$<br>Re $s >$ Re $k$ if $p=q$ |

| | | f(t) | g(s) | |
|---|---|---|---|---|
| 32.2 (Contd.) | 15 | $t^c {}_pF_q\left[\begin{matrix}(a); \\ (b);\end{matrix} kt\right]$ | $\frac{\Gamma(c+1)}{s^{c+1}} {}_{p+1}F_q\left[\begin{matrix}(a), c+1; \\ (b) \;\; ;\end{matrix} \frac{k}{s}\right]$ | $p \leqslant q$<br>$\mathrm{Re}\, c > 1$<br>$\mathrm{Re}\, s > 0$ if $p < q$<br>$\mathrm{Re}\, s > \mathrm{Re}\, k$ if $p = q$ |
| | 16 | $\frac{1}{t^{\frac{1}{2}}} {}_{2p}F_{2q}\left[\begin{matrix}\frac{a_1}{2}, \frac{a_1+1}{2}, \ldots, \frac{a_p}{2}, \frac{a_p+1}{2}; \\ \frac{b_1}{2}, \frac{b_1+1}{2}, \ldots, \frac{b_q}{2}, \frac{b_q+1}{2};\end{matrix} -2^{p-q-2}\frac{k^2}{t}\right]$ | $\left(\frac{\pi}{s}\right)^{\frac{1}{2}} {}_pF_q\left[\begin{matrix}a_1, \ldots, a_p; \\ b_1, \ldots, b_q;\end{matrix} -ks^{\frac{1}{2}}\right]$ | $k > 0$<br>$p \leqslant q$<br>$\mathrm{Re}\, s > 0$ |
| | 17 | $\frac{1}{t^{2\nu+1}} S_1(\nu, \nu-\frac{1}{2}, -\nu-\frac{1}{2}, \nu+\frac{1}{2}; at)$ | $\frac{s^{2\nu}}{2^{2\nu+\frac{3}{2}}\pi^{\frac{1}{2}}} \mathbf{H}_{2\nu}\left(\frac{4a}{s}\right)$ | $\mathrm{Re}\, s > 0$ |
| | 18 | $\frac{1}{t^{2\mu+1}} S_1(\nu-\frac{1}{2}, -\nu-\frac{1}{2}, \mu, \mu+\frac{1}{2}; at)$ | $\frac{s^{2\mu}}{2^{2\mu+1}\pi^{\frac{1}{2}}} J_{2\nu}\left(\frac{4a}{s}\right)$ | $\mathrm{Re}(\nu-\mu) > 0$<br>$\mathrm{Re}\, s > 0$ |
| | 19 | $\frac{1}{t^{2\nu}} S_1(\nu, \nu-\frac{1}{2}, -\nu-\frac{1}{2}, \nu-\frac{1}{2}; at)$ | $\frac{s^{2\nu-1}}{2^{2\nu+\frac{1}{2}}\pi^{\frac{1}{2}}} \mathbf{H}_{2\nu}\left(\frac{4a}{s}\right)$ | $\mathrm{Re}\, s > 0$ |
| | 20 | $\frac{1}{t^{2\nu}} S_2(\nu, \nu-\frac{1}{2}, -\nu-\frac{1}{2}, \nu-\frac{1}{2}; at)$ | $\frac{\pi^{\frac{1}{2}} s^{2\nu-1}}{2^{2\nu}}\left[I_{2\nu}\left(\frac{4a}{s}\right) - \mathbf{L}_{2\nu}\left(\frac{4a}{s}\right)\right]$ | $\mathrm{Re}\, s > 0$ |
| | 21 | $\frac{1}{t^{2\nu}} S_2(\nu, -\nu-\frac{1}{2}, \nu-\frac{1}{2}, \nu-\frac{1}{2}; at)$ | $\frac{\pi^{\frac{1}{2}}}{2^{2\nu}} \sec(2\nu\pi) s^{2\nu-1}\left[I_{-2\nu}\left(\frac{4a}{s}\right) - \mathbf{L}_{2\nu}\left(\frac{4a}{s}\right)\right]$ | $\mathrm{Re}\, \nu < \frac{1}{2}$<br>$\mathrm{Re}\, s > 0$ |
| | 22 | $\frac{1}{t^{2\nu+1}} S_2(\nu, -\nu-\frac{1}{2}, \nu-\frac{1}{2}, \nu+\frac{1}{2}; at)$ | $\frac{\pi^{\frac{1}{2}}}{2^{2\nu+1}} \sec(2\nu\pi) s^{2\nu}\left[I_{-2\nu}\left(\frac{4a}{s}\right) - \mathbf{L}_{2\nu}\left(\frac{4a}{s}\right)\right]$ | $\mathrm{Re}\, \nu < 0$<br>$\mathrm{Re}\, s > 0$ |
| | 23 | $\frac{1}{t^{2\mu+1}} S_2(\nu, -\nu-1, \mu+\frac{1}{2}, \mu; at)$ | $\pi^{-\frac{1}{2}}\left(\frac{s}{2}\right)^{2\mu} K_{2\nu+1}\left(\frac{4a}{s}\right)$ | $\mathrm{Re}(\mu+\nu) < -\frac{1}{2}$<br>$\mathrm{Re}(\mu-\nu) < \frac{1}{2}$<br>$\mathrm{Re}\, s > 0$ |

| | | f(t) | g(s) | |
|---|---|---|---|---|
| 32.2 (Contd.) | 24 | $\frac{1}{t^{2\nu}} S_3(\nu, \nu-\frac{1}{2}, -\nu-\frac{1}{2}, \nu-\frac{1}{2}; at)$ | $\frac{\pi^{\frac{3}{2}}}{2^{2\nu}} \sec(2\nu\pi) s^{2\nu-1}\left[\mathbf{H}_{2\nu}\left(\frac{4a}{s}\right) - Y_{2\nu}\left(\frac{4a}{s}\right)\right]$ | Re $\nu < \frac{1}{2}$ <br> Re $s > 0$ |
| | 25 | $t^{a_{m+1}-1} E(m; a_r : n; b_j : \frac{1}{t})$ | $s^{-a_{m+1}} E(m+1; a_r : n; b_j : s)$ | Re $a_{m+1} > 0$ <br> Re $s > 0$ |
| 32.2.1 | 1 | $t^{\frac{1}{2}} {}_0F_2\left[\begin{matrix} ; & -a^3t^3 \\ \frac{7}{6}, \frac{5}{6}; & \end{matrix}\right]$ | $\frac{3\Gamma(\frac{7}{6})\Gamma(\frac{5}{6})}{2\pi^{\frac{1}{2}}(s^3+27a^3)^{\frac{1}{2}}}$ | Re $s >$ Max $-3$Re $a$, $\frac{3\text{Re } a + 3^{\frac{3}{2}}\lvert\text{Im } a\rvert}{2}$ |
| 32.2.1 | 2 | $\frac{1}{t^{\frac{1}{6}}} {}_0F_2\left[\begin{matrix} ; & -a^3t^3 \\ \frac{7}{6}, \frac{1}{6}; & \end{matrix}\right]$ | $\frac{\Gamma(\frac{7}{6})\Gamma(\frac{1}{6})s}{2\pi^{\frac{1}{2}}a^{\frac{1}{3}}(s^3+27a^3)^{\frac{1}{2}}}$ | Re $s >$ Max $-3$Re $a$, $\frac{3\text{Re } a + 3^{\frac{3}{2}}\lvert\text{Im } a\rvert}{2}$ |
| | 3 | $\frac{1}{t^{\frac{1}{2}}} {}_0F_2\left[\begin{matrix} ; & \frac{t^3}{108} \\ \frac{7}{6}, \frac{5}{6}; & \end{matrix}\right]$ | $\frac{3\Gamma(\frac{7}{6})\Gamma(\frac{5}{6})}{\pi^{\frac{1}{2}}}\int_s^\infty \frac{du}{(4u^3-1)^{\frac{1}{2}}}$ | Re $s > 0$ |
| | 4 | $\frac{1}{t^{\frac{3}{2}}} {}_0F_2\left[\begin{matrix} ; & \frac{t^3}{108} \\ \frac{5}{6}, \frac{1}{6}; & \end{matrix}\right]$ | $\frac{\Gamma(\frac{5}{6})\Gamma(\frac{1}{6})}{\pi^{\frac{1}{2}}}\int_s^\infty \frac{u\,du}{(4\mu^3-1)^{\frac{1}{2}}}$ | Re $s > 0$ |
| | 5 | $t^{2\nu} {}_0F_2\left[\begin{matrix} ; & -t^2 \\ 2\nu+1, \nu+1; & \end{matrix}\right]$ | $\frac{\Gamma(2\nu+1)\Gamma(\nu+1)}{s^2} e^{-\frac{2}{s^2}} I_\nu\left(\frac{2}{s^2}\right)$ | Re $\nu > -1$ <br> Re $s > 0$ |
| | 6 | $t^a {}_0F_2\left[\begin{matrix} ; & -t^3 \\ \mu, \nu; & \end{matrix}\right]$ | $\frac{\Gamma(a+1)}{s^{a+1}} {}_3F_2\left[\begin{matrix} \frac{a+1}{3}, \frac{a+2}{3}, \frac{a+3}{3}; & -\frac{27}{s^3} \\ \mu, \nu; & \end{matrix}\right]$ | Re $a > -1$ <br> Re $s > \frac{3}{2}$ |
| | 7 | $t^{2\mu-1} {}_0F_3\left[\begin{matrix} ; & -a^2t^2 \\ \nu, \mu, \mu+\frac{1}{2}; & \end{matrix}\right]$ | $\frac{\Gamma(\nu)\Gamma(2\mu)s^{\nu-1-2\mu}}{(2a)^{\nu-1}} J_{\nu-1}\left(\frac{4a}{s}\right)$ | Re $\mu > 0$ <br> Re $s > 0$ |
| | 8 | $t^{2\mu-1} {}_0F_3\left[\begin{matrix} ; & a^2t^2 \\ \nu, \mu, \mu+\frac{1}{2}; & \end{matrix}\right]$ | $\frac{\Gamma(\nu)\Gamma(2\mu)}{(2a)^{\nu-1}s^{2\mu-\nu+1}} I_{\nu-1}\left(\frac{4a}{s}\right)$ | Re $\mu > 0$ <br> Re $s > 0$ |
| | 9 | $t^{2\mu-1} {}_1F_2\left[\begin{matrix} \nu; & -a^2t^2 \\ \mu, \mu+\frac{1}{2}; & \end{matrix}\right]$ | $\frac{\Gamma(2\mu)}{s^{2\mu-2\nu}(s^2+4a^2)^\nu}$ | Re $\mu > 0$ <br> Re $s > 2\lvert\text{Im } a\rvert$ |

32.2.1 (Contd.)

| | $f(t)$ | $g(s)$ | |
|---|---|---|---|
| 10 | $t^{3\mu-1}{}_1F_3\left[\begin{matrix}\nu\,; \\ \mu,\mu+\frac{1}{3},\mu+\frac{2}{3}\,;\end{matrix}\; -a^3t^3\right]$ | $\dfrac{\Gamma(3\mu)}{s^{3\mu-3\nu}(s^3+27a^3)^{\nu}}$ | $\operatorname{Re}\mu>0$<br>$\operatorname{Re}s>3\lvert\operatorname{Im}a\rvert$ |
| 11 | $t^{2\mu}{}_1F_4\left[\begin{matrix}1\,; \\ \frac{3}{2},\nu+\frac{3}{2},\mu+\frac{1}{2},\mu+1\,;\end{matrix}\; a^2t^2\right]$ | $\dfrac{\pi^{\frac{1}{2}}\Gamma(\nu+\frac{3}{2})\Gamma(2\mu+1)}{2(2a)^{\nu+1}s^{2\mu-\nu}}\mathbf{L}_{\nu}\left(\dfrac{4a}{s}\right)$ | $\operatorname{Re}\mu>-\frac{1}{2}$<br>$\operatorname{Re}s>0$ |
| 12 | $t^{2\mu}{}_1F_4\left[\begin{matrix}1\,; \\ \frac{3}{2},\nu+\frac{3}{2},\mu+\frac{1}{2},\mu+1\,;\end{matrix}\; -a^2t^2\right]$ | $\dfrac{\pi^{\frac{1}{2}}\Gamma(\nu+\frac{3}{2})\Gamma(2\mu+1)}{2(2a)^{\nu+1}s^{2\mu-\nu}}\mathbf{H}_{\nu}\left(\dfrac{4a}{s}\right)$ | $\operatorname{Re}\mu>-\frac{1}{2}$<br>$\operatorname{Re}s>0$ |
| 13 | $t^{2a-1}{}_3F_2\left[\begin{matrix}1,\frac{1}{2}-\mu+\nu,\frac{1}{2}-\mu-\nu\,; \\ a,\ a+\frac{1}{2}\,;\end{matrix}\; -k^2t^2\right]$ | $\Gamma(2a)k^{2\mu-1}s^{1-2a-2\mu}S_{2\mu,2\nu}\left(\dfrac{s}{k}\right)$ | $\operatorname{Re}k>0$<br>$\operatorname{Re}a>0$<br>$\operatorname{Re}s>0$ |
| 14 | $t^{2a-1}{}_4F_3\left[\begin{matrix}\frac{1}{2}+\mu+\nu,\frac{1}{2}-\mu+\nu,\frac{1}{2}+\mu-\nu,\frac{1}{2}-\mu-\nu\,; \\ \frac{1}{2},\ a,\ a+\frac{1}{2}\,;\end{matrix}\; -\frac{k^2t^2}{4}\right]$ | $\dfrac{\pi\Gamma(2a)}{4ks^{2a-1}}\left[e^{(\mu-\nu)\pi i}H^{(1)}_{2\mu}\left(\dfrac{s}{k}\right)H^{(2)}_{2\nu}\left(\dfrac{s}{k}\right)\right.$<br>$\left.+\,e^{(\nu-\mu)\pi i}H^{(2)}_{2\mu}\left(\dfrac{s}{k}\right)H^{(1)}_{2\nu}\left(\dfrac{s}{k}\right)\right]$ | $\operatorname{Re}a>0$<br>$\operatorname{Re}k>0$<br>$\operatorname{Re}s>0$ |
| 15 | $t^{2a-1}{}_4F_3\left[\begin{matrix}1+\mu+\nu,1-\mu+\nu,1+\mu-\nu,1-\mu-\nu\,; \\ \frac{3}{2},\ a,\ a+\frac{1}{2}\,;\end{matrix}\; -\frac{k^2t^2}{4}\right]$ | $\dfrac{\pi\Gamma(2a)s^{2-2a}}{8ik^2(\mu^2-\nu^2)}\left[e^{(\mu-\nu)\pi i}H^{(1)}_{2\mu}\left(\dfrac{s}{k}\right)H^{(2)}_{2\nu}\left(\dfrac{s}{k}\right)\right.$<br>$\left.+\,e^{(\nu-\mu)\pi i}H^{(2)}_{2\mu}\left(\dfrac{s}{k}\right)H^{(1)}_{2\nu}\left(\dfrac{s}{k}\right)\right]$ | $\operatorname{Re}k>0$<br>$\operatorname{Re}a>0$<br>$\operatorname{Re}s>0$ |
| 16 | $t^{2a-1}{}_4F_3\left[\begin{matrix}\frac{1}{2}-\mu+\nu,\frac{1}{2}-\mu-\nu,\frac{1}{2}-\mu,1-\mu\,; \\ 1-2\mu,\ a,\ a+\frac{1}{2}\,;\end{matrix}\; -k^2t^2\right]$ | $\dfrac{\Gamma(2a)k^{2\mu}}{s^{2a+2\mu}}W_{\mu,\nu}\left(\dfrac{is}{k}\right)W_{\mu,\nu}\left(-\dfrac{is}{k}\right)$ | $\operatorname{Re}k>0$<br>$\operatorname{Re}a>0$<br>$\operatorname{Re}s>0$ |
| 17 | $t^{2c-1}{}_pF_{q+2}\left[\begin{matrix}(a)\,; \\ (b),c,c+\frac{1}{2}\,;\end{matrix}\; k^2t^2\right]$ | $\dfrac{\Gamma(2c)}{s^{2c}}{}_pF_q\left[\begin{matrix}(a)\,; \\ (b)\,;\end{matrix}\; \dfrac{4k^2}{s^2}\right]$ | $p\leqslant q+1$<br>$\operatorname{Re}c>0$<br>$\operatorname{Re}s>0$<br>if $p<q+1$<br>$\operatorname{Re}s>\lvert\operatorname{Re}k\rvert$<br>if $p=q+1$ |
| 18 | $t^{2c-1}{}_pF_q\left[\begin{matrix}(a)\,; \\ (b)\,;\end{matrix}\; k^2t^2\right]$ | $\dfrac{\Gamma(2c)}{s^{2c}}{}_{p+2}F_q\left[\begin{matrix}(a),\frac{c}{2},\frac{c+1}{2}\,; \\ (b)\,;\end{matrix}\; \dfrac{4k^2}{s^2}\right]$ | $p<q$<br>$\operatorname{Re}c>0$<br>$\operatorname{Re}s>0$ if $p<q-1$<br>$\operatorname{Re}s>\lvert\operatorname{Re}k\rvert$ if $p=q-1$ |

| | | f(t) | g(s) | |
|---|---|---|---|---|
| 32.2.1 (Contd.) | 19 | $t^{c}\,{}_pF_q\left[\begin{matrix}(a); \\ (b);\end{matrix}\ (kt)^{n}\right]$ | $\frac{\Gamma(c+1)}{s^{c+1}}\,{}_{p+n}F_q\left[\begin{matrix}(a), \frac{c+1}{n}, \frac{c+2}{n}, \ldots, \frac{c+n}{n}; \\ (b) \qquad ;\end{matrix}\ \left(\frac{nk}{s}\right)^{n}\right]$ | $n = 1,2,3,\ldots$<br>$p+n \leq q+1$<br>$\mathrm{Re}\, c > -1$<br>$\mathrm{Re}\, s > 0$ if $p+n \leq q$<br>$\mathrm{Re}(s+nke^{2\pi ir/n}) > 0$<br>$(r = 0,1,\ldots,n-1)$<br>if $p+n = q+1$ |
| | 20 | $\frac{1}{t^{\frac{1}{3}}}\frac{d}{dt}\left\{t^{2\nu}\,{}_0F_2\left[\begin{matrix} ; \\ 2\nu+1,\nu+1;\end{matrix}\ -\frac{t^{2}}{2}\right]\right\}$ | $\frac{\Gamma(2\nu+1)\Gamma(\nu+1)}{2^{\frac{7}{6}-\nu}\,s}\, e^{-\frac{1}{s^{2}}}\, I_{\nu}\left(\frac{1}{s^{2}}\right)$ | $\mathrm{Re}\,\nu > 0$<br>$\mathrm{Re}\, s > 0$ |
| 32.3 | 1 | $(1-e^{-t})^{c}\,{}_pF_q\left[\begin{matrix}(a); \\ (b);\end{matrix}\ ke^{-t}\right]$ | $B(c+1,s)\,{}_{p+1}F_{q+1}\left[\begin{matrix}(a),s; \\ (b),s+c+1;\end{matrix}\ k\right]$ | $\mathrm{Re}\, c > -1$<br>$p \leq q$<br>Valid for $p=q+1$ if $\lvert k\rvert < 1$<br>$\mathrm{Re}\, s > 0$ |
| | 2 | $(1-e^{-t})^{c}\,{}_pF_q\left[\begin{matrix}(a); \\ (b);\end{matrix}\ k(1-e^{-t})\right]$ | $B(c+1,s)\,{}_{p+1}F_{q+1}\left[\begin{matrix}(a),c+1 \ ; \\ (b),s+c+1;\end{matrix}\ k\right]$ | $\mathrm{Re}\, c > -1$<br>$p \leq q$<br>Valid for $p=q+1$ if $\lvert k\rvert < 1$<br>$\mathrm{Re}\, s > 0$ |
| | 3 | $(e^{t}-1)^{a_{m+1}}\, E\left(m;a_r:n;b_j:\frac{k}{1-e^{-t}}\right)$ | $\Gamma(s-a_{m+1})E(m+1;a_r:n;b_j,s:k)$ | $n,m = 0,1,2,\ldots$<br>$\mathrm{Re}\, a_{m+1} > -1$<br>$\mathrm{Re}\, s > \mathrm{Re}\, a_{m+1}$ |
| 32.3.2 | 1 | $t^{\nu-1}e^{-bt}\,{}_2F_2\left[\begin{matrix}-n,n+1; \\ 1,\ \nu\ ;\end{matrix}\ at\right]$ | $\frac{\Gamma(\nu)P_n\left(\frac{s+b-2a}{s+b}\right)}{(s+b)^{\nu}}$ | $\mathrm{Re}\,\nu > 0$<br>$n = 0,1,2,\ldots$<br>$\mathrm{Re}\, s > -\mathrm{Re}\, b$ |
| | 2 | $t^{\mu-1}e^{-bt}\,{}_2F_2\left[\begin{matrix}-n,n+2\nu; \\ \mu,\nu+\frac{1}{2};\end{matrix}\ at\right]$ | $\frac{n\,B(n,2\nu)\Gamma(\mu)\,C_n^{\nu}\left(\frac{s+b-2a}{s+b}\right)}{(s+b)^{\mu}}$ | $\mathrm{Re}\,\mu > 0$<br>$\mathrm{Re}\,\nu > 0$<br>$n = 0,1,2,\ldots$<br>$\mathrm{Re}\, s > -\mathrm{Re}\, b$ |
| 32.3.2.1 | 1 | $t^{\mu+\nu-1}e^{-\frac{a^{2}t^{2}}{2}}\,{}_2F_2\left[\begin{matrix}\mu, \quad \nu\ ; \\ \frac{\mu+\nu}{2},\frac{\mu+\nu+1}{2};\end{matrix}\ \frac{a^{2}t^{2}}{4}\right]$ | $\frac{\Gamma(\mu+\nu)}{a^{\mu+\nu}}e^{\frac{s^{2}}{4a^{2}}}D_{-\mu}\left(\frac{s}{a}\right)D_{-\nu}\left(\frac{s}{a}\right)$ | $\mathrm{Re}(\mu+\nu) > 0$<br>$\mathrm{Re}\, s > -\infty$ |

| | | f(t) | | g(s) | |
|---|---|---|---|---|---|
| 33 | 1 | 1 | $o < t < b$ | $\dfrac{1-e^{-bs}}{s}$ | Re $s > -\infty$ |
| | | 0 | $t > b$ | | |

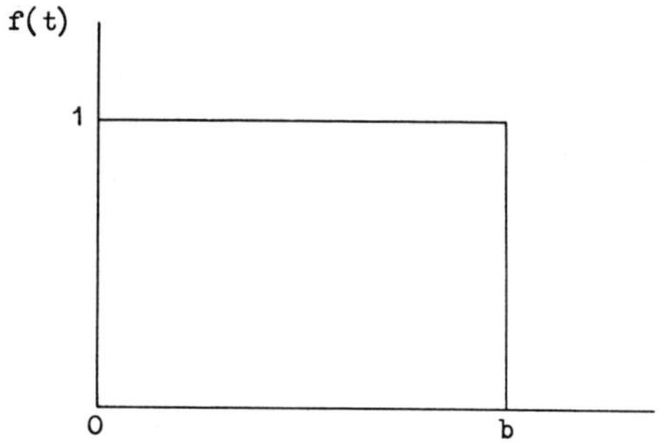


| | | | | |
|---|---|---|---|---|
| 2 | 0 | $o < t < a$ | $\dfrac{e^{-as}-e^{-bs}}{s}$ | Re $s > -\infty$ |
| | 1 | $a < t < b$ | | |
| | 0 | $t > b$ | | |

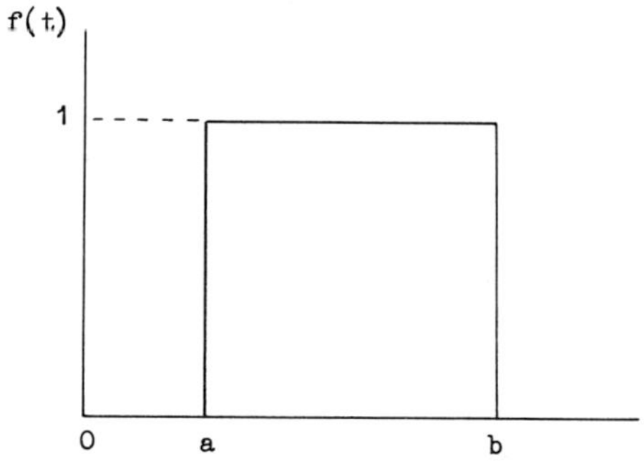


| | | | | |
|---|---|---|---|---|
| 3 | 1 | $o < t < b$ | $\dfrac{(1-e^{-bs})^2}{s}$ | Re $s > -\infty$ |
| | -1 | $b < t < 2b$ | | |
| | 0 | $t > 2b$ | | |

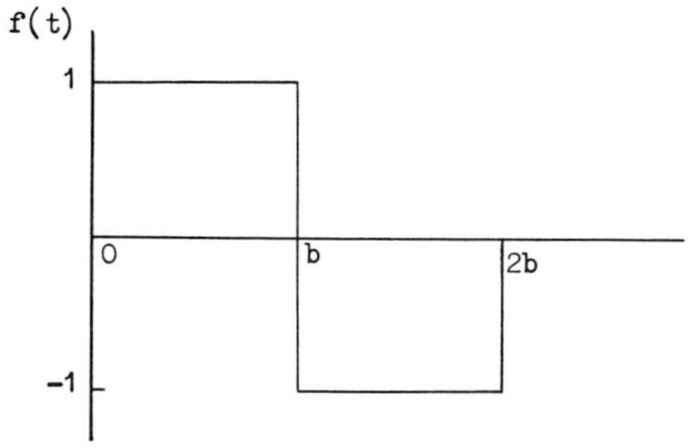

| | | f(t) | | g(s) | |
|---|---|---|---|---|---|
| 33 (Contd.) | 4 | 0 | $o < t < 2a$ | $\frac{(e^{-as}-e^{-bs})^2}{s}$ | Re $s > -\infty$ |
| | | 1 | $2a < t < a+b$ | | |
| | | -1 | $a+b < t < 2b$ | | |
| | | 0 | $t > 2b$ | | |

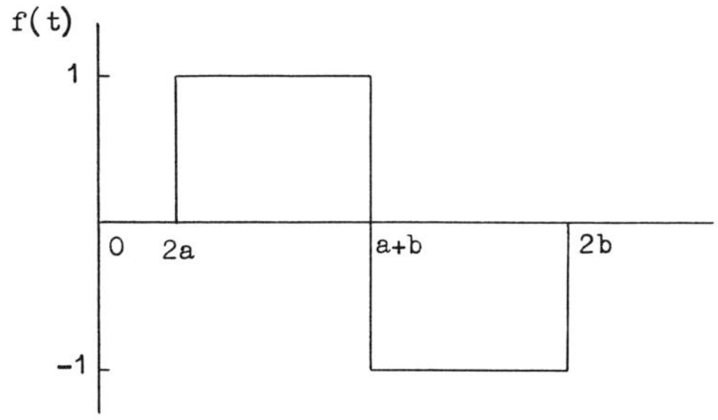


| | | | | | |
|---|---|---|---|---|---|
| 33.1 | 1 | $1-\frac{t}{b}$ | $o < t < b$ | $\frac{e^{-bs}+bs-1}{bs^2}$ | Re $s > -\infty$ |
| | | 0 | $t > b$ | | |

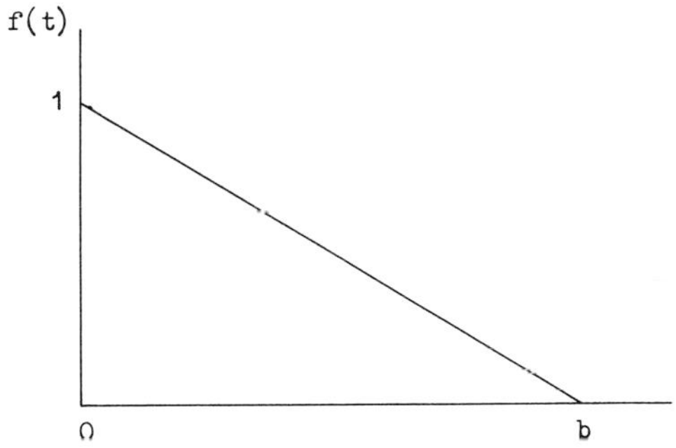


| | | | | | |
|---|---|---|---|---|---|
| | 2 | $t$ | $o < t < b$ | $\frac{(1-e^{-bs})^2}{s^2}$ | Re $s > -\infty$ |
| | | $2b-t$ | $b < t < 2b$ | | |
| | | 0 | $t > 2b$ | | |

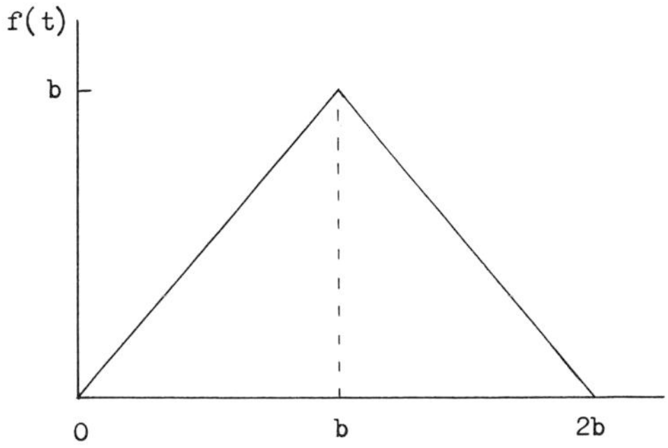

| | f(t) | g(s) | |
|---|---|---|---|
| 33.1 (Contd.) 3 | $\begin{cases} 0 & t < a \\ t-a & a < t < \frac{a+b}{2} \\ b-t & \frac{a+b}{2} < t < b \\ 0 & t > b \end{cases}$ | $\dfrac{\left(e^{-\frac{as}{2}} - e^{-\frac{bs}{2}}\right)^2}{s^2}$ | Re $s > -\infty$ |

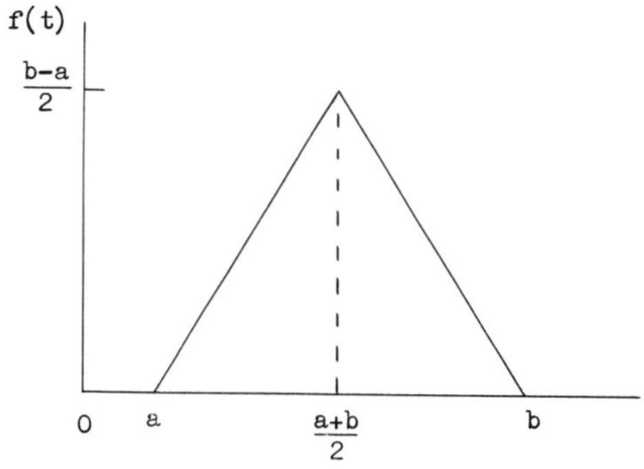


| | f(t) | g(s) | |
|---|---|---|---|
| 4 | $\begin{cases} 0 & o < t < b \\ \frac{1}{t+a} & b < t < c \\ 0 & t > c \end{cases}$ <br> $-a$ not between b and c | $e^{as}\left\{ \mathrm{Ei}[-(a+c)s] - \mathrm{Ei}[-(a+b)a] \right\}$ | Re $s > -\infty$ |
| 5 | $\begin{cases} \frac{1}{2}t^2 & o < t < 1 \\ \frac{3}{4} - (t - \frac{3}{2})^2 & 1 < t < 2 \\ \frac{1}{2}(t-3)^2 & 2 < t < 3 \\ 0 & t > 3 \end{cases}$ | $\dfrac{(1-e^{-s})^3}{s^3}$ | Re $s > -\infty$ |
| 6 | $\begin{cases} 0 & t < a \\ \frac{1}{2}(t-a)^2 & a < t < \frac{2a+b}{3} \\ \frac{1}{12}(b-a)^2 - [t - \frac{1}{2}(a+b)]^2 & \frac{2a+b}{3} < t < \frac{a+2b}{3} \\ \frac{1}{2}(b-t)^2 & \frac{a+2b}{3} < t < b \\ 0 & t > b \end{cases}$ | $\dfrac{\left(e^{-\frac{as}{3}} - e^{-\frac{bs}{3}}\right)^3}{s^3}$ | Re $s > -\infty$ |
| 7 | $\begin{cases} t^n & o < t < b \\ 0 & t > b \end{cases}$ | $\dfrac{n!}{s^{n+1}} - e^{-bs} \sum_{m=o}^{n} \dfrac{n!}{m!} \dfrac{b^m}{s^{n-m+1}}$ | $n = 0, 1, 2, \ldots$ <br> Re $s > -\infty$ |

| | | f(t) | g(s) | |
|---|---|---|---|---|
| 33.2 | 1 | $\frac{1}{t^{\frac{1}{2}}}$ $\quad 0<t<b$ <br> $0 \quad t>b$ | $\left(\frac{\pi}{s}\right)^{\frac{1}{2}} \operatorname{Erf}\left[(bs)^{\frac{1}{2}}\right]$ | $\operatorname{Re} s > -\infty$ |
| | 2 | $t^{\nu} \quad 0<t<b$ <br> $0 \quad t>b$ | $\frac{\gamma(\nu+1,bs)}{s^{\nu+1}}$ | $\operatorname{Re}\nu > -1$ <br> $\operatorname{Re} s > -\infty$ |
| | 3 | $(1+t)^{\nu} \quad 0<t<b$ <br> $0 \quad t>b$ | $\sum_{n=0}^{\infty} L_n^{(\nu+1)}(s) \frac{b^{n+1}}{(n+1)(b+1)^{n+1}}$ | $\operatorname{Re} s > -\infty$ |
| | 4 | $(1+t)^{\nu} \quad 0<t<b$ <br> $0 \quad t>b$ | $\sum_{n=0}^{\infty} L_n^{(\nu-n)}(s) \frac{b^{n+1}}{n+1}$ | $b<1$ <br> $\operatorname{Re} s > -\infty$ |
| | 5 | $(b-t)^{\nu} \quad 0<t<b$ <br> $0 \quad t>b$ | $\frac{\gamma(\nu+1,-bs)}{s^{\nu+1}\, e^{bs}}$ | $\operatorname{Re}\nu > -1$ <br> $\operatorname{Re} s > -\infty$ |
| | 6 | $t^{a}(1-t)^{b} \quad 0<t<1$ <br> $0 \quad t>1$ | $\frac{\Gamma(a+1)\Gamma(b+1)}{\Gamma(a+b+2)} {}_1F_1[a+1;a+b+2;-s]$ | $\operatorname{Re}(a+b+1) > \operatorname{Re} a > -1$ <br> $\operatorname{Re} s > -\infty$ |
| | 7 | $0 \quad 0<t<a$ <br> $(t-a)^{2\mu-1}(b-t)^{2\nu-1} \quad a<t<b$ <br> $0 \quad t>b$ | $B(2\mu,2\nu)(b-a)^{\mu+\nu-1} s^{-\mu-\nu}$ <br> $\cdot\, e^{-\frac{(a+b)s}{2}} M_{\mu-\nu,\mu+\nu-\frac{1}{2}}[(b-a)s]$ | $\operatorname{Re}\mu > 0$ <br> $\operatorname{Re}\nu > 0$ <br> $\operatorname{Re} s > -\infty$ |
| | 8 | $\frac{1}{(1-t^2)^{\frac{1}{2}}} \quad 0<t<1$ <br> $0 \quad t>1$ | $\frac{\pi}{2}[I_0(s)-\mathbf{L}_0(s)]$ | $\operatorname{Re} s > -\infty$ |
| | 9 | $(b^2-t^2)^{\nu} \quad 0<t<b$ <br> $0 \quad t>b$ | $\frac{1}{2}\pi^{\frac{1}{2}}\Gamma(\nu+1)\left(\frac{2b}{s}\right)^{\nu+\frac{1}{2}}\left[I_{\nu+\frac{1}{2}}(bs)-\mathbf{L}_{\nu+\frac{1}{2}}(bs)\right]$ | $\operatorname{Re}\nu > -1$ <br> $\operatorname{Re} s > -\infty$ |

| | | f(t) | g(s) | |
|---|---|---|---|---|
| 33.2 (Contd.) | 10 | $\frac{1}{(bt-t^2)^{\frac{1}{2}}}$ $\quad 0 < t < b$ <br> $0 \quad t > b$ | $\pi e^{-\frac{b}{2}s} I_0\left(\frac{bs}{2}\right)$ | $\mathrm{Re}\, s > -\infty$ |
| | 11 | $(bt-t^2)^{\nu} \quad 0 < t < b$ <br> $0 \quad t > b$ | $\pi^{\frac{1}{2}}\Gamma(\nu+1)e^{-\frac{bs}{2}} b^{\nu+\frac{1}{2}} s^{-\nu-\frac{1}{2}} I_{\nu+\frac{1}{2}}\left(\frac{bs}{2}\right)$ | $\mathrm{Re}\, \nu > -1$ <br> $\mathrm{Re}\, s > -\infty$ |
| | 12 | $(bt-t^2)^{\nu} \quad 0 < t < \frac{b}{2}$ <br> $-(bt-t^2)^{\nu} \quad \frac{b}{2} < t < b$ <br> $0 \quad t > b$ | $\pi^{\frac{1}{2}}\Gamma(\nu+1)\left(\frac{b}{s}\right)^{\nu+\frac{1}{2}} e^{-\frac{bs}{2}} \mathbf{L}_{\nu+\frac{1}{2}}\left(\frac{bs}{2}\right)$ | $\mathrm{Re}\, \nu > -1$ <br> $\mathrm{Re}\, s > -\infty$ |
| | 13 | $\frac{t^a(1-t)^b}{(1-ht)^c} \quad 0 < t < 1$ <br> $0 \quad t > 1$ | $B(a+1,b+1)\, \Phi_1(a+1,c,a+b+2;h,-s)$ | $\mathrm{Re}\, a > -1$ <br> $\mathrm{Re}\, b > -1$ <br> $\lvert \arg(1-h) \rvert < \pi$ <br> $\mathrm{Re}\, s > -\infty$ |
| 33.2.1 | 1 | $\frac{b-t}{(2bt-t^2)^{\frac{1}{2}}} \quad 0 < t < 2b$ <br> $0 \quad t > 2b$ | $\pi b e^{-bs} I_1(bs)$ | $\mathrm{Re}\, s > -\infty$ |
| | 2 | $\frac{t}{(b^2-t^2)^{\frac{1}{2}}} \quad 0 < t < b$ <br> $0 \quad t > b$ | $\frac{\pi b}{2}[\mathbf{L}_1(bs) - I_1(bs)]+b$ | $\mathrm{Re}\, s > -\infty$ |
| 33.3 | 1 | $e^{it} \quad 0 < t < 2n\pi$ <br> $0 \quad t > 2n\pi$ | $\frac{1-e^{-2n\pi s}}{s-i}$ | $n = 1,2,3,\ldots$ <br> $\mathrm{Re}\, s > -\infty$ |
| | 2 | $0 \quad 0 < t < \log a$ <br> $e^{-e^t} \quad \log a < t < \log b$ <br> $0 \quad t > \log b$ | $\gamma(-s,b)-\gamma(-s,a)$ <br> $= \Gamma(-s,a)-\Gamma(-s,b)$ | $1 \leq a < b$ <br> $\mathrm{Re}\, s > -\infty$ |

| | | f(t) | | g(s) | |
|---|---|---|---|---|---|
| 33.4 | 1 | $\log\frac{t}{b}$ | $0 < t < b$ | $\frac{Ei(-bs) - \log(\gamma bs)}{s}$ | $Re\ s > -\infty$ |
| | | $0$ | $t > b$ | | |
| 33.4.1 | 1 | $\frac{\log t}{1+t}$ | $0 < t < 1$ | $\sum_{n=0}^{\infty} \frac{(-s)^n}{n!}\left[\psi'\left(\frac{n+2}{2}\right) - \psi'\left(\frac{n+1}{2}\right)\right]$ | $Re\ s > -\infty$ |
| | | $0$ | $t > 1$ | | |
| 33.4.2.1 | 1 | $\frac{\log\frac{4t(2b-t)}{b^2}}{t^{\frac{1}{2}}(2b-t)^{\frac{1}{2}}}$ | $0 < t < 2b$ | $\pi e^{-bs}\left[\frac{\pi}{2} Y_0(ibs) - \log(\frac{\gamma}{2}) J_0(ibs)\right]$ | $Re\ s > -\infty$ |
| | | $0$ | $t > 2b$ | | |
| 33.5 | 1 | $\sin t$ | $0 < t < \pi$ | $\frac{1+e^{-\pi s}}{s^2+1}$ | $Re\ s > -\infty$ |
| | | $0$ | $t > \pi$ | | |
| | 2 | $\sin(at)$ | $0 < t < b\pi$ | $a\frac{1-e^{-b\pi s}}{s^2+a^2}$ | $Re\ s > -\infty$ |
| | | $0$ | $t > b\pi$ | | |
| | 3 | $0$ | $0 < t < a$ | $\frac{e^{-as}[c\cos(ac) + s\sin(ac)] - e^{-bs}[c\cos(bc) + s\sin(bc)]}{s^2+c^2}$ | $Re\ s > -\infty$ |
| | | $\sin(ct)$ | $a < t < b$ | | |
| | | $0$ | $t > b$ | | |
| | 4 | $t\sin t$ | $0 < t < \frac{\pi}{2}$ | [illegible] $e^{-\frac{\pi}{2}s}[\frac{\pi}{2}$ [illegible] $(1$ [illegible] $)$ [illegible] $1]$ / $(1+s^2)^2$ | $Re\ s > -\infty$ |
| | | $0$ | $t > \frac{\pi}{2}$ | | |
| | 5 | $\sin^2(at)$ | $0 < t < b\pi$ | $\frac{2a^2(1-e^{-b\pi s})}{s(s^2+4a^2)}$ | $Re\ s > -\infty$ |
| | | $0$ | $t > b\pi$ | | |
| | 6 | $0$ | $0 < t < \frac{n\pi}{a}$ | $\frac{2a^2}{s(s^2+4a^2)} e^{-\frac{n\pi s}{a}}\left(1-e^{-\frac{\pi s}{2a}}\right)$ | $n = 1,2,3,\ldots$ |
| | | $\sin^2(at)$ | $\frac{n\pi}{a} < t < \frac{(n+\frac{1}{2})\pi}{a}$ | | $Re\ s > -\infty$ |
| | | $0$ | $t > \frac{(n+\frac{1}{2})\pi}{a}$ | | |

| | | f(t) | | g(s) | |
|---|---|---|---|---|---|
| 33.5 (Contd.) | 7 | $0$ <br> $\sin^2(ct)$ <br> $0$ | $o<t<a$ <br> $a<t<b$ <br> $t>b$ | $\dfrac{\{e^{-as}[\frac{2c^2}{s}+s\sin^2(ac)+c\sin(2ac)] - e^{-bs}[\frac{2c^2}{s}+s\sin^2(bc)+c\sin(2bc)]\}}{s^2+4c^2}$ | Re $s>-\infty$ |
| | 8 | $\sin^{2n}t$ <br> $0$ | $o<t<\frac{\pi}{2}$ <br> $t>\frac{\pi}{2}$ | $(2n)!\,\dfrac{1-e^{-\frac{\pi}{2}s}\left\{1+\frac{s^2}{2!}+\dots+\frac{s^2[s^2+2^2]\dots[s^2+(2n-2)^2]}{(2n)!}\right\}}{s[s^2+2^2][s^2+4^2]\dots[s^2+(2n)^2]}$ | $n=1,2,3,\dots$ <br> Re $s>-\infty$ |
| | 9 | $\sin^{2n}t$ <br> $0$ | $o<t<m\pi$ <br> $t>m\pi$ | $\dfrac{(2n)!(1-e^{-m\pi s})}{s(s^2+2^2)(s^2+4^2)\dots(s^2+4n^2)}$ | $n,m=1,2,3,\dots$ <br> Re $s>-\infty$ |
| | 10 | $\sin^{2n+1}t$ <br> $0$ | $o<t<\frac{\pi}{2}$ <br> $t>\frac{\pi}{2}$ | $(2n+1)!\,\dfrac{1-s\,e^{-\frac{\pi}{2}s}\left\{1+\frac{s^2+1^2}{3!}+\dots+\frac{[s^2+1^2][s^2+3^2]\dots[s^2+(2n-1)^2]}{(2n+1)!}\right\}}{[s^2+1^2][s^2+3^2]\dots[s^2(2n+1)^2]}$ | $n=1,2,3,\dots$ <br> Re $s>-\infty$ |
| | 11 | $\sin^{2n+1}t$ <br> $0$ | $o<t<m\pi$ <br> $t>m\pi$ | $\dfrac{(2n+1)![1-(-1)^m e^{-m\pi s}]}{[s^2+1^2][s^2+3^2]\dots[s^2+(2n+1)^2]}$ | $n=0,1,2,\dots$ <br> $m=1,2,3,\dots$ <br> Re $s>-\infty$ |
| | 12 | $\sin^{\nu}t$ <br> $0$ | $o<t<\pi$ <br> $t>\pi$ | $\dfrac{\pi\Gamma(\nu+1)e^{-\frac{\pi s}{2}}}{2^{\nu}\Gamma\left(1+\frac{\nu+is}{2}\right)\Gamma\left(1+\frac{\nu-is}{2}\right)}$ | Re $\nu>1$ <br> Re $s>-\infty$ |
| | 13 | $\cos t$ <br> $0$ | $o<t<\pi$ <br> $t>\pi$ | $\dfrac{s(1+e^{-\pi s})}{s^2+1}$ | Re $s>-\infty$ |
| | 14 | $\cos(at)$ <br> $0$ | $o<t<\frac{2n\pi}{a}$ <br> $t>\frac{2n\pi}{a}$ | $\dfrac{s}{s^2+a^2}\left(1-e^{-\frac{2n\pi s}{a}}\right)$ | $n=1,2,3,\dots$ <br> Re $s>-\infty$ |
| | 15 | $0$ <br> $\cos(ct)$ <br> $0$ | $o<t<a$ <br> $a<t<b$ <br> $t>b$ | $\dfrac{\{e^{-as}[s\cos(ac)-c\sin(ac)] - e^{-bs}[s\cos(bc)-c\sin(bc)]\}}{s^2+c^2}$ | Re $s>-\infty$ |

|  | f(t) |  | g(s) |  |
|---|---|---|---|---|

33.5
(Contd.)

**16** $t \cos t$, $0 < t < \dfrac{\pi}{2}$

$0$, $t > \dfrac{\pi}{2}$

$$\frac{s^2 - 1 + e^{-\frac{\pi}{2}s}[\frac{\pi}{2}(s^2+1)+2s]}{(s^2+1)^2}$$

$\mathrm{Re}\ s > -\infty$

**17** $1 - \cos(at)$, $0 < t < \dfrac{2n\pi}{a}$

$0$, $t > \dfrac{2n\pi}{a}$

$$\frac{a^2\left(1 - e^{-\frac{2n\pi s}{a}}\right)}{s(s^2+a^2)}$$

$n = 1,2,3,\ldots$
$\mathrm{Re}\ s > -\infty$

**18** $\cos^2(at)$, $0 < t < \dfrac{n\pi}{a}$

$0$, $t > \dfrac{n\pi}{a}$

$$\frac{s^2 + 2a^2}{s(s^2+4a^2)}\left(1 - e^{-\frac{n\pi s}{a}}\right)$$

$n = 1,2,3,\ldots$
$\mathrm{Re}\ s > -\infty$

**19** $0$, $0 < t < a$

$\cos^2(ct)$, $a < t < b$

$0$, $t > b$

$$\frac{\left\{e^{-as}\left[\frac{2c^2}{s} + s\cos^2(ac) - c\sin(2ac)\right] - e^{-bs}\left[\frac{2c^2}{s} + s\cos^2(bc) - c\sin(2bc)\right]\right\}}{s^2 + 4c^2}$$

$\mathrm{Re}\ s > -\infty$

**20** $0$, $0 < t < \dfrac{n\pi}{a}$

$\cos^2(at)$, $\dfrac{n\pi}{a} < t < \dfrac{(n+\frac{1}{2})\pi}{a}$

$0$, $t \dfrac{(n+\frac{1}{2})\pi}{a}$

$$\frac{s^2 + 2a^2}{s(s^2+4a^2)}e^{-\frac{n\pi s}{a}}\left(1 - e^{-\frac{\pi s}{2a}}\right)$$

$n = 1,2,3,\ldots$
$\mathrm{Re}\ s > -\infty$

**21** $\cos^{2n}t$, $0 < t < \dfrac{\pi}{2}$

$0$, $t > \dfrac{\pi}{2}$

$$(2n)!\ \frac{-e^{-\frac{\pi}{2}s} + 1 + \frac{s^2}{2!} + \cdots + \frac{s^2[s^2+2^2]\cdots[s^2+4(n-1)^2]}{(2n)!}}{s(s^2+2^2)(s^2+4^2)\cdots(s^2+4n^2)}$$

$n = 1,2,3,\ldots$
$\mathrm{Re}\ s > -\infty$

**22** $0$, $0 < t < \dfrac{\pi}{2}$

$\cos^{2n}t$, $\dfrac{\pi}{2} < t < (m+\frac{1}{2})\pi$

$0$, $t (m+\frac{1}{2})\pi$

$$\frac{(2n)!\ e^{-\frac{\pi}{2}s}\left(1 - e^{-m\pi s}\right)}{s(s^2+2^2)(s^2+4^2)\cdots(s^2+4n^2)}$$

$n,m = 1,2,3,\ldots$

33.5

**23** $\cos^{2n+1}t$, $0 < t < \dfrac{\pi}{2}$

$0$, $t > \dfrac{\pi}{2}$

$$(2n+1)!\ \frac{e^{-\frac{\pi}{2}s} + s\left\{1 + \frac{s^2+1^2}{3!} + \cdots + \frac{[s^2+1^2][s^2+3^2]\cdots[s^2+(2n-1)^2]}{(2n+1)!}\right\}}{[s^2+1^2][s^2+3^2]\cdots[s^2+(2n+1)^2]}$$

$n = 0,1,2,\ldots$
$\mathrm{Re}\ s > -\infty$

| | | f(t) | | g(s) | |
|---|---|---|---|---|---|
| 33.5.1 | 1 | $\sin(at+b)$ <br> $0$ | $0<t<\frac{2n\pi}{a}$ <br> $t>\frac{2n\pi}{a}$ | $\frac{\left(1-e^{-\frac{2n\pi s}{a}}\right)(a\cos b+s\sin b)}{s^2+a^2}$ | $n=1,2,3,\ldots$ <br> $\mathrm{Re}\, s>-\infty$ |
| | 2 | $\cos(at+b)$ <br> $0$ | $0<t<\frac{2n\pi}{a}$ <br> $t>\frac{2n\pi}{a}$ | $\frac{\left(1-e^{-\frac{2n\pi s}{a}}\right)(s\cos b-a\sin b)}{s^2+a^2}$ | $n=1,2,3,\ldots$ <br> $\mathrm{Re}\, s>-\infty$ |
| | 3 | $0$ <br> $\cos(t-b)$ <br> $0$ | $0<t<b$ <br> $b<t<b+2n\pi$ <br> $t>b+2n\pi$ | $\frac{s\, e^{-bs}(1-e^{-2n\pi s})}{s^2+1}$ | $n=1,2,3,\ldots$ <br> $\mathrm{Re}\, s>-\infty$ |
| 33.5.2 | 1 | $\frac{\cos[a(2t-t^2)^{\frac{1}{2}}]}{(2t-t^2)^{\frac{1}{2}}}$ <br> $0$ | $0<t<2$ <br> $t>2$ | $\pi e^{-s} J_0[(a^2-s^2)^{\frac{1}{2}}]$ <br> $=\pi e^{-s} I_0[(s^2-a^2)^{\frac{1}{2}}]$ | $\mathrm{Re}\, s>-\infty$ |
| 33.6 | 1 | $\sin^{-1}\frac{t}{b}$ <br> $0$ | $0<t<b$ <br> $t>b$ | $\frac{\pi}{2s}[I_0(bs)-L_0(bs)]$ | $\mathrm{Re}\, s>-\infty$ |
| | 2 | $t\sin^{-1} t$ <br> $0$ | $0<t<1$ <br> $t>1$ | $\frac{\pi}{2s^2}[L_0(s)-I_0(s)+s L_1(s)$ <br> $-s I_1(s)]+\frac{1}{s}$ | $\mathrm{Re}\, s>-\infty$ |
| 33.6.5.2 | 1 | $\frac{\cos[(2n+\frac{1}{2})\cos^{-1}\frac{t}{b}]}{t^{\frac{1}{2}}(b^2-t^2)^{\frac{1}{2}}}$ <br> $0$ | $0<t<b$ <br> $t>b$ | $(-1)^n(\frac{\pi}{2}s)^{\frac{1}{2}} I_n(\frac{bs}{2}) K_{n+\frac{1}{2}}(\frac{bs}{2})$ | $n=0,1,2,\ldots$ <br> $\mathrm{Re}\, s>-\infty$ |
| | 2 | $\frac{\cos(\nu\cos^{-1}\frac{t}{b})}{t^{\frac{1}{2}}(b^2-t^2)^{\frac{1}{2}}}$ <br> $0$ | $0<t<b$ <br> $t>b$ | $(\frac{\pi}{2})^{\frac{3}{2}} s^{\frac{1}{2}}\left[I_{\frac{\nu}{2}-\frac{1}{4}}\left(\frac{bs}{2}\right) I_{-\frac{\nu}{2}-\frac{1}{4}}\left(\frac{bs}{2}\right)\right.$ <br> $\left.-I_{\frac{\nu}{2}+\frac{1}{4}}\left(\frac{bs}{2}\right) I_{-\frac{\nu}{2}+\frac{1}{4}}\left(\frac{bs}{2}\right)\right]$ | $\mathrm{Re}\, s>-\infty$ |

| | | f(t) | | g(s) | |
|---|---|---|---|---|---|
| 33.6.5.2.1 | 1 | $0$ | $0<t<a$ | | |
| | | $\dfrac{\cos\left(n\cos^{-1}\dfrac{2t-a-b}{b-a}\right)}{(t-a)^{\frac{1}{2}}(b-t)^{\frac{1}{2}}}$ | $a<t<b$ | $\pi e^{-\frac{1}{2}(a+b)s} I_n\left[\frac{1}{2}(b-a)s\right]$ | $n=0,1,2,\ldots$ Re $s>-\infty$ |
| | | $0$ | $t>b$ | | |
| 33.7 | 1 | $0$ | $0<t<a$ | | |
| | | $\sinh(ct)$ | $a<t<b$ | $\dfrac{\{e^{-as}[c\cosh(ac)+s\sinh(ac)] - e^{-bs}[c\cosh(bc)+s\sinh(bc)]\}}{s^2-c^2}$ | Re $s>-\infty$ |
| | | $0$ | $t>b$ | | |
| | 2 | $\dfrac{\sinh(at)}{t}$ | $0<t<1$ | $\frac{1}{2}\log\frac{s+a}{s-a}+\frac{1}{2}\mathrm{Ei}(a-s)-\frac{1}{2}\mathrm{Ei}(-a-s)$ | Re $s>-\infty$ |
| | | $0$ | $t>1$ | | |
| | 3 | $0$ | $0<t<a$ | | |
| | | $\sinh^2(ct)$ | $a<t<b$ | $\dfrac{\{e^{-as}[s\sinh^2(ac)+\frac{2c^2}{s}+c\sinh(2ab)] - e^{-bs}[s\sinh^2(bc)+\frac{2c^2}{s}+c\sinh(2bc)]\}}{s^2-4c^2}$ | Re $s>-\infty$ |
| | | $0$ | $t>b$ | | |
| | 4 | $0$ | $0<t<a$ | | |
| | | $\cosh(ct)$ | $a<t<b$ | $\dfrac{\{e^{-as}[s\cosh(ac)+c\sinh(ac)] - e^{-bs}[s\cosh(bc)+c\sinh(bc)]\}}{s^2-c^2}$ | Re $s>-\infty$ |
| | | $0$ | $t>b$ | | |
| | 5 | $0$ | $0<t<a$ | | |
| | | $\cosh^2(ct)$ | $a<t<b$ | $\dfrac{\{e^{-as}[s\cosh^2(ac)-\frac{2c^2}{s}+c\sinh(2ac)] - e^{-bs}[s\cosh^2(bc)-\frac{2c^2}{s}+c\sinh(2bc)]\}}{s^2-4c^2}$ | Re $s>-\infty$ |
| | | $0$ | $t>b$ | | |
| 33.9.1 | 1 | $P_n(1-t)$ | $0<t<2$ | $\left(\frac{2\pi}{s}\right)^{\frac{1}{2}} e^{-s} I_{n+\frac{1}{2}}(s)$ | $n=0,1,2,\ldots$ Re $s>-\infty$ |
| | | $0$ | $t>2$ | | |
| 33.9.2.1 | 1 | $[t(b-t)]^{\nu-\frac{1}{2}} C_n^{\nu}\left(\frac{2t}{b}-1\right)$ | $0<t<b$ | $\dfrac{(-1)^n\pi\Gamma(2\nu+n)}{n!\,\Gamma(\nu)}\left(\frac{b}{4s}\right)^{\nu} e^{-\frac{bs}{2}} I_{\nu+n}\left(\frac{bs}{2}\right)$ | Re $\nu>-\frac{1}{2}$ $n=0,1,2,\ldots$ Re $s>-\infty$ |
| | | $0$ | $t>b$ | | |
| 33.10.2 | 1 | $\dfrac{1}{t^{\frac{\nu}{2}}} J_\nu(2t^{\frac{1}{2}})$ | $0<t<b$ | $\displaystyle\sum_{n=0}^{\infty}\frac{(-1)^n b^{n+1} s^n L_n^{(\nu)}(-\frac{1}{s})}{(n+1)\,\Gamma(n+\nu+1)}$ | Re $s>-\infty$ |
| | | $0$ | $t>b$ | | |

| | | f(t) | g(s) | |
|---|---|---|---|---|
| 33.12.9.2.1 | 1 | $(2t-t^2)^{\frac{\nu}{2}} C_n^{\nu+\frac{1}{2}}(t-1) I_\nu[a(2t-t^2)^{\frac{1}{2}}]$ $\quad 0 < t < 2$ <br> $0 \quad t > 2$ | $\frac{(-1)^n (2\pi)^{\frac{1}{2}} a^\nu e^{-s} C_n^{\nu+\frac{1}{2}}\left[\frac{s}{(s^2+a^2)^{\frac{1}{2}}}\right]}{(s^2+a^2)^{\frac{\nu}{2}+\frac{1}{4}}}$ <br> $\cdot I_{\nu+\frac{1}{2}+n}[(s^2+a^2)^{\frac{1}{2}}]$ | $Re\,\nu > -1$ <br> $n = 0, 1, 2, \ldots$ <br> $Re\,s > -\infty$ |
| 34 | 1 | $[t]$ | $\frac{1}{s(e^s-1)}$ | $Re\,s > 0$ |

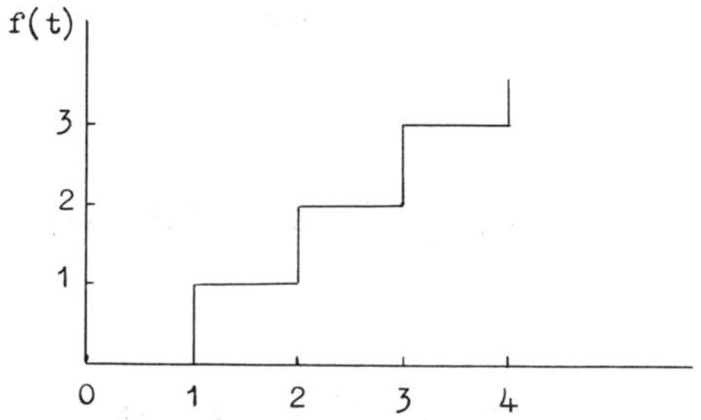


| | | | | |
|---|---|---|---|---|
| 34.1 | 1 | $[t+1]$ | $\frac{1}{s(1-e^{-s})}$ | $Re\,s > 0$ |

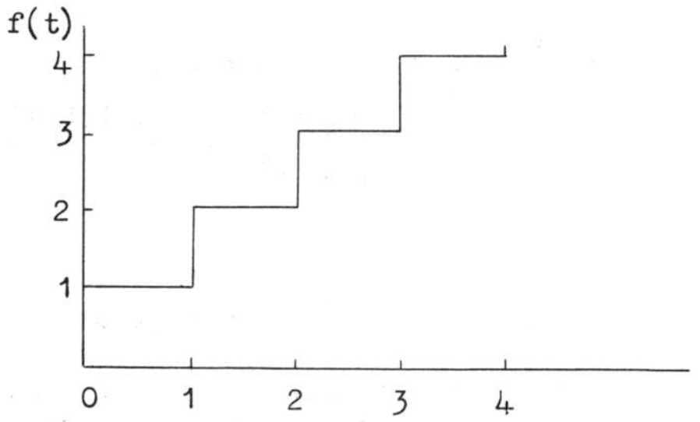


| | | | | |
|---|---|---|---|---|
| | 2 | $[2t+1]$ | $\frac{1}{s} \coth \frac{s}{2}$ | $Re\,s > 0$ |

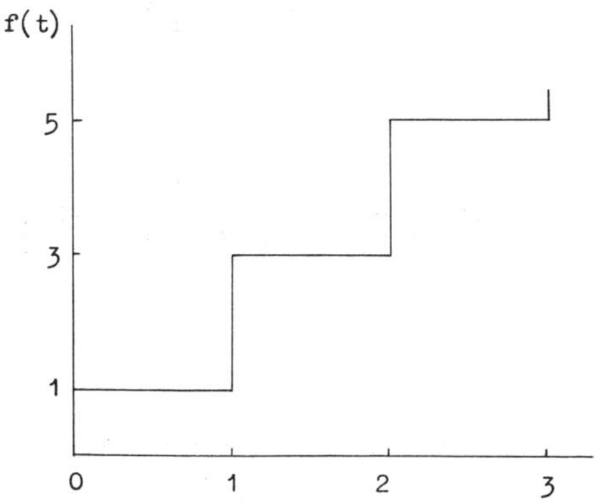

| | | f(t) | g(s) | |
|---|---|---|---|---|
| 34.1 (Contd.) | 3 | $[t(t-1)]$ | $\dfrac{2}{s^2(e^s-1)}$ | Re s > 0 |

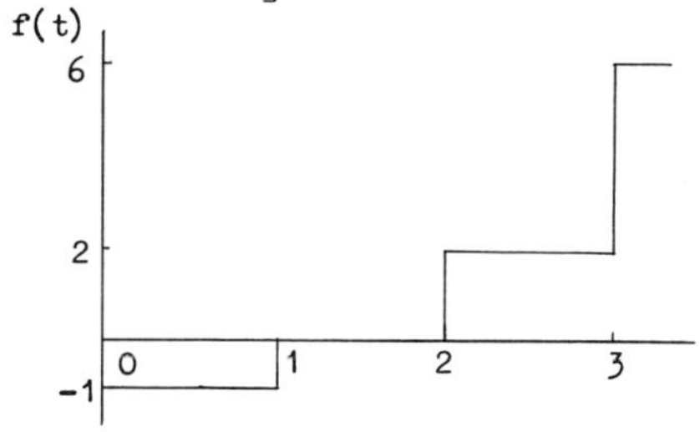


| | | | | |
|---|---|---|---|---|
| | 4 | $[t^2]$ | $\dfrac{e^s+1}{s(e^s-1)^2}$ | Re s > 0 |

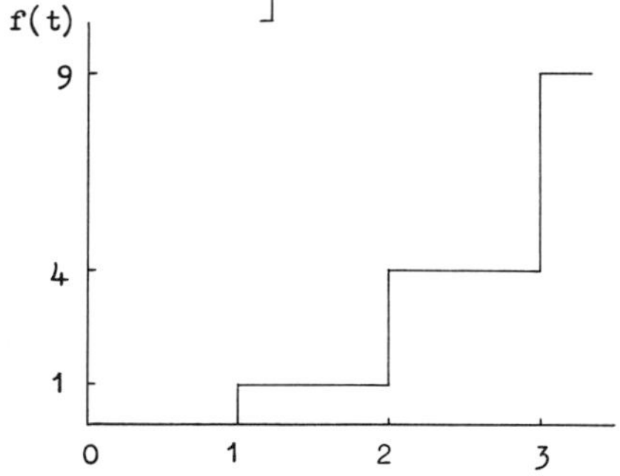


| | | | | |
|---|---|---|---|---|
| | 5 | $[t^3]$ | $\dfrac{e^{2s}+4e^s+1}{s(e^s-1)^3}$ | Re s > 0 |

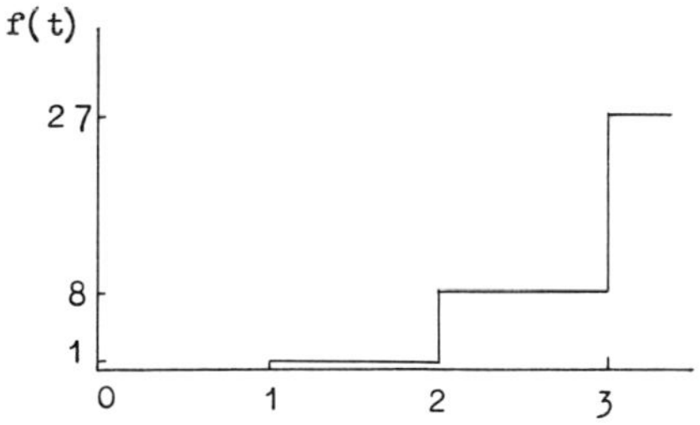


| | | | | |
|---|---|---|---|---|
| | 6 | $[t^4]$ | $\dfrac{e^{3s}+11e^{2s}+11e^s+1}{s(e^s-1)^4}$ | Re s > 0 |

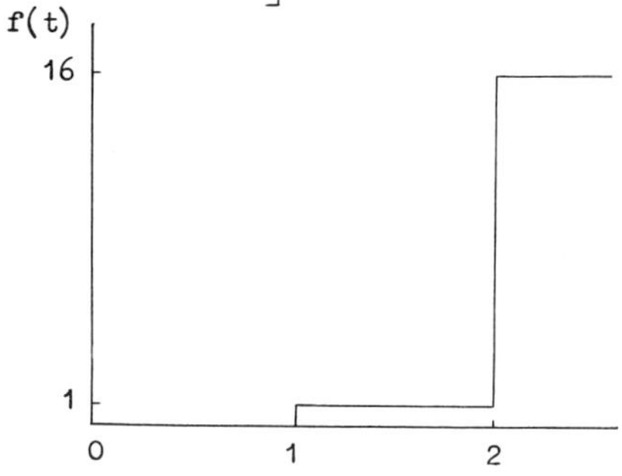

| | | f(t) | g(s) | |
|---|---|---|---|---|
| 34.1 (Contd.) | 7 | $[t^n]$ | $(-1)^n \frac{1-e^{-s}}{s} \frac{d^n}{ds^n}\left(\frac{1}{1-e^{-s}}\right)$ | $n=0,1,2,\ldots$ Re $s > 0$ |
| 34.3 | 1 | $[a^t]$ | $\frac{e^s-1}{s(e^s-a)}$ | Re $s >$ Re$(\log a)$ |
| | 2 | $[1-a^t]$ | $\frac{1-a}{s(e^s-a)}$ | Re $s <$ Max $0$, Re$(\log a)$ |
| | 3 | $\left[\frac{a^t-1}{a-1}\right] - [t]$ | $\frac{a-1}{s(e^s-1)(e^s-a)}$ | Re $s >$ Max $0$, Re$(\log a)$ |
| | 4 | $[ca^t-db^t]$ | $\frac{(e^s-1)[(c-d)e^s-cb+da]}{s(e^s-a)(e^s-b)}$ | Re $s >$ Max Re$(\log a)$, Re$(\log b)$ |
| 34.3.1 | 1 | $[ta^{t-1}]$ | $\frac{e^s-1}{s(e^s-a)^2}$ | Re $s >$ Re$(\log a)$ |
| | 2 | $[a^{t-1}-b^{t-1}]$ | $-\frac{a-b}{ab} \frac{e^s-1}{s} \frac{e^s-(a+b)}{(e^s-a)(e^s-b)}$ | Re $s >$ Max Re$(\log a)$, Re$(\log b)$ |
| | 3 | $[t^2 a^{t-1}]$ | $\frac{(e^s-1)(e^s+a)}{s(e^s-a)^3}$ | Re $s >$ Re$(\log a)$ |
| | 4 | $[t(t-1)a^{t-2}]$ | $\frac{2(e^s-1)}{s(e^s-a)^3}$ | Re $s >$ Re$(\log a)$ |
| 34.5 | 1 | $[\sin(at)]$ | $\frac{(e^s-1)\sin a}{s(e^{2s}-2e^s\cos a+1)}$ | Re $s > \lvert \text{Im}\, a \rvert$ |
| | 2 | $[\cos(at)]$ | $\frac{(e^s-1)(e^s-\cos a)}{s(e^{2s}-2e^s\cos a+1)}$ | Re $s > \lvert \text{Im}\, a \rvert$ |
| 34.5.3 | 1 | $[a^t\sin(bt)]$ | $\frac{a\sin b\,(e^s-1)}{s(e^{2s}-2ae^s\cos b+a^2)}$ | Re $s >$ Re$(\log a) + \lvert \text{Im}\, b \rvert$ |
| | 2 | $[a^t\cos(bt)]$ | $\frac{(e^s-1)(e^s-a\cos b)}{s(e^{2s}-2ae^s\cos b+a^2)}$ | Re $s >$ Re$(\log a) + \lvert \text{Im}\, b \rvert$ |

| | | f(t) | g(s) | |
|---|---|---|---|---|
| 34.21 | 1 | $\left[\binom{t}{n}\right.$ | $\dfrac{1}{s(e^{s}-1)^{n}}$ | $n=0,1,2,\ldots$<br>$\mathrm{Re}\, s>0$ |
| 34.21.1 | 1 | $\left[\dfrac{\Gamma(t+a+1)}{\Gamma(t+a+1-n)}\right.$ | $\dfrac{n!\, e^{as}}{s(e^{s}-1)^{n}}$ | $n=0,1,2,\ldots$<br>$a\leqslant n$<br>$\mathrm{Re}\, s>0$ |
| 34.21.3.1 | 1 | $\left[\binom{t}{n} a^{t-n}\right.$ | $\dfrac{e^{s}-1}{s(e^{s}-a)^{n+1}}$ | $n=0,1,2,\ldots$<br>$\mathrm{Re}\, s>\mathrm{Re}(\log a)$ |
| 35 | 1 | 1 $\quad 2nb<t<(2n+1)b$<br>0 $\quad (2n+1)b<t<(2n+2)b$ | $\dfrac{1}{s(1+e^{-bs})}$ | $n=0,1,2,\ldots$<br>$\mathrm{Re}\, s>0$ |

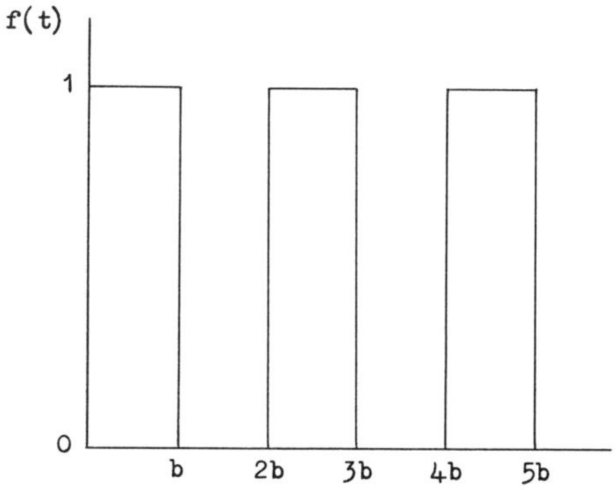


| | | f(t) | g(s) | |
|---|---|---|---|---|
| | 2 | 1 $\quad na<t<na+b$<br>0 $\quad na+b<t<(n+1)a$ | $\dfrac{1-e^{-bs}}{s(1-e^{-as})}$ | $n=0,1,2,\ldots$<br>$\mathrm{Re}\, s>0$ |

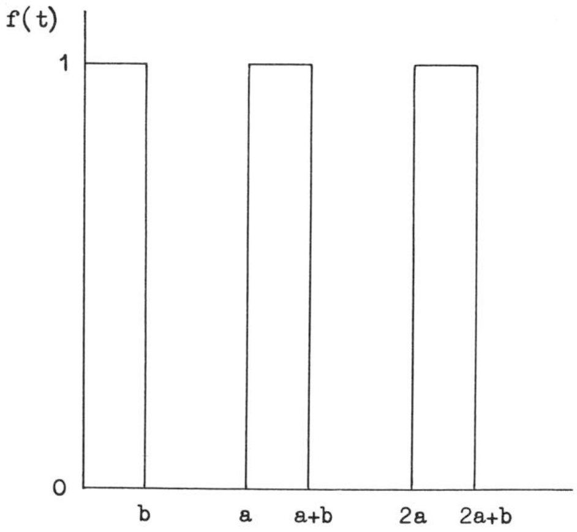

| | f(t) | | g(s) | |
|---|---|---|---|---|
| 35 (Contd.) 3 | 1 | $2nb < t < (2n+1)b$ | $\frac{1}{s}\tanh\frac{bs}{2} = \frac{1-e^{-bs}}{s(1+e^{-bs})}$ | $n = 0,1,2,\ldots$ / $\text{Re } s > 0$ |
| | $-1$ | $(2n+1)b < t < (2n+2)b$ | | |

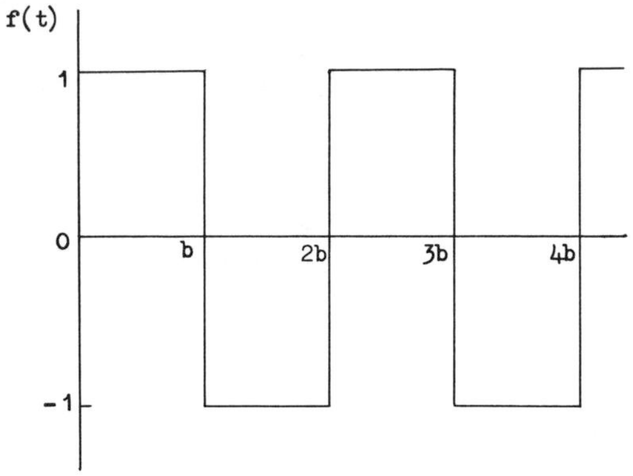


| | f(t) | | g(s) | |
|---|---|---|---|---|
| 4 | 1 | $0 < t < b$ | $\frac{1-\operatorname{sech}(bs)}{s}$ | $n = 1,2,3,\ldots$ / $\text{Re } s > 0$ |
| | $-1$ | $(4n-3)b < t < (4n-1)b$ | | |
| | 1 | $(4n-1)b < t < (4n+1)b$ | | |

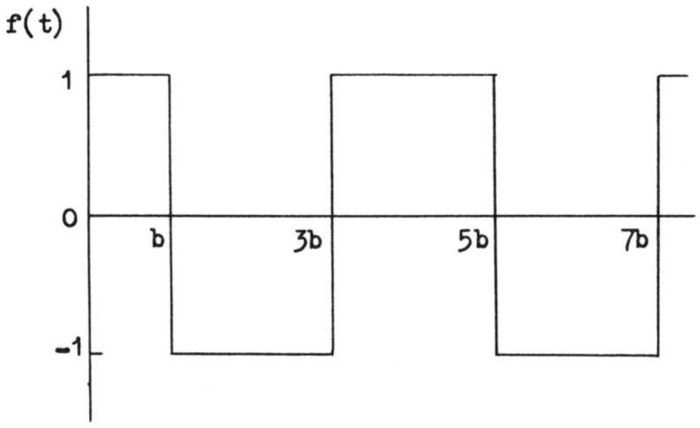


| | f(t) | | g(s) | |
|---|---|---|---|---|
| 5 | 1 | $(2n)^2\pi^2 < t < (2n+1)^2\pi^2$ | $\frac{1}{s}\theta_4(0\|s)$ | $n = 0,1,2,\ldots$ / $\text{Re } s > 0$ |
| | $-1$ | $(2n+1)^2\pi^2 < t < (2n+2)^2\pi^2$ | | |

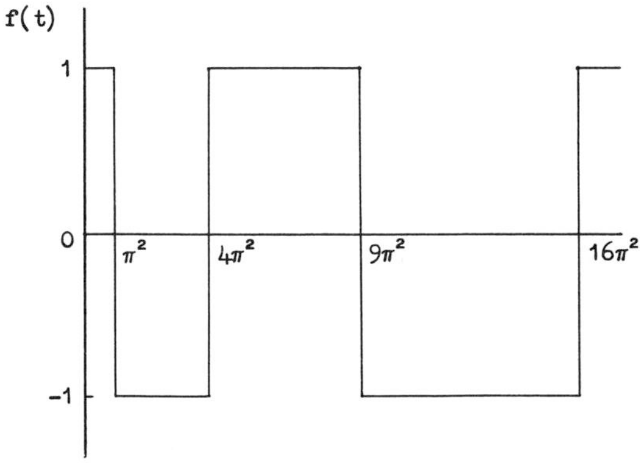

| | | f(t) | | g(s) | |
|---|---|---|---|---|---|
| 35 (Contd.) | 6 | $n$ | $\log n < t < \log(n+1)$ | $\frac{\zeta(s)}{s}$ | $n = 1,2,3,\ldots$ <br> Re $s > 1$ |

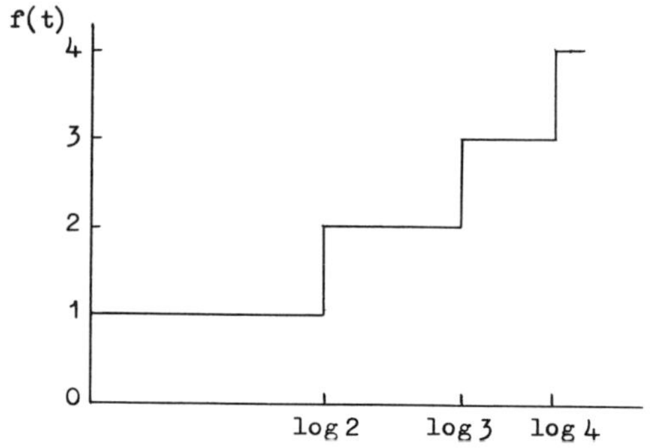


| | | | | |
|---|---|---|---|---|
| 7 | $n$ | $\log(2n-1) < t < \log(2n+1)$ | $\frac{1}{s}(1-2^{2-s})\zeta(s-1)$ | $n = 1,2,3,\ldots$ <br> Re $s > 0$ |

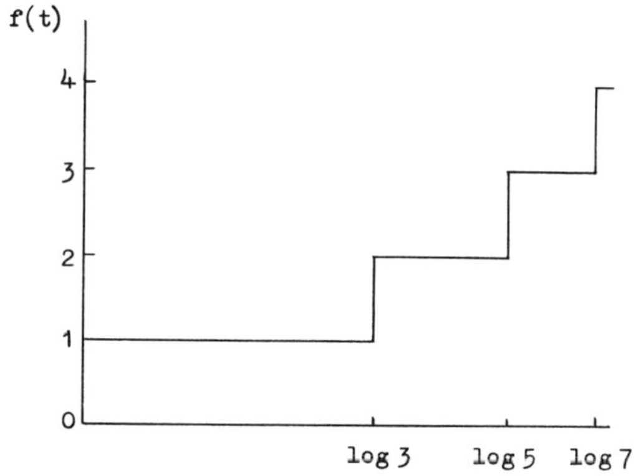


| | | | | |
|---|---|---|---|---|
| 8 | $2n+1$ | $\pi^2 n^2 < t < \pi^2(n+1)^2$ | $\frac{1}{s}\,\theta_3(0\|s)$ | $n = 0,1,2,\ldots$ <br> Re $s > 0$ |

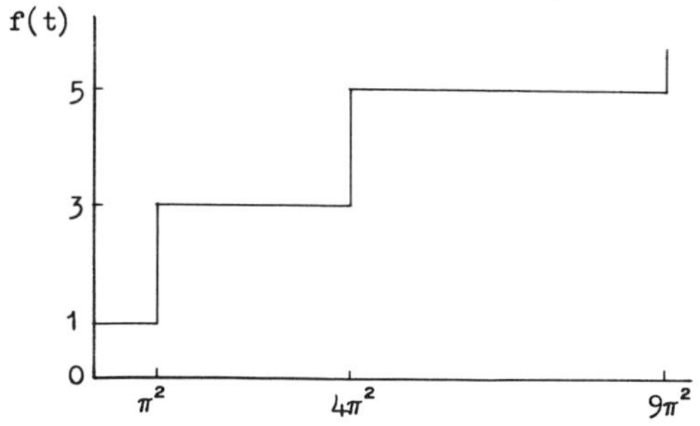


| | | | | |
|---|---|---|---|---|
| 9 | $\frac{1}{2}-(-\frac{1}{2})^{n+1}$ | $nb < t < (n+1)b$ | $\frac{4-e^{-bs}}{s(4+2e^{-bs})}$ | $n = 0,1,2,\ldots$ <br> Re $s > 0$ |

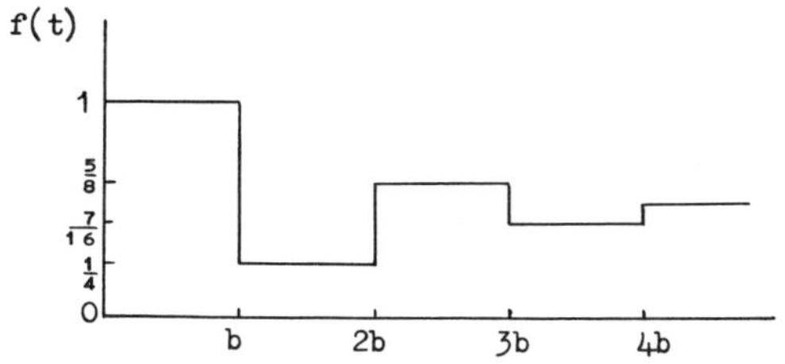

| | | f(t) | | g(s) | |
|---|---|---|---|---|---|
| 35 (Contd.) | 10 | $\binom{n}{m}$ | $nb < t < (n+1)b$ | $\dfrac{e^{-bs}}{s(e^{bs}-1)^m}$ | $n = 0,1,2,\ldots$ <br> $m = 0,1,2,\ldots$ |
| | 11 | $\sum\limits_{1 \leqslant n \leqslant e^t} \dfrac{1}{n^a}$ | | $\dfrac{1}{s}\zeta(s+a)$ | Re s >- Re a - 1 |
| | 12 | $t$ <br> $b$ | $o < t < b$ <br> $t > b$ | $\dfrac{1-e^{-bs}}{s^2}$ | Re s > o |

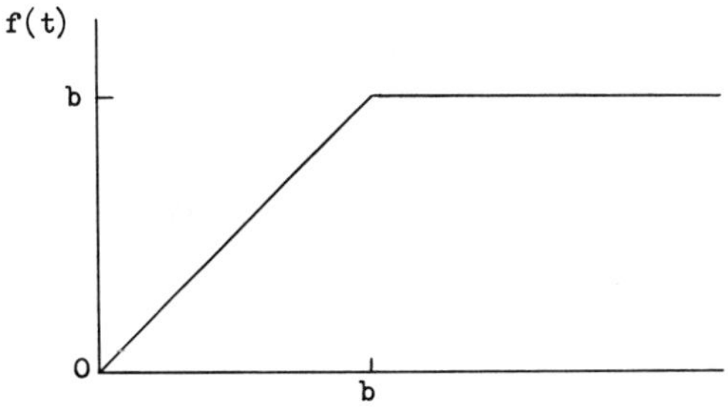


| | | f(t) | | g(s) | |
|---|---|---|---|---|---|
| 35.1 | 1 | $\dfrac{2t}{b} - 4n-1$ <br> $4n+3-\dfrac{2t}{b}$ | $2nb < t < (2n+1)b$ <br> $(2n+1)b < t < (2n+2)b$ | $\dfrac{2(1-e^{-as})}{as^2(1+e^{-as})} - \dfrac{1}{s}$ | $n = 0,1,2,\ldots$ <br> Re s > o |

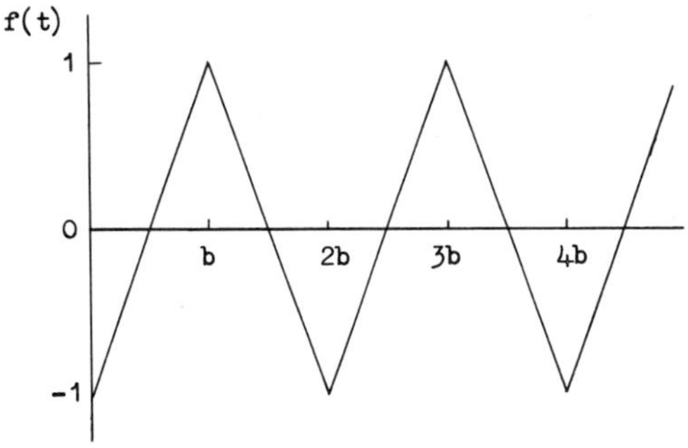


| | | f(t) | | g(s) | |
|---|---|---|---|---|---|
| | 2 | $b-(-1)^n(2bn+b-t)$ | $2nb < t < 2(n+1)b$ | $\dfrac{\tanh(bs)}{s^2}$ | $n = 0,1,2,\ldots$ <br> Re s > o |

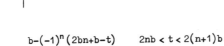

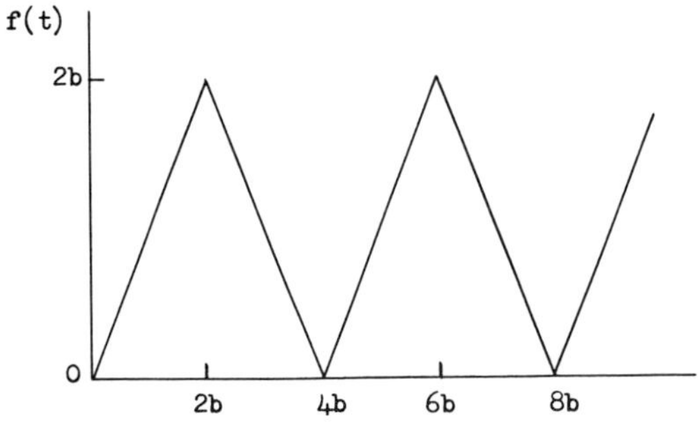

| | | f(t) | g(s) | |
|---|---|---|---|---|
| 35.1 (Contd.) | 3 | $$f(t)=\begin{cases}\dfrac{t-4na}{a} & 4na<t<(4n+1)a\\ \dfrac{4na+2a-t}{a} & (4n+1)a<t<(4n+2)a\\ 0 & (4n+2)a<t<(4n+4)a\end{cases}$$ | $$\frac{(1-e^{-as})^2}{as^2(1-e^{-4as})}$$ | $n=0,1,2,\ldots$ Re $s>0$ |

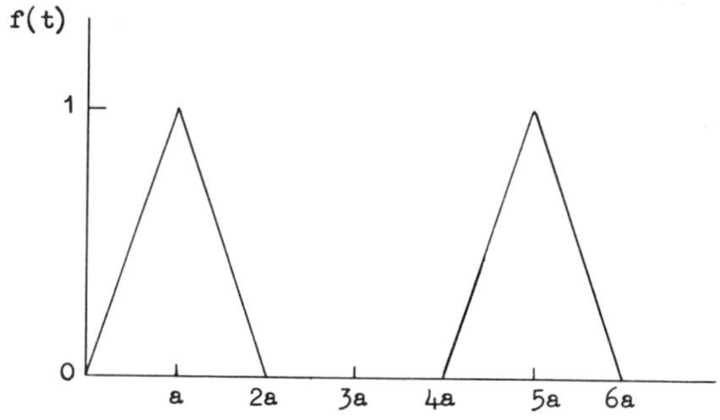


| | | f(t) | g(s) | |
|---|---|---|---|---|
| | 4 | $$f(t)=\begin{cases}\dfrac{2(t-na)}{b} & na<t<na+\dfrac{b}{2}\\ \dfrac{2(b+na-t)}{b} & na+\dfrac{b}{2}<t<na+b\\ 0 & na+b<t<(n+1)a\end{cases}$$ | $$\frac{2(1-e^{-\frac{bs}{2}})^2}{bs^2(1-e^{-as})}$$ | $n=0,1,2,\ldots$ Re $s>0$ |

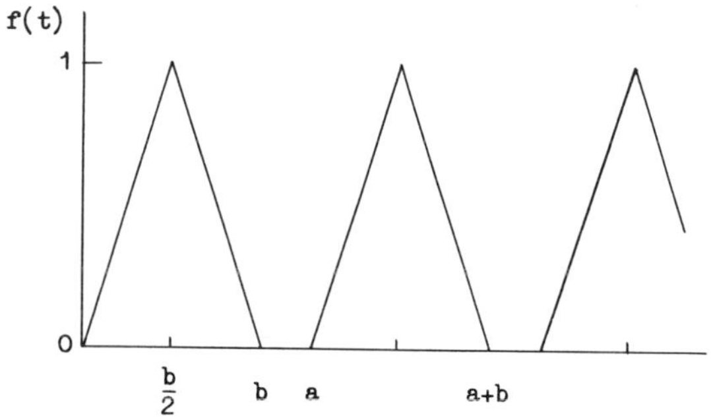


| | | f(t) | g(s) | |
|---|---|---|---|---|
| | 5 | $$f(t)=\begin{cases}-\dfrac{b}{a} & 0<t<\dfrac{a-b}{2}\\ \dfrac{2t}{a}-(4n+1) & \dfrac{(4n+1)a-b}{2}<t<\dfrac{(4n+1)a+b}{2}\\ \dfrac{b}{a} & \dfrac{(4n+1)a+b}{2}<t<\dfrac{(4n+3)a-b}{2}\\ -\dfrac{2t}{a}+(4n+3) & \dfrac{(4n+3)a-b}{2}<t<\dfrac{(4n+3)a+b}{2}\\ -\dfrac{b}{a} & \dfrac{(4n+3)a+b}{2}<t<\dfrac{(4n+5)a-b}{2}\end{cases}$$ | $$\frac{2(e^{-\frac{a-b}{2}s}-e^{-\frac{a+b}{2}s})}{as^2(1+e^{-as})}-\frac{b}{as}$$ | $n=0,1,2,\ldots$ Re $s>0$ |

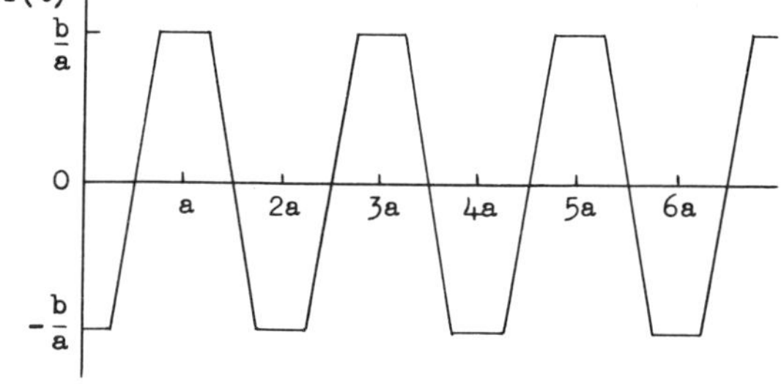

| | | f(t) | | g(s) | |
|---|---|---|---|---|---|
| 35.1 (Contd.) | 6 | $\frac{t-2na}{a}$ | $2na < t < 2na+b$ | $\frac{(1-e^{-bs})[1-e^{-(2-\frac{b}{a})as}]}{as^2(1-e^{-2as})}$ | $n=0,1,2,\ldots$<br>$\text{Re } s > 0$ |
| | | $\frac{b}{a}$ | $2na+b < t < (2n+2)a-b$ | | |
| | | $\frac{(2n+2)a-t}{a}$ | $(2n+2)a-b < t < (2n+2)a$ | | |

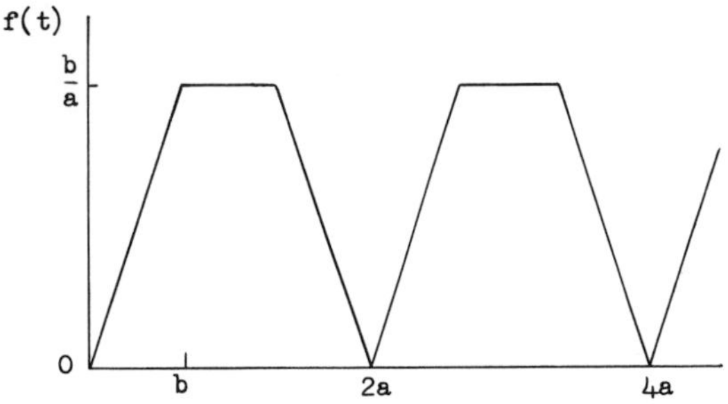


| | | f(t) | | g(s) | |
|---|---|---|---|---|---|
| | 7 | $\frac{t-4na}{a}$ | $4na < t < 4na+b$ | $\frac{(1-e^{-bs})[1-e^{-(2-\frac{b}{a})as}]}{as^2(1-e^{-4as})}$ | $n=0,1,2,\ldots$<br>$\text{Re } s > 0$ |
| | | $\frac{b}{a}$ | $4na+b < t < (4n+2)a-b$ | | |
| | | $\frac{(4n+2)a-t}{a}$ | $(4n+2)a-b < t < (4n+2)a$ | | |
| | | $0$ | $(4n+2)a < t < (4n+4)a$ | | |

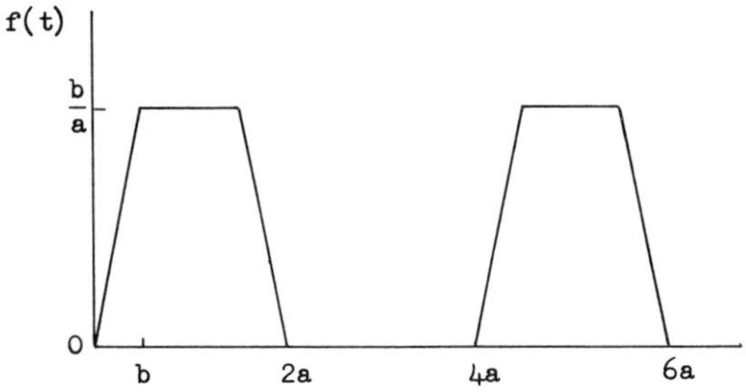


| | | f(t) | | g(s) | |
|---|---|---|---|---|---|
| | 8 | $\frac{2(t-na)}{b}$ | $na < t < na+c$ | $2\,\frac{1-e^{-cs}-e^{-(b-c)s}+e^{-bs}}{bs^2(1-e^{-as})}$ | $n=0,1,2,\ldots$<br>$\text{Re } s > 0$ |
| | | $\frac{2c}{b}$ | $na+c < t < na+b-c$ | | |
| | | $\frac{2(b+na-t)}{b}$ | $na+b-c < t < na+b$ | | |
| | | $0$ | $na+b < t < (n+1)a$ | | |

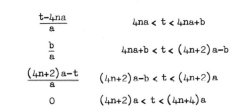

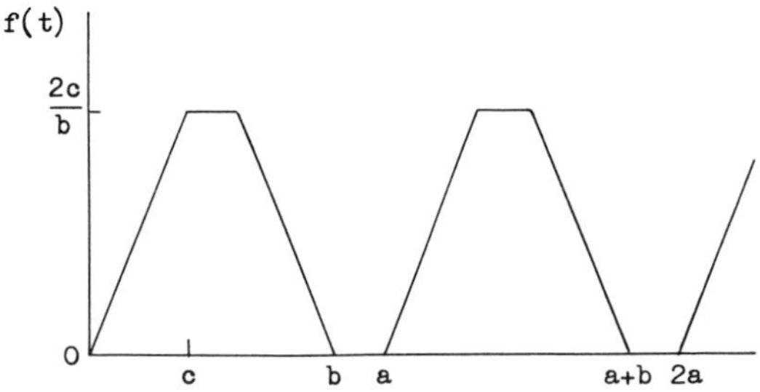

| | | $f(t)$ | | $g(s)$ | |
|---|---|---|---|---|---|
| 35.1 (Contd.) | 9 | $\frac{2t}{b} - 2n-1$ | $nb < t < (n+1)b$ | $\frac{2}{bs^2} - \frac{1+e^{-bs}}{s(1-e^{-bs})}$ | $n = 0,1,2,\dots$ Re $s > 0$ |

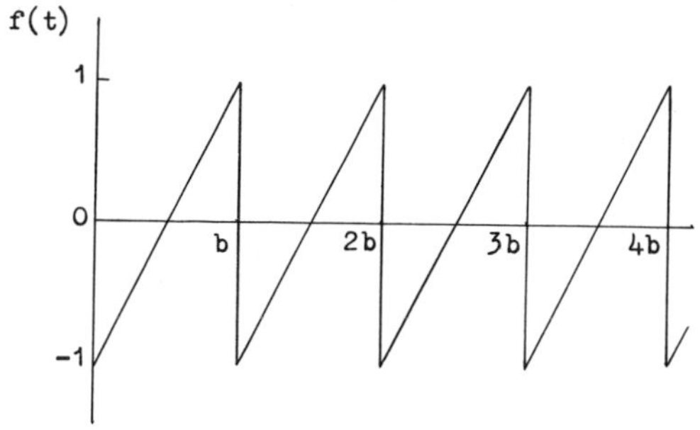


| | | | | |
|---|---|---|---|---|
| 10 | $t-nb$ | $nb < t < (n+1)b$ | $\frac{1}{s^2} - \frac{b}{2s}\left[\coth\frac{bs}{2} - 1\right]$ $= \frac{e^{bs}-bs-1}{s^2(e^{bs}-1)}$ | $n = 0,1,2,\dots$ Re $s > 0$ |

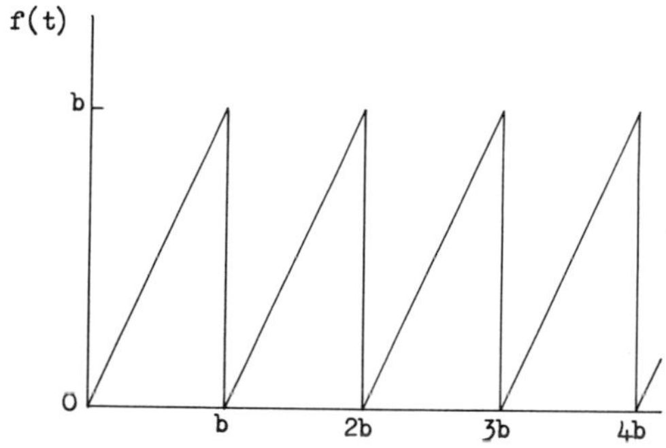


| | | | | |
|---|---|---|---|---|
| 11 | $t-an$<br>$0$ | $na < t < na+b$<br>$na+b < t < (n+1)a$ | $\frac{b}{a}\ \frac{1-(1+bs)e^{-bs}}{s^2(1-e^{-as})}$ | $n = 0,1,2,\dots$ Re $s > 0$ |

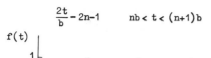

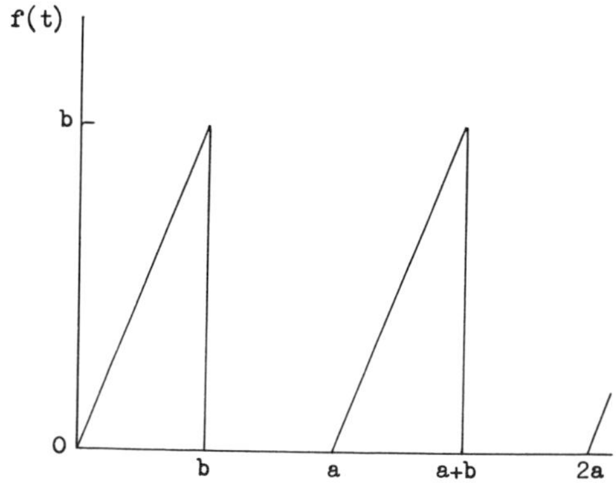

| | f(t) | | g(s) | |
|---|---|---|---|---|
| 35.1 (Contd.) 12 | $n+1-\frac{t}{b}$ | $nb<t<(n+1)b$ | $\frac{e^{-bs}+bs-1}{bs^2(1-e^{-bs})}$ | $n=0,1,2,\ldots$ Re $s>0$ |

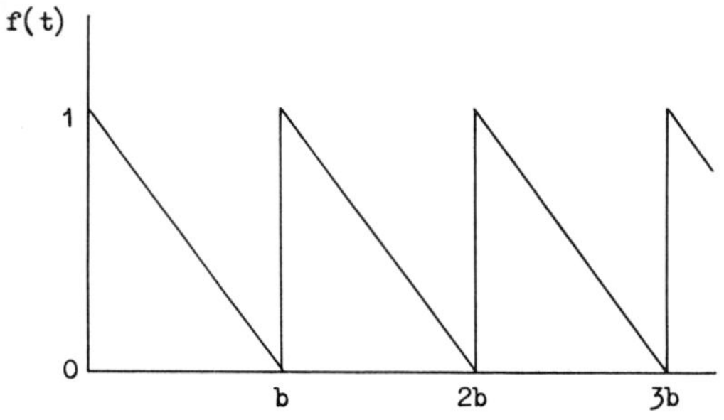


| | | | |
|---|---|---|---|
| 13 | $-\frac{b}{a}$ | $na<t<\frac{(2n+1)a-b}{2}$ | $\frac{2e^{-\frac{as}{2}}\left(e^{\frac{bs}{2}}-e^{-\frac{bs}{2}}\right)-bs\,(1+e^{-as})}{as^2(1-e^{-as})}$   $n=0,1,2,\ldots$ Re $s>0$ |
| | $\frac{2t}{a}-(2n+1)$ | $\frac{(2n+1)a-b}{2}<t<\frac{(2n+1)a+b}{2}$ | |
| | $\frac{b}{a}$ | $\frac{(2n+1)a+b}{2}<t<(n+1)a$ | |

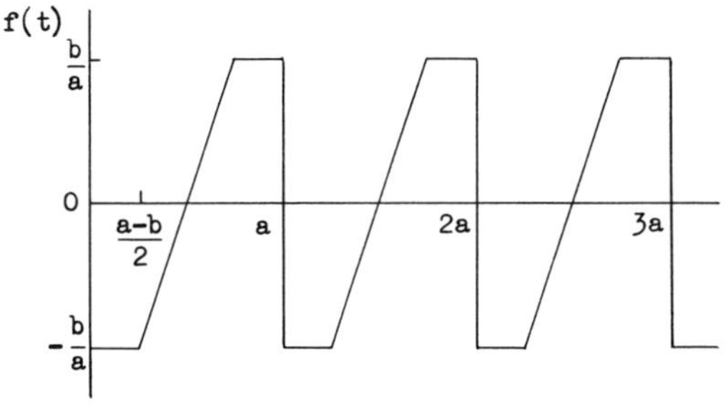


| | | | |
|---|---|---|---|
| 14 | $\frac{t-na}{a}$ | $na<t<na+b$ | $\frac{1-e^{-bs}-bse^{-as}}{as^2(1-e^{-as})}$   $n=0,1,2,\ldots$ Re $s>0$ |
| | $\frac{b}{a}$ | $na+b<t<(n+1)a$ | |

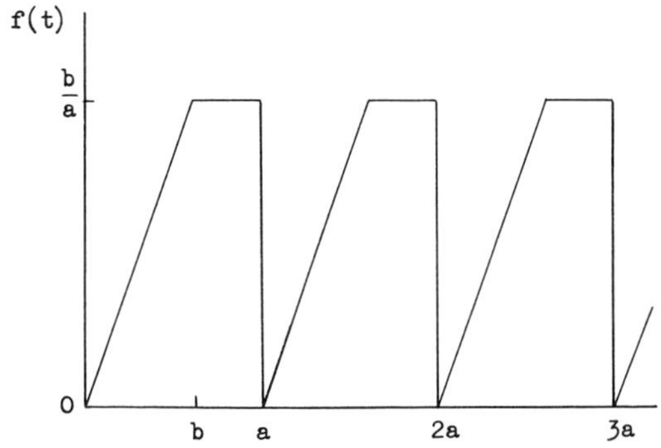

| | | f(t) | | g(s) | |
|---|---|---|---|---|---|
| 35.1 (Contd.) | 15 | $\frac{t-2na}{a}$ | $2na < t < 2na+b$ | $\frac{1-e^{-bs}-bse^{-as}}{as^2(1-e^{-2as})}$ | $n=0,1,2,\ldots$ |
| | | $\frac{b}{a}$ | $2na+b < t < (2n+1)a$ | | Re $s > 0$ |
| | | 0 | $(2n+1)a < t < (2n+2)a$ | | |

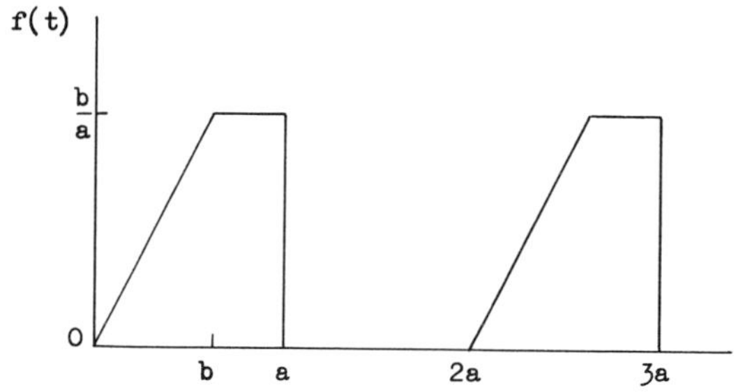


| | | | | | |
|---|---|---|---|---|---|
| | 16 | $\frac{t-na}{b}$ | $na < t < na+c$ | $\frac{1-e^{-cs}-cse^{-bs}}{bs^2(1-e^{-as})}$ | $n=0,1,2,\ldots$ |
| | | $\frac{c}{b}$ | $na+c < t < na+b$ | | Re $s > 0$ |
| | | 0 | $na+b < t < (n+1)a$ | | |

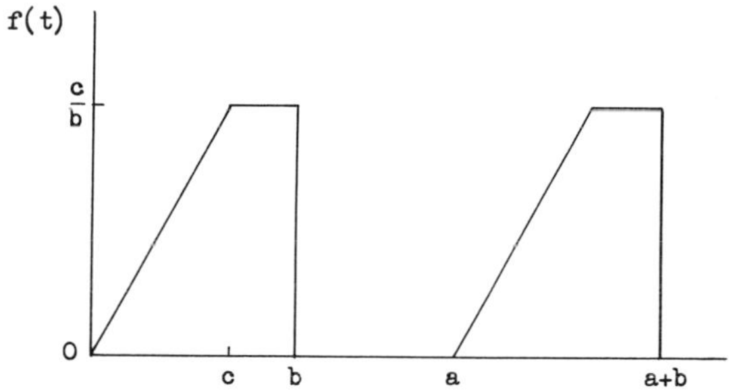


| | | | | | |
|---|---|---|---|---|---|
| | 17 | $\frac{t}{b}-2n$ | $2nb < t < (2n+1)b$ | $\frac{1-e^{-bs}}{bs^2(1+e^{-bs})}$ | $n=0,1,2,\ldots$ |
| | | $2(n+1)-\frac{t}{b}$ | $(2n+1)b < t < (2n+2)b$ | | Re $s > 0$ |

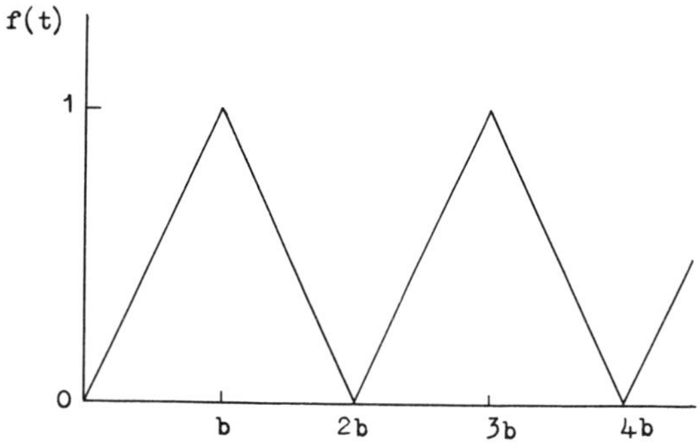

| | f(t) | | g(s) | |
|---|---|---|---|---|
| 35.1 (Contd.) 18 | $\frac{t}{b} - 2n$ | $2nb < t < (2n+1)b$ | $\frac{1-(1+bs)e^{-bs}}{bs^2(1-e^{-2bs})}$ | $n = 0,1,2,\ldots$ Re $s > 0$ |
| | $0$ | $(2n+1)b < t < (2n+2)b$ | | |

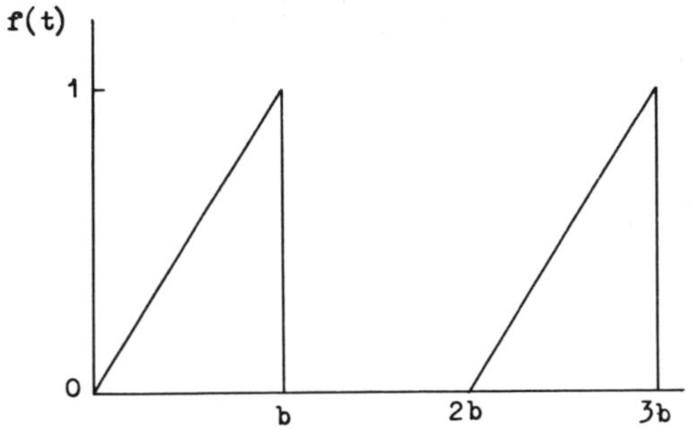


| | | | | |
|---|---|---|---|---|
| 19 | $\frac{t-an}{b}$ | $na < t < na+b$ | $\frac{1}{(a-b)s^2}\left[\frac{a(1-e^{-bs})}{b(1-e^{-as})} - 1\right]$ | $n = 0,1,2,\ldots$ Re $s > 0$ |
| | $\frac{a(n+1)-t}{a-b}$ | $na+b < t < (n+1)a$ | | |

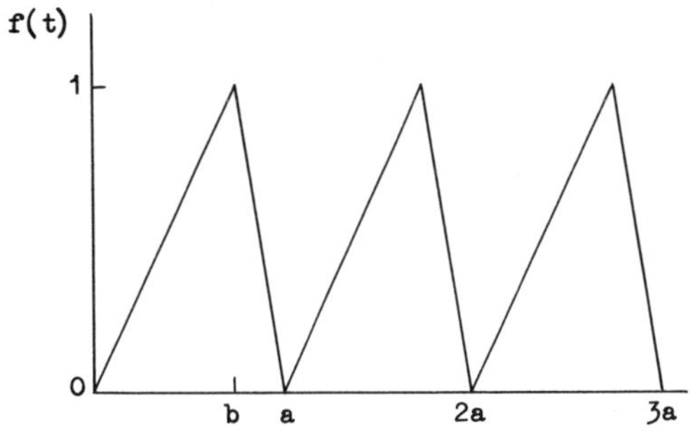


| | | | | |
|---|---|---|---|---|
| 20 | $\frac{t-na}{c}$ | $na < t < na+c$ | | |
| | $\frac{na+b-t}{b-c}$ | $na+c < t < na+b$ | $\frac{b(1-e^{-cs})-c(1-e^{-bs})}{c(b-c)s^2(1-e^{-as})}$ | $n = 0,1,2,\ldots$ Re $s > 0$ |
| | $0$ | $na+b < t < (n+1)a$ | | |

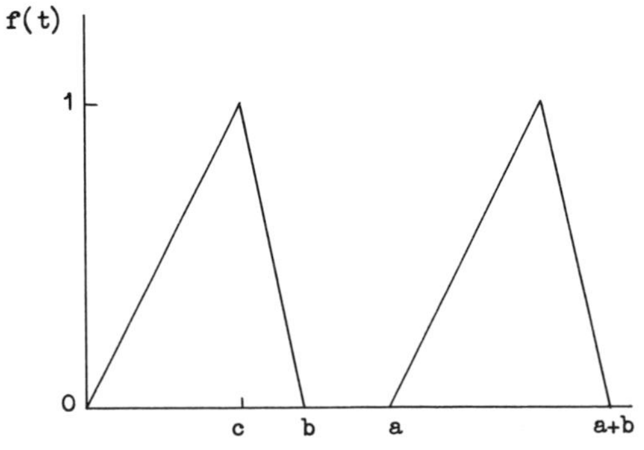

| | | f(t) | | g(s) | |
|---|---|---|---|---|---|
| 5.1 (Contd.) | 21 | $\frac{t-2na}{b}$<br>$\frac{(2n+1)a-t}{a-b}$<br>$0$ | $2na < t < 2na+b$<br>$2na+b < t < (2n+1)a$<br>$(2n+1)a < t < (2n+2)a$ | $\frac{a(1-e^{-bs})-b(1-e^{-as})}{b(a-b)s^2(1-e^{-2as})}$ | $n=0,1,2,\ldots$<br>$\text{Re } s > 0$ |

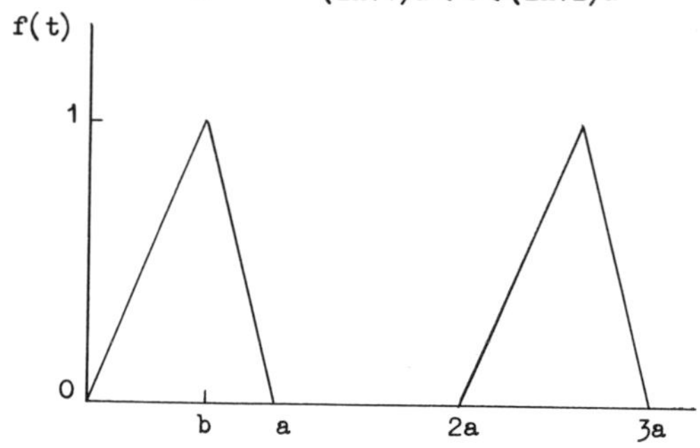


| | | f(t) | | g(s) | |
|---|---|---|---|---|---|
| | 22 | $(2n+1)t-bn(n+1)$ | $nb < t < (n+1)b$ | $\frac{\coth(\frac{bs}{2})}{s^2}$ | $n=0,1,2,\ldots$<br>$\text{Re } s > 0$ |

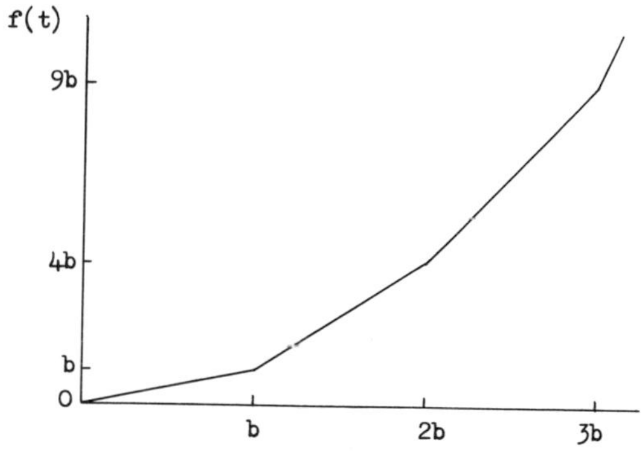


| | | f(t) | | g(s) | |
|---|---|---|---|---|---|
| | 23 | $\frac{1}{2}t^2$<br>$1-\frac{1}{2}(t-2)^2$<br>$1$ | $0 < t < 1$<br>$1 < t < 2$<br>$t > 2$ | $\frac{(1-e^{-s})^2}{s^3}$ | $\text{Re } s > 0$ |
| | 24 | $(t-nb)^2$ | $nb < t < (n+1)b$ | $\frac{2}{s^3} - \frac{b(b+2s)}{s^2(e^{bs}-1)}$ | $n=0,1,2,\ldots$<br>$\text{Re } s > 0$ |
| 5.2 | 1 | $[b(t-nb)-(t-nb)^2]^\nu$ | $nb < t < (n+1)b$ | $\frac{\pi \,\text{cosech}\, \frac{bs}{2}\Gamma(2\nu+1)}{\Gamma(\nu+\frac{1}{2})}\left(\frac{b}{4s}\right)^{\nu+\frac{1}{2}} \cdot I_{\nu+\frac{1}{2}}\left(\frac{bs}{2}\right)$ | $n=0,1,2,\ldots$<br>$\text{Re } \nu > -1$<br>$\text{Re } s > 0$ |

| | | f(t) | g(s) | |
|---|---|---|---|---|
| 35.2 (Contd.) | 2 | $[2b(t-2nb)-(t-2nb)^2]^{\nu}$ $\quad 2nb < t < (2n+1)b$ <br> $-[2b(t-2nb)-(t-2nb)^2]^{\nu}$ $\quad (2n+1)b < t < (2n+2)b$ | $\pi\left(\frac{b}{2s}\right)^{\nu+\frac{1}{2}} \frac{\Gamma(2\nu+1)}{\Gamma(\nu+\frac{1}{2})} \frac{L_{\nu+\frac{1}{2}}(bs)}{\sinh(bs)}$ | $n=0,1,2,\ldots$ <br> $\mathrm{Re}\,\nu > -1$ <br> $\mathrm{Re}\,s > 0$ |
| | 3 | $\frac{\cos[2\pi(\nu-\frac{1}{2})]}{(bt-t^2)^{\nu}}$ $\quad 0 < t < b$ <br> $-\frac{\sin[2\pi(\nu-\frac{1}{2})]}{(t^2-bt)^{\nu}}$ $\quad t > b$ | $\frac{\pi^{\frac{3}{2}} e^{-\frac{bs}{2}} s^{\nu-\frac{1}{2}}}{\Gamma(\nu) b^{\nu-\frac{1}{2}}} I_{\nu-\frac{1}{2}}\left(\frac{bs}{2}\right)$ | $\mathrm{Re}\,\nu < 1$ <br> $\mathrm{Re}\,s > 0$ |
| | 4 | $\sum_{1 \leq n \leq e^t} (t-\log n)^a$ | $\frac{\Gamma(a+1)\zeta(s)}{s^{a+1}}$ | $\mathrm{Re}\,a > -1$ <br> $\mathrm{Re}\,s > 0$ |
| 35.4 | 1 | $\log b \quad 0 < t < b$ <br> $\log t \quad t > b$ | $\frac{1}{s}[\log b - \mathrm{Ei}(-bs)]$ | $\mathrm{Re}\,s > 0$ |
| | 2 | $\log t \quad 0 < t < b$ <br> $\log b \quad t > b$ | $\frac{1}{s}[\mathrm{Ei}(-bs) - \log(\gamma s)]$ | $\mathrm{Re}\,s > -\infty$ |
| 35.4.1 | 1 | $\log\lvert b-t\rvert$ | $\frac{1}{s}[\log b - e^{-bs}\,\overline{\mathrm{Ei}}(bs)]$ | $\mathrm{Re}\,s > 0$ |
| | 2 | $\log\lvert t^2-b^2\rvert$ | $\frac{1}{s}[2\log b - e^{bs}\mathrm{Ei}(-bs) - e^{-bs}\overline{\mathrm{Ei}}(bs)]$ | $\mathrm{Re}\,s > 0$ <br> $b > 0$ |
| | 3 | $\frac{1}{t}\log\lvert 1-b^2t^2\rvert$ | $\overline{\mathrm{Ei}}(\frac{s}{b})\mathrm{Ei}(-\frac{s}{b})$ | $b > 0$ <br> $\mathrm{Re}\,s > 0$ |

| | | f(t) | | g(s) | |
|---|---|---|---|---|---|
| 5.5 | 1 | $\sin bt$ | $\frac{2n\pi}{b} < t < \frac{(2n+1)\pi}{b}$ | $\frac{b}{s^2+b^2} \cdot \frac{1}{1-e^{-\frac{\pi}{b}s}}$ | $n = 0,1,2,\ldots$ <br> $\operatorname{Re} s > 0$ |
| | | $0$ | $\frac{(2n+1)\pi}{b} < t < \frac{(2n+2)\pi}{b}$ | | |
| | 2 | $\sin(at)$ | $2nb\pi < t < (2n+1)b\pi$ | $\frac{a}{(s^2+a^2)(1+e^{-b\pi s})}$ | $n = 0,1,2,\ldots$ <br> $\operatorname{Re} s > \lvert \operatorname{Im} a \rvert$ |
| | | $0$ | $(2n+1)b\pi < t < (2n+2)b\pi$ | | |
| | 3 | $\lvert \sin(bt) \rvert$ | | $\frac{b}{s^2+b^2} \; \frac{1+e^{-\frac{\pi s}{b}}}{1-e^{-\frac{\pi s}{b}}} = \frac{b}{s^2+b^2} \coth \frac{\pi s}{2b}$ | $\operatorname{Re} s > \lvert \operatorname{Im} b \rvert$ |
| | 4 | $\lvert \sin(bt) \rvert^{2\nu}$ | | $\frac{B(1+\frac{is}{2b}, 1-\frac{is}{2b})}{(2\nu+1) 2^{2\nu} s \, B(\nu+1+\frac{is}{2b}, \nu+1-\frac{is}{2b})}$ | $\operatorname{Re} \nu > -\frac{1}{2}$ <br> $\operatorname{Re} s > \lvert \operatorname{Im} b \rvert$ |
| | 5 | $\sin^2(at)$ | $2nb\pi < t < (2n+1)b\pi$ | $\frac{2a^2}{s(s^2+4a^2)(1+e^{-b\pi s})}$ | $n = 0,1,2,\ldots$ <br> $\operatorname{Re} s > 2\lvert \operatorname{Im} a \rvert$ |
| | | $0$ | $(2n+1)b\pi < t < (2n+2)b\pi$ | | |
| | 6 | $\cos(bt)$ | $2n\pi < bt < (2n+1)\pi$ | $\frac{s}{s^2+b^2} \coth \frac{\pi s}{2b}$ | $n = 0,1,2,\ldots$ <br> $\operatorname{Re} s > 0$ |
| | | $-\cos(bt)$ | $(2n+1)\pi < bt < (2n+2)\pi$ | | |
| | 7 | $\cos(at)$ | $2nb\pi < t < (2n+1)b\pi$ | $\frac{s}{(s^2+a^2)(1+e^{-b\pi s})}$ | $n = 0,1,2,\ldots$ <br> $\operatorname{Re} s > \lvert \operatorname{Im} a \rvert$ |
| | | $0$ | $(2n+1)b\pi < t < (2n+2)b\pi$ | | |
| | 8 | $1-\cos(bt)$ | $2n < \frac{bt}{2m\pi} < 2n+1$ | $\frac{b^2}{s(s^2+b^2)(1+e^{-\frac{2m\pi s}{b}})}$ | $m = 1,2,3,\ldots$ <br> $n = 0,1,2,\ldots$ <br> $\operatorname{Re} s > 0$ |
| | | $0$ | $2n+1 < \frac{bt}{2m\pi} < 2n+2$ | | |

| | | f(t) | | g(s) | |
|---|---|---|---|---|---|
| 35.5 (Contd.) | 9 | $\lvert\cos(bt)\rvert$ | | $\dfrac{s+b\ \operatorname{cosech}\left(\frac{\pi s}{2b}\right)}{s^2+b^2}$ | |
| | | | | $= \dfrac{1}{s^2+b^2}\left(s+\dfrac{2be^{-\frac{\pi s}{2b}}}{1-e^{-\frac{\pi s}{b}}}\right)$ | $\operatorname{Re} s > \lvert \operatorname{Im} b \rvert$ |
| | 10 | $\lvert\cos(bt)\rvert-\cos(bt)$ | | $\dfrac{b\ \operatorname{cosech}\frac{\pi s}{2b}}{s^2+b^2}$ | $\operatorname{Re} s > \lvert \operatorname{Im} b \rvert$ |
| | 11 | $\cos^2(at)$ | $2nb\pi < t < (2n+1)b\pi$ | $\dfrac{s^2+2a^2}{s(s^2+4a^2)(1+e^{-b\pi s})}$ | $n = 0,1,2,\ldots$ |
| | | $0$ | $(2n+1)b\pi < t < (2n+2)b\pi$ | | $\operatorname{Re} s > 2\lvert \operatorname{Im} a \rvert$ |
| 35.16 | 1 | $\operatorname{Erf}(at)$ | $0 < t < \frac{b}{a}$ | $\frac{1}{s}\, e^{\frac{s^2}{4a^2}}\left[\operatorname{Erf}\left(\frac{s}{2a}\right)-\operatorname{Erf}\left(\frac{s}{2a}+b\right)\right]$ | $\operatorname{Re} s > 0$ |
| | | $\operatorname{Erf}(b)$ | $t > \frac{b}{a}$ | | |
| 36 | 1 | $0$ | $0 < t < b$ | $\frac{1}{s}\, e^{-bs}$ | $\operatorname{Re} s > 0$ |
| | | $1$ | $t > b$ | | |
| | 2 | $0$ | $0 < t < b$ | $\left(\frac{b}{s}+\frac{1}{s^2}\right)e^{-bs}$ | $\operatorname{Re} s > 0$ |
| | | $t$ | $t > b$ | | |
| | 3 | $0$ | $0 < t < b$ | $-\operatorname{Ei}(-bs)$ | $\operatorname{Re} s > 0$ |
| | | $\frac{1}{t}$ | $t > b$ | | |
| 36.1 | 1 | $0$ | $0 < t < b$ | $\left(\frac{2}{s^3}+\frac{2b}{s^2}+\frac{b^2}{s}\right)e^{-bs}$ | $\operatorname{Re} s > 0$ |
| | | $t^2$ | $t > b$ | | |

| | | f(t) | | g(s) | |
|---|---|---|---|---|---|
| 36.1 (Contd.) | 2 | $0$ <br> $t^n$ | $0<t<b$ <br> $t>b$ | $e^{-bs}\sum_{m=0}^{n}\frac{n!}{m!}\frac{b^m}{s^{n-m+1}}$ | $n=0,1,2,\ldots$ <br> $\mathrm{Re}\, s>0$ |
| | 3 | $0$ <br> $\frac{1}{t^2}$ | $0<t<b$ <br> $t>b$ | $\frac{e^{-bs}}{b}+s\mathrm{Ei}(-bs)$ | $\mathrm{Re}\, s>0$ |
| | 4 | $0$ <br> $\frac{1}{t+a}$ | $0<t<b$ <br> $t>b$ | $-e^{as}\mathrm{Ei}[-(a+b)s]$ | $\lvert\arg(a+b)\rvert<\pi$ <br> $\mathrm{Re}\, s>0$ |
| | 5 | $0$ <br> $\frac{1}{(t+a)^n}$ | $0<t<b$ <br> $t>b$ | $e^{-bs}\sum_{m=1}^{n-1}\frac{(m-1)!}{(n-1)!}\frac{(-s)^{n-m-1}}{(a+b)^m}$ <br> $-\frac{(-s)^{n-1}}{(n-1)!}e^{as}\mathrm{Ei}[-(a+b)s]$ | $n=2,3,4,\ldots$ <br> $\lvert\arg(a+b)\rvert<\pi$ <br> $\mathrm{Re}\, s>0$ |
| 36.2 | 1 | $0$ <br> $\frac{1}{t^{\frac{1}{2}}}$ | $0<t<b$ <br> $t>b$ | $(\frac{\pi}{s})^{\frac{1}{2}}\mathrm{Erfc}[(bs)^{\frac{1}{2}}]$ | $\mathrm{Re}\, s>0$ |
| | 2 | $0$ <br> $\frac{1}{t^{\frac{3}{2}}}$ | $0<t<b$ <br> $t>b$ | $\frac{2}{b^{\frac{1}{2}}}e^{-bs}-2(\pi s)^{\frac{1}{2}}\mathrm{Erfc}[(bs)^{\frac{1}{2}}]$ | $\mathrm{Re}\, s\geqslant 0$ |
| | 3 | $0$ <br> $t^{\nu}$ | $0<t<b$ <br> $t>b$ | $\frac{\Gamma(\nu+1,bs)}{s^{\nu+1}}$ | $\mathrm{Re}\, s>0$ |
| | 4 | $0$ <br> $(t-b)^{\nu}$ | $0<t<b$ <br> $t>b$ | $\frac{\Gamma(\nu+1)e^{-bs}}{s^{\nu+1}}$ | $\mathrm{Re}\,\nu>-1$ <br> $\mathrm{Re}\, s>0$ |

| | | f(t) | g(s) | |
|---|---|---|---|---|
| 36.2 (Contd.) | 5 | $0 \quad 0<t<b$ ; $\dfrac{(t-b)^{\frac{1}{2}}}{t} \quad t>b$ | $\pi^{\frac{1}{2}}s^{\frac{1}{2}}e^{-bs}-\pi b^{\frac{1}{2}}\mathrm{Erfc}(b^{\frac{1}{2}}s^{\frac{1}{2}})$ | Re $s>0$ |
| | 6 | $0 \quad 0<t<b$ ; $\dfrac{(t-b)^{\nu}}{t} \quad t>b$ | $\Gamma(\nu+1)b^{\nu}\Gamma(-\nu,bs)$ | Re $\nu>-1$ <br> Re $s>0$ |
| | 7 | $0 \quad 0<t<b$ ; $\dfrac{1}{t(t-b)^{\frac{1}{2}}} \quad t>b$ | $\pi b^{-\frac{1}{2}}\mathrm{Erfc}(b^{\frac{1}{2}}s^{\frac{1}{2}})$ | Re $s\geqslant 0$ |
| | 8 | $0 \quad 0<t<b$ ; $\dfrac{(t-b)^{\nu-1}}{(t+b)^{\nu+\frac{1}{2}}} \quad t>b$ | $2^{\nu-\frac{1}{2}}\Gamma(\nu)b^{-\frac{1}{2}}D_{-2\nu}(2b^{\frac{1}{2}}s^{\frac{1}{2}})$ | Re $\nu>0$ <br> Re $s\geqslant 0$ |
| | 9 | $0 \quad 0<t<b$ ; $\dfrac{(t-b)^{\nu-1}}{(t+b)^{\nu-\frac{1}{2}}} \quad t>b$ | $2^{\nu-\frac{1}{2}}\Gamma(\nu)s^{-\frac{1}{2}}D_{1-2\nu}(2b^{\frac{1}{2}}s^{\frac{1}{2}})$ | Re $\nu>0$ <br> Re $s>0$ |
| | 10 | $0 \quad 0<t<b$ ; $(t+a)^{\mu}(t-b)^{\nu} \quad t>b$ | $\dfrac{\Gamma(\nu+1)(a+b)^{\frac{\mu+\nu}{2}}}{s^{\frac{\mu+\nu}{2}+1}}e^{\frac{(a-b)s}{2}}\cdot W_{\frac{\mu-\nu}{2},\frac{\mu+\nu+1}{2}}[(a+b)s]$ | Re $\nu>-1$ <br> $\lvert\arg(a+b)\rvert<\pi$ <br> Re $s>0$ |
| | 11 | $0 \quad 0<t<b$ ; $[(t+b)^{\frac{1}{2}}+(t-b)^{\frac{1}{2}}]^{\nu}-[(t+b)^{\frac{1}{2}}-(t-b)^{\frac{1}{2}}]^{\nu} \quad t>b$ | $(2b)^{\frac{\nu}{2}}\dfrac{\nu}{s}K_{\frac{\nu}{2}}(bs)$ | Re $s>0$ |

| | | f(t) | | g(s) | |
|---|---|---|---|---|---|
| 36.2 (Contd.) | 12 | $0$ | $0 < t < b$ | $K_0(bs)$ | Re $s > 0$ |
| | | $\frac{1}{(t^2-b^2)^{\frac{1}{2}}}$ | $t > b$ | | |
| | 13 | $0$ | $0 < t < b$ | $bK_1(bs)$ | Re $s > 0$ |
| | | $\frac{t}{(t^2-b^2)^{\frac{1}{2}}}$ | $t > b$ | | |
| | 14 | $0$ | $0 < t < b$ | $\frac{1}{\pi^{\frac{1}{2}}}\Gamma(\nu+1)\left(\frac{2b}{s}\right)^{\nu+\frac{1}{2}} K_{\nu+\frac{1}{2}}(bs)$ | Re $\nu > -1$<br>Re $s > 0$ |
| | | $(t^2-b^2)^{\nu}$ | $t > b$ | | |
| | 15 | $0$ | $0 < t < 1$ | $2K_{\nu}(s)$ | Re $s > 0$ |
| | | $\frac{[t+(t^2-1)^{\frac{1}{2}}]^{\nu}+[t-(t^2-1)^{\frac{1}{2}}]^{\nu}}{(t^2-1)^{\frac{1}{2}}}$ | $t > 1$ | | |
| | 16 | $0$ | $0 < t < 1$ | $\left(\frac{2s}{\pi}\right)^{\frac{1}{2}} K_{\frac{\nu}{2}+\frac{1}{4}}\left(\frac{s}{2}\right) K_{\frac{\nu}{2}-\frac{1}{4}}\left(\frac{s}{2}\right)$ | Re $s > 0$ |
| | | $\frac{[t+(t^2-1)^{\frac{1}{2}}]^{\nu}+[t-(t^2-1)^{\frac{1}{2}}]^{\nu}}{t^{\frac{1}{2}}(t^2-1)^{\frac{1}{2}}}$ | $t > 1$ | | |
| 36.3 | 1 | $0$ | $0 < t < a \log b$ | $\frac{a\,n!\,b^{-as}\Gamma(as)}{\Gamma(as+n+1)}$ | $n = 0, 1, 2, \ldots$<br>Re $s > 0$ |
| | | $(1-be^{-\frac{t}{a}})^n$ | $t > a \log b$ | | |
| | 2 | $0$ | $0 < t < \log b$ | $\frac{B(s, a+1)}{b^s}$ | Re $a > -1$<br>$b > 1$<br>Re $s > 0$ |
| | | $(1-be^{-t})^a$ | $t > \log b$ | | |

| | | f(t) | | g(s) | |
|---|---|---|---|---|---|
| 36.3 (Contd.) | 3 | $0$ | $0 < t < b$ | $\frac{\pi^{\frac{1}{2}}\Gamma(s)\Gamma(\nu+1)e^{-\frac{b(s+\nu)}{2}}}{2^{\frac{s+\nu}{2}}\Gamma(\frac{s+\nu+1}{2})} \cdot P^{-\frac{s+\nu}{2}}_{\frac{\nu-s}{2}}[(1-e^{-2b})^{\frac{1}{2}}]$ | $\operatorname{Re}\nu > -1$ <br> $\operatorname{Re}s > 0$ |
| | | $\frac{[e^{-b}(1-e^{-2t})^{\frac{1}{2}} - e^{-t}(1-e^{-2b})^{\frac{1}{2}}]^{\nu}}{(1-e^{-2t})^{\frac{1}{2}}}$ | $t > b$ | | |
| 36.3.1 | 1 | $0$ | $0 < t < b$ | $\frac{e^{-bs}}{s+a}$ | $\operatorname{Re}s > -\operatorname{Re}a$ |
| | | $e^{-a(t-b)}$ | $t > b$ | | |
| | 2 | $0$ | $0 < t < b$ | $\frac{a\,e^{-bs}}{s(s+a)}$ | $\operatorname{Re}s > \operatorname{Max}\ 0, -\operatorname{Re}a$ |
| | | $1-e^{-a(t-b)}$ | $t > b$ | | |
| | 3 | $0$ | $0 < t < b$ | $\pi^{\frac{1}{2}}a^{\frac{1}{2}}e^{as^2}\operatorname{Erfc}\left(a^{\frac{1}{2}}s + \frac{b}{2a^{\frac{1}{2}}}\right)$ | $\operatorname{Re}a > 0$ <br> $\operatorname{Re}s > -\infty$ |
| | | $e^{-\frac{t^2}{4a}}$ | $t > b$ | | |
| 36.3.2 | 1 | $0$ | $0 < t < b$ | $\frac{Q(as,\nu+1)}{(s-b)s^{\nu+1}}$ | $\operatorname{Re}s > b$ |
| | | $e^{bt}\int_a^t e^{-bu}u^{\nu}du$ | $t > b$ | | |
| 36.4 | 1 | $0$ | $0 < t < b$ | $\frac{1}{s}[e^{-bs}\log b - \operatorname{Ei}(-bs)]$ | $\operatorname{Re}s > 0$ |
| | | $\log t$ | $t > b$ | | |
| 36.4.1 | 1 | $0$ | $0 < t < b$ | $\frac{1}{2}e^{bs}[\operatorname{Ei}(-bs)]^2$ | $\operatorname{Re}s > 0$ |
| | | $\frac{\log\frac{t}{b}}{t+b}$ | $t > b$ | | |

| | | f(t) | | g(s) | |
|---|---|---|---|---|---|
| 36.4.1 (Contd.) | 2 | $0$ | $0<t<b$ | $e^{bs}\{\frac{1}{2}[Ei(-bs)]^2-\log b\, Ei(-2bs)\}$ | Re s > 0 |
| | | $\frac{\log t}{t+b}$ | $t>b$ | | |
| | 3 | $0$ | $0<t<1$ | $\frac{1}{2}[Ei(-\frac{s}{2})]^2$ | Re s > 0 |
| | | $\frac{1}{t}\log(2t-1)$ | $t>1$ | | |
| | 4 | $0$ | $0<t<a+b$ | $Ei(-as)Ei(-bs)$ | a > 0<br>b > 0<br>Re s > 0 |
| | | $\frac{1}{t}\log\frac{(t-a)(t-b)}{ab}$ | $t>a+b$ | | |
| 36.4.2 | 1 | $0$ | $0<t<b$ | $\frac{1}{2s}K_0(bs)$ | Re s > 0 |
| | | $\log\frac{(t+b)^{\frac{1}{2}}+(t-b)^{\frac{1}{2}}}{(2b)^{\frac{1}{2}}}$ | $t>b$ | | |
| 36.5 | 1 | $0$ | $0<t<\frac{\pi}{2}$ | $\frac{(2n)!e^{-\frac{\pi}{2}s}\left\{1+\frac{s^2}{2!}+\cdots+\frac{s^2(s^2+2^2)\cdots[s^2+(2n-2)^2]}{(2n)!}\right\}}{s[s^2+2^2][s^2+4^2]\cdots[s^2+(2n)^2]}$ | n = 1,2,3,...<br>Re s > 0 |
| | | $\sin^{2n}t$ | $t>\frac{\pi}{2}$ | | |
| | 2 | $0$ | $0<t<\frac{\pi}{2}$ | $\frac{(2n+1)!se^{-\frac{\pi}{2}s}\left\{1+\frac{s^2+1^2}{3!}+\cdots+\frac{(s^2+1^2)(s^2+3^2)\cdots[s^2+(2n-1)^2]}{(2n+1)!}\right\}}{[s^2+1^2][s^2+3^2]\cdots[s^2+(2n+1)^2]}$ | n = 0,1,2,...<br>Re s > 0 |
| | | $\sin^{2n+1}t$ | $t>\frac{\pi}{2}$ | | |
| | 3 | $0$ | $0<t<\frac{\pi}{2}$ | $\frac{e^{-\frac{\pi}{2}s}}{(1+s^2)^2}[\frac{\pi}{2}s(1+s^2)+s^2-1]$ | Re s > 0 |
| | | $t\sin t$ | $t>\frac{\pi}{2}$ | | |
| | 4 | $0$ | $0<t<\frac{\pi}{2}$ | $\frac{(2n)!e^{-\frac{\pi}{2}s}}{s(s^2+2^2)(s^2+4^2)\cdots(s^2+4n^2)}$ | n = 1,2,3,...<br>Re s > 0 |
| | | $\cos^{2n}t$ | $t>\frac{\pi}{2}$ | | |

| | | f(t) | | g(s) | |
|---|---|---|---|---|---|
| 36.5 (Contd.) | 5 | $0$ | $0 < t < \frac{\pi}{2}$ | $\frac{-(2n+1)!\,e^{-\frac{\pi}{2}s}}{[s^2+1^2][s^2+3^2]\cdots[s^2+(2n+1)^2]}$ | $n = 0,1,2,\ldots$ Re $s > 0$ |
| | | $\cos^{2n+1} t$ | $t > \frac{\pi}{2}$ | | |
| | 6 | $0$ | $0 < t < \frac{\pi}{2}$ | $-e^{\frac{\pi}{2}s}\,\frac{\frac{\pi}{2}(1+s^2)+2s}{(1+s^2)^2}$ | Re $s > 0$ |
| | | $t\cos t$ | $t > \frac{\pi}{2}$ | | |
| 36.5.1 | 1 | $0$ | $0 < t < b$ | $\frac{s+ac}{s^2+a^2}\,e^{-bs}$ | Re $s > \lvert \mathrm{Im}\, a\rvert$ |
| | | $\cos[a(t-b)]+c\sin[a(t-b)]$ | $t > b$ | | |
| 36.5.2 | 1 | $0$ | $0 < t < b$ | $\frac{a\pi^{\frac{1}{2}}e^{-b(s^2+a^2)^{\frac{1}{2}}}}{2^{\frac{1}{2}}(s^2+a^2)^{\frac{1}{2}}[s+(s^2+a^2)^{\frac{1}{2}}]^{\frac{1}{2}}}$ | Re $s > \lvert \mathrm{Im}\, a\rvert$ |
| | | $\frac{\sin[a(t^2-b^2)^{\frac{1}{2}}]}{(t+b)^{\frac{1}{2}}}$ | $t > b$ | | |
| | 2 | $0$ | $0 < t < b$ | $ab\,\frac{K_1[b(s^2+a^2)^{\frac{1}{2}}]}{(s^2+a^2)^{\frac{1}{2}}}$ | Re $s > \lvert \mathrm{Im}\, a\rvert$ |
| | | $\sin[a(t^2-b^2)^{\frac{1}{2}}]$ | $t > b$ | | |
| | 3 | $0$ | $0 < t < b$ | $\left(\frac{\pi}{2}\right)^{\frac{1}{2}}\frac{[s+(s^2+a^2)^{\frac{1}{2}}]^{\frac{1}{2}}}{(s^2+a^2)^{\frac{1}{2}}}e^{-b(s^2+a^2)^{\frac{1}{2}}}$ | Re $s > \lvert \mathrm{Im}\, a\rvert$ |
| | | $\frac{\cos[a(t^2-b^2)^{\frac{1}{2}}]}{(t+b)^{\frac{1}{2}}}$ | $t > b$ | | |
| 36.6 | 1 | $0$ | $0 < t < b$ | $\frac{b}{s}\int_s^\infty K_0(bu)\,du$ | Re $s > 0$ |
| | | $\cos^{-1}\frac{b}{t}$ | $t > b$ | | |
| 36.7 | 1 | $0$ | $0 < t < 1$ | $-\frac{1}{2}\mathrm{Ei}(a-s)+\frac{1}{2}\mathrm{Ei}(-a-s)$ | Re $s > \lvert \mathrm{Re}\, a\rvert$ |
| | | $\frac{\sinh(at)}{t}$ | $t > 1$ | | |

| | | f(t) | | g(s) | |
|---|---|---|---|---|---|
| 36.7 (Contd.) | 2 | $0$ | $0<t<1$ | $-\frac{1}{2}\mathrm{Ei}(a-s)-\frac{1}{2}\mathrm{Ei}(-a-s)$ | $\mathrm{Re}\, s>\lvert\mathrm{Re}\, a\rvert$ |
| | | $\frac{\cosh(at)}{t}$ | $t>1$ | | |
| | 3 | $0$ | $0<t<b$ | $-i(\frac{2}{\pi})^{\frac{1}{2}}e^{i\nu\pi}\Gamma(\nu)\sinh^{\nu-\frac{1}{2}}b\; Q_{s-\frac{1}{2}}^{\frac{1}{2}-\nu}(\cosh b)$ | $\mathrm{Re}\,\nu>0$ |
| | | $(\cosh t-\cosh b)^{\nu-1}$ | $t>b$ | | $\mathrm{Re}\, s>\mathrm{Re}(\nu-1)$ |
| 36.7.1 | 1 | $0$ | $0<t<b$ | $\frac{s+ac}{s^2-a^2}e^{-bs}$ | $\mathrm{Re}\, s>\lvert\mathrm{Re}\, a\rvert$ |
| | | $\cosh[a(t-b)+c\sinh[a(t-b)]$ | $t>b$ | | |
| 36.7.2 | 1 | $0$ | $0<t<b$ | $(\frac{\pi}{2})^{\frac{1}{2}}e^{-b(s^2-a^2)^{\frac{1}{2}}}\left[\frac{s-(s^2-a^2)^{\frac{1}{2}}}{s^2-a^2}\right]^{\frac{1}{2}}$ | $\mathrm{Re}\, s>\lvert\mathrm{Re}\, a\rvert$ |
| | | $\frac{\sinh[a(t^2-b^2)^{\frac{1}{2}}]}{(t+b)^{\frac{1}{2}}}$ | $t>b$ | | |
| | 2 | $0$ | $0<t<b$ | $(\frac{\pi}{2})^{\frac{1}{2}}e^{-b(s^2-a^2)^{\frac{1}{2}}}\left[\frac{(s^2-a^2)^{\frac{1}{2}}+s}{s^2-a^2}\right]^{\frac{1}{2}}$ | $\mathrm{Re}\, s>\lvert\mathrm{Re}\, a\rvert$ |
| | | $\frac{\cosh[a(t^2-b^2)^{\frac{1}{2}}]}{(t+b)^{\frac{1}{2}}}$ | $t>b$ | | |
| 36.7.3 | 1 | $0$ | $0<t<\cosh^{-1}a$ | $(\frac{2}{\pi})^{\frac{1}{2}}\frac{\Gamma(-\mu)}{[-(a^2-1)^{\frac{1}{2}}]^{\mu-\frac{1}{2}}}Q_s^{\mu-\frac{1}{2}}(a)$ | $\mathrm{Re}\,\mu<1$ |
| | | $\frac{e^{-\frac{t}{2}}}{(\cosh t-a)^{\mu}}$ | $t>\cosh^{-1}a$ | | $\mathrm{Re}\, s>-\mathrm{Re}(\mu+\frac{1}{2})$ |
| 36.8 | 1 | $0$ | $0<t<b$ | $\frac{1}{s}K_0(bs)$ | $\mathrm{Re}\, s>0$ |
| | | $\cosh^{-1}\frac{t}{b}$ | $t>b$ | | |
| 36.8.7 | 1 | $0$ | $0<t<b$ | $\frac{\nu}{s}K_{\nu}(bs)$ | $\mathrm{Re}\, s>0$ |
| | | $\sinh[\nu\cosh^{-1}\frac{t}{b}]$ | $t>b$ | | |

| | | f(t) | | g(s) | |
|---|---|---|---|---|---|
| 36.8.7.2 | 1 | $0$ | $0 < t < b$ | $K_{\nu}(bs)$ | Re s > 0 |
| | | $\dfrac{\cosh(\nu\cosh^{-1}\frac{t}{b})}{(t^2-b^2)^{\frac{1}{2}}}$ | $t > b$ | | |
| | 2 | $0$ | $0 < t < b$ | $(\frac{s}{2\pi})^{\frac{1}{2}}\, K_{\frac{\nu}{2}+\frac{1}{4}}(\frac{bs}{2}) K_{\frac{\nu}{2}-\frac{1}{4}}(\frac{bs}{2})$ | Re s > 0 |
| | | $\dfrac{\cosh(\nu\cosh^{-1}\frac{t}{b})}{t^{\frac{1}{2}}(t^2-b^2)^{\frac{1}{2}}}$ | $t > b$ | | |
| 36.9.2 | 1 | $0$ | $0 < t < 1$ | $\frac{n}{s} K_n(s)$ | $n = 0,1,2,\ldots$ Re s > 0 |
| | | $(t^2-1)^{\frac{1}{2}} U_n(t)$ | $t > 1$ | | |
| | 2 | $0$ | $0 < t < 1$ | $K_n(s)$ | $n = 0,1,2,\ldots$ Re s > 0 |
| | | $\dfrac{T_n(t)}{(t^2-1)^{\frac{1}{2}}}$ | $t > 1$ | | |
| 36.10.2 | 1 | $0$ | $0 < t < b$ | $(\frac{2}{\pi})^{\frac{1}{2}} \dfrac{K_{\frac{1}{2}}[b(s^2+a^2)^{\frac{1}{2}}]}{(s^2+a^2)^{\frac{1}{4}}}$ | Re s > 0 |
| | | $\dfrac{J_0[a(t^2-b^2)^{\frac{1}{2}}]}{t^{\frac{1}{2}}}$ | $t > b$ | | |
| | 2 | $0$ | $0 < t < b$ | $\dfrac{e^{-b(s^2+a^2)^{\frac{1}{2}}}}{(s^2+a^2)^{\frac{1}{2}}}$ | Re s > \|Im a\| |
| | | $J_0[a(t^2-b^2)^{\frac{1}{2}}]$ | $t > b$ | | |
| | 3 | $0$ | $0 < t < b$ | $\dfrac{s[b(s^2+a^2)^{\frac{1}{2}}+1]}{(s^2+a^2)^{\frac{3}{2}}} e^{-b(s^2+a^2)^{\frac{1}{2}}}$ | Re s > \|Im a\| |
| | | $t\, J_0[a(t^2-b^2)^{\frac{1}{2}}]$ | $t > b$ | | |
| | 4 | $0$ | $0 < t < b$ | $\dfrac{a[b(s^2+a^2)^{\frac{1}{2}}+1]}{(s^2+a^2)^{\frac{3}{2}}} e^{-b(s^2+a^2)^{\frac{1}{2}}}$ | Re s > \|Im a\| |
| | | $(t^2-b^2)^{\frac{1}{2}} J_1[a(t^2-b^2)^{\frac{1}{2}}]$ | $t > b$ | | |

| | f(t) | | g(s) | |
|---|---|---|---|---|
| 36.10.2 (Contd.) 5 | $0$ | $0<t<b$ | $\frac{e^{-bs}-e^{-b(s^2+a^2)^{\frac{1}{2}}}}{ab}$ | $\mathrm{Re}\, s>\lvert\mathrm{Im}\, a\rvert$ |
| | $\frac{J_1[a(t^2-b^2)^{\frac{1}{2}}]}{(t^2-b^2)^{\frac{1}{2}}}$ | $t>b$ | | |
| 6 | $0$ | $0<t<b$ | $\frac{1}{a}\left[e^{-bs}-\frac{s}{(s^2+a^2)^{\frac{1}{2}}}e^{-b(s^2+a^2)^{\frac{1}{2}}}\right]$ | $\mathrm{Re}\, s>\lvert\mathrm{Im}\, a\rvert$ |
| | $\frac{t\, J_1[a(t^2-b^2)^{\frac{1}{2}}]}{(t^2-b^2)^{\frac{1}{2}}}$ | $t>b$ | | |
| 7 | $0$ | $0<t<b$ | $\frac{1}{a}\left[1-\frac{s}{(s^2+a^2)^{\frac{1}{2}}}\right]e^{-b(s^2+a^2)^{\frac{1}{2}}}$ | $\mathrm{Re}\, s>\lvert\mathrm{Im}\, a\rvert$ |
| | $\left(\frac{t-b}{t+b}\right)^{\frac{1}{2}}J_1[a(t^2-b^2)^{\frac{1}{2}}]$ | $t>b$ | | |
| 8 | $0$ | $0<t<b$ | $I_{\frac{\nu}{2}}\{\frac{b}{2}[(s^2+a^2)^{\frac{1}{2}}-s]\}K_{\frac{\nu}{2}}\{\frac{b}{2}[(s^2+a^2)^{\frac{1}{2}}+s]\}$ | $\mathrm{Re}\,\nu>-1$ <br> $\mathrm{Re}\, s>\lvert\mathrm{Im}\, a\rvert$ |
| | $\frac{J_\nu[a(t^2-b^2)^{\frac{1}{2}}]}{(t^2-b^2)^{\frac{1}{2}}}$ | $t>b$ | | |
| 9 | $0$ | $0<t<b$ | $\frac{a^\nu e^{-b(s^2+a^2)^{\frac{1}{2}}}}{(s^2+a^2)^{\frac{1}{2}}[s+(s^2+a^2)^{\frac{1}{2}}]^\nu}$ | $\mathrm{Re}\,\nu>-1$ <br> $\mathrm{Re}\, s>\lvert\mathrm{Im}\, a\rvert$ |
| | $\left(\frac{t-b}{t+b}\right)^{\frac{\nu}{2}}J_\nu[a(t^2-b^2)^{\frac{1}{2}}]$ | $t>b$ | | |
| 10 | $0$ | $0<t<b$ | $\frac{2^{\frac{1}{2}}a^\nu b^{\nu+\frac{1}{2}}K_{\nu+\frac{1}{2}}[b(s^2+a^2)^{\frac{1}{2}}]}{\pi^{\frac{1}{2}}(s^2+a^2)^{\frac{\nu}{2}+\frac{1}{4}}}$ | $\mathrm{Re}\,\nu>-1$ <br> $\mathrm{Re}\, s>\lvert\mathrm{Im}\, a\rvert$ |
| | $(t^2-b^2)^{\frac{\nu}{2}}J_\nu[a(t^2-b^2)^{\frac{1}{2}}]$ | $t>b$ | | |
| 11 | $0$ | $0<t<b$ | $\sum_{n=0}^{\infty}\frac{(-1)^n(ab)^{2\nu+2n}(2b)^{2\mu+1}\Gamma(\mu+\nu+n+1)}{\pi^{\frac{1}{2}}n!\Gamma(2\nu+n+1)(2s)^{\mu+\nu+n+\frac{1}{2}}}\cdot K_{\mu+\nu+n+\frac{1}{2}}(bs)$ | $\mathrm{Re}(\mu+\nu)>-1$ <br> $\mathrm{Re}\, s>\lvert\mathrm{Im}\, a\rvert$ |
| | $(t^2-b^2)^\mu J_{2\nu}[a(t^2-b^2)^{\frac{1}{2}}]$ | $t>b$ | | |

| | | f(t) | | g(s) | |
|---|---|---|---|---|---|
| 36.10.2 (Contd.) | 12 | $0$ | $0<t<b$ | $\dfrac{e^{-b(s^2+a^2)^{\frac{1}{2}}}\log[s+(s^2+a^2)^{\frac{1}{2}}]}{(s^2+a^2)^{\frac{1}{2}}}$ | $\mathrm{Re}\, s>\lvert \mathrm{Im}\, a\rvert$ |
| | | $\log a\, J_0[a(t^2-b^2)^{\frac{1}{2}}] -\frac{\pi}{2}Y_0[a(t^2-b^2)^{\frac{1}{2}}]$ | $t>b$ | | |
| 36.10.2.1 | 1 | $0$ | $0<t<b$ | $-e^{-b(s^2+a^2)^{\frac{1}{2}}}\int_0^\infty e^{-u}\{u^2-2[cs-b(s^2+a^2)^{\frac{1}{2}}]u + c^2[(s^2+a^2)^{\frac{1}{2}}-s]^2\}^{-\frac{1}{2}}du$ | $\lvert\arg(b-c)\rvert<\pi$, $\mathrm{Re}\, s>\lvert \mathrm{Im}\, a\rvert$ |
| | | $\dfrac{J_0[a(t^2-b^2)^{\frac{1}{2}}]}{t-c}$ | $t>b$ | | |
| | 2 | $0$ | $0<t<b$ | $\dfrac{e^{-b(s^2+a^2)^{\frac{1}{2}}}}{s^2+a^2}$ | $\mathrm{Re}\, s>\lvert \mathrm{Im}\, a\rvert$ |
| | | $\int_b^t J_0[a(t-u)]\,J_0[a(u^2-b^2)^{\frac{1}{2}}]du$ | $t>b$ | | |
| 36.10.5.2 | 1 | $0$ | $0<t<b$ | $\dfrac{2}{\pi a}\,\dfrac{s e^{-b(s^2+a^2)^{\frac{1}{2}}}}{s^2+a^2}$ | $\mathrm{Re}\, s>\lvert \mathrm{Im}\, a\rvert$ |
| | | $Y_0[a(t^2-b^2)^{\frac{1}{2}}]*[ab\, J_0(at)+\sin(at)] -(t^2-b^2)^{\frac{1}{2}}Y_0[a(t^2-b^2)^{\frac{1}{2}}]$ | $t>b$ | | |
| 36.12.2 | 1 | $0$ | $0<t<b$ | $\dfrac{e^{-b(s^2-a^2)^{\frac{1}{2}}}}{(s^2-a^2)^{\frac{1}{2}}}$ | $\mathrm{Re}\, s>\lvert \mathrm{Re}\, a\rvert$ |
| | | $I_0[a(t^2-b^2)^{\frac{1}{2}}]$ | $t>b$ | | |
| | 2 | $0$ | $0<t<b$ | $s\,e^{-b(s^2-a^2)^{\frac{1}{2}}}\left[\dfrac{b}{s^2-a^2}+\dfrac{1}{(s^2-a^2)^{\frac{3}{2}}}\right]$ | $\mathrm{Re}\, s>\lvert \mathrm{Re}\, a\rvert$ |
| | | $t\, I_0[a(t^2-b^2)^{\frac{1}{2}}]$ | $t>b$ | | |
| | 3 | $0$ | $0<t<b$ | $a\,e^{-b(s^2-a^2)^{\frac{1}{2}}}\left[\dfrac{b}{s^2-a^2}+\dfrac{1}{(s^2-a^2)^{\frac{3}{2}}}\right]$ | $\mathrm{Re}\, s>\lvert \mathrm{Re}\, a\rvert$ |
| | | $(t^2-b^2)^{\frac{1}{2}}I_1[a(t^2-b^2)^{\frac{1}{2}}]$ | $t>b$ | | |

| | | f(t) | | g(s) | |
|---|---|---|---|---|---|
| 36.12.2 (Contd.) | 4 | $0$ | $0 < t < b$ | $\dfrac{e^{-b(s^2-a^2)^{\frac{1}{2}}}-e^{-bs}}{ab}$ | $\mathrm{Re}\, s > \lvert \mathrm{Re}\, a \rvert$ |
| | | $\dfrac{I_1[a(t^2-b^2)^{\frac{1}{2}}]}{(t^2-b^2)^{\frac{1}{2}}}$ | $t > b$ | | |
| | 5 | $0$ | $0 < t < b$ | $\dfrac{s\,e^{-b(s^2-a^2)^{\frac{1}{2}}}}{a(s^2-a^2)^{\frac{1}{2}}} - \dfrac{e^{-bs}}{a}$ | $\mathrm{Re}\, s > \lvert \mathrm{Re}\, a \rvert$ |
| | | $\dfrac{t\, I_1[a(t^2-b^2)^{\frac{1}{2}}]}{(t -b^2)^{\frac{1}{2}}}$ | $t > b$ | | |
| | 6 | $0$ | $0 < t < b$ | $\dfrac{1}{a}\left[\dfrac{s}{(s^2-a^2)^{\frac{1}{2}}} - 1\right] e^{-b(s^2-a^2)^{\frac{1}{2}}}$ | $\mathrm{Re}\, s > \lvert \mathrm{Re}\, a \rvert$ |
| | | $\left(\dfrac{t-b}{t+b}\right)^{\frac{1}{2}} I_1\, [a(t^2-b^2)^{\frac{1}{2}}]$ | $t > b$ | | |
| | 7 | $0$ | $0 < t < b$ | $\left(\dfrac{2}{\pi}\right)^{\frac{1}{2}} \dfrac{a^{\nu} b^{\nu+\frac{1}{2}}}{(s^2-a^2)^{\frac{\nu}{2}+\frac{1}{4}}} K_{\nu+\frac{1}{2}}[b(s^2-a^2)^{\frac{1}{2}}]$ | $\mathrm{Re}\, \nu > -1$ <br> $\mathrm{Re}\, s > \lvert \mathrm{Re}\, a \rvert$ |
| | | $(t^2-b^2)^{\frac{\nu}{2}} I_{\nu}[a(t^2-b^2)^{\frac{1}{2}}]$ | $t > b$ | | |
| | 8 | $0$ | $0 < t < b$ | $\dfrac{a^{\nu} e^{-b(s^2-a^2)^{\frac{1}{2}}}}{(s^2-a^2)^{\frac{1}{2}}[s+(s^2-a^2)^{\frac{1}{2}}]^{\nu}}$ | $\mathrm{Re}\, \nu > -1$ <br> $\mathrm{Re}\, s > \lvert \mathrm{Re}\, a \rvert$ |
| | | $\left(\dfrac{t-b}{t+b}\right)^{\frac{\nu}{2}} I_{\nu}[a(t^2-b^2)^{\frac{1}{2}}]$ | $t > b$ | | |
| 36.12.2.1 | 1 | $0$ | $0 < t < b$ | $\dfrac{e^{-b(s^2-a^2)^{\frac{1}{2}}}}{s^2-a^2}$ | $\mathrm{Re}\, s > \lvert \mathrm{Re}\, a \rvert$ |
| | | $\int_b^t I_0[a(t-u)] I_0[a(u^2-b^2)^{\frac{1}{2}}]\, du$ | $t > b$ | | |
| 36.12.3.2 | 1 | $0$ | $0 < t < b$ | $\dfrac{e^{-b(s+a+c)^{\frac{1}{2}}(s-a+c)^{\frac{1}{2}}}}{(s+a+c)^{\frac{1}{2}}(s-a+c)^{\frac{1}{2}}}$ | $\mathrm{Re}\, s > \mathrm{Max}\; -\mathrm{Re}(a+c),$ <br> $\mathrm{Re}(a-c)$ |
| | | $e^{-ct} I_0[a(t^2-b^2)^{\frac{1}{2}}]$ | $t > b$ | | |

| | | $f(t)$ | | $g(s)$ | |
|---|---|---|---|---|---|
| 36.12.3.2 (Contd.) | 2 | $0$ | $0<t<b$ | | |
| | | $\left(\frac{t-b}{t+b}\right)^{\frac{\nu}{2}} e^{-(a+b)t} I_\nu[a(t^2-b^2)^{\frac{1}{2}}]$ | $t>b$ | $\frac{a^\nu e^{-b(s+2a+b)^{\frac{1}{2}}(s+b)^{\frac{1}{2}}}}{(s+2a+b)^{\frac{1}{2}}(s+b)^{\frac{1}{2}}} \cdot \frac{1}{[s+(a+b)+(s+2a+b)^{\frac{1}{2}}(s+b)^{\frac{1}{2}}]^\nu}$ | $\operatorname{Re}\nu>-1$ <br> $\operatorname{Re}s>\lvert\operatorname{Re}a\rvert-\operatorname{Re}(a+b)$ |
| | 3 | $0$ | $0<t<b$ | | |
| | | $e^{-at}I_0[c(t^2-b^2)^{\frac{1}{2}}]+(a-c)\int_b^t e^{-au}I_0[c(u^2-b^2)^{\frac{1}{2}}]\,du$ | $t>b$ | $\frac{1}{s}\left(\frac{s+a-c}{s+a+c}\right)^{\frac{1}{2}} e^{-b[(s+a+c)(s+a-c)]^{\frac{1}{2}}}$ | $\operatorname{Re}s>\operatorname{Max}-\operatorname{Re}(a+c),-\operatorname{Re}(a-c),0$ |
| | 4 | $0$ | $0<t<b$ | | |
| | | $\left(\frac{t-b}{t+b}\right)^{\frac{\nu}{2}} K_\nu[a(t^2-b^2)]$ | $t>b$ | $\frac{\pi\operatorname{cosec}(\nu\pi)}{2a^\nu}\frac{e^{-b(s^2-a^2)^{\frac{1}{2}}}}{(s^2-a^2)^{\frac{1}{2}}} \cdot \left[\left\{s+(s^2-a^2)^{\frac{1}{2}}\right\}^\nu-\left\{s-(s^2-a^2)^{\frac{1}{2}}\right\}^\nu\right]$ | $\lvert\operatorname{Re}\nu\rvert<1$ <br> $\operatorname{Re}s>\lvert\operatorname{Re}a\rvert$ |
| 36.13.12.2 | 1 | $0$ | $0<t<b$ | | |
| | | $K_0[a(t^2-b^2)^{\frac{1}{2}}]+\log a\, I_0[a(t^2-b^2)^{\frac{1}{2}}]$ | $t>b$ | $\frac{e^{-b(s^2-a^2)^{\frac{1}{2}}}\log[s+(s^2-a^2)^{\frac{1}{2}}]}{(s^2-a^2)^{\frac{1}{2}}}$ | $\operatorname{Re}s>\lvert\operatorname{Re}a\rvert$ |
| 36.16 | 1 | $0$ | $0<t<b$ | | |
| | | $\operatorname{Erf}(\frac{t}{2})-\operatorname{Erf}(\frac{b}{2})$ | $t>b$ | $\frac{1}{s}e^{s^2}\operatorname{Erfc}(s+\frac{b}{2})$ | $\operatorname{Re}s>0$ |
| 36.19 | 1 | $0$ | $0<t<b$ | | |
| | | $\operatorname{Ei}(-ba)-\operatorname{Ei}(-at)$ | $t>b$ | $\frac{1}{s}\operatorname{Ei}[-b(s+a)]$ | $a\neq 0$ <br> $\operatorname{Re}s>-\operatorname{Re}a$ |
| 36.21 | 1 | $0$ | $0<t<b$ | | |
| | | $\Gamma(\nu,at)$ | $t>b$ | $\frac{e^{-bs}}{s}\Gamma(\nu,ab)-\frac{a^\nu}{s(s+a)^\nu}\Gamma[\nu,b(s+a)]$ | $\operatorname{Re}s>-\operatorname{Re}a$ |

| | | f(t) | | g(s) | |
|---|---|---|---|---|---|
| 36.23.2 | 1 | $0$ | $0<t<b$ | $\left(\frac{2b}{\pi}\right)^{\frac{1}{2}} \frac{K_{\nu+\frac{1}{2}}(bs)}{s^{\mu+\frac{1}{2}}}$ | Re $s>0$ |
| | | $(t^2-b^2)^{\frac{\mu}{2}} P_{\nu}^{-\mu}(\frac{t}{b})$ | $t>b$ | | |
| | 2 | $0$ | $0<t<b$ | $\frac{1}{s} W_{\mu,\nu+\frac{1}{2}}(2bs)$ | Re $\mu>1$<br>$\nu \neq 0, \pm 1, \pm 2, \ldots$<br>Re $s>0$ |
| | | $\left(\frac{t+b}{t-b}\right)^{\frac{\mu}{2}} P_{\nu}^{\mu}(\frac{t}{b})$ | $t>b$ | | |
| 36.24.2 | 1 | $0$ | $0<t<b$ | $\frac{e^{-b(s^2-ia^2)^{\frac{1}{2}}}}{(s^2-ia^2)^{\frac{1}{2}}}$ | $\mathrm{Re}(s \pm a i^{\frac{1}{2}})>0$ |
| | | $\mathrm{ber}[a(t^2-b^2)^{\frac{1}{2}}]+i\,\mathrm{bei}[a(t^2-b^2)^{\frac{1}{2}}]$ | $t>b$ | | |
| | 2 | $0$ | $0<t<b$ | $\frac{s[b(s^2-ia^2)^{\frac{1}{2}}+1]}{(s^2-ia^2)^{\frac{3}{2}}} e^{-b(s^2-ia^2)^{\frac{1}{2}}}$ | $\mathrm{Re}(s \pm a i^{\frac{1}{2}})>0$ |
| | | $t\{\mathrm{ber}[a(t^2-b^2)^{\frac{1}{2}}]+i\,\mathrm{bei}[a(t^2-b^2)^{\frac{1}{2}}]\}$ | $t>b$ | | |
| | 3 | $0$ | $0<t<b$ | $\frac{a[b(s^2-ia^2)^{\frac{1}{2}}+1]}{(s^2-ia^2)^{\frac{3}{2}}} e^{-b(s^2-ia^2)^{\frac{1}{2}}+\frac{3\pi}{4}i}$ | $\mathrm{Re}(s \pm a i^{\frac{1}{2}})>0$ |
| | | $(t^2-b^2)^{\frac{1}{2}}\{\mathrm{ber}_1[a(t^2-b^2)^{\frac{1}{2}}]+$ $i\,\mathrm{bei}_1[a(t-b^2)^{\frac{1}{2}}]\}$ | $t>b$ | | |
| | 4 | $0$ | $0<t<b$ | $\frac{\left\{e^{-bs}-e^{-b(s^2-ia^2)^{\frac{1}{2}}}\right\} e^{-\frac{3\pi}{4}i}}{ab}$ | $\mathrm{Re}(s \pm a i^{\frac{1}{2}})>0$ |
| | | $\frac{\mathrm{ber}_1[a(t^2-b^2)^{\frac{1}{2}}]+i\,\mathrm{bei}_1[a(t^2-b^2)^{\frac{1}{2}}]}{(t^2-b^2)^{\frac{1}{2}}}$ | $t>b$ | | |
| | 5 | $0$ | $0<t<b$ | $\frac{e^{-\frac{3\pi}{4}i}}{a}\left[e^{-bs}-\frac{s}{(s^2-ia^2)^{\frac{1}{2}}} e^{-b(s^2-ia^2)^{\frac{1}{2}}}\right]$ | $\mathrm{Re}(s \pm a i^{\frac{1}{2}})>0$ |
| | | $\frac{t\{\mathrm{ber}_1[a(t^2-b^2)^{\frac{1}{2}}]+i\,\mathrm{bei}_1[a(t^2-b^2)^{\frac{1}{2}}]\}}{(t^2-b^2)^{\frac{1}{2}}}$ | $t>b$ | | |

| | | f(t) | | g(s) | |
|---|---|---|---|---|---|
| 36.24.2 (Contd.) | 6 | $0$ | $0<t<b$ | $\dfrac{a^{\nu}e^{\frac{3}{4}\nu\pi i-b(s^2-ia^2)^{\frac{1}{2}}}}{(s^2-ia^2)^{\frac{1}{2}}[s+(s^2-ia^2)^{\frac{1}{2}}]^{\nu}}$ | $\mathrm{Re}\,\nu>-1$<br>$\mathrm{Re}(s\pm ai^{\frac{1}{2}})>0$ |
| | | $\left(\dfrac{t-b}{t+b}\right)^{\frac{\nu}{2}}\{\mathrm{ber}_{\nu}[a(t^2-b^2)^{\frac{1}{2}}]+i\,\mathrm{bei}_{\nu}[a(t^2-b^2)^{\frac{1}{2}}]\}$ | $t>b$ | | |
| | 7 | $0$ | $0<t<b$ | $\dfrac{e^{-b(s^2-ia^2)^{\frac{1}{2}}}}{ia^2-s^2}\left\{1+\left[bs-\dfrac{s}{(s^2-ia^2)^{\frac{1}{2}}}\right]\cdot\log\dfrac{[s+(s^2-ia^2)^{\frac{1}{2}}]}{i^{\frac{1}{2}}a}\right\}$ | $\mathrm{Re}(s+ai^{\frac{1}{2}})>0$ |
| | | $t\{\mathrm{ker}[a(t^2-b^2)^{\frac{1}{2}}]+i\,\mathrm{kei}[a(t^2-b^2)^{\frac{1}{2}}]\}$ | $t>b$ | | |
| | 8 | $0$ | $0<t<b$ | $\dfrac{e^{-b(s^2-ia^2)^{\frac{1}{2}}}}{(s^2-ia^2)^{\frac{1}{2}}}\log\dfrac{[s+(s^2-ia^2)^{\frac{1}{2}}]}{i^{\frac{1}{2}}a}$ | $\mathrm{Re}(s+ai^{\frac{1}{2}})>0$ |
| | | $\mathrm{ker}[a(t^2-b^2)^{\frac{1}{2}}]+i\,\mathrm{kei}[a(t^2-b^2)^{\frac{1}{2}}]$ | $t>b$ | | |
| | 9 | $0$ | $0<t<b$ | $\dfrac{e^{-b(s^2-ia^2)^{\frac{1}{2}}}}{s^2-ia^2}\left\{\dfrac{i^{\frac{1}{2}}s}{a}+i^{\frac{3}{2}}a\left[b+\dfrac{1}{(s^2-ia^2)^{\frac{1}{2}}}\right]\cdot\log\dfrac{[s+(s^2-ia^2)^{\frac{1}{2}}]}{i^{\frac{1}{2}}a}\right\}$ | $\mathrm{Re}(s+ai^{\frac{1}{2}})>0$ |
| | | $(t^2-b^2)^{\frac{1}{2}}\{\mathrm{ker}_1[a(t^2-b^2)^{\frac{1}{2}}]+i\,\mathrm{kei}_1[a(t^2-b^2)^{\frac{1}{2}}]\}$ | $t>b$ | | |
| | 10 | $0$ | $0<t<b$ | $\dfrac{\pi e^{-bs-\frac{i\nu\pi}{2}}}{2(s^2-ia^2)^{\frac{1}{2}}\sin(\nu\pi)}\left\{\left[\dfrac{s+(s^2-ia^2)^{\frac{1}{2}}}{ai^{\frac{1}{2}}}\right]^{\nu}-\left[\dfrac{ai^{\frac{1}{2}}}{s+(s^2-ia^2)^{\frac{1}{2}}}\right]^{\nu}\right\}$ | $\lvert\mathrm{Re}\,\nu\rvert<1$<br>$\mathrm{Re}(s+ai^{\frac{1}{2}})>0$ |
| | | $\left(\dfrac{t-b}{t+b}\right)^{\frac{\nu}{2}}\{\mathrm{ker}_{\nu}[a(t^2-b^2)^{\frac{1}{2}}]+i\,\mathrm{kei}_{\nu}[a(t^2-b^2)^{\frac{1}{2}}]\}$ | $t>b$ | | |
| 36.31.2.1 | 1 | $0$ | $0<t<b$ | $\left(\dfrac{2b}{s}\right)^{\mu+\nu}\dfrac{\Gamma(\mu+\nu+\frac{1}{2})}{\pi^{\frac{1}{2}}}K_{\nu-\mu}(bs)$ | $\mathrm{Re}(\mu+\nu)>-\frac{1}{2}$<br>$\mathrm{Re}\,s>0$ |
| | | $(t^2-b^2)^{\mu+\nu-\frac{1}{2}}{}_2F_1[\mu,\nu;\mu+\nu+\frac{1}{2};1-\frac{t^2}{b^2}]$ | $t>b$ | | |

| | | f(t) | | g(s) | |
|---|---|---|---|---|---|
| 36.35 | 1 | 0 | $2nb < t < (2n+1)b$ | $\frac{1}{s(1+e^{bs})}$ | $n = 0,1,2,\ldots$ <br> $\operatorname{Re} s > 0$ |
| | | 1 | $(2n+1)b < t < (2n+2)b$ | | |

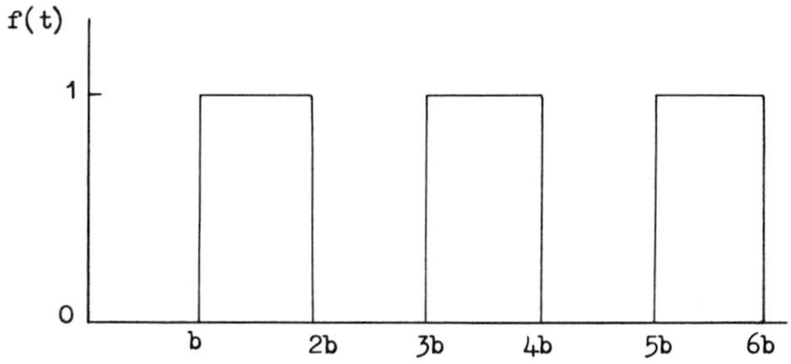


| | | | | | |
|---|---|---|---|---|---|
| | 2 | 0 | $0 < t < b$ | $\frac{\operatorname{sech}(bs)}{2s}$ | $n = 0,1,2,\ldots$ <br> $\operatorname{Re} s < 0$ |
| | | 1 | $(4n+1)b < t < (4n+3)b$ | | |
| | | 0 | $(4n+3)b < t < (4n+5)b$ | | |

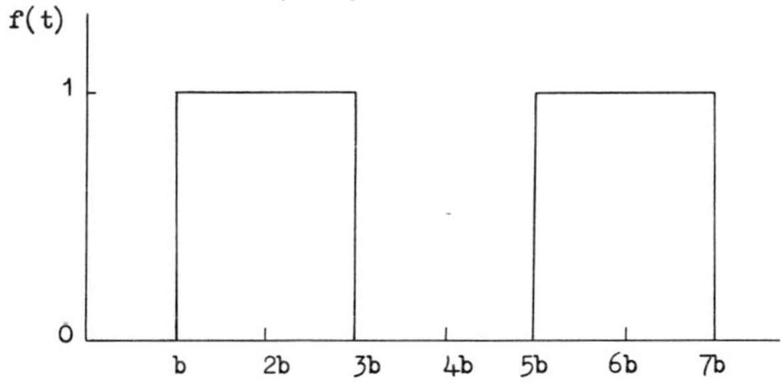


| | | | | | |
|---|---|---|---|---|---|
| | 3 | 0 | $0 < t < b$ | $\frac{1-e^{-bs}}{s(1+e^{bs})}$ | $n = 0,1,2,\ldots$ <br> $\operatorname{Re} s > 0$ |
| | | 1 | $(2n+1)b < t < (2n+2)b$ | | |
| | | -1 | $(2n+2)b < t < (2n+3)b$ | | |

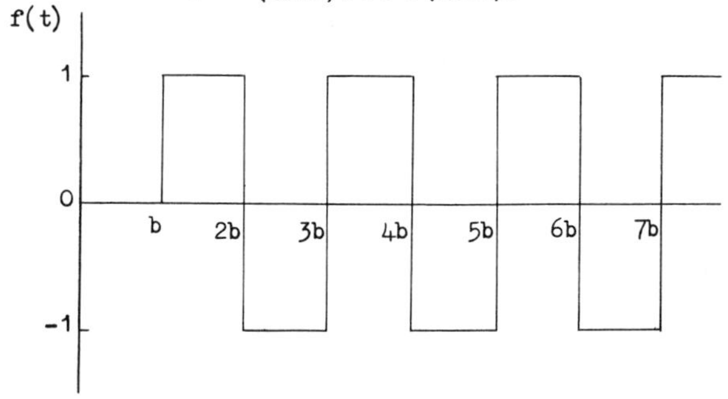

| | f(t) | | g(s) | |
|---|---|---|---|---|
| 36.35 (Contd.) 4 | 1 | $(8n-7)b < t < (8n-5)b$ | $\frac{\sinh(bs)}{s\cosh(2bs)}$ | $n = 1,2,3,\ldots$; Re $s > 0$ |
| | -1 | $(8n-3)b < t < (8n-1)b$ | | |
| | 0 | otherwise | | |

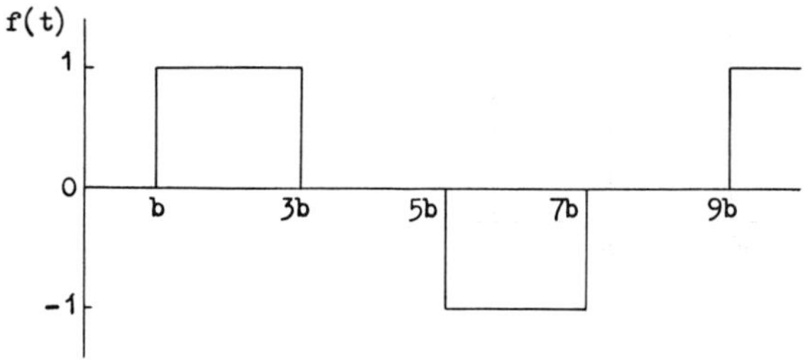


| | f(t) | | g(s) | |
|---|---|---|---|---|
| 5 | 1 | $(4n+1)b < t < (4n+2)b$ | $\frac{1-e^{-bs}}{s(e^{bs}+e^{-bs})}$ | $n = 0,1,2,\ldots$; Re $s > 0$ |
| | -1 | $(4n+3)b < t < (4n+4)b$ | | |
| | 0 | otherwise | | |

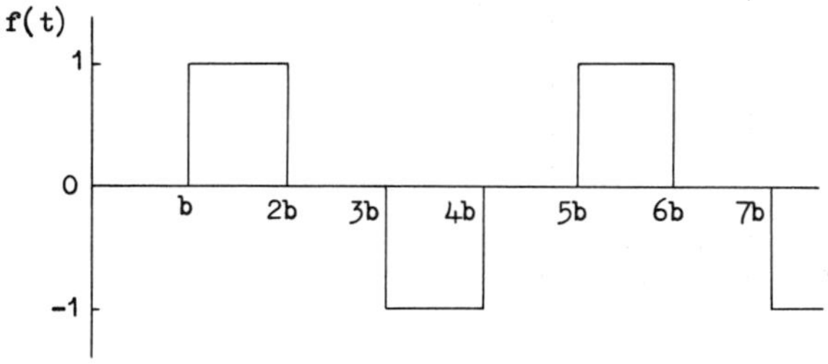


| | f(t) | | g(s) | |
|---|---|---|---|---|
| 6 | 0 | $na < t < na+b$ and $na+c < t < na+d$ | | |
| | 1 | $na+b < t < na+c$ | $\frac{e^{-bs}-e^{-cs}+e^{-as}-e^{-ds}}{s(1-e^{-as})}$ | $n = 0,1,2,\ldots$; $a > d > c > b$; Re $s > 0$ |
| | -1 | $na+d < t < (n+1)a$ | | |

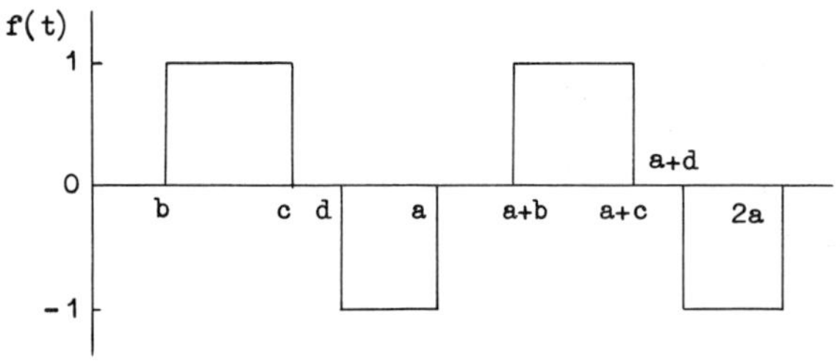

| | | f(t) | | g(s) | |
|---|---|---|---|---|---|
| 36.35 (Contd.) | 7 | 1 | $(4n-3)b < t < (4n-1)b$ | | |
| | | 2 | $(8n-5)b < t < (8n-3)b$ | $\dfrac{\cosh(bs)}{s\cosh(2bs)}$ | $n = 1,2,3,\ldots$ Re $s > 0$ |
| | | 0 | otherwise | | |

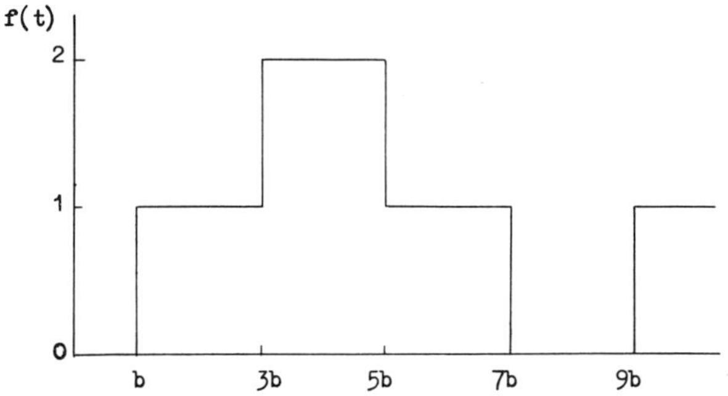


| | | | | | |
|---|---|---|---|---|---|
| | 8 | 0 | $0 < t < b$ | $\dfrac{\text{cosech } bs}{2s}$ | $n = 1,2,3,\ldots$ Re $s > 0$ |
| | | n | $(2n-1)b < t < (2n+1)b$ | | |

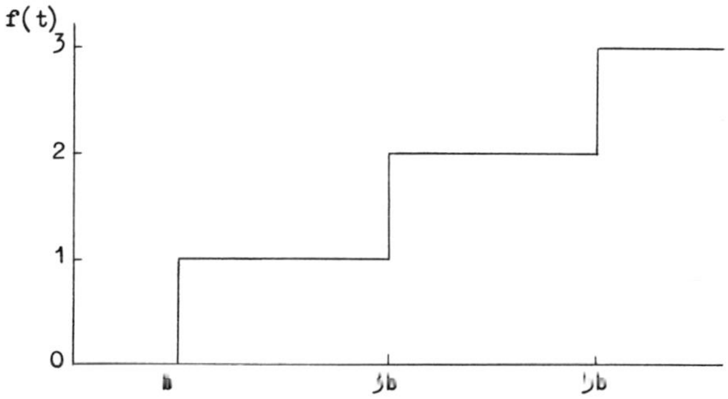


| | | | | | |
|---|---|---|---|---|---|
| | 9 | n | $b\pi^2 n^2 < t < b\pi^2(n+1)^2$ | $\dfrac{1}{2s}[\theta_3(0 \mid bs)-1]$ | $n = 0,1,2,\ldots$ Re $s > 0$ |

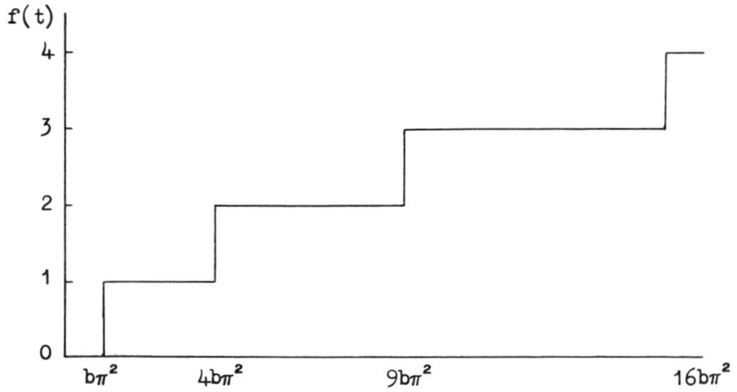

| | f(t) | | g(s) | |
|---|---|---|---|---|
| 36.35 (Contd.) 10 | 0 | $0 < t < \frac{\pi^2}{4}$ | $\frac{1}{2s}\,\theta_2(0\|s)$ | $n = 0,1,2,\ldots$ Re s > 0 |
| | n+1 | $\pi^2(n+\frac{1}{2})^2 < t < \pi^2(n+\frac{3}{2})^2$ | | |

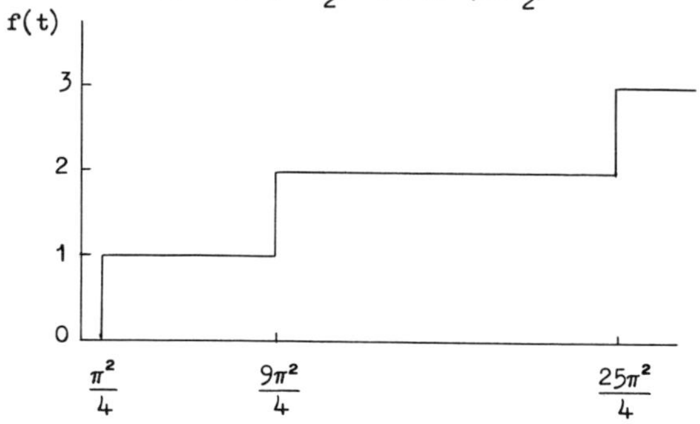


| | f(t) | | g(s) | |
|---|---|---|---|---|
| 11 | 0 | $0 < t < b$ | $\frac{\sinh(bs)}{2s\cosh^2(bs)}$ | $n = 1,2,3,\ldots$ Re s > 0 |
| | 2n−1 | $(4n-3)b < t < (4n-1)b$ | | |
| | −2n | $(4n-1)b < t < (4n+1)b$ | | |

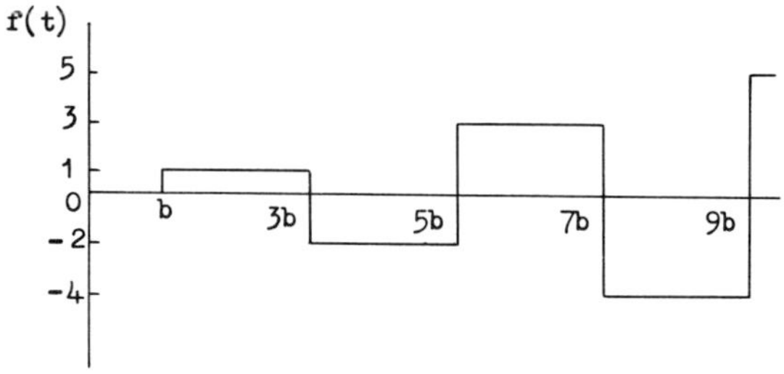


| | f(t) | | g(s) | |
|---|---|---|---|---|
| 12 | 0 | $0 < t < b$ | $\frac{1+bs\tanh(bs)}{2s^2\cosh(bs)}$ | $n = 1,2,3,\ldots$ Re s > 0 |
| | t | $(4n-3)b < t < (4n-1)b$ | | |
| | 0 | $(4n-1)b < t < (4n+1)b$ | | |

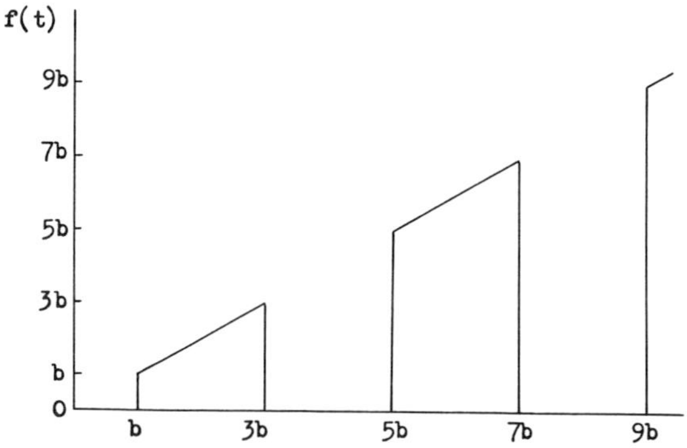

| | f(t) | | g(s) | |
|---|---|---|---|---|
| 36.35.1 | | | | |
| 1 | $0$ | $0 < t < a$ | $\frac{e^{-as} - e^{-bs}}{s^2}$ | Re $s > 0$ |
| | $t-a$ | $a < t < b$ | | |
| | $b-a$ | $t > b$ | | |

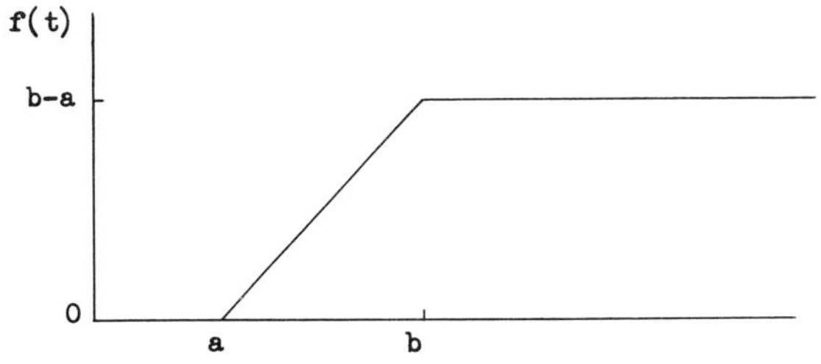


| | f(t) | | g(s) | |
|---|---|---|---|---|
| 2 | $0$ | $0 < t < b$ | $\frac{\sinh(bs)}{s^2 \cosh(2bs)}$ | $n = 0, 1, 2, \ldots$ Re $s > 0$ |
| | $t-(8n+1)b$ | $(8n+1)b < t < (8n+3)b$ | | |
| | $2b$ | $(8n+3)b < t < (8n+5)b$ | | |
| | $-t+(8n+7)b$ | $(8n+5)b < t < (8n+7)b$ | | |
| | $0$ | $(8n+7)b < t < (8n+9)b$ | | |

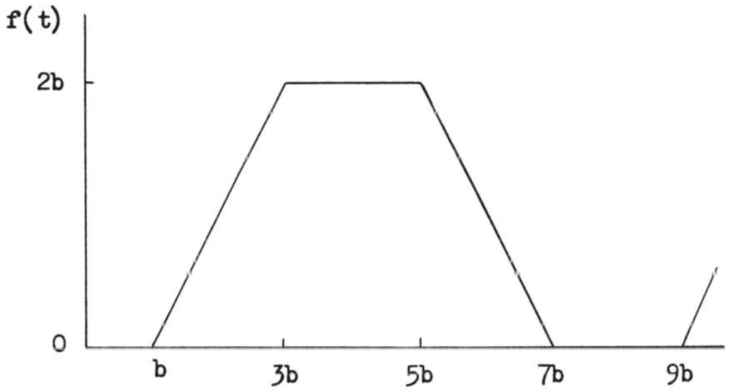


| | f(t) | | g(s) | |
|---|---|---|---|---|
| 3 | | $0 < t < b$ | $\frac{\text{sech}(bs)}{s^2}$ | $n = 1, 2, 3, \ldots$ Re $s > 0$ |
| | $t-(-1)^n(t-2nb)$ | $(2n-1)b < t < (2n+1)b$ | | |

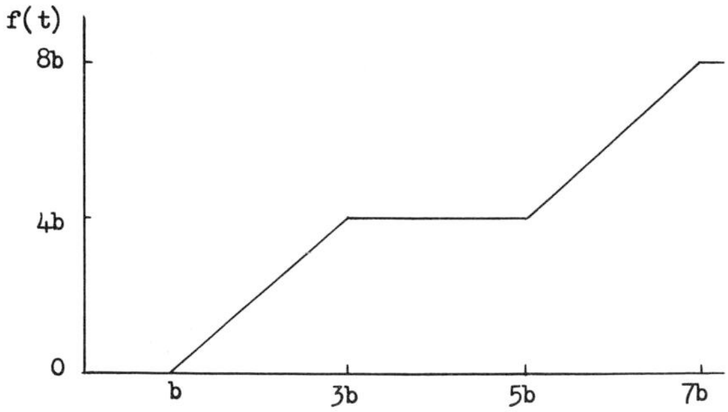

| | | f(t) | | g(s) | |
|---|---|---|---|---|---|
| 36.35.1 (Contd.) | 4 | $\frac{1}{4}[1-(-1)^n](2t-b)+\frac{1}{2}(-1)^n bn$ | $nb < t < (n+1)b$ | $\frac{1}{s^2(e^{bs}+1)}$ | $n=0,1,2,\ldots$ Re $s > 0$ |

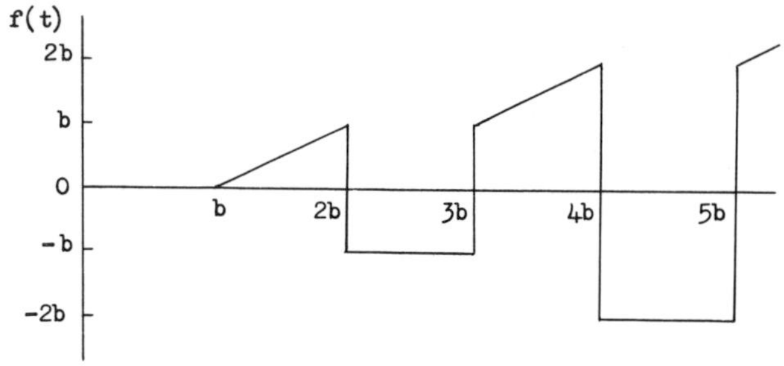


| | | | | | |
|---|---|---|---|---|---|
| | 5 | $0$ | $0 < t < b$ | $\frac{\operatorname{cosech}(bs)}{2s^2}$ | $n=1,2,3,\ldots$ Re $s > 0$ |
| | | $n(t-bn)$ | $(2n-1)b < t < (2n+1)b$ | | |

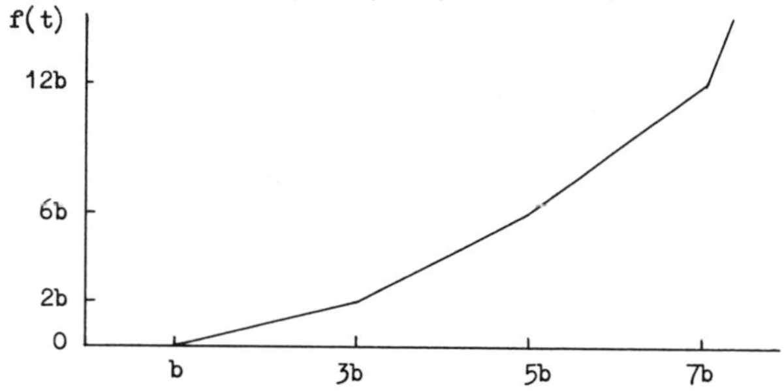


| | | | | | |
|---|---|---|---|---|---|
| | 6 | $nt-\frac{1}{2}bn(n+1)$ | $nb < t < (n+1)b$ | $\frac{1}{s^2(e^{bs}-1)}$ | $n=0,1,2,\ldots$ Re $s > 0$ |

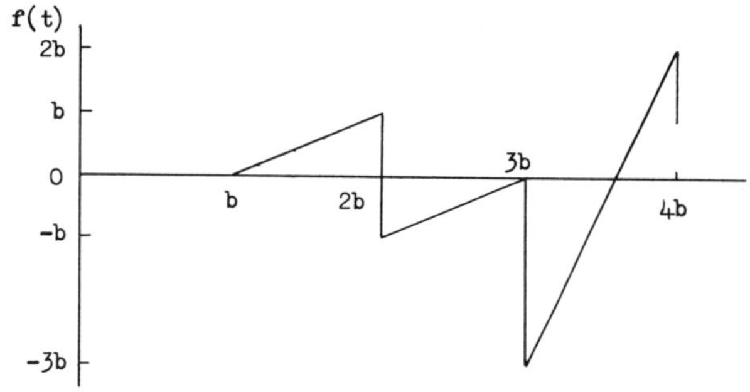


| | | | | | |
|---|---|---|---|---|---|
| | 7 | $\frac{1-a^n}{1-a}t-b\,\frac{1-(n+1)a^n+na^{n+1}}{(1-a)^2}$ | $nb < t < (n+1)b$ | $\frac{1}{s^2(e^{bs}-a)}$ | $n=0,1,2,\ldots$ Re $s >$ Max o, $\frac{1}{b}$ Re(log a) |
| | 8 | $0$ | $0 < t < a$ | $\frac{e^{-as}-e^{-bs}}{s^3}$ | Re $s > 0$ |
| | | $\frac{1}{2}(t-a)^2$ | $a < t < b$ | | |
| | | $t(b-a)+\frac{1}{2}(a^2-b^2)$ | $t > b$ | | |

| | | f(t) | | g(s) | |
|---|---|---|---|---|---|
| 36.35.1 (Contd.) | 9 | $0$ | $t<a$ | | |
| | | $\frac{1}{2}(t-a)^2$ | $a<t<\frac{a+b}{2}$ | $\frac{(e^{-\frac{as}{2}}-e^{-\frac{bs}{2}})^2}{s^3}$ | Re $s>0$ |
| | | $\frac{1}{4}(b-a)^2-\frac{1}{2}(t-b)^2$ | $\frac{a+b}{2}<t<b$ | | |
| | | $\frac{1}{4}(b-a)^2$ | $t>b$ | | |
| 36.35.2 | 1 | $0$ | $0<t<\frac{1}{2}$ | $\frac{\pi^{\frac{1}{2}}\Gamma(\nu+1)\operatorname{cosech}\frac{s}{2}[I_{\nu+\frac{1}{2}}(s)-L_{\nu+\frac{1}{2}}(s)]}{4s^{\nu+\frac{1}{2}}}$ | $n=0,1,2,\ldots$ Re $\nu>-1$ Re $s>0$ |
| | | $[\frac{3}{4}+t-n-(t-n)^2]^{\nu}$ | $n+\frac{1}{2}<t<n+\frac{3}{2}$ | | |
| 36.35.5 | 1 | $0$ | $\frac{2n\pi}{b}<t<\frac{(2n+1)\pi}{b}$ | $\frac{b}{s^2+b^2}\,\frac{1}{e^{\frac{\pi}{b}s}-1}$ | $n=0,1,2,\ldots$ Re $s>0$ |
| | | $-\sin(bt)$ | $\frac{(2n+1)\pi}{b}<t<\frac{(2n+2)\pi}{b}$ | | |
| 37 | 1 | $\mathrm{Cih}(at)-\log a$ | | $-\frac{1}{2s}\log(s^2-a^2)$ | Re $s>\lvert\mathrm{Re}\,a\rvert$ |
| | 2 | $J_n^m(at)$ | | $\frac{2^m a^{n-m}(s^2+a^2)^{\frac{m-1}{2}}}{[s+(s^2+a^2)^{\frac{1}{2}}]^n}$ | $n>m-1$ $n,m=0,1,2,\ldots$ Re $s>\lvert\mathrm{Im}\,a\rvert$ |
| | 3 | $U^{m,n}(at)$ | | $\frac{1}{s+a}P_m(\frac{s-a}{s+a})P_n(\frac{s-a}{s+a})$ | $m,n=0,1,2,\ldots$ Re $s>-$ Re $a$ |
| | 4 | $V_n(at)$ | | $\frac{2}{s-a}Q_n(\frac{s+a}{s-a})$ | Re $s>0$ |
| | 5 | $\mu(at,b)$ | | $\frac{\Gamma(b+1)}{s(\log\frac{s}{a})^{b+1}}$ | Re $b>-1$ Re $s>$ Re $a$ |

| | | f(t) | g(s) | |
|---|---|---|---|---|
| 37 (Contd.) | 6 | $\nu(at,b)$ | $\dfrac{a^b}{s^{b+1}\log\frac{s}{a}}$ | Re b > −1<br>Re s > Re a |
| | 7 | $\nu(at)$ | $\dfrac{1}{s\log\frac{s}{a}}$ | Re s > o |
| 37.2 | 1 | $\dfrac{1}{t^{\frac{1}{2}}}\mu(at^{\frac{1}{2}},b)$ | $\dfrac{2^{b+1}\pi^{\frac{1}{2}}}{s^{\frac{1}{2}}}\mu(\frac{a^2}{4s},b)$ | Re s > o |
| | 2 | $\dfrac{\nu(at^{\frac{1}{2}})}{t^{\frac{1}{2}}}$ | $\dfrac{2\pi^{\frac{1}{2}}}{s^{\frac{1}{2}}}\nu(\frac{a^2}{4s})$ | Re s > o |
| | 3 | $\nu(at^{\frac{1}{2}},b)$ | $\dfrac{a\pi^{\frac{1}{2}}}{4s^{\frac{3}{2}}}\nu(\frac{a^2}{4s},\frac{b-1}{2})$ | Re b > − 2<br>Re s > o |
| | 4 | $\dfrac{1}{t^{\frac{1}{2}}}\nu(at^{\frac{1}{2}},b)$ | $\dfrac{\pi^{\frac{1}{2}}}{s^{\frac{1}{2}}}\nu(\frac{a^2}{4s},\frac{b}{2})$ | Re b > −1<br>Re s > o |
| 37.3 | 1 | $\dfrac{\nu(at)}{1-e^{-at}}$ | $\dfrac{1}{a}\int_0^\infty \zeta(u+1,\frac{s}{a})\,du$ | Re s > Re a |
| | 2 | $\nu(e^{-at})$ | $\int_0^\infty \dfrac{du}{(s+au)\Gamma(u+1)}$ | Re s > o |
| | 3 | $\nu(1-e^{-at})$ | $\frac{1}{a}\,\Gamma(\frac{s}{a})\,\nu(1,\frac{s}{a})$ | Re s > o |
| 37.7 | 1 | $t\,\mathrm{Cih}(at)-\dfrac{\sinh(at)}{a}-t\log a$ | $-\dfrac{1}{2s^2}\log(s^2-a^2)$ | Re a > o<br>Re s > Re a |

# Part II

# INVERSE TRANSFORMS

# Section 1 • Operations

| | g(s) | f(t) | |
|---|---|---|---|
| inearity, Scale Change & Translation | | | |
| • | $a\,g(s)$ | $a f(t)$ | |
| • | $g(as)$ | $\frac{1}{a} f(\frac{t}{a})$ | $a > 0$ |
| • | $g(as-b)$ | $a^{-1} e^{\frac{b}{a}t} f(\frac{t}{a})$ | $a > 0$ |
| • | $g_1(s) \pm g_2(s)$ | $f_1(t) \pm f_2(t)$ | |
| • | $g(s+a)-g(s)$ | $(e^{-at}-1)f(t)$ | |
| • | $g(s-a)+g(s+a)$ | $2f(t)\cosh(at)$ | |
| • | $g(s-a)-g(s+a)$ | $2f(t)\sinh(at)$ | |
| • | $g(s-ia)+g(s+ia)$ | $2f(t)\cos(at)$ | |

| | g(s) | f(t) | |
|---|---|---|---|
| 9. | $g(s-ia)-g(s+ia)$ | $2if(t)\sin(at)$ | |
| 10. | $\Delta_a^n g(s)$ | $(e^{-at}-1)^n f(t)$ | $n=1,2,3,\ldots$ |

Multiplication by a Function

| | | | |
|---|---|---|---|
| 11. | $s\,g(s)$ | $\frac{df(t)}{dt}+f(o)$ | |
| 12. | $s^n g(s)$ | $\frac{d^n f(t)}{dt^n}+\sum_{k=0}^{n-1} f^{(k)}(o)\,s^{n-k-1}$ | $n=1,2,3,\ldots$ |
| 13. | $\frac{1}{s^n}g(s)$ | $\int_o^t \cdots \int_o^t f(u)\,(du)^n$ | $n=1,2,3,\ldots$ |
| 14. | $(s-1)\ldots(s-n)\,g(s-n)$ | $\left(e^{t}\frac{d}{dt}\right)^n f(t)$ if $f^{(k)}(o)=0$ for $k=0,1,\ldots,n-1$ | $n=1,2,3,\ldots$ |
| 15. | $\frac{g(\frac{s}{a})}{ae^{\frac{b}{a}s}}$ | $0 \quad t<\frac{b}{a}$; $f(at-b) \quad t>\frac{b}{a}$ | $a,b>o$ |
| 16. | $g(s)\,\frac{1+e^{-as}}{1-e^{-as}}$ | $f(t)+2\sum_{1\leqslant n<\frac{t}{a}} f(t-an)$ | $a>o$ |
| 17. | $\frac{g(s)}{(e^{as}+b)^{\nu}}$ | $\sum_{o\leqslant n<\frac{t}{a}-\nu} \binom{-\nu}{n} b^n f(t-a\nu-an)$ | $a,\nu>o$ |
| 18. | $g(s)\,(1+be^{-as})^{\nu}$ | $\sum_{o\leqslant n\leqslant\frac{t}{a}} \binom{\nu}{n} b^n f(t-an)$ | $a>o$ |
| 19. | $g_1(s)\,g_2(s)$ | $\int_o^t f_1(u)\,f_2(t-u)\,du$ | |

| | g(s) | f(t) | |
|---|---|---|---|
| Composite Functions | | | |
| 20. | $\frac{1}{s^{\frac{1}{2}}}g(\frac{1}{s})$ | $\frac{1}{(\pi t)^{\frac{1}{2}}}\int_0^\infty \cos(2u^{\frac{1}{2}}t^{\frac{1}{2}})f(u)\,du$ | |
| 21. | $\frac{1}{s}\,g(\frac{1}{s})$ | $\int_0^\infty J_0(2t^{\frac{1}{2}}u^{\frac{1}{2}})f(u)\,du$ | |
| 22. | $\frac{1}{s^{\frac{3}{2}}}\,g(\frac{1}{s})$ | $\pi^{-\frac{1}{2}}\int_0^\infty u^{-\frac{1}{2}}\sin(2u^{\frac{1}{2}}t^{\frac{1}{2}})f(u)\,du$ | |
| 3. | $\frac{1}{s^{2\nu+1}}g(\frac{1}{s})$ | $t^{\nu}\int_0^\infty J_{2\nu}(2u^{\frac{1}{2}}t^{\frac{1}{2}})u^{-\nu}f(u)\,du$ | $\mathrm{Re}\,\nu > -\frac{1}{2}$ |
| 4. | $\frac{1}{s^{\frac{1}{2}}}\,g(-\frac{1}{s})$ | $\frac{1}{(\pi t)^{\frac{1}{2}}}\int_0^\infty \cosh(2t^{\frac{1}{2}}u^{\frac{1}{2}})f(u)\,du$ | |
| 5. | $\frac{1}{s^{\frac{3}{2}}}\,g(-\frac{1}{s})$ | $\pi^{-\frac{1}{2}}\int_0^\infty \frac{\sinh(2t^{\frac{1}{2}}u^{\frac{1}{2}})}{u^{\frac{1}{2}}}f(u)\,du$ | |
| 6. | $\frac{1}{s}\,g(\frac{1}{s^n})$ | $\int_0^\infty {}_0F_n\left[\frac{1}{n},\frac{2}{n},\dots,\frac{n-1}{n},1;\ -\frac{ut^n}{n^n}\right]f(u)\,du$ | $n = 1,2,3,\dots$ |
| 7. | $\frac{1}{s}\,g(s+\frac{1}{s})$ | $\int_0^t J_0[2(t-u)^{\frac{1}{2}}u^{\frac{1}{2}}]f(u)\,du$ | |
| 8. | $\frac{1}{s^{2\nu+1}}g(s+\frac{a}{s})$ | $\int_0^t \left(\frac{t-u}{au}\right)^{\nu}J_{2\nu}[2(aut-au^2)^{\frac{1}{2}}]f(u)\,du$ | |
| 9. | $g(s^{\frac{1}{2}})$ | $\frac{1}{2\pi^{\frac{1}{2}}t^{\frac{3}{2}}}\int_0^\infty ue^{-\frac{u^2}{4t}}f(u)\,du$ | |
| 0. | $\frac{1}{s^{\frac{1}{2}}}\,g(s^{\frac{1}{2}})$ | $\frac{1}{(\pi t)^{\frac{1}{2}}}\int_0^\infty e^{-\frac{u^2}{4t}}f(u)\,du$ | |
| . | $s^{\frac{n-1}{2}}\,g(s^{\frac{1}{2}})$ | $\frac{1}{2^{\frac{n}{2}}\pi^{\frac{1}{2}}t^{\frac{n+1}{2}}}\int_0^\infty e^{-\frac{u^2}{4t}}He_n\left[\frac{u}{(2t)^{\frac{1}{2}}}\right]f(u)\,du$ | $n = 0,1,2,\dots$ |

| | g(s) | f(t) |
|---|---|---|
| 32. | $s^{\nu} g(s^{\frac{1}{2}})$ | $\dfrac{2^{\frac{1}{2}}}{\pi^{\frac{1}{2}}(2t)^{\nu+1}} \int_0^{\infty} e^{-\frac{u^2}{8t}} D_{2\nu+1}\left(\dfrac{u}{2^{\frac{1}{2}} t^{\frac{1}{2}}}\right) f(u)\,du$ |
| 33. | $g[(s+1)^{\frac{1}{2}}]$ | $\dfrac{1}{2\pi^{\frac{1}{2}} t^{\frac{3}{2}}}\left[\int_0^{\infty} u\, e^{-\frac{u^2}{4t}} f(u)\,du - \int_0^{\infty} u\, e^{-\frac{u^2}{4t}} \int_0^{u} J_1(v) f[(u^2-v^2)^{\frac{1}{2}}]\,dv\,du\right]$ |
| 34. | $s^{\frac{n-1}{2}} g[(s+1)^{\frac{1}{2}}]$ | $\dfrac{1}{2^{\frac{n}{2}} \pi^{\frac{1}{2}} t^{\frac{n+1}{2}}} \int_0^{\infty} e^{-\frac{u^2}{4t}} He\left(\dfrac{u}{2^{\frac{1}{2}} t^{\frac{1}{2}}}\right)\left[f(u) - \int_0^{u} f[(u^2-v^2)^{\frac{1}{2}}] J_1(v)\,dv\right] du$ |
| 35. | $g[(s-1)^{\frac{1}{2}}]$ | $\dfrac{1}{2\pi^{\frac{1}{2}} t^{\frac{3}{2}}}\left[\int_0^{\infty} u\, e^{-\frac{u^2}{4t}} f(u)\,du + \int_0^{\infty} u\, e^{-\frac{u^2}{4t}} \int_0^{u} I_1(v) f[(u^2-v^2)^{\frac{1}{2}}]\,dv\,du\right]$ |
| 36. | $s^{\frac{n-1}{2}} g[(s-1)^{\frac{1}{2}}]$ | $\dfrac{1}{2^{\frac{n}{2}} \pi^{\frac{1}{2}} t^{\frac{n+1}{2}}} \int_0^{\infty} e^{-\frac{u^2}{4t}} He\left(\dfrac{u}{2^{\frac{1}{2}} t^{\frac{1}{2}}}\right)\left[f(u) + \int_0^{u} f[(u^2-v^2)^{\frac{1}{2}}] I_1(v)\,dv\right] du$ |
| 37. | $g(s+s^{\frac{1}{2}})$ | $\dfrac{1}{2\pi^{\frac{1}{2}}} \int_0^{t} u(t-u)^{-\frac{3}{2}} e^{-\frac{u^2}{4(t-u)}} f(u)\,du$ |
| 38. | $\dfrac{1}{s^{\frac{1}{2}}} g(s+s^{\frac{1}{2}})$ | $\pi^{-\frac{1}{2}} \int_0^{t} (t-u)^{-\frac{1}{2}} e^{-\frac{u^2}{4(t-u)}} f(u)\,du$ |
| 39. | $g[(s^2+a^2)^{\frac{1}{2}}]$ | $f(t) - a\int_0^{t} f[(t^2-u^2)^{\frac{1}{2}}] J_1(au)\,du$ |

| | g(s) | f(t) | |
|---|---|---|---|
| 0. | $\dfrac{g[(s^2+a^2)^{\frac{1}{2}}]}{(s^2+a^2)^{\frac{1}{2}}}$ | $\int_0^t J_0[a(t^2-u^2)^{\frac{1}{2}}]f(u)\,du$ | |
| 1. | $\dfrac{sg[(s^2+a^2)^{\frac{1}{2}}]}{(s^2+a^2)^{\frac{1}{2}}}$ | $f(t)-at\int_0^t (t^2-u^2)^{-\frac{1}{2}}J_1[a(t^2-u^2)^{\frac{1}{2}}]f(u)\,du$ | |
| 2. | $\dfrac{[(s^2+a^2)^{\frac{1}{2}}-s]^{2\nu}g[(s^2+a^2)^{\frac{1}{2}}]}{(s^2+a^2)^{\frac{1}{2}}}$ | $a^{2\nu}\int_0^t \left(\frac{t-u}{t+u}\right)^{\nu} J_{2\nu}[a(t^2-u^2)^{\frac{1}{2}}]f(u)\,du$ | $\mathrm{Re}\,\nu > -\frac{1}{2}$ |
| 3. | $g[(s^2-a^2)^{\frac{1}{2}}]$ | $f(t)+a\int_0^t f[(t^2-u^2)^{\frac{1}{2}}]I_1(u)\,du$ | |
| 4. | $\dfrac{g[(s^2-a^2)^{\frac{1}{2}}]}{(s^2-a^2)^{\frac{1}{2}}}$ | $\int_0^t I_0[a(t^2-u^2)^{\frac{1}{2}}]f(u)\,du$ | |
| 5. | $\dfrac{s\,g[(s^2-a^2)^{\frac{1}{2}}]}{(s^2-a^2)^{\frac{1}{2}}}$ | $f(t)+at\int_0^t (t^2-u^2)^{-\frac{1}{2}}I_1[a(t^2-u^2)^{\frac{1}{2}}]f(u)\,du$ | |
| 6. | $\dfrac{[s-(s^2-a^2)^{\frac{1}{2}}]^{2\nu}g[(s^2-a^2)^{\frac{1}{2}}]}{(s^2-a^2)^{\frac{1}{2}}}$ | $a^{2\nu}\int_0^t \left(\frac{t-u}{t+u}\right)^{\nu} I_{2\nu}[a(t^2-u^2)^{\frac{1}{2}}]f(u)\,du$ | $\mathrm{Re}\,\nu > -\frac{1}{2}$ |
| 7. | $\dfrac{1}{(s+a)^{\nu}}g[bs+(s+a)^{\frac{1}{2}}]$ | $\dfrac{2^{\nu-\frac{1}{2}}}{\pi^{\frac{1}{2}}}\int_0^{\frac{t}{b}} (t-bu)^{\nu-1}\exp\left[-a(t-bu)-\dfrac{u^2}{8(t-bu)}\right]D_{1-2\nu}\left[\dfrac{u}{2^{\frac{1}{2}}(t-bu)^{\frac{1}{2}}}\right]f(u)\,du$ | $b>0$ |
| 3. | $\dfrac{[(s^2+a^2)^{\frac{1}{2}}-s]^{2\nu}g[(s^2+a^2)^{\frac{1}{2}}-s]}{(s^2+a^2)^{\frac{1}{2}}}$ | $a^{2\nu}t^{\nu}\int_0^{\infty} (t+2u)^{-\nu}J_{2\nu}[a(t^2+2tu)^{\frac{1}{2}}]f(u)\,du$ | $\mathrm{Re}\,\nu > -\frac{1}{2}$ |
| . | $\dfrac{[(s^2+a^2)^{\frac{1}{2}}-s]^{2\nu}g[s-(s^2+a^2)^{\frac{1}{2}}]}{(s^2+a^2)^{\frac{1}{2}}}$ | $a^{2\nu}t^{\nu}\int_0^{\infty} (t-2u)^{-\nu}J_{2\nu}[a(t^2-2tu)^{\frac{1}{2}}]f(u)\,du$ | $\mathrm{Re}\,\nu > -\frac{1}{2}$ |

| | g(s) | f(t) | |
|---|---|---|---|
| 50. | $\dfrac{[s-(s^2-a^2)^{\frac{1}{2}}]^{2\nu}g[(s^2-a^2)^{\frac{1}{2}}-s]}{(s^2-a^2)^{\frac{1}{2}}}$ | $a^{2\nu}t^{\nu}\int_0^\infty (t+2u)^{-\nu}I_{2\nu}[a(t^2+2tu)^{\frac{1}{2}}]f(u)\,du$ | Re $\nu$ > - |
| 51. | $\dfrac{[s-(s^2-a^2)^{\frac{1}{2}}]^{2\nu}g[s-(s^2-a^2)^{\frac{1}{2}}]}{(s^2-a^2)^{\frac{1}{2}}}$ | $a^{2\nu}t^{\nu}\int_0^\infty (t-2u)^{-\nu}I_{2\nu}[a(t^2-2tu)^{\frac{1}{2}}]f(u)\,du$ | Re $\nu$ > - |
| 52. | $g[b+(s^2+a^2)^{\frac{1}{2}}-s]-g(b)$ | $-at^{-\frac{1}{2}}\int_0^\infty e^{-bu}(t+2u)^{-\frac{1}{2}}J_1[at^{\frac{1}{2}}(t+2u)^{\frac{1}{2}}]uf(u)\,du$ | |
| 53. | $g[b+(s^2-a^2)^{\frac{1}{2}}-s]-g(b)$ | $at^{-\frac{1}{2}}\int_0^\infty e^{-bu}(t+2u)^{-\frac{1}{2}}I_1[at^{\frac{1}{2}}(t+2u)^{\frac{1}{2}}]uf(u)\,du$ | |
| 54. | $g(\log s^a)$ | $\int_0^\infty \dfrac{t^{au-1}}{\Gamma(au)}f(u)\,du$ | |
| 55. | $\dfrac{1}{s}g(\log s)$ | $\int_0^\infty \dfrac{t^u}{\Gamma(u+1)}f(u)\,du$ | |
| 56. | $g[w(s)]$ | $\int_0^\infty r(u,t)f(u)\,du$ where the inverse transform of $e^{-uw(s)}$ is $r(u,t)$ | |

Differentiation

| | | | |
|---|---|---|---|
| 57. | $\dfrac{d^n g(s)}{ds^n}$ | $(-1)^n t^n f(t)$ | $n = 0,1,2,\ldots$ |
| 58. | $s^n g^{(m)}(s)$ | $(-1)^m \dfrac{d^n}{dt^n}[t^m f(t)]$ | $m \geqslant n$<br>$m,n = 0,1,2,\ldots$ |
| 59. | $\left(-\dfrac{d}{ds}\right)^m [s^n g(s)]$ | $t^m f^{(n)}(t)$ | $m \geqslant n$<br>$m,n = 0,1,2,\ldots$ |

| | g(s) | f(t) | |
|---|---|---|---|
| | $\left(-s\frac{d}{ds}\right)^n g(s)$ | $\left(\frac{d}{dt}t\right)^n f(t)$ | $n=0,1,2,\ldots$ |
| | $\left(-\frac{d}{ds}s\right)^n g(s)$ | $\left(t\frac{d}{dt}\right)^n f(t)$ | $n=0,1,2,\ldots$ |
| | $\frac{\partial}{\partial a} g(s,a)$ | $\frac{\partial}{\partial a} f(t,a)$ | |

tegration

| | g(s) | f(t) | |
|---|---|---|---|
| | $\int_s^\infty g(u)\,du$ | $\frac{f(t)}{t}$ | |
| | $\frac{1}{s}\int_s^\infty g(u)\,du$ | $\int_0^t v^{-1} f(v)\,dv$ | |
| | $\frac{1}{s}\int_0^s g(u)\,du$ | $\int_t^\infty v^{-1} f(v)\,dv$ | |
| | $\int_{a_0}^a g(s,u)\,du$ | $\int_{a_0}^a f(t,v)\,dv$ | |
| | $\int_s^\infty \cdots \int_s^\infty g(u)(du)^n$ | $t^{-n} f(t)$ | $n=1,2,3,\ldots$ |
| | $\int_s^\infty u \int_s^\infty \cdots u \int_s^\infty u\, g(u)\,(du)^n$ | $\left(\frac{1}{t}\frac{d}{dt}\right)^n f(t)$<br>if $\left(\frac{1}{t}\frac{d}{dt}\right)^k f(t)=0$<br>for $t=0,\ k=0,1,\ldots,n-1$ | $n=1,2,3,\ldots$ |
| | $\frac{1}{1-e^{-as}}\int_0^a e^{-su} f(u)\,du$ | $f(t+a)=f(t)$ | $a>0$ |

| | $g(s)$ | $f(t)$ | |
|---|---|---|---|
| 70. | $\frac{1}{1+e^{-as}}\int_0^a e^{-su}f(u)\,du$ | $f(t+a)=-f(t)$ | $a>0$ |
| 71. | $\int_0^\infty (e^{su}-1)^{-1}f(u)\,du$ | $\sum_{n=1}^{\infty}\frac{1}{n}f(\frac{t}{n})$ | |
| 72. | $e^{as}[g(s)-\int_0^a e^{-su}f(u)\,du]$ | $f(t+a)$ | $a\geqslant$ |
| 73. | $\int_0^\infty e^{-\frac{s^2}{4u^2}}g(u^2)\,du$ | $\pi^{\frac{1}{2}}f(t^2)$ | |
| 74. | $\int_0^\infty u^{-\frac{1}{2}}e^{-\frac{s^2}{4u}}g(u)\,du$ | $2\pi^{\frac{1}{2}}f(t^2)$ | |
| 75. | $s\int_0^\infty u^{-\frac{3}{2}}e^{-\frac{s^2}{4u}}g(u)\,du$ | $4\pi^{\frac{1}{2}}t\,f(t^2)$ | |
| 76. | $\int_0^\infty J_0(2s^{\frac{1}{2}}u^{\frac{1}{2}})g(u)\,du$ | $\frac{1}{t}f(\frac{1}{t})$ | |
| 77. | $\frac{1}{s^{\frac{1}{2}}}\int_0^\infty u^{\frac{1}{2}}J_1(2s^{\frac{1}{2}}u^{\frac{1}{2}})g(u)\,du$ | $f(\frac{1}{t})$ | |
| 78. | $\int_0^\infty J_s(au)g(u)\,du$ | $f(a\sinh t)$ | $a>$ |
| 79. | $\int_0^\infty u^{n-2}e^{-\frac{s^2u^2}{4}}He_n(2^{-\frac{1}{2}}su)g(\frac{1}{u^2})\,du$ | $2^{\frac{n}{2}}\pi^{\frac{1}{2}}t^n f(t^2)$ | $n=0,1,2,\ldots$ |
| 80. | $\int_0^\infty u^{\nu-2}e^{-\frac{s^2u^2}{4}}D_\nu(su)g(\frac{1}{2u^2})\,du$ | $2^{\frac{1}{2}}\pi^{\frac{1}{2}}t^\nu f(t^2)$ | |
| 81. | $\frac{1}{2\pi i}\int_{c-i\infty}^{c+i\infty}g_1(u)g_2(s-u)\,du$ | $f_1(t)f_2(t)$ | |

| | g(s) | f(t) |
|---|---|---|

Limiting Values

| | | |
|---|---|---|
| 32. | $\lim_{s \to \infty} s\,g(s)$ | $\lim_{t \to 0} f(t)$ |
| 33. | $\lim_{s \to 0} s\,g(s)$<br>if sg(s) is analytic on the imaginary axis and in the right half-plane | $\lim_{t \to \infty} f(t)$ |
| 34. | $\lim_{a \to a_0} g(s,a)$ | $\lim_{a \to a_0} f(t,a)$ |

# Section 2 • Inverse Transform Pairs

Because of the large number of inverse transforms of polynomials in s (code #1) immediately following, a sub-coding system is used to facilitate the location of particular entries. It makes use of the denominators of the polynomial expressions. The denominators can be expressed as the product of one or more of the following polynomial expressions, where $\alpha$ and $\beta$ are arbitrary constants.

| Code Letter | Polynomial Expression |
|---|---|
| A | $s$ |
| B | $s^2$ |
| C | $s^3$ |
| D | $s^4$ |
| E | $s^5$ |
| F | $s+\alpha$ |
| G | $(s+\alpha)^2$ |
| H | $(s+\alpha)^3$ |
| I | $(s+\alpha)^4$ |
| J | $(s+\alpha)^5$ |
| K | $s^2+\alpha^2$ |

| Code Letter | Polynomial Expression |
|---|---|
| L | $(s^2+\alpha^2)^2$ |
| M | $s^2-\alpha^2$ |
| N | $(s^2-\alpha^2)^2$ |
| O | $s^2+\alpha s+\beta$ |
| P | $s^3+\alpha^3$ |
| Q | $s^3-\alpha^3$ |
| R | $s^4+\alpha^4$ |
| S | $s^4-\alpha^4$ |

For example, $s^2(s+\alpha)(s+\beta)$ is of the form BFF

and $s(s+\alpha)^2$ is of the form AG

Specific entries in the table are listed in strict alphabetical order according to this scheme. Most denominators having orders up to $s^4$ are listed together with a few having higher orders.

Immediately following the alphabetically coded group are listed some inverse transforms of more general polynomials.

| | No. | | g(s) | f(t) | |
|---|---|---|---|---|---|
| 1 | 1 | A | $\frac{1}{s}$ | $1$ | $\mathrm{Re}\ s > o$ |
| | 2 | AF | $\frac{1}{s(s+\alpha)}$ | $\frac{1-e^{-\alpha t}}{\alpha}$ | $\mathrm{Re}\ s > \mathrm{Max}\ o,\ -\mathrm{Re}\ \alpha$ |
| | 3 | | $\frac{s+a}{s(s+\alpha)}$ | $\frac{a}{\alpha} + (1-\frac{a}{\alpha})e^{-\alpha t}$ | $\mathrm{Re}\ s > \mathrm{Max}\ o,\ -\mathrm{Re}\ \alpha$ |
| | 4 | AFF | $\frac{1}{s(s+\alpha)(s+\beta)}$ | $\frac{1}{\alpha\beta} + \frac{\beta\, e^{-\alpha t} - \alpha\, e^{-\beta t}}{\alpha\beta(\alpha-\beta)}$ | $\mathrm{Re}\ s > \mathrm{Max}\ o,\ -\mathrm{Re}\ \alpha,\ -\mathrm{Re}\ \beta$ |
| | 5 | | $\frac{s+a}{s(s+\alpha)(s+\beta)}$ | $\frac{a}{\alpha\beta} + \frac{a-\alpha}{\alpha(\alpha-\beta)} e^{-\alpha t} + \frac{a-\beta}{\beta(\beta-\alpha)} e^{-\beta t}$ | $\mathrm{Re}\ s > \mathrm{Max}\ o,\ -\mathrm{Re}\ \alpha,\ -\mathrm{Re}\ \beta$ |
| | 6 | | $\frac{s^2+as+b}{s(s+\alpha)(s+\beta)}$ | $\frac{b}{\alpha\beta} + \frac{\alpha^2-a\alpha+b}{\alpha(\alpha-\beta)} e^{-\alpha t} - \frac{\beta^2-a\beta+b}{\beta(\alpha-\beta)} e^{-\beta t}$ | $\mathrm{Re}\ s > \mathrm{Max}\ o,\ -\mathrm{Re}\ \alpha,\ -\mathrm{Re}\ \beta$ |
| | 7 | AFFF | $\frac{1}{s(s+\alpha)(s+\beta)(s+\gamma)}$ | $\frac{1}{\alpha\beta\gamma} - \frac{e^{-\alpha t}}{\alpha(\alpha-\beta)(\alpha-\gamma)} - \frac{e^{-\beta t}}{\beta(\beta-\alpha)(\beta-\gamma)} - \frac{e^{-\gamma t}}{\gamma(\gamma-\alpha)(\gamma-\beta)}$ | $\mathrm{Re}\ s > \mathrm{Max}\ o,\ -\mathrm{Re}\ \alpha,\ -\mathrm{Re}\ \beta,\ -\mathrm{Re}\ \gamma$ |
| | 8 | | $\frac{s+a}{s(s+\alpha)(s+\beta)(s+\gamma)}$ | $\frac{a}{\alpha\beta\gamma} - \frac{a-\alpha}{\alpha(\beta-\alpha)(\gamma-\alpha)} e^{-\alpha t} - \frac{a-\beta}{\beta(\alpha-\beta)(\gamma-\beta)} e^{-\beta t} - \frac{a-\gamma}{\gamma(\alpha-\gamma)(\beta-\gamma)} e^{-\gamma t}$ | $\mathrm{Re}\ s > \mathrm{Max}\ o,\ -\mathrm{Re}\ \alpha,\ -\mathrm{Re}\ \beta,\ -\mathrm{Re}\ \gamma$ |
| | 9 | | $\frac{s^2+as+b}{s(s+\alpha)(s+\beta)(s+\gamma)}$ | $\frac{b}{\alpha\beta\gamma} - \frac{\alpha^2-a\alpha+b}{\alpha(\alpha-\beta)(\alpha-\gamma)} e^{-\alpha t} - \frac{\beta^2-a\beta+b}{\beta(\beta-\alpha)(\beta-\gamma)} e^{-\beta t} - \frac{\gamma^2-a\gamma+b}{\gamma(\gamma-\alpha)(\gamma-\beta)} e^{-\gamma t}$ | $\mathrm{Re}\ s > \mathrm{Max}\ o,\ -\mathrm{Re}\ \alpha,\ -\mathrm{Re}\ \beta,\ -\mathrm{Re}\ \gamma$ |
| | 10 | | $\frac{s^3+as^2+bs+c}{s(s+\alpha)(s+\beta)(s+\gamma)}$ | $\frac{c}{\alpha\beta\gamma} + \frac{\alpha^3-a\alpha^2+b\alpha-c}{\alpha(\beta-\alpha)(\gamma-\alpha)} e^{-\alpha t} + \frac{\beta^3-a\beta^2+b\beta-c}{\beta(\alpha-\beta)(\gamma-\beta)} e^{-\beta t} + \frac{\gamma^3-a\gamma^2+b\gamma-c}{\gamma(\alpha-\gamma)(\beta-\gamma)} e^{-\gamma t}$ | $\mathrm{Re}\ s > \mathrm{Max}\ o,\ -\mathrm{Re}\ \alpha,\ -\mathrm{Re}\ \beta,\ -\mathrm{Re}\ \gamma$ |

| | | g(s) | f(t) | |
|---|---|---|---|---|
| 1(Contd.) | | | | |
| 11 | AG | $\frac{1}{s(s+\alpha)^2}$ | $\frac{1}{\alpha^2}-\frac{1}{\alpha}(\frac{1}{\alpha}+t)e^{-\alpha t}$ | Re s > Max o, − Re α |
| 12 | | $\frac{s+a}{s(s+\alpha)^2}$ | $\frac{a}{\alpha^2}+[(1-\frac{a}{\alpha})t-\frac{a}{\alpha^2}]e^{-\alpha t}$ | Re s > Max o, − Re α |
| 13 | | $\frac{s^2+as+b}{s(s+\alpha)^2}$ | $\frac{b}{\alpha^2}-[\frac{b}{\alpha^2}-1+(\alpha-a+\frac{b}{\alpha})t]e^{-\alpha t}$ | Re s > Max o, − Re α |
| 14 | AH | $\frac{1}{s(s+\alpha)^3}$ | $\frac{1}{\alpha^3}(1-e^{-\alpha t})-\frac{t}{\alpha^2}e^{-\alpha t}-\frac{t^2}{2\alpha}e^{-\alpha t}$ | Re s > Max o, − Re α |
| 15 | | $\frac{s+a}{s(s+\alpha)^3}$ | $\frac{a}{\alpha^3}(1-e^{-\alpha t})-\frac{a}{\alpha^2}te^{-\alpha t}+\frac{\alpha-a}{2\alpha}t^2e^{-\alpha t}$ | Re s > Max o, − Re α |
| 16 | | $\frac{s^2+as+b}{s(s+\alpha)^3}$ | $\frac{b}{\alpha^3}(1-e^{-\alpha t})+(1-\frac{b}{\alpha^2})te^{-\alpha t}$ $+\frac{1}{2}(a-\alpha-\frac{b}{\alpha})t^2e^{-\alpha t}$ | Re s > Max o, − Re α |
| 17 | | $\frac{s^3+as^2+bs+c}{s(s+\alpha)^3}$ | $\frac{c}{\alpha^3}+(1-\frac{c}{\alpha^3})e^{-\alpha t}+(a-2\alpha-\frac{c}{\alpha^2})te^{-\alpha t}$ $+\frac{1}{2}(b+\alpha^2-a\alpha-\frac{c}{\alpha})t^2e^{-\alpha t}$ | Re s > Max o, − Re α |
| 18 | AK | $\frac{1}{s(s^2+\alpha^2)}$ | $\frac{1-\cos(\alpha t)}{\alpha^2}$ $=\left(\frac{\pi t}{2\alpha^3}\right)^{\frac{1}{2}}\mathbf{H}_{\frac{1}{2}}(\alpha t)$ | Re s > \|Im α\| |
| 19 | | $\frac{s^2+2\alpha^2}{s(s^2+4\alpha^2)}$ | $\cos^2(\alpha t)$ | Re s > 2\|Im α\| |
| 20 | | $\frac{s+a}{s(s^2+\alpha^2)}$ | $\frac{a}{\alpha^2}-\frac{(a^2+\alpha^2)^{\frac{1}{2}}}{\alpha^2}\cos(\alpha t+\tan^{-1}\frac{\alpha}{a})$ | Re s > \|Im a\| |

| | | g(s) | f(t) | |
|---|---|---|---|---|
| 1(Contd.) | | | | |
| 21 | AK | $\frac{s^2+as+b}{s(s^2+\alpha^2)}$ | $\frac{b-[(b-\alpha^2)^2+a^2\alpha^2]^{\frac{1}{2}}\cos(\alpha t+\tan^{-1}\frac{a\alpha}{b-\alpha^2})}{\alpha^2}$ | Re s > \| Im α \| |
| 22 | AM | $\frac{1}{s(s^2-\alpha^2)}$ | $\frac{2\sinh^2\frac{\alpha t}{2}}{\alpha^2} = \frac{\cosh(\alpha t)-1}{\alpha^2}$ <br> $= \left(\frac{\pi t}{2\alpha^3}\right)^{\frac{1}{2}} L_{\frac{1}{2}}(\alpha t)$ | Re s > \|Re α \| |
| 23 | | $\frac{s+a}{s(s^2-\alpha^2)}$ | $\frac{1}{\alpha}\sinh(\alpha t)+\frac{a}{\alpha^2}\cosh(\alpha t)-\frac{a}{\alpha^2}$ | Re s > \|Re α \| |
| 24 | | $\frac{s^2+as+b}{s(s^2-\alpha^2)}$ | $\frac{a}{\alpha}\sinh(\alpha t)+\frac{\alpha^2+b}{\alpha^2}\cosh(\alpha t)-\frac{b}{\alpha^2}$ | Re s > \|Re α \| |
| 25 | | $\frac{s^2-2\alpha^2}{s(s^2-4\alpha^2)}$ | $\cosh^2(\alpha t)$ | Re s > 2\|Re α \| |
| 26 | AO | $\frac{1}{s(s^2+\alpha s+\beta)}$ | $\frac{1}{\beta}-\frac{1}{r_1-r_2}\left(\frac{e^{-r_2 t}}{r_2}-\frac{e^{-r_1 t}}{r_1}\right)$ if $\alpha^2 \neq 4\beta$ <br> where $-r_1$ and $-r_2$ are the roots of <br> $s^2+\alpha s+\beta = 0$ <br> $\frac{1}{\beta}[1-(1+\frac{\alpha t}{2})e^{-\frac{\alpha t}{2}}]$ if $\alpha^2 = 4\beta$ <br> If $4\beta-\alpha^2$ is real and positive a convenient form is <br> $\frac{1}{\beta}-\frac{e^{-\alpha t}}{(\beta^2-\frac{\alpha^2\beta}{4})^{\frac{1}{2}}}\sin[(\beta-\frac{\alpha^2}{4})^{\frac{1}{2}}t+\tan^{-1}(\frac{4\beta}{\alpha^2}-1)^{\frac{1}{2}}]$ | Re s > Max o, − Re $r_1$, − Re $r_2$ |
| 27 | | $\frac{s+a}{s(s^2+\alpha s+\beta)}$ <br> $= \frac{1}{s^2+\alpha s+\beta}+\frac{a}{s(s^2+\alpha s+\beta)}$ | See under AO and O. | Re s > Max o, $-\frac{1}{2}$ Re α <br> $+ \mid \mathrm{Im}(\beta-\frac{\alpha^2}{4})^{\frac{1}{2}} \mid$ |

| | | g(s) | f(t) | |
|---|---|---|---|---|
| 1(Contd.) | | | | |
| 28 | AO | $\frac{s^2+as+b}{s(s^2+\alpha s+\beta)} = \frac{s+a}{s^2+\alpha s+\beta} + \frac{b}{s(s^2+\alpha s+\beta)}$ | See under AO and O. | Re s > Max o, $-\frac{1}{2}$ Re α + $\left\lvert \mathrm{Im}(\beta - \frac{\alpha^2}{4})^{\frac{1}{2}} \right\rvert$ |
| 29 | AP | $\frac{1}{s(s^3+\alpha^3)}$ | $\frac{1}{\alpha^3}\left[1 - \frac{1}{3}e^{-\alpha t} - \frac{2}{3}e^{\frac{\alpha t}{2}}\cos\frac{3^{\frac{1}{2}}\alpha t}{2}\right]$ | Re s > Max o, − Re α, $\frac{1}{2}$ Re α + $\frac{3^{\frac{1}{2}}}{2}$\| Im α \| |
| 30 | | $\frac{s+a}{s(s^3+\alpha^3)}$ | $\frac{a}{\alpha^3} - \frac{1}{3\alpha^3}\left[(a-\alpha)e^{-\alpha t}+(2a+\alpha)e^{\frac{\alpha t}{2}}\cos\frac{3^{\frac{1}{2}}\alpha t}{2} - 3^{\frac{1}{2}}\alpha e^{\frac{\alpha t}{2}}\sin\frac{3^{\frac{1}{2}}\alpha t}{2}\right]$ | Re s> Max o, − Re a, $\frac{1}{2}$ Re α + $\frac{3^{\frac{1}{2}}}{2}$\| Im α \| |
| 31 | | $\frac{s^2+as+b}{s(s^3+\alpha^3)}$ | $\frac{b}{\alpha^3} - \frac{1}{3\alpha^3}\left[(b+\alpha^2-a\alpha)e^{-\alpha t}+(2b-\alpha^2+a\alpha)\,.\,e^{\frac{\alpha t}{2}}\cos\frac{3^{\frac{1}{2}}\alpha t}{2} - 3^{\frac{1}{2}}\alpha(\alpha+a)e^{\frac{\alpha t}{2}}\sin\frac{3^{\frac{1}{2}}\alpha t}{2}\right]$ | Re s > Max o, − Re α, $\frac{1}{2}$ Re α + $\frac{3^{\frac{1}{2}}}{2}$\| Im α \| |
| 32 | | $\frac{s^3+as^2+bs+c}{s(s^3+\alpha^3)}$ | $\frac{c}{\alpha^3} + \frac{1}{3\alpha^3}\left[(\alpha^3-c-a\alpha^2+b\alpha)e^{-\alpha t} + (2\alpha^3-2c+a\alpha^2-b\alpha)e^{\frac{\alpha t}{2}}\cos\frac{3^{\frac{1}{2}}\alpha t}{2} + 3^{\frac{1}{2}}\alpha(a\alpha+b)e^{\frac{\alpha t}{2}}\sin\frac{3^{\frac{1}{2}}\alpha t}{2}\right]$ | Re s > Max o, − Re a, $\frac{1}{2}$ Re α + $\frac{3^{\frac{1}{2}}}{2}$\| Im α \| |
| 33 | AQ | $\frac{1}{s(s^3-\alpha^3)}$ | $\frac{1}{\alpha^3}\left[\frac{1}{3}e^{\alpha t} + \frac{2}{3}e^{-\frac{\alpha t}{2}}\cos\left(\frac{3^{\frac{1}{2}}\alpha t}{2}\right) - 1\right]$ | Re s > Max o, Re α, $\frac{1}{2}(-\mathrm{Re}\,\alpha + 3^{\frac{1}{2}}\lvert \mathrm{Im}\,\alpha \rvert)$ |
| 34 | | $\frac{s+a}{s(s^3-\alpha^3)}$ | $\frac{1}{3\alpha^3}\left[(a+\alpha)e^{\alpha t}+(2a-\alpha)e^{-\frac{\alpha t}{2}}\cos\left(\frac{3^{\frac{1}{2}}\alpha t}{2}\right) - 3^{\frac{1}{2}}\alpha e^{-\frac{\alpha t}{2}}\sin\left(\frac{3^{\frac{1}{2}}\alpha t}{2}\right)\right] - \frac{a}{\alpha^3}$ | Re s > Max o, Re α, $\frac{1}{2}(-\mathrm{Re}\,\alpha + 3^{\frac{1}{2}}\lvert \mathrm{Im}\,\alpha \rvert)$ |

| | | g(s) | f(t) | |
|---|---|---|---|---|
| (Contd.) | | | | |
| 35 | AQ | $\frac{s^2+as+b}{s(s^3-\alpha^3)}$ | $\frac{1}{3\alpha^3}\left[(b+\alpha^2+a\alpha)e^{\alpha t}+(2b-\alpha^2-a\alpha)e^{-\frac{\alpha t}{2}}\cos\left(\frac{3^{\frac{1}{2}}\alpha t}{2}\right) + 3^{\frac{1}{2}}\alpha(\alpha-a)e^{-\frac{\alpha t}{2}}\sin\left(\frac{3^{\frac{1}{2}}\alpha t}{2}\right)\right]-\frac{b}{\alpha^3}$ | Re s > Max o, Re $\alpha$, $\frac{1}{2}(-\mathrm{Re}\,\alpha + 3^{\frac{1}{2}}\lvert \mathrm{Im}\,\alpha \rvert)$ |
| 36 | | $\frac{s^3+as^2+bs+c}{s(s^3-\alpha^3)}$ | $\frac{1}{3\alpha^3}\left[(\alpha^3+c+a\alpha^2+b\alpha)e^{\alpha t} + (2\alpha^3+2c-a\alpha^2-b\alpha)e^{-\frac{\alpha t}{2}}\cos\left(\frac{3^{\frac{1}{2}}\alpha t}{2}\right) + 3^{\frac{1}{2}}\alpha(a\alpha-b)e^{-\frac{\alpha t}{2}}\sin\left(\frac{3^{\frac{1}{2}}\alpha t}{2}\right)\right]-\frac{c}{\alpha^3}$ | Re s > Max o, Re $\alpha$, $\frac{1}{2}(-\mathrm{Re}\,\alpha + 3^{\frac{1}{2}}\lvert \mathrm{Im}\,\alpha \rvert)$ |
| 37 | B | $\frac{1}{s^2}$ | $t$ | Re s > o |
| 38 | | $\frac{s+a}{s^2}$ | $1+at$ | Re s > o |
| 39 | BF | $\frac{1}{s^2(s+\alpha)}$ | $\frac{1}{\alpha^2}\left(e^{-\alpha t}+\alpha t-1\right)$ | Re s > Max o, − Re $\alpha$ |
| 0 | | $\frac{s+a}{s^2(s+\alpha)}$ | $\left(\frac{1}{\alpha}-\frac{a}{\alpha^2}\right)\left(1-e^{-\alpha t}\right)+\frac{a}{\alpha}t$ | Re s > Max o, − Re $\alpha$ |
| 1 | | $\frac{s^2+as+b}{s^2(s+\alpha)}$ | $\frac{bt}{\alpha}+\frac{a}{\alpha}-\frac{b}{\alpha^2}-\left(\frac{a}{\alpha}-\frac{b}{\alpha^2}-1\right)e^{-\alpha t}$ | Re s > Max o, − Re $\alpha$ |
| 2 | BFF | $\frac{1}{s^2(s+\alpha)(s+\beta)}$ | $-\frac{\alpha+\beta}{\alpha^2\beta^2}+\frac{t}{\alpha\beta}-\frac{e^{-\alpha t}}{\alpha^2(\alpha-\beta)}+\frac{e^{-\beta t}}{\beta^2(\alpha-\beta)}$ | Re s > Max o, − Re $\alpha$, − Re $\beta$ |
| 3 | | $\frac{s+a}{s^2(s+\alpha)(s+\beta)}$ | $\frac{\alpha\beta-(\alpha+\beta)a}{\alpha^2\beta^2}+\frac{at}{\alpha\beta}-\frac{\alpha-a}{\alpha^2(\alpha-\beta)}e^{-\alpha t} - \frac{\beta-a}{\beta^2(\alpha-\beta)}e^{-\beta t}$ | Re s > Max o, − Re $\alpha$, − Re $\beta$ |

| | | g(s) | f(t) | |
|---|---|---|---|---|
| 1(Contd.) | | | | |
| 44 | BFF | $\dfrac{s^2+as+b}{s^2(s+\alpha)(s+\beta)}$ | $\dfrac{\alpha\beta a-(\alpha+\beta)b}{\alpha^2\beta^2}+\dfrac{bt}{\alpha\beta}-\dfrac{\alpha^2-\alpha a+b}{\alpha^2(\alpha-\beta)}e^{-\alpha t}+\dfrac{\beta^2-\beta a+b}{\beta^2(\alpha-\beta)}e^{-\beta t}$ | Re s > Max o, − Re α, − Re β |
| 45 | | $\dfrac{s^3+as^2+bs+c}{s^2(s+\alpha)(s+\beta)}$ | $\dfrac{\alpha\beta b-(\alpha+\beta)c}{\alpha^2\beta^2}+\dfrac{ct}{\alpha\beta}+\dfrac{\alpha^3-\alpha^2 a+\alpha b-c}{\alpha^2(\alpha-\beta)}e^{-\alpha t}-\dfrac{\beta^3-\beta^2 a+\beta b-c}{\beta^2(\alpha-\beta)}e^{-\beta t}$ | Re s > Max o, − Re α, − Re β |
| 46 | BG | $\dfrac{1}{s^2(s+\alpha)^2}$ | $-\dfrac{2}{\alpha^3}+\dfrac{t}{\alpha^2}+\dfrac{2}{\alpha^3}e^{-\alpha t}+\dfrac{t}{\alpha^2}e^{-\alpha t}$ | Re s > Max o, − Re α |
| 47 | | $\dfrac{s+a}{s^2(s+\alpha)^2}$ | $\dfrac{1}{\alpha^2}-\dfrac{2a}{\alpha^3}+\dfrac{a}{\alpha^2}t+\left(-\dfrac{1}{\alpha^2}+\dfrac{2a}{\alpha^3}\right)e^{-\alpha t}+\left(-\dfrac{1}{\alpha}+\dfrac{a}{\alpha^2}\right)te^{-\alpha t}$ | Re s > Max o, − Re α |
| 48 | | $\dfrac{s^2+as+b}{s^2(s+\alpha)^2}$ | $\dfrac{a}{\alpha^2}-\dfrac{2b}{\alpha^3}+\dfrac{b}{\alpha^2}t+\left(-\dfrac{a}{\alpha^2}+\dfrac{2b}{\alpha^3}\right)e^{-\alpha t}+\left(1-\dfrac{a}{\alpha}+\dfrac{b}{\alpha^2}\right)t\,e^{-\alpha t}$ | Re s > Max o, − Re α |
| 49 | | $\dfrac{s^3+as^2+bs+c}{s^2(s+a)^2}$ | $\dfrac{b}{\alpha^2}-\dfrac{2c}{\alpha^3}+\dfrac{c}{\alpha^2}t+\left(1-\dfrac{b}{\alpha^2}+\dfrac{2c}{\alpha^3}\right)e^{-\alpha t}+\left(-\alpha+a-\dfrac{b}{\alpha}+\dfrac{c}{\alpha^2}\right)te^{-\alpha t}$ | Re s > Max o, − Re α |
| 50 | BK | $\dfrac{1}{s^2(s^2+\alpha^2)}$ | $\dfrac{t}{\alpha^2}-\dfrac{\sin(\alpha t)}{\alpha^3}$ | Re s > \|Im α\| |
| 51 | | $\dfrac{s+a}{s^2(s^2+\alpha^2)}$ | $\dfrac{1}{\alpha^2}+\dfrac{at}{\alpha^2}-\dfrac{1}{\alpha^2}\cos(\alpha t)-\dfrac{a}{\alpha^3}\sin(\alpha t)$ | Re s > \|Im α\| |

| | | g(s) | f(t) | |
|---|---|---|---|---|
| 1(Contd.) | | | | |
| 52 | BK | $\dfrac{s^2+as+b}{s^2(s^2+\alpha^2)}$ | $\dfrac{a}{\alpha^2}+\dfrac{b}{\alpha^2}t-\dfrac{a}{\alpha^2}\cos(\alpha t)+(\dfrac{1}{\alpha}-\dfrac{b}{\alpha^3})\sin(\alpha t)$ | $\text{Re } s > \lvert \text{Im } \alpha \rvert$ |
| 53 | | $\dfrac{s^3+as^2+bs+c}{s^2(s^2+\alpha^2)}$ | $\dfrac{b}{\alpha^2}+\dfrac{c}{\alpha^2}t+\left(1-\dfrac{b}{\alpha^2}\right)\cos(\alpha t)+\left(\dfrac{a}{\alpha}-\dfrac{c}{\alpha^3}\right)\sin(\alpha t)$ | $\text{Re } s > \lvert \text{Im } \alpha \rvert$ |
| 54 | BM | $\dfrac{1}{s^2(s^2-\alpha^2)}$ | $\dfrac{\sinh(\alpha t)}{\alpha^3}-\dfrac{t}{\alpha^2}$ | $\text{Re } s > \lvert \text{Re } \alpha \rvert$ |
| 55 | | $\dfrac{s+a}{s^2(s^2-\alpha^2)}$ | $\dfrac{\cosh(\alpha t)}{\alpha^2}+\dfrac{a\sinh(\alpha t)}{\alpha^3}-\dfrac{1}{\alpha^2}-\dfrac{at}{\alpha^2}$ | $\text{Re } s > \lvert \text{Re } \alpha \rvert$ |
| 56 | | $\dfrac{s^2+as+b}{s^2(s^2-\alpha^2)}$ | $\dfrac{a}{\alpha^2}\cosh(\alpha t)+\left(\dfrac{1}{\alpha}+\dfrac{b}{\alpha^3}\right)\sinh(\alpha t)-\dfrac{a}{\alpha^2}-\dfrac{bt}{\alpha^2}$ | $\text{Re } s > \lvert \text{Re } \alpha \rvert$ |
| 57 | | $\dfrac{s^3+as^2+bs+c}{s^2(s^2-\alpha^2)}$ | $\left(1+\dfrac{b}{\alpha^2}\right)\cosh(\alpha t)+\left(\dfrac{a}{\alpha}+\dfrac{c}{\alpha^3}\right)\sinh(\alpha t)$ $-\dfrac{b}{\alpha^2}-\dfrac{ct}{\alpha^2}$ | $\text{Re } s > \lvert \text{Re } \alpha \rvert$ |
| 58 | BO | $\dfrac{1}{s^2(s^2+\alpha s+\beta)}$ $=\dfrac{\beta-\alpha s}{\beta^2 s^2}+\dfrac{\alpha s+\alpha^2-\beta}{\beta^2(s^2+\alpha s+\beta)}$ | See under B and O. | $\text{Re } s > \text{Max } o, -\frac{1}{2}\text{Re } \alpha$ $+\lvert \text{Im}(\beta-\frac{\alpha^2}{4})^{\frac{1}{2}}\rvert$ |
| 59 | | $\dfrac{s+a}{s^2(s^2+\alpha s+\beta)}$ $=\dfrac{(\beta-\alpha a)s+\beta a}{\beta^2 s^2}+\dfrac{(\alpha a-\beta)s+(\alpha^2 a-\beta a-\alpha\beta)}{\beta^2(s^2+\alpha s+\beta)}$ | See under B and O | $\text{Re } s > \text{Max } o, -\frac{1}{2}\text{Re } \alpha$ $+\lvert \text{Im}(\beta-\frac{\alpha^2}{4})^{\frac{1}{2}}\rvert$ |
| 60 | | $\dfrac{s^2+as+b}{s^2(s^2+\alpha s+\beta)}$ $=\dfrac{(\beta a-\alpha b)s+\beta b}{\beta^2 s^2}+\dfrac{(\alpha b-\beta a)s+(\beta^2-\alpha\beta a+\alpha^2 b-\beta b)}{\beta^2(s^2+\alpha s+\beta)}$ | See under B and O | $\text{Re } s > \text{Max } o, -\frac{1}{2}\text{Re } \alpha$ $+\lvert \text{Im}(\beta-\frac{\alpha^2}{4})^{\frac{1}{2}}\rvert$ |

| | | $g(s)$ | $f(t)$ | |
|---|---|---|---|---|
| 1(Contd.) | | | | |
| 61 | BO | $\dfrac{s^3+as^2+bs+c}{s^2(s^2+\alpha s+\beta)}$ <br> $=\dfrac{(\beta b-\alpha c)s+\beta c}{\beta^2 s^2}+\dfrac{(\beta^2-\beta b+\alpha c)s+(\beta^2 a-\alpha\beta b+\alpha^2 c-\beta c)}{\beta^2(s^2+\alpha s+\beta)}$ | See under B and O | $\mathrm{Re}\, s > \mathrm{Max}\, o,\ -\frac{1}{2}\mathrm{Re}\,\alpha$ <br> $+\lvert \mathrm{Im}(\beta-\frac{\alpha^2}{4})^{\frac{1}{2}}\rvert$ |
| 62 | C | $\dfrac{1}{s^3}$ | $\dfrac{t^2}{2}$ | $\mathrm{Re}\, s > o$ |
| 63 | | $\dfrac{s+a}{s^3}$ | $t+\dfrac{at^2}{2}$ | $\mathrm{Re}\, s > o$ |
| 64 | | $\dfrac{s^2+as+b}{s^3}$ | $1+at+\dfrac{bt^2}{2}$ | $\mathrm{Re}\, s > o$ |
| 65 | CF | $\dfrac{1}{s^2(s+\alpha)}$ | $\dfrac{1}{\alpha^3}(1-e^{-\alpha t})-\dfrac{t}{\alpha^2}+\dfrac{t^2}{2\alpha}$ | $\mathrm{Re}\, s > \mathrm{Max}\, o,\ -\mathrm{Re}\,\alpha$ |
| 66 | | $\dfrac{s+a}{s^3(s+\alpha)}$ | $\dfrac{\alpha-a}{\alpha^2}t+\dfrac{a}{2\alpha}t^2-\dfrac{\alpha-a}{\alpha^3}(1-e^{-\alpha t})$ | $\mathrm{Re}\, s > \mathrm{Max}\, o,\ -\mathrm{Re}\,\alpha$ |
| 67 | | $\dfrac{s^2+as+b}{s^3(s+\alpha)}$ | $\dfrac{a\alpha-b}{\alpha^2}t+\dfrac{b}{2\alpha}t^2+\dfrac{\alpha^2-a\alpha+b}{\alpha^3}(1-e^{-\alpha t})$ | $\mathrm{Re}\, s > \mathrm{Max}\, o,\ -\mathrm{Re}\,\alpha$ |
| 68 | | $\dfrac{s^3+as^2+bs+c}{s^3(s+\alpha)}$ | $\dfrac{a\alpha^2-b\alpha+c}{\alpha^3}+\dfrac{b\alpha-c}{\alpha^2}t+\dfrac{c}{2\alpha}t^2+\dfrac{\alpha^3-a\alpha^2+b\alpha-c}{\alpha^3}e^{-\alpha t}$ | $\mathrm{Re}\, s > \mathrm{Max}\, o,\ -\mathrm{Re}\,\alpha$ |
| 69 | CKK | $\dfrac{3s^2+\alpha^2}{s^3(s^2+\alpha^2)^2}$ | $\left(\dfrac{\pi t^3}{2\alpha^5}\right)^{\frac{1}{2}} \mathbf{H}_{\frac{3}{2}}(\alpha t)$ | $\mathrm{Re}\, s > \lvert \mathrm{Im}\,\alpha \rvert$ |
| 70 | CMM | $\dfrac{3s^2-\alpha^2}{s^3(s^2-\alpha^2)^2}$ | $\left(\dfrac{\pi t^3}{2\alpha^5}\right)^{\frac{1}{2}} \mathbf{L}_{\frac{3}{2}}(\alpha t)$ | $\mathrm{Re}\, s > \lvert \mathrm{Re}\,\alpha \rvert$ |
| 71 | D | $\dfrac{1}{s^4}$ | $\dfrac{t^3}{6}$ | $\mathrm{Re}\, s > o$ |

1(Contd.)

| | | g(s) | f(t) | |
|---|---|---|---|---|
| 72 | D | $\frac{s+a}{s^4}$ | $\frac{t^2}{2}+\frac{at^3}{6}$ | Re s > o |
| 73 | | $\frac{s^2+as+b}{s^4}$ | $t+\frac{at^2}{2}+\frac{bt^3}{6}$ | Re s > o |
| 74 | | $\frac{s^3+as^2+bs+c}{s^4}$ | $1+at+\frac{bt^2}{2}+\frac{ct^3}{6}$ | Re s > o |
| 75 | E | $\frac{1}{s^5}$ | $\frac{t^4}{24}$ | Re s > o |
| 76 | F | $\frac{1}{s+\alpha}$ | $e^{-\alpha t}$ | Re s > - Re a |
| 77 | FF | $\frac{1}{(s+\alpha)(s+\beta)}$ | $\frac{e^{-\alpha t}-e^{-\beta t}}{\beta-\alpha}$ | Re s > Max - Re α, - Re β |
| 78 | | $\frac{s+a}{(s+\alpha)(s+\beta)}$ | $\frac{\alpha-a}{\alpha-\beta}e^{-\alpha t}+\frac{\beta-a}{\beta-\alpha}e^{-\beta t}$ | Re s > Max - Re α, - Re β |
| 79 | FFF | $\frac{1}{(s+\alpha)(s+\beta)(s+\gamma)}$ | $\frac{e^{-\alpha t}}{(\beta-\alpha)(\gamma-\alpha)}+\frac{e^{-\beta t}}{(\alpha-\beta)(\gamma-\beta)}+\frac{e^{-\gamma t}}{(\alpha-\gamma)(\beta-\gamma)}$ | Re s > Max - Re α, - Re β, - Re γ |
| 80 | | $\frac{s+a}{(s+\alpha)(s+\beta)(s+\gamma)}$ | $\frac{a-\alpha}{(\beta-\alpha)(\gamma-\alpha)}e^{-\alpha t}+\frac{a-\beta}{(\alpha-\beta)(\gamma-\beta)}e^{-\beta t}+\frac{a-\gamma}{(\alpha-\gamma)(\beta-\gamma)}e^{-\gamma t}$ | Re s > Max - Re α, - Re β, - Re γ |
| 81 | | $\frac{s^2+as+b}{(s+\alpha)(s+\beta)(s+\gamma)}$ | $\frac{\alpha^2-a\alpha+b}{(\alpha-\beta)(\alpha-\gamma)}e^{-\alpha t}+\frac{\beta^2-a\beta+b}{(\beta-\alpha)(\beta-\gamma)}e^{-\beta t}+\frac{\gamma^2-a\gamma+b}{(\gamma-\alpha)(\gamma-\beta)}e^{-\gamma t}$ | Re s > Max - Re α, - Re β, - Re γ |

| | | $g(s)$ | $f(t)$ | |
|---|---|---|---|---|
| 1(Contd.) | | | | |
| 82 | FFFF | $\dfrac{1}{(s+\alpha)(s+\beta)(s+\gamma)(s+\delta)}$ | $-\dfrac{e^{-\alpha t}}{(\alpha-\beta)(\alpha-\gamma)(\alpha-\delta)}-\dfrac{e^{-\beta t}}{(\beta-\alpha)(\beta-\gamma)(\beta-\delta)}-\dfrac{e^{-\gamma t}}{(\gamma-\alpha)(\gamma-\beta)(\gamma-\delta)}-\dfrac{e^{-\delta t}}{(\delta-\alpha)(\delta-\beta)(\delta-\gamma)}$ | Re $s>$ Max $-$Re $\alpha$, $-$Re $\beta$, $-$Re $\gamma$, $-$Re $\delta$ |
| 83 | | $\dfrac{s+a}{(s+\alpha)(s+\beta)(s+\gamma)(s+\delta)}$ | $-\dfrac{\alpha-a}{(\beta-\alpha)(\gamma-\alpha)(\delta-\alpha)}e^{-\alpha t}-\dfrac{\beta-a}{(\alpha-\beta)(\gamma-\beta)(\delta-\beta)}e^{-\beta t}-\dfrac{\gamma-a}{(\alpha-\gamma)(\beta-\gamma)(\delta-\gamma)}e^{-\gamma t}-\dfrac{\delta-a}{(\alpha-\delta)(\beta-\delta)(\gamma-\delta)}e^{-\delta t}$ | Re $s>$ Max $-$Re $\alpha$, $-$Re $\beta$, $-$Re $\gamma$, $-$Re $\delta$ |
| 84 | | $\dfrac{s^2+as+b}{(s+\alpha)(s+\beta)(s+\gamma)(s+\delta)}$ | $-\dfrac{\alpha^2-a\alpha+b}{(\alpha-\beta)(\alpha-\gamma)(\alpha-\delta)}e^{-\alpha t}-\dfrac{\beta^2-a\beta+b}{(\beta-\alpha)(\beta-\gamma)(\beta-\delta)}e^{-\beta t}-\dfrac{\gamma^2-a\gamma+b}{(\gamma-\alpha)(\gamma-\beta)(\gamma-\delta)}e^{-\gamma t}-\dfrac{\delta^2-a\delta+b}{(\delta-\alpha)(\delta-\beta)(\delta-\gamma)}e^{-\delta t}$ | Re $s>$ Max $-$Re $\alpha$, $-$Re $\beta$, $-$Re $\gamma$, $-$Re $\delta$ |
| 85 | | $\dfrac{s^3+as^2+bs+c}{(s+\alpha)(s+\beta)(s+\gamma)(s+\delta)}$ | $-\dfrac{\alpha^3-a\alpha^2+b\alpha-c}{(\beta-\alpha)(\gamma-\alpha)(\delta-\alpha)}e^{-\alpha t}-\dfrac{\beta^3-a\beta^2+b\beta-c}{(\alpha-\beta)(\gamma-\beta)(\delta-\beta)}e^{-\beta t}-\dfrac{\gamma^3-a\gamma^2+b\gamma-c}{(\alpha-\gamma)(\beta-\gamma)(\delta-\gamma)}e^{-\gamma t}-\dfrac{\delta^3-a\delta^2+b\delta-c}{(\alpha-\delta)(\beta-\delta)(\gamma-\delta)}e^{-\delta t}$ | Re $s>$ Max $-$Re $\alpha$, $-$Re $\beta$, $-$Re $\gamma$, $-$Re $\delta$ |
| 86 | FG | $\dfrac{1}{(s+\alpha)^2(s+\beta)}$ | $\dfrac{1}{(\beta-\alpha)^2}e^{-\beta t}+\dfrac{(\beta-\alpha)t-1}{(\beta-\alpha)^2}e^{-\alpha t}$ | Re $s>$ Max $-$Re $\alpha$, $-$Re $\beta$ |
| 87 | | $\dfrac{s+a}{(s+\alpha)^2(s+\beta)}$ | $\dfrac{a-\beta}{(\alpha-\beta)^2}e^{-\beta t}+\left[\dfrac{a-\alpha}{\beta-\alpha}t+\dfrac{\beta-a}{(\beta-\alpha)^2}\right]e^{-\alpha t}$ | Re $s>$ Max $-$Re $\alpha$, $-$Re $\beta$ |
| 88 | | $\dfrac{s^2+as+b}{(s+\alpha)^2(s+\beta)}$ | $\left[\dfrac{\alpha(\alpha-2\beta)+a\beta-b}{(\alpha-\beta)^2}-\dfrac{\alpha^2-a\alpha+b}{\alpha-\beta}t\right]e^{-\alpha t}+\dfrac{\beta^2-a\beta+b}{(\alpha-\beta)^2}e^{-\beta t}$ | Re $s>$ Max $-$Re $\alpha$, $-$Re $\beta$ |

| | | $g(s)$ | $f(t)$ | |
|---|---|---|---|---|
| 1(Contd.) | | | | |
| 89 | FH | $\dfrac{1}{(s+\alpha)(s+\beta)^3}$ | $\dfrac{[1-(\alpha-\beta)t+\frac{1}{2}(\alpha-\beta)^2t^2]e^{-\beta t}-e^{-\alpha t}}{(\alpha-\beta)^3}$ | Re s > Max − Re α, − Re β |
| 90 | | $\dfrac{s+a}{(s+\alpha)(s+\beta)^3}$ | $\dfrac{\alpha-a}{(\alpha-\beta)^3}(e^{-\alpha t}-e^{-\beta t})+\dfrac{e^{-\beta t}}{(\alpha-\beta)^3}\left[(\alpha-\beta)(\alpha-a)t+\dfrac{1}{2}\dfrac{a-\beta}{\alpha-\beta}t^2\right]$ | Re s > Max − Re α, − Re β |
| 91 | | $\dfrac{s^2+as+b}{(s+\alpha)(s+\beta)^3}$ | $\dfrac{\alpha^2-a\alpha+b}{(\beta-\alpha)^3}e^{-\alpha t}-\dfrac{\alpha^2-a\alpha+b}{(\beta-\alpha)^3}e^{-\beta t}$ $+\dfrac{\beta^2-2\alpha\beta+a\alpha-b}{(\alpha-\beta)^2}te^{-\beta t}$ $+\dfrac{\beta^2-a\beta+b}{2(\alpha-\beta)}t^2e^{-\beta t}$ | Re s > Max − Re α, − Re β |
| 92 | | $\dfrac{s^3+as^2+bs+c}{(s+\alpha)(s+\beta)^3}$ | $\dfrac{\alpha^3-a\alpha^2+b\alpha-c}{(\alpha-\beta)^3}e^{-\alpha t}$ $+\dfrac{3\alpha\beta^2-3\alpha^2\beta-\beta^3+a\alpha^2-\alpha b+c}{(\alpha-\beta)^3}e^{-\beta t}$ $+\dfrac{(a+3\alpha)\beta^2-2\beta^3-2a\alpha\beta+\alpha b-c}{(\alpha-\beta)^2}te^{-\beta t}$ $+\dfrac{a\beta^2-\beta^3-b\beta+c}{2(\alpha-\beta)}t^2e^{-\beta t}$ | Re s > Max − Re α, − Re β |
| 93 | FK | $\dfrac{1}{(s+\alpha)(s^2+\beta^2)}$ | $\dfrac{1}{\alpha^2+\beta^2}e^{-\alpha t}+\dfrac{\sin(\beta t-\tan^{-1}\frac{\beta}{\alpha})}{\beta(\alpha^2+\beta^2)^{\frac{1}{2}}}$ | Re s > Max − Re α, \| Im β \| |
| 94 | | $\dfrac{s+a}{(s+\alpha)(s^2+\beta^2)}$ | $\dfrac{a-\alpha}{\alpha^2+\beta^2}e^{-\alpha t}$ $+\dfrac{(a^2+\beta^2)^{\frac{1}{2}}}{\beta(\alpha^2+\beta^2)^{\frac{1}{2}}}\sin(\beta t+\tan^{-1}\frac{\beta}{a}-\tan^{-1}\frac{\beta}{\alpha})$ | Re s > Max − Re α, \| Im β \| |

| | | g(s) | f(t) | |
|---|---|---|---|---|
| 1(Contd.) | | | | |
| 95 | FK | $\frac{s^2+as+b}{(s+\alpha)(s^2+\beta^2)}$ | $\frac{\alpha^2-a\alpha+b}{\alpha^2+\beta^2}e^{-\alpha t}+\left[\frac{(\frac{b}{\beta}-\beta)^2+a^2}{\alpha^2+b^2}\right]^{\frac{1}{2}}\cdot \sin(\beta t+\tan^{-1}\frac{a\beta}{b-\beta^2}-\tan^{-1}\frac{\beta}{\alpha})$ | Re s > Max − Re α, \|Im β\| |
| 96 | FM | $\frac{1}{(s+\alpha)(s^2-\beta^2)}$ | $\frac{-e^{-\alpha t}+\cosh(\beta t)-\frac{\alpha}{\beta}\sinh(\beta t)}{\beta^2-\alpha^2}$ | Re s > Max − Re α, \|Re β |
| 97 | | $\frac{s+a}{(s+\alpha)(s^2-\beta^2)}$ | $\frac{(\alpha-a)e^{-\alpha t}-(\alpha-a)\cosh(\beta t)+(\beta-\frac{a\alpha}{\beta})\sinh(\beta t)}{\beta^2-\alpha^2}$ | Re s > Max − Re α, \|Re β |
| 98 | | $\frac{s^2+as+b}{(s+\alpha)(s^2-\beta^2)}$ | $\frac{1}{\alpha^2-\beta^2}\left[(\alpha^2-a\alpha+b)e^{-\alpha t}-(\beta^2-a\alpha+b)\cosh(\beta t)+(\alpha\beta-a\beta+\frac{b\alpha}{\beta})\sinh(\beta t)\right]$ | Re s > Max − Re α, \|Re β |
| 99 | FO | $\frac{1}{(s+\alpha)(s^2+\beta s+\gamma)}$ $=\frac{1}{(\alpha^2-\alpha\beta+\gamma)(s+\alpha)}+\frac{\alpha-\beta-s}{(\alpha^2-\alpha\beta+\gamma)(s^2+\beta s+\gamma)}$ | See under F and O | Re s > Max − Re α, $-\frac{1}{2}\text{Re}\,\beta+\left\|\text{Im}(\gamma-\frac{\beta^2}{4})^{\frac{1}{2}}\right.$ |
| 100 | | $\frac{s+a}{(s+\alpha)(s^2+\beta s+\gamma)}$ $=\frac{a-\alpha}{(\alpha^2-\alpha\beta+\gamma)(s+a)}+\frac{(\alpha-a)s+a\alpha-a\beta+\gamma}{(\alpha^2-\alpha\beta+\gamma)(s^2+\beta s+\gamma)}$ | See under F and O | Re s > Max − Re α, $-\frac{1}{2}\text{Re}\,\beta+\left\|\text{Im}(\gamma-\frac{\beta^2}{4})^{\frac{1}{2}}\right.$ |
| 101 | | $\frac{s^2+as+b}{(s+\alpha)(s^2+\beta s+\gamma)}$ $=\frac{\alpha^2-a\alpha+b}{(\alpha^2-\alpha\beta+\gamma)(s+\alpha)}+\frac{(a\alpha-\alpha\beta+\gamma-b)s+b(\alpha-\beta)+\gamma(a-\alpha)}{(\alpha^2-\alpha\beta+\gamma)(s^2+\beta s+\gamma)}$ | See under F and O | Re s > Max − Re α, $-\frac{1}{2}\text{Re}\,\beta+\left\|\text{Im}(\gamma-\frac{\beta^2}{4})^{\frac{1}{2}}\right\|$ |

| | | g(s) | f(t) | |
|---|---|---|---|---|
| 1(Contd.) | | | | |
| 102 | FP | $\dfrac{1}{(s+\alpha)(s^3+\beta^3)}$ | $\dfrac{1}{\beta^3-\alpha^3}e^{-\alpha t}+\dfrac{1}{3\beta^2(\alpha-\beta)}e^{-\beta t}+\dfrac{2\beta^2-\alpha\beta-\alpha^2}{3\beta^2(\alpha^3-\beta^3)}e^{\frac{\beta t}{2}}\cos\dfrac{3^{\frac{1}{2}}\beta t}{2}+\dfrac{\alpha}{3^{\frac{1}{2}}\beta^2(\alpha^2+\alpha\beta+\beta^2)}e^{\frac{\beta t}{2}}\sin\dfrac{3^{\frac{1}{2}}\beta t}{2}$ | $\mathrm{Re}\, s > \mathrm{Max} - \mathrm{Re}\,\alpha,\ -\mathrm{Re}\,\beta,\ \frac{1}{2}\mathrm{Re}\,\beta+\frac{3^{\frac{1}{2}}}{2}\lvert \mathrm{Im}\,\beta\rvert$ |
| 103 | | $\dfrac{s+a}{(s+\alpha)(s^3+\beta^3)}$ | $\dfrac{\alpha-a}{\alpha^2-\beta^3}e^{-\alpha t}+\dfrac{a-\beta}{3\beta^2(\alpha-\beta)}e^{-\beta t}+\dfrac{\beta(\alpha-\beta)-a(2\beta+\alpha)}{3\beta^2(\alpha^2+\alpha\beta+\beta^2)}e^{\frac{\beta t}{2}}\cos\dfrac{3^{\frac{1}{2}}\beta t}{2}+\dfrac{a\alpha+\alpha\beta+\beta^2}{3^{\frac{1}{2}}\beta^2(\alpha^2+\alpha\beta+\beta^2)}e^{\frac{\beta t}{2}}\sin\dfrac{3^{\frac{1}{2}}\beta t}{2}$ | $\mathrm{Re}\, s > \mathrm{Max} - \mathrm{Re}\,\alpha,\ -\mathrm{Re}\,\beta,\ \frac{1}{2}\mathrm{Re}\,\beta+\frac{3^{\frac{1}{2}}}{2}\lvert \mathrm{Im}\,\beta\rvert$ |
| 104 | | $\dfrac{s^2+as+b}{(s+\alpha)(s^3+\beta^3)}$ $=\dfrac{-\alpha^2+\alpha a-b}{(\alpha^3-\beta^3)(s+\alpha)}+\dfrac{(\alpha^2-\alpha a+b)s^2+(-\beta^3+\alpha^2 a-\alpha b)s+(\alpha\beta^3-\beta^3 a+\alpha^2 b)}{(\alpha^3-\beta^3)(s^3+\beta^3)}$ | See under F and P | $\mathrm{Re}\, s > \mathrm{Max} - \mathrm{Re}\,\alpha,\ -\mathrm{Re}\,\beta,\ \frac{1}{2}\mathrm{Re}\,\beta+\frac{3^{\frac{1}{2}}}{2}\lvert \mathrm{Im}\,\beta\rvert$ |
| 105 | | $\dfrac{s^3+as^2+bs+c}{(s+\alpha)(s^3+\beta^3)}$ $=\dfrac{\alpha^3-\alpha^2 a+\alpha b-c}{(\alpha^3-\beta^3)(s+\alpha)}+\dfrac{(-\beta^3+\alpha^2 a-\alpha b+c)s^2+(\alpha\beta^3-\beta^3 a+\alpha^2 b-\alpha c)s+(-\alpha^2\beta^3+\alpha\beta^3 a-\beta^3 b+\alpha^2 c)}{(\alpha^3-\beta^3)(s^3+\beta^3)}$ | See under F and P | $\mathrm{Re}\, s > \mathrm{Max} - \mathrm{Re}\,\alpha,\ -\mathrm{Re}\,\beta,\ \frac{1}{2}\mathrm{Re}\,\beta+\frac{3^{\frac{1}{2}}}{2}\lvert \mathrm{Im}\,\beta\rvert$ |
| 106 | G | $\dfrac{1}{(s+\alpha)^2}$ | $t\,e^{-\alpha t}$ | $\mathrm{Re}\, s > -\mathrm{Re}\,\alpha$ |
| 107 | | $\dfrac{s+a}{(s+\alpha)^2}$ | $[1+(a-\alpha)t]e^{-\alpha t}$ | $\mathrm{Re}\, s > -\mathrm{Re}\,\alpha$ |

| | | g(s) | f(t) | |
|---|---|---|---|---|
| 1(Contd.) | | | | |
| 108 | GK | $\frac{1}{(s+\alpha)^2(s^2+\beta^2)}$ | $\frac{2\alpha}{(\alpha^2+\beta^2)^2} e^{-\alpha t} + \frac{t}{\alpha^2+\beta^2} e^{-\alpha t}$ | Re s > Max − Re α, \|Im β\| |
| | | | $- \frac{2\alpha}{(\alpha^2+\beta^2)^2} \cos(\beta t) + \frac{\alpha^2-\beta^2}{\beta(\alpha^2+\beta^2)^2} \sin(\beta t)$ | |
| 109 | | $\frac{s+a}{(s+\alpha)^2(s^2+\beta^2)}$ | $- \frac{\alpha^2-\beta^2-2\alpha a}{(\alpha^2+\beta^2)^2} e^{-\alpha t} - \frac{\alpha-a}{\alpha^2+\beta^2} t e^{-\alpha t}$ | Re s > Max − Re α, \|Im β\| |
| | | | $+ \frac{\alpha^2-\beta^2-2\alpha a}{(\alpha^2+\beta^2)^2} \cos(\beta t) + \frac{2\alpha\beta^2+a(\alpha^2-\beta^2)}{\beta(\alpha^2+\beta^2)^2} \sin(\beta t)$ | |
| 110 | | $\frac{s^2+as+b}{(s+\alpha)^2(s^2+\beta^2)}$ | $- Ae^{-\alpha t} + Bte^{-\alpha t} + A\cos(\beta t) + C\sin(\beta t)$ | Re s > Max − Re α, \|Im β\| |
| | | | where $A = \frac{(\alpha^2-\beta^2)a+2\alpha(\beta^2-b)}{(\alpha^2+\beta^2)^2}$ | |
| | | | $B = \frac{\alpha^2-\alpha a+b}{\alpha^2+\beta^2}$ | |
| | | | $C = \frac{2\alpha\beta^2 a-(\alpha^2-\beta^2)(\beta^2-b)}{\beta(\alpha^2+\beta^2)^2}$ | |
| 111 | | $\frac{s^3+as^2+bs+c}{(s+\alpha)^2(s^2+\beta^2)}$ | $Ae^{-\alpha t} + Bte^{-\alpha t} + C\cos(\beta t) + D\sin(\beta t)$ | Re s > Max − Re α, \|Im β\| |
| | | | where $A = \frac{\alpha^2(\alpha^2+3\beta^2)-(\alpha^2-\beta^2)b-2\alpha(\beta^2 a-c)}{(\alpha^2+\beta^2)^2}$ | |
| | | | $B = \frac{-\alpha^3+\alpha^2 a-\alpha b+c}{\alpha^2+\beta^2}$ | |
| | | | $C = \frac{(\alpha^2-\beta^2)(b-\beta^2)+2\alpha(\beta^2 a-c)}{(\alpha^2+\beta^2)^2}$ | |
| | | | $D = \frac{2\alpha\beta^2(b-\beta^2)-(\alpha^2-\beta^2)(\beta^2 a-c)}{\beta(\alpha^2+\beta^2)^2}$ | |
| 112 | GM | $\frac{1}{(s+\alpha)^2(s^2-\beta^2)}$ | $\frac{2\alpha}{(\alpha^2-\beta^2)^2} e^{-\alpha t} + \frac{t}{\alpha^2-\beta^2} e^{-\alpha t} - \frac{2\alpha}{(\alpha^2-\beta^2)^2} \cosh(\beta t)$ | Re s > Max − Re α, \|Re β\| |
| | | | $+ \frac{\alpha^2+\beta^2}{\beta(\alpha^2-\beta^2)} \sinh(\beta t)$ | |

| | | g(s) | f(t) | |
|---|---|---|---|---|
| 1(Contd.) | | | | |
| 113 | GM | $\frac{s+a}{(s+\alpha)^2(s^2-\beta^2)}$ | $\frac{-\alpha^2-\beta^2+2\alpha a}{(\alpha^2-\beta^2)^2}e^{-\alpha t}+\frac{a-\alpha}{\alpha^2-\beta^2}te^{-\alpha t}$ $+\frac{\alpha^2+\beta^2-2\alpha a}{(\alpha^2-\beta^2)^2}\cosh(\beta t)+\frac{-2\alpha\beta^2+(\alpha^2+\beta^2)a}{\beta(\alpha^2-\beta^2)^2}\sinh(\beta t)$ | $\mathrm{Re}\, s > \mathrm{Max} - \mathrm{Re}\,\alpha, \lvert\mathrm{Re}\,\beta\rvert$ |
| 114 | | $\frac{s^2+as+b}{(s+\alpha)^2(s^2-\beta^2)}$ | $Ae^{-\alpha t}+Bte^{-\alpha t}-A\cosh(\beta t)+C\sinh(\beta t)$ where $A=\frac{-(\alpha^2+\beta^2)a+2\alpha(\beta^2+b)}{(\alpha^2-\beta^2)^2}$, $B=\frac{\alpha^2-\alpha a+b}{\alpha^2-\beta^2}$, $C=\frac{-2\alpha\beta^2 a+(\alpha^2+\beta^2)(\beta^2+b)}{\beta(\alpha^2-\beta^2)^2}$ | $\mathrm{Re}\, s > \mathrm{Max} - \mathrm{Re}\,\alpha, \lvert\mathrm{Re}\,\beta\rvert$ |
| 115 | | $\frac{s^3+as^2+bs+c}{(s+\alpha)^2(s^2-\beta^2)}$ | $Ae^{-\alpha t}+Bte^{-\alpha t}+C\cosh(\beta t)+D\sinh(\beta t)$ where $A=\frac{\alpha^2(\alpha^2-3\beta^2)-(\alpha^2+\beta^2)b+2\alpha(\beta^2a+c)}{(\alpha^2-\beta^2)^2}$, $B=\frac{-\alpha^3+\alpha^2a-\alpha b+c}{\alpha^2-\beta^2}$, $C=\frac{(\alpha^2+\beta^2)(b+\beta^2)-2\alpha(\beta^2a+c)}{(\alpha^2-\beta^2)^2}$, $D=\frac{-2\alpha\beta^2(b+\beta^2)+(\alpha^2+\beta^2)(\beta^2a+c)}{\beta(\alpha^2-\beta^2)^2}$ | $\mathrm{Re}\, s > \mathrm{Max} - \mathrm{Re}\,\alpha, \lvert\mathrm{Re}\,\beta\rvert$ |
| 116 | H | $\frac{1}{(s+\alpha)^3}$ | $\frac{t^2}{2}e^{-\alpha t}$ | $\mathrm{Re}\, s > -\mathrm{Re}\,\alpha$ |
| 117 | | $\frac{s+a}{(s+\alpha)^3}$ | $t(1+\frac{a-\alpha}{2}t)e^{-\alpha t}$ | $\mathrm{Re}\, s > -\mathrm{Re}\,\alpha$ |
| 118 | | $\frac{s^2+as+b}{(s+\alpha)^3}$ | $[1+(a-2\alpha)t+\frac{1}{2}(\alpha^2-a\alpha+b)t^2]e^{-\alpha t}$ | $\mathrm{Re}\, s > -\mathrm{Re}\,\alpha$ |

| | | g(s) | f(t) | |
|---|---|---|---|---|
| 1(Contd.) | | | | |
| 119 | I | $\frac{1}{(s+\alpha)^4}$ | $\frac{t^3 e^{-\alpha t}}{6}$ | Re s > - Re α |
| 120 | | $\frac{s+a}{(s+\alpha)^4}$ | $t^2\left(\frac{1}{2}+\frac{a-\alpha}{6}t\right)e^{-\alpha t}$ | Re s > - Re α |
| 121 | | $\frac{s^2+as+b}{(s+\alpha)^4}$ | $t\left[1+(\frac{a}{2}-\alpha)t+\frac{b+\alpha^2-a\alpha}{6}t^2\right]e^{-\alpha t}$ | Re s > - Re α |
| 122 | | $\frac{s^3+as^2+bs+c}{(s+\alpha)^4}$ | $\left[1+(a-3\alpha)t+\frac{b-2a\alpha+3\alpha^2}{2}t^2+\frac{c-b\alpha+a\alpha^2-\alpha^3}{6}t^3\right]e^{-\alpha t}$ | Re s > - Re α |
| 123 | J | $\frac{1}{(s+\alpha)^5}$ | $\frac{t^4 e^{-\alpha t}}{24}$ | Re s > - Re α |
| 124 | K | $\frac{1}{s^2+\alpha^2}$ | $\frac{\sin(\alpha t)}{\alpha}$ $=\left(\frac{\pi t}{2\alpha}\right)^{\frac{1}{2}} H_{-\frac{1}{2}}(\alpha t)$ | Re s > \|Im α\| |
| 125 | | $\frac{s}{s^2+\alpha^2}$ | $\cos(\alpha t)$ | Re s > \|Im α\| |
| 126 | | $\frac{s+a}{s^2+\alpha^2}$ | $\cos(\alpha t)+\frac{a}{\alpha}\sin(\alpha t)$ | Re s > \|Im α\| |
| 127 | | $\frac{s\sin b+\alpha\cos b}{s^2+\alpha^2}$ | $\sin(\alpha t+b)$ | Re s > \|Im α\| |
| 128 | | $\frac{s\cos b-\alpha\sin b}{s^2+\alpha^2}$ | $\cos(\alpha t+b)$ | Re s > \|Im α\| |
| 129 | KK | $\frac{1}{(s^2+\alpha^2)(s^2+\beta^2)}$ | $\frac{\alpha\sin(\beta t)-\beta\sin(\alpha t)}{\alpha\beta(\alpha^2-\beta^2)}$ | Re s > Max \|Im α\|, \|Im β\| |

| | | $g(s)$ | $f(t)$ | |
|---|---|---|---|---|
| 1(Contd.) | | | | |
| 130 | KK | $\frac{s}{(s^2+\alpha^2)(s^2+\beta^2)}$ | $\frac{2}{\alpha^2-\beta^2}\sin\left(\frac{\alpha+\beta}{2}t\right)\sin\left(\frac{\alpha-\beta}{2}t\right)$ $=\frac{\cos(\alpha t)-\cos(\beta t)}{\beta^2-\alpha^2}$ | Re s > Max $\lvert \mathrm{Im}\,\alpha \rvert, \lvert \mathrm{Im}\,\beta \rvert$ |
| 131 | | $\frac{s+a}{(s^2+\alpha^2)(s^2+\beta^2)}$ | $\frac{1}{\beta^2-\alpha^2}\left[\left(1+\frac{a^2}{\alpha^2}\right)^{\frac{1}{2}}\sin(\alpha t+\tan^{-1}\frac{\alpha}{a}) - \left(1+\frac{a^2}{\beta^2}\right)^{\frac{1}{2}}\sin(\beta t+\tan^{-1}\frac{\beta}{a})\right]$ | Re s > Max $\lvert \mathrm{Im}\,\alpha \rvert, \lvert \mathrm{Im}\,\beta \rvert$ |
| 132 | | $\frac{s^2-\alpha\beta}{(s^2+\alpha^2)(s^2+\beta^2)}$ | $\frac{2}{\alpha-\beta}[\sin(\alpha t)-\sin(\beta t)]$ | Re s > Max $\lvert \mathrm{Im}\,\alpha \rvert, \lvert \mathrm{Im}\,\beta \rvert$ |
| 133 | | $\frac{s^2+as+b}{(s^2+\alpha^2)(s^2+\beta^2)}$ | $\frac{a}{\beta^2-\alpha^2}\left[\left\{1+\frac{(b-\alpha^2)^2}{a^2\alpha^2}\right\}^{\frac{1}{2}}\sin(\alpha t+\tan^{-1}\frac{a\alpha}{b-\alpha^2}) - \left\{1+\frac{(b-\beta^2)^2}{a^2\beta^2}\right\}^{\frac{1}{2}}\sin(\beta t+\tan^{-1}\frac{a\beta}{b-\beta^2})\right]$ | Re s > Max $\lvert \mathrm{Im}\,\alpha \rvert, \lvert \mathrm{Im}\,\beta \rvert$ |
| 134 | | $\frac{s(s^2+7\alpha^2)}{(s^2+\alpha^2)(s^2+9\alpha^2)}$ | $\cos^3(\alpha t)$ | Re s > 3 $\lvert \mathrm{Im}\,\alpha \rvert$ |
| 135 | | $\frac{s(s^2+\frac{\alpha^2+\beta^2}{2})}{(s^2+\alpha^2)(s^2+\beta^2)}$ | $\frac{1}{2}[\cos(\alpha t)+\cos(\beta t)]$ | Re s > Max $\lvert \mathrm{Im}\,\alpha \rvert, \lvert \mathrm{Im}\,\beta \rvert$ |
| 136 | | $\frac{s^3+as^2+bs+c}{(s^2+\alpha^2)(s^2+\beta^2)}$ | $\frac{1}{\beta^2-\alpha^2}[(b-\alpha^2)\cos(\alpha t)+(\frac{c}{\alpha}-a\alpha)\cdot\sin(\alpha t)-(b-\beta^2)\cos(\beta t)-(\frac{c}{\beta}-a\beta)\sin(\beta t)]$ | Re s > Max $\lvert \mathrm{Im}\,\alpha \rvert, \lvert \mathrm{Im}\,\beta \rvert$ |
| 137 | KM | $\frac{1}{(s^2+\alpha^2)(s^2-\beta^2)}$ | $\frac{\alpha\sinh(\beta t)-\beta\sin(\alpha t)}{\alpha\beta(\alpha^2+\beta^2)}$ | Re s > Max $\lvert \mathrm{Im}\,\alpha \rvert, \lvert \mathrm{Re}\,\beta \rvert$ |
| 138 | | $\frac{s+a}{(s^2+\alpha^2)(s^2-\beta^2)}$ | $\frac{\cosh(\beta t)-\cos(\alpha t)}{\alpha^2+\beta^2}+\frac{a\alpha\sinh(\beta t)-a\beta\sin(\alpha t)}{\alpha\beta(\alpha^2+\beta^2)}$ | Re s > Max $\lvert \mathrm{Im}\,\alpha \rvert, \lvert \mathrm{Re}\,\beta \rvert$ |

| | | g(s) | f(t) | |
|---|---|---|---|---|
| 1(Contd.) | | | | |
| 139 | KM | $\frac{s^2+as+b}{(s^2+\alpha^2)(s^2-\beta^2)}$ | $\frac{a}{\alpha^2+\beta^2}[\cosh(\beta t)-\cos(\alpha t)] - \frac{b-\alpha^2}{\alpha(\alpha^2+\beta^2)}\sin(\alpha t)$ $+ \frac{b+\beta^2}{\beta(\alpha^2+\beta^2)}\sinh(\beta t)$ | Re s > Max \|Im α\|, \|Re β\| |
| 140 | | $\frac{s^3+as^2+bs+c}{(s^2+\alpha^2)(s^2-\beta^2)}$ | $\frac{\alpha^2-b}{\alpha^2+\beta^2}\cos(\alpha t) - \frac{c-a\alpha^2}{\alpha(\alpha^2+\beta^2)}\sin(\alpha t)$ $+ \frac{\beta^2+b}{\alpha^2+\beta^2}\cosh(\beta t) + \frac{c+a\beta^2}{\beta(\alpha^2+\beta^2)}\sinh(\beta t)$ | Re s > Max \|Im α\|, \|Re β\| |
| 141 | L | $\frac{1}{(s^2+\alpha^2)^2}$ | $\frac{\sin(\alpha t)-\alpha t\cos(\alpha t)}{2\alpha^3}$ | Re s > \|Im α\| |
| 142 | | $\frac{s+a}{(s^2+\alpha^2)^2}$ | $\frac{(\alpha^2 t+a)\sin(\alpha t)-a\,\alpha\, t\,\cos(\alpha t)}{2\alpha^3}$ | Re s > \|Im α\| |
| 143 | | $\frac{s^2+as+b}{(s^2+\alpha^2)^2}$ | $\frac{(a\alpha^2 t+b+\alpha^2)\sin(\alpha t)-\alpha(b-\alpha^2)\,t\cos(\alpha t)}{2\alpha^3}$ | Re s > \|Im α\| |
| 144 | | $\frac{s^3+as^2+bs+c}{(s^2+\alpha^2)^2}$ | $\left(1-\frac{c-a\alpha^2}{2\alpha^2}t\right)\cos(\alpha t)$ $+\left(\frac{c+a\alpha^2}{2\alpha^3}+\frac{b-\alpha^2}{2\alpha}t\right)\sin(\alpha t)$ | Re s > \|Im α\| |
| 145 | M | $\frac{1}{s^2-\alpha^2}$ | $\frac{\sinh(\alpha t)}{\alpha}$ $=\left(\frac{\pi t}{2\alpha}\right)^{\frac{1}{2}} L_{-\frac{1}{2}}(\alpha t)$ | Re s > \|Re α\| |
| 146 | | $\frac{s}{s^2-\alpha^2}$ | $\cosh(\alpha t)$ | Re s > \|Re α\| |
| 147 | | $\frac{s+a}{s^2-\alpha^2}$ | $\cosh(\alpha t)+\frac{a}{\alpha}\sinh(\alpha t)$ | Re s > \|Re α\| |

| | g(s) | f(t) | |
|---|---|---|---|
| 1(Contd.) | | | |
| 148 N | $\frac{1}{(s^2-\alpha^2)^2}$ | $\frac{\alpha t\cosh(\alpha t)-\sinh(\alpha t)}{2\alpha^3}$ | $\mathrm{Re}\,s>\lvert\mathrm{Re}\,\alpha\rvert$ |
| 149 | $\frac{s+a}{(s^2-\alpha^2)^2}$ | $\frac{(\alpha^2 t-a)\sinh(\alpha t)+a\alpha t\cosh(\alpha t)}{2\alpha^3}$ | $\mathrm{Re}\,s>\lvert\mathrm{Re}\,\alpha\rvert$ |
| 150 | $\frac{s^2+as+b}{(s^2-\alpha^2)^2}$ | $\frac{(\alpha^2 at+\alpha^2-b)\sinh(\alpha t)+(\alpha^2+b)\alpha t\cosh(\alpha t)}{2\alpha^3}$ | $\mathrm{Re}\,s>\lvert\mathrm{Re}\,\alpha\rvert$ |
| 151 | $\frac{s^3+as^2+bs+c}{(s^2-\alpha^2)^2}$ | $\frac{1}{2\alpha^3}[\alpha^2(\alpha^2+b)t+a\alpha^2-c]\sinh(\alpha t)+\frac{1}{2\alpha^2}[2\alpha^2+(a\alpha^2+c)t]\cosh(\alpha t)$ | $\mathrm{Re}\,s>\lvert\mathrm{Re}\,\alpha\rvert$ |
| 152 O | $\frac{1}{s^2+\alpha s+\beta}$ | $\frac{e^{-r_1 t}-e^{-r_2 t}}{r_2-r_1}$ if $\alpha^2\neq 4\beta$ | $\mathrm{Re}\,s>\mathrm{Max}-\mathrm{Re}\,r_1,-\mathrm{Re}\,r_2$ |

where $-r_1$ and $-r_2$ are the roots of $s^2+\alpha s+\beta=0$

$$te^{-\frac{\alpha t}{2}}\ \text{if}\ \alpha^2=4\beta$$

If $4\beta-\alpha^2$ is real and positive a convenient form is

$$\frac{e^{-\frac{\alpha t}{2}}\sin[(\beta-\frac{\alpha^2}{4})^{\frac{1}{2}}t]}{(\beta-\frac{\alpha^2}{4})^{\frac{1}{2}}}$$

If $\alpha^2-4\beta$ is real and positive a convenient form is

$$\frac{e^{-\frac{\alpha t}{2}}\sinh[(\frac{\alpha^2}{4}-\beta)^{\frac{1}{2}}t]}{(\frac{\alpha^2}{4}-\beta)^{\frac{1}{2}}}$$

| | | g(s) | f(t) | |
|---|---|---|---|---|
| 1(Contd.) | | | | |
| 153 | O | $\frac{s+a}{s^2+\alpha s+\beta}$ | $\frac{(a-r_1)e^{-r_1 t}-(a-r_2)e^{-r_2 t}}{r_2-r_1}$ if $\alpha^2 \neq 4\beta$ | Re $s >$ Max $-$Re $r_1$, $-$Re $r_2$ |

where $-r_1$ and $-r_2$ are the roots of $s^2+\alpha s+\beta=0$

$$e^{-\frac{\alpha t}{2}}[1+(a-\tfrac{\alpha}{2})t] \text{ if } \alpha^2=4\beta$$

If $4\beta-\alpha^2$ is real and positive a convenient form is

$$\frac{a e^{-\frac{\alpha t}{2}}}{(\beta-\frac{\alpha^2}{4})^{\frac{1}{2}}}\sin[(\beta-\tfrac{\alpha^2}{4})^{\frac{1}{2}}t]-\frac{\beta^{\frac{1}{2}}e^{-\frac{\alpha t}{2}}}{(\beta-\frac{\alpha^2}{4})^{\frac{1}{2}}}\cdot$$

$$\sin[(\beta-\tfrac{\alpha^2}{4})^{\frac{1}{2}}t-\tan^{-1}\frac{2(\beta-\frac{\alpha^2}{4})^{\frac{1}{2}}}{\alpha}]$$

| | | g(s) | f(t) | |
|---|---|---|---|---|
| 154 | P | $\frac{1}{s^3+\alpha^3}$ | $\frac{1}{3\alpha^2}e^{-\alpha t}-\frac{1}{3\alpha^2}e^{\frac{\alpha t}{2}}\cos\left(\frac{3^{\frac{1}{2}}\alpha t}{2}\right)+\frac{1}{3^{\frac{1}{2}}\alpha^2}e^{\frac{\alpha t}{2}}\sin\left(\frac{3^{\frac{1}{2}}\alpha t}{2}\right)$ | Re $s >$ Max $-$Re $\alpha$, $\frac{1}{2}$(Re $\alpha + 3^{\frac{1}{2}}\lvert$Im $\alpha\rvert$) |
| 155 | | $\frac{s+a}{s^3+\alpha^3}$ | $\frac{a-\alpha}{3\alpha^2}e^{-\alpha t}-\frac{a-\alpha}{3\alpha^2}e^{\frac{\alpha t}{2}}\cos\left(\frac{3^{\frac{1}{2}}\alpha t}{2}\right)+\frac{a+\alpha}{3^{\frac{1}{2}}\alpha}e^{\frac{\alpha t}{2}}\sin\left(\frac{3^{\frac{1}{2}}\alpha t}{2}\right)$ | Re $s >$ Max $-$Re $\alpha$, $\frac{1}{2}$(Re $\alpha + 3^{\frac{1}{2}}\lvert$Im $\alpha\rvert$) |
| 156 | | $\frac{s^2+as+b}{s^3+\alpha^3}$ | $\frac{\alpha^2-a\alpha+b}{3\alpha^2}e^{-\alpha t}+\frac{2\alpha^2+a\alpha-b}{3\alpha^2}e^{\frac{\alpha t}{2}}\cos\left(\frac{3^{\frac{1}{2}}\alpha t}{2}\right)$ $+\frac{1}{3^{\frac{1}{2}}\alpha^2}(a\alpha+b)e^{\frac{\alpha t}{2}}\sin\left(\frac{3^{\frac{1}{2}}\alpha t}{2}\right)$ | Re $s >$ Max $-$ Re $\alpha$, $\frac{1}{2}$(Re $\alpha + 3^{\frac{1}{2}}\lvert$Im $\alpha\rvert$) |
| 157 | Q | $\frac{1}{s^3-\alpha^3}$ | $\frac{1}{3\alpha^2}e^{\alpha t}-\frac{1}{3\alpha^2}e^{-\frac{\alpha t}{2}}\cos\left(\frac{3^{\frac{1}{2}}\alpha t}{2}\right)-\frac{1}{3^{\frac{1}{2}}\alpha^2}e^{-\frac{\alpha t}{2}}\sin\left(\frac{3^{\frac{1}{2}}\alpha t}{2}\right)$ | Re $s >$ Max Re $\alpha$, $-\frac{1}{2}$(Re $\alpha - 3^{\frac{1}{2}}\lvert$Im $\alpha\rvert$) |
| 158 | | $\frac{s+a}{s^3-\alpha^3}$ | $\frac{a+\alpha}{3\alpha^2}e^{\alpha t}-\frac{a+\alpha}{3\alpha^2}e^{-\frac{\alpha t}{2}}\cos\left(\frac{3^{\frac{1}{2}}\alpha t}{2}\right)+\frac{a-\alpha}{3^{\frac{1}{2}}\alpha}e^{-\frac{\alpha t}{2}}\sin\left(\frac{3^{\frac{1}{2}}\alpha t}{2}\right)$ | Re $s >$ Max Re $\alpha$, $-\frac{1}{2}$(Re $\alpha - 3^{\frac{1}{2}}\lvert$Im $\alpha\rvert$) |

| | | g(s) | f(t) | |
|---|---|---|---|---|
| 1(Contd.) | | | | |
| 159 | Q | $\dfrac{s^2+as+b}{s^3-\alpha^3}$ | $\dfrac{\alpha^2+a\alpha+b}{3\alpha^2}e^{\alpha t}+\dfrac{2\alpha^2-a\alpha-b}{3\alpha^2}e^{-\frac{\alpha t}{2}}\cos\left(\dfrac{3^{\frac{1}{2}}\alpha t}{2}\right) - \dfrac{1}{3^{\frac{1}{2}}\alpha^2}(b-a\alpha)e^{-\frac{\alpha t}{2}}\sin\left(\dfrac{3^{\frac{1}{2}}\alpha t}{2}\right)$ | $\mathrm{Re}\, s > \mathrm{Max}\ \mathrm{Re}\,\alpha,\ -\frac{1}{2}(\mathrm{Re}\,\alpha - 3^{\frac{1}{2}}\lvert\mathrm{Im}\,\alpha\rvert)$ |
| 160 | R | $\dfrac{1}{s^4+\alpha^4}$ | $\dfrac{1}{2^{\frac{1}{2}}\alpha^3}\left[\sin\left(\dfrac{\alpha t}{2^{\frac{1}{2}}}\right)\cosh\left(\dfrac{\alpha t}{2^{\frac{1}{2}}}\right)-\cos\left(\dfrac{\alpha t}{2^{\frac{1}{2}}}\right)\sinh\left(\dfrac{\alpha t}{2^{\frac{1}{2}}}\right)\right]$ | $\mathrm{Re}\, s > \frac{1}{2^{\frac{1}{2}}}(\lvert\mathrm{Re}\,\alpha\rvert+\lvert\mathrm{Im}\,\alpha\rvert)$ |
| 161 | | $\dfrac{s}{s^4+\alpha^4}$ | $\dfrac{1}{\alpha^2}\sin\left(\dfrac{\alpha t}{2^{\frac{1}{2}}}\right)\sinh\left(\dfrac{\alpha t}{2^{\frac{1}{2}}}\right)$ | $\mathrm{Re}\, s > \frac{1}{2^{\frac{1}{2}}}(\lvert\mathrm{Re}\,\alpha\rvert+\lvert\mathrm{Im}\,\alpha\rvert)$ |
| 162 | | $\dfrac{s+a}{s^4+\alpha^4}$ | $\dfrac{a}{2^{\frac{1}{2}}\alpha^3}\left[\sin\left(\dfrac{\alpha t}{2^{\frac{1}{2}}}\right)\cosh\left(\dfrac{\alpha t}{2^{\frac{1}{2}}}\right)-\cos\left(\dfrac{\alpha t}{2^{\frac{1}{2}}}\right)\sinh\left(\dfrac{\alpha t}{2^{\frac{1}{2}}}\right)\right] + \dfrac{1}{\alpha^2}\sin\left(\dfrac{\alpha t}{2^{\frac{1}{2}}}\right)\sinh\left(\dfrac{\alpha t}{2^{\frac{1}{2}}}\right)$ | $\mathrm{Re}\, s > \frac{1}{2^{\frac{1}{2}}}(\lvert\mathrm{Re}\,\alpha\rvert+\lvert\mathrm{Im}\,\alpha\rvert)$ |
| 163 | | $\dfrac{s^2+2\alpha^2}{s^4+4\alpha^4}$ | $\dfrac{\sin(\alpha t)\cosh(\alpha t)}{\alpha}$ | $\mathrm{Re}\, s > \lvert\mathrm{Re}\,\alpha\rvert+\lvert\mathrm{Im}\,\alpha\rvert$ |
| 164 | | $\dfrac{s^2-2\alpha^2}{s^4+4\alpha^4}$ | $\dfrac{\cos(\alpha t)\sinh(\alpha t)}{\alpha}$ | $\mathrm{Re}\, s > \lvert\mathrm{Re}\,\alpha\rvert+\lvert\mathrm{Im}\,\alpha\rvert$ |
| 165 | | $\dfrac{s^2+as+b}{s^4+\alpha^4}$ | $\dfrac{1}{2^{\frac{1}{2}}\alpha^3}\left[(\alpha^2-b)\cos\left(\dfrac{\alpha t}{2^{\frac{1}{2}}}\right)\sinh\left(\dfrac{\alpha t}{2^{\frac{1}{2}}}\right) + (\alpha^2+b)\sin\left(\dfrac{\alpha t}{2^{\frac{1}{2}}}\right)\cosh\left(\dfrac{\alpha t}{2^{\frac{1}{2}}}\right) + 2^{\frac{1}{2}}a\alpha\sin\left(\dfrac{\alpha t}{2^{\frac{1}{2}}}\right)\sinh\left(\dfrac{\alpha t}{2^{\frac{1}{2}}}\right)\right]$ | $\mathrm{Re}\, s > \frac{1}{2^{\frac{1}{2}}}(\lvert\mathrm{Re}\,\alpha\rvert+\lvert\mathrm{Im}\,\alpha\rvert)$ |
| 166 | | $\dfrac{s^3}{s^4+\alpha^4}$ | $\cos\left(\dfrac{\alpha t}{2^{\frac{1}{2}}}\right)\cosh\left(\dfrac{\alpha t}{2^{\frac{1}{2}}}\right)$ | $\mathrm{Re}\, s > \frac{1}{2^{\frac{1}{2}}}(\lvert\mathrm{Re}\,\alpha\rvert+\lvert\mathrm{Im}\,\alpha\rvert)$ |

| | | g(s) | f(t) | |
|---|---|---|---|---|
| 1(Contd.) | | | | |
| 167 | R | $\dfrac{s^3+as^2+bs+c}{s^4+\alpha^4}$ | $\dfrac{1}{2^{\frac{1}{2}}\alpha^3}\Big[2^{\frac{1}{2}}\alpha^3\cos\left(\dfrac{\alpha t}{2^{\frac{1}{2}}}\right)\cosh\left(\dfrac{\alpha t}{2^{\frac{1}{2}}}\right)$ $+(a\alpha^2-c)\cos\left(\dfrac{\alpha t}{2^{\frac{1}{2}}}\right)\sinh\left(\dfrac{\alpha t}{2^{\frac{1}{2}}}\right)$ $+(a\alpha^2+c)\sin\left(\dfrac{\alpha t}{2^{\frac{1}{2}}}\right)\cosh\left(\dfrac{\alpha t}{2^{\frac{1}{2}}}\right)$ $+2^{\frac{1}{2}}b\alpha\sin\left(\dfrac{\alpha t}{2^{\frac{1}{2}}}\right)\sinh\left(\dfrac{\alpha t}{2^{\frac{1}{2}}}\right)\Big]$ | $\text{Re } s > \dfrac{1}{2^{\frac{1}{2}}}(\lvert\text{Re }\alpha\rvert + \lvert\text{Im }\alpha\rvert)$ |
| 168 | S | $\dfrac{1}{s^4-\alpha^4}$ | $\dfrac{\sinh(\alpha t)-\sin(\alpha t)}{2\alpha^3}$ | $\text{Re } s > \text{Max } \lvert\text{Re }\alpha\rvert, \lvert\text{Im }\alpha\rvert$ |
| 169 | | $\dfrac{s+a}{s^4-\alpha^4}$ | $\dfrac{\cosh(\alpha t)-\cos(\alpha t)}{2\alpha^2} + a\,\dfrac{\sinh(\alpha t)-\sin(\alpha t)}{2\alpha^3}$ | $\text{Re } s > \text{Max } \lvert\text{Re }\alpha\rvert, \lvert\text{Im }\alpha\rvert$ |
| 170 | | $\dfrac{s^2+as+b}{s^4-\alpha^4}$ | $\dfrac{1}{2\alpha^3}[\alpha a\cosh(\alpha t)+(\alpha^2+b)\sinh(\alpha t)$ $-\alpha a\cos(\alpha t)+(\alpha^2-b)\sin(\alpha t)]$ | $\text{Re } s > \text{Max } \lvert\text{Re }\alpha\rvert, \lvert\text{Im }\alpha\rvert$ |
| 171 | | $\dfrac{s^3+as^2+bs+c}{s^4-\alpha^4}$ | $\dfrac{1}{2\alpha^3}[(\alpha^3-\alpha b)\cos(\alpha t)+(\alpha^2 a-c)\sin(\alpha t)$ $+(\alpha^3+\alpha b)\cosh(\alpha t)+(\alpha^2 a+c)\sinh(\alpha t)]$ | $\text{Re } s > \text{Max } \lvert\text{Re }\alpha\rvert, \lvert\text{Im }\alpha\rvert$ |
| 172 | | $1$ | $\delta(t)$ | $\text{Re } s > 0$ |
| 173 | | $s$ | $\delta'(t)$ | $\text{Re } s > 0$ |
| 174 | | $\dfrac{1}{s^{n+1}}$ | $\dfrac{t^n}{n!}$ | $n=0,1,2,\ldots$ $\text{Re } s > 0$ |
| 175 | | $\dfrac{1}{(s+a)^n}$ | $\dfrac{t^{n-1}e^{-at}}{(n-1)!}$ | $n=1,2,3,\ldots$ $\text{Re } s > -\text{Re } a$ |

| | g(s) | f(t) | |
|---|---|---|---|
| 1(Contd.) | | | |
| 176 | $\frac{1}{s(as+1)_n}$ | $\frac{\left(1-e^{-\frac{t}{a}}\right)^n}{n!}$ | $n = 0,1,2,\ldots$ <br> $\mathrm{Re}\, s > \mathrm{Max}\ o,\ -n\,\mathrm{Re}\,\frac{1}{a}$ |
| 177 | $\frac{1}{s(s+a)^n}$ | $a^{-n}\left\{1-e^{-at}\left[1+\frac{at}{1!}+\cdots+\frac{(at)^{n-1}}{(n-1)!}\right]\right\}$ | $n = 1,2,3,\ldots$ <br> $\mathrm{Re}\, s > -\mathrm{Re}\, a$ |
| 178 | $\frac{(s-1)^n}{s^{n+1}}$ | $L_n(t)$ | $n = 0,1,2,\ldots$ <br> $\mathrm{Re}\, s > o$ |
| 179 | $\frac{(s-1)^n}{s^m}$ | $\frac{t^{m-1}p_n(m-1;t)}{(m-1)!}$ | $n = 0,1,2,\ldots$ <br> $m = 1,2,3,\ldots$ <br> $\mathrm{Re}\, s > o$ |
| 180 | $\frac{(s-\frac{1}{2})^n}{(s+\frac{1}{2})^{n+1}}$ | $e^{-\frac{t}{2}}L_n(t)$ | $n = 0,1,2,\ldots$ <br> $\mathrm{Re}\, s > -\frac{1}{2}$ |
| 181 | $\frac{(a-s)^n}{(a+s)^{n+2}}$ | $\frac{k_{2n+2}(at)}{2a}$ | $n = 0,1,2,\ldots$ <br> $\mathrm{Re}\, s > -\mathrm{Re}\, a$ |
| 182 | $\frac{1}{P(s)}$ <br> $P(s)=(s-b_1)(s-b_2)\ldots(s-b_n)$ <br> $b_i \neq b_k$ for $i \neq k$ | $\sum_{m=1}^{n}\frac{e^{b_m t}}{P_m(b_m)}$ <br> $P_m(s) = \frac{P(s)}{s-b_m}$ | $\mathrm{Re}\, s > \mathrm{Max}\ \mathrm{Re}\, b_i\ (i = 1,2,\ldots,n)$ |
| 183 | $\frac{1}{sP(s)}$ <br> $P(s)=(s-b_1)(s-b_2)\ldots(s-b_n)$ <br> $b_i \neq b_k$ for $i \neq k$ | $\frac{1}{P(o)}+\sum_{m=1}^{n}\frac{e^{b_m t}}{b_m P_m(b_m)}$ <br> $P_m(s) = \frac{P(s)}{s-b_m}$ | $\mathrm{Re}\, s > \mathrm{Max}\ \mathrm{Re}\, b_i\ (i = 1,2,\ldots,n)$ |

| | $g(s)$ | $f(t)$ | |
|---|---|---|---|
| 1(Contd.) | | | |
| 184 | $\frac{Q(s)}{P(s)}$ <br> $P(s)=(s-b_1)^{m_1}\ldots(s-b_n)^{m_n}$ <br> $Q(s)$ = polynomial of degree $< m_1+\ldots+m_n-1$ <br> $b_i \neq b_k$ for $i \neq k$ | $\sum_{k=1}^{n}\sum_{\tau=1}^{m_k}\frac{\Phi_{k\tau}(b_k)}{(m_k-\tau)!(\tau-1)!}t^{m_k-\tau}e^{b_k t}$ <br> $\Phi_{k\tau}(s)=\frac{d^{\tau-1}}{ds^{\tau-1}}\left[\frac{Q(s)}{P_k(s)}\right]$ <br> $P_k(s)=\frac{P(s)}{(s-b_k)^{m_k}}$ | Re $s >$ Max Re $b_i$ $(i=1,2,\ldots,n)$ |
| 185 | $\frac{Q(s)}{P(s)}$ <br> $P(s)=(s-b_1)(s-b_2)\ldots(s-b_n)$ <br> $Q(s)$ = polynomial of degree $\leqslant n-1$ <br> $n=1,2,3,\ldots$ <br> $b_i \neq b_k$ for $i \neq k$ | $\sum_{m=1}^{n}\frac{Q(b_m)}{P_m(b_m)}e^{b_m t}$ <br> $P_m(s)=\frac{P(s)}{s-b_m}$ | Re $s >$ Max Re $b_i$ $(i=1,2,\ldots,n)$ |
| 186 | $\frac{Q(s)+sN(s)}{P(s)}$ <br> $P(s)=(s^2+b_1{}^2)\ldots(s^2+b_n{}^2)$ <br> $Q(s),N(s)$ = polvnomials of even degree $\leqslant (2n-2)$ $n=1,2,3,\ldots$ <br> $b_i \neq b_k$ for $i \neq k$ | $\sum_{m=1}^{n}\frac{1}{P_m(ib_m)}[N(ib_m)\cos(b_m t)$ $+(b_m)^{-1}Q(ib_m)\sin(b_m t)]$ <br> $P_m(s)=\frac{P(s)}{s^2+b_m{}^2}$ | Re $s >$ Max$\lvert$Im $b_i\rvert$ $(i=1,2,\ldots,n)$ |
| 187 | $\frac{1}{[s^2+a^2][s^2+(3a)^2]\ldots[s^2+\{(2n+1)a\}^2]}$ | $\frac{\sin^{2n+1}(at)}{(2n+1)!\,a^{2n+1}}$ | $n=0,1,2,\ldots$ <br> Re $s > (2n+1)\lvert$Im $a\rvert$ |
| 188 | $\frac{1}{s[s^2+(2a)^2][s^2+(4a)^2]\ldots[s^2+(2na)^2]}$ | $\frac{\sin^{2n}(at)}{(2n)!\,a^{2n}}$ | $n=1,2,3,\ldots$ <br> Re $s > 2n\,\lvert$Im $a\rvert$ |
| 189 | $\frac{[s^2+a^2][s^2+(3a)^2]\ldots[s^2+(2na-a)^2]}{s[s^2+(2a)^2][s^2+(4a)^2]\ldots[s^2+(2na)^2]}$ | $P_{2n}[\cos(at)]$ | $n=1,2,3,\ldots$ <br> Re $s > 2n\,\lvert$Im $a\rvert$ |
| 190 | $\frac{s[s^2+(2a)^2][s^2+(4a)^2]\ldots[s^2+(2na)^2]}{[s^2+a^2][s^2+(3a)^2]\ldots[s^2+(2na+a)^2]}$ | $P_{2n+1}[\cos(at)]$ | $n=1,2,3,\ldots$ <br> Re $s > (2n+1)\,\lvert$Im $a\rvert$ |

| | g(s) | f(t) | |
|---|---|---|---|
| 1(Contd.) | | | |
| 191 | $\dfrac{[s^2-a^2][s^2-(3a)^2]\ldots[s^2-(2na-a)^2]}{s[s^2-(2a)^2][s^2-(4a)^2]\ldots[s^2-(2na)^2]}$ | $P_{2n}[\cosh(at)]$ | $n=1,2,3,\ldots$ <br> Re $s > 2n\lvert\text{Re } a\rvert$ |
| 192 | $\dfrac{s[s^2-(2a)^2][s^2-(4a)^2]\ldots[s^2-(2na)^2]}{[s^2-a^2][s^2-(3a)^2]\ldots[s^2-(2na+a)^2]}$ | $P_{2n+1}[\cosh(at)]$ | $n=1,2,3,\ldots$ <br> Re $s > (2n+1)\lvert\text{Re } a\rvert$ |
| 193 | $\dfrac{1+\dfrac{s^2}{2!a^2}+\ldots+\dfrac{s^2[s^2+4a^2]\ldots[s^2+4(na-a)^2]}{(2n)!a^{2n}}}{s[s^2+(2a)^2][s^2+(4a)^2]\ldots[s^2+(2na)^2]}$ | $\dfrac{\cos^{2n}(at)}{(2n)!a^{2n}}$ | $n=1,2,3,\ldots$ <br> Re $s > 2n\lvert\text{Im } a\rvert$ |
| 194 | $\dfrac{s\left\{1+\dfrac{s^2+a^2}{3!a^2}+\ldots+\dfrac{[s^2+a^2][s^2+(3a)^2]\ldots[s^2+(2na-a)^2]}{(2n+1)!a^{2n}}\right\}}{[s^2+a^2][s^2+(3a)^2]\ldots[s^2+(2na+a)^2]}$ | $\dfrac{\cos^{2n+1}(at)}{(2n+1)!a^{2n}}$ | $n=1,2,3,\ldots$ <br> Re $s > (2n+1)\lvert\text{Im } a\rvert$ |
| 195 | $\dfrac{1}{s}\left(\dfrac{a}{s}-1\right)\left(\dfrac{a}{s}-\dfrac{1}{2}\right)\cdots\left(\dfrac{a}{s}-\dfrac{1}{n}\right)$ | $A_n(at)$ | Re $s > 0$ |
| 196 | $\dfrac{(s-1)(s-2)\ldots(s-n+1)}{(s+n)(s+n-2)\ldots(s-n+2)}$ | $P_n(e^{-t})$ | $n=2,3,4,\ldots$ <br> Re $s > 0$ |
| 197 | $\displaystyle\sum_{m=0}^{n}\binom{a+m-1}{m}\frac{(s-1)^{n-m}}{s^{n-m+1}}$ | $L_n^a(t)$ | $n=0,1,2,\ldots$ <br> Re $s > 0$ |
| 198 | $\dfrac{a_1 s^{n-1}+a_2 s^{n-2}+\ldots+a_n}{(s+b)^n}$ | $\Big\{a_1+\left[a_2-\binom{n-1}{1}a_1 b\right]t$ $+\left[a_3-\binom{n-2}{1}a_2 b+\binom{n-1}{2}a_1 b^2\right]\dfrac{t^2}{2!}$ $+\ldots+[a_n-a_{n-1}b+\ldots+a_1(-b)^{n-1}]\cdot\dfrac{t^{n-1}}{(n-1)!}\Big\}e^{-bt}$ | $n=1,2,3,\ldots$ <br> Re $s > -$Re $b$ |

| | g(s) | f(t) | |
|---|---|---|---|
| 1(Contd.) | | | |
| 199 | $\dfrac{a_1 s^{n-1}+a_2 s^{n-2}+\dots+a_n}{(s+b_1)(s+b_2)\dots(s+b_n)}$ | $\displaystyle\sum_{k=1}^{n} \frac{a_1(-b_k)^{n-1}+a_2(-b_k)^{n-2}+\dots+a_n}{\prod_{\substack{i=1\\ i\neq k}}^{n}(b_i-b_k)} e^{-b_k t}$ | $n=1,2,3,\dots$ <br> Re $s >$ Max $-$Re $b_i$ $(i=1,2,3,\dots,n)$ |
| 200 | $\dfrac{1}{s}+\displaystyle\sum_{m=1}^{n}\frac{2s}{s^2+4m^2}$ | $\dfrac{\sin[(2n+1)t]}{\sin t}$ | $n=1,2,3,\dots$ <br> Re $s>0$ |
| 201 | $\dfrac{2n+1}{s^2+(2n+1)^2}+2\displaystyle\sum_{m=0}^{n-1}\frac{(-1)^m(2m+1)}{s^2+(2m+1)^2}$ | $\tan t\cos[(2n+1)t]$ | $n=1,2,3,\dots$ <br> Re $s>0$ |
| 202 | $\left(\dfrac{s}{s^2+a^2}\right)^{n+1}\displaystyle\sum_{0\leq 2m\leq n}(-1)^m\binom{n+1}{2m+1}\left(\frac{a}{s}\right)^{2m+1}$ | $\dfrac{t^n\sin(at)}{n!}$ | $n=0,1,2,\dots$ <br> Re $s>\lvert\text{Im } a\rvert$ |
| 203 | $\left(\dfrac{s}{s^2+a^2}\right)^{n+1}\displaystyle\sum_{0\leq 2m\leq n+1}(-1)^m\binom{n+1}{2m}\left(\frac{a}{s}\right)^{2m}$ | $\dfrac{t^n\cos(at)}{n!}$ | $n=0,1,2,\dots$ <br> Re $s>\lvert\text{Im } a\rvert$ |
| 204 | $s^n\left(1+\dfrac{1}{2}\dfrac{d}{ds}\right)^n\left(\dfrac{1}{s^{n+1}}\right)$ | $P_n(1-t)$ | $n=0,1,2,\dots$ <br> Re $s>0$ |

Functions of s only

| | g(s) | f(t) | |
|---|---|---|---|
| 2 1 | $\dfrac{1}{s^{\frac{1}{2}}}$ | $\dfrac{1}{(\pi t)^{\frac{1}{2}}}$ | Re $s>0$ |
| 2 | $\dfrac{1}{s^{\frac{3}{2}}}$ | $2\left(\dfrac{t}{\pi}\right)^{\frac{1}{2}}$ | Re $s>0$ |
| 3 | $\dfrac{1}{s^{n+\frac{1}{2}}}$ | $\dfrac{t^{n-\frac{1}{2}}}{\pi^{\frac{1}{2}}\left(\frac{1}{2}\right)\left(\frac{3}{2}\right)\dots\left(\frac{2n-1}{2}\right)}$ | $n=1,2,3,\dots$ <br> Re $s>0$ |
| 4 | $\dfrac{1}{s^{\nu}}$ | $\dfrac{t^{\nu-1}}{\Gamma(\nu)}$ | Re $\nu>0$ <br> Re $s>0$ |

| | $g(s)$ | $f(t)$ | |
|---|---|---|---|
| 2(Contd.) | | | |
| 5 | $\sum_{m=0}^{[\frac{n}{2}]} \frac{n!\Gamma(a+n-2m)}{m!(n-2m)!}(-\frac{1}{2})^m s^{2m-a-n}$ | $t^{a-1}He_n(t)$ | $n=0,1,2,\ldots$ <br> Re $a>0$ for $n$ even <br> Re $a>-1$ for $n$ odd <br> Re $s>0$ |
| Functions of $(s\pm a)$ only | | | |
| 6 | $\frac{1}{(s+a)^{\frac{1}{2}}}$ | $\frac{e^{-at}}{(\pi t)^{\frac{1}{2}}}$ <br> $=\frac{(2a)^{\frac{1}{2}}}{\pi}K_{\frac{1}{2}}(at)$ | Re $s>-$ Re $a$ |
| 7 | $\frac{1}{(s+a)^{\nu}}$ | $\frac{t^{\nu-1}e^{-at}}{\Gamma(\nu)}$ | Re $\nu>0$ <br> Re $s>-$ Re $a$ |
| 8 | $(s-a)^{\frac{1}{2}}-(s-b)^{\frac{1}{2}}$ | $\frac{e^{bt}-e^{at}}{2\pi^{\frac{1}{2}}t^{\frac{3}{2}}}$ | Re $s>$ Max Re $a$, Re $b$ |
| 9 | $\frac{1}{(s-a)^{\nu}}+\frac{1}{(s+a)^{\nu}}$ | $\frac{2t^{\nu-1}\cosh(at)}{\Gamma(\nu)}$ | Re $\nu>0$ <br> Re $s>\lvert$Re $a\rvert$ |
| 0 | $\frac{1}{(s-a)^{\nu}}-\frac{1}{(s+a)^{\nu}}$ | $\frac{2t^{\nu-1}\sinh(at)}{\Gamma(\nu)}$ | Re $\nu>-1$ <br> Re $s>\lvert$Re $a\rvert$ |
| 1 | $\frac{1}{(s-ia)^{\nu}}+\frac{1}{(s+ia)^{\nu}}$ | $\frac{2}{\Gamma(\nu)}t^{\nu-1}\cos(at)$ | Re $\nu>0$ <br> Re $s>\lvert$Im $a\rvert$ |
| 2 | $\frac{1}{(s+ia)^{\nu}}-\frac{1}{(s-ia)^{\nu}}$ | $-\frac{2i}{\Gamma(\nu)}t^{\nu-1}\sin(at)$ | Re $\nu>-1$ <br> Re $s>\lvert$Im $a\rvert$ |
| 3 | $\sum_{n=1}^{\infty}\frac{1}{(s+n)^{\nu}}$ | $\frac{t^{\nu-1}}{\Gamma(\nu)(e^{t}-1)}$ | Re $\nu>1$ <br> Re $s>-1$ |

| | $g(s)$ | $f(t)$ | |
|---|---|---|---|
| 2(Contd.) | | | |
| 14 | $\sum_{n=1}^{\infty} \frac{(-1)^{n-1}}{(s+n)^{\nu}}$ | $\frac{t^{\nu-1}}{\Gamma(\nu)(1+e^{t})}$ | Re $\nu > 1$<br>Re $s > -1$ |
| 15 | $\sum_{n=0}^{\infty} \frac{a^n}{(s+n)^{\nu}}$ | $\frac{t^{\nu-1}}{\Gamma(\nu)(1-ae^{-t})}$ | Re $\nu > 0$<br>$\|a\| < 1$<br>Re $s > 0$ |
| 16 | $\left(\frac{s+a}{s-a}\right)^{\frac{1}{2}} - 1$ | $a[I_0(at) + I_1(at)]$ | Re $s > \|$Re $a\|$ |
| 17 | $\frac{(s+a)^{\frac{1}{2}}}{(s+b)^{\frac{3}{2}}}$ | $e^{-\frac{a+b}{2}t}[\{1+(a-b)t\}I_0(\frac{a-b}{2}t)+(a-b)tI_1(\frac{a-b}{2}t)]$ | Re $s >$ Max $-$Re $a$, $-$Re $b$ |
| 18 | $\frac{1}{(s+a)^{\frac{1}{2}}(s+b)^{\frac{1}{2}}}$ | $e^{-\frac{a+b}{2}t} I_0(\frac{a-b}{2}t)$ | Re $s >$ Max $-$Re $a$, $-$Re $b$ |
| 19 | $\frac{1}{(s+a)^{\frac{1}{2}}(s+b)^{\frac{3}{2}}}$ | $t e^{-\frac{a+b}{2}t} [I_0(\frac{a-b}{2}t) + I_1(\frac{a-b}{2}t)]$ | Re $s >$ Max $-$Re $a$, $-$Re $b$ |
| 20 | $\frac{1}{[(s-a)(s-b)(s-c)]^{\frac{1}{2}}}$ | $\frac{1}{\pi^{\frac{3}{2}}} \frac{e^{at}}{t^{\frac{1}{2}}} * \frac{e^{bt}}{t^{\frac{1}{2}}} * \frac{e^{ct}}{t^{\frac{1}{2}}}$<br>$= \frac{e^{at}}{(\pi t)^{\frac{1}{2}}} * I_0(\frac{b-c}{2}t) e^{\frac{b+c}{2}t}$ | Re $s >$ Max Re $a$, Re $b$, Re $c$ |
| 21 | $\frac{(s-a)^{\nu}}{(s+a)^{\nu+\frac{1}{2}}}$ | $\frac{\Gamma(\frac{1}{2}-\nu)}{2^{\nu+1}\pi t^{\frac{1}{2}}}[D_{2\nu}(2a^{\frac{1}{2}}t^{\frac{1}{2}}) + D_{2\nu}(-2a^{\frac{1}{2}}t^{\frac{1}{2}})]$ | Re $s > \|$Re $a\|$ |
| 22 | $\frac{(s-a)^{\nu}}{(s-b)^{\nu+\frac{1}{2}}}$ | $\frac{\Gamma(\frac{1}{2}-\nu)\, e^{\frac{a+b}{2}t}}{2^{\nu+1}\pi t^{\frac{1}{2}}} \left\{D_{2\nu}[-2^{\frac{1}{2}}(a-b)^{\frac{1}{2}}t^{\frac{1}{2}}]\right.$<br>$\left. + D_{2\nu}[2^{\frac{1}{2}}(a-b)^{\frac{1}{2}}t^{\frac{1}{2}}]\right\}$ | Re $s >$ Max Re $a$, Re $b$ |

| | g(s) | f(t) | |
|---|---|---|---|
| 2(Contd.) | | | |
| 23 | $\dfrac{(s-a)^{\nu}}{(s+a)^{\nu+\frac{3}{2}}}$ | $\dfrac{\Gamma(-\nu-\frac{1}{2})}{2^{\nu+2}\pi a^{\frac{1}{2}}}[D_{2\nu+1}(-2a^{\frac{1}{2}}t^{\frac{1}{2}})-D_{2\nu+1}(2a^{\frac{1}{2}}t^{\frac{1}{2}})]$ | Re s > \|Re a\| |
| 24 | $\dfrac{(s-a)^{\nu}}{(s-b)^{\nu+\frac{3}{2}}}$ | $\dfrac{\Gamma(-\frac{1}{2}-\nu)\, e^{\frac{a+b}{2}t}}{2^{\nu+\frac{3}{2}}\pi(a-b)^{\frac{1}{2}}}\Big\{D_{2\nu+1}[-2^{\frac{1}{2}}(a-b)^{\frac{1}{2}}t^{\frac{1}{2}}] - D_{2\nu+1}[2^{\frac{1}{2}}(a-b)^{\frac{1}{2}}t^{\frac{1}{2}}]\Big\}$ | Re s > Max Re a, Re b |
| 25 | $\dfrac{1}{(s+a)^{\nu}(s+b)^{\nu}}$ | $\dfrac{\pi^{\frac{1}{2}}}{\Gamma(\nu)}\left(\dfrac{t}{a-b}\right)^{\nu-\frac{1}{2}} e^{-\frac{a+b}{2}t} I_{\nu-\frac{1}{2}}\left(\dfrac{a-b}{2}t\right)$ | Re ν > o<br>Re s > Max - Re a, - Reb |
| 26 | $\dfrac{(s-a)^{\nu}}{(s+a)^{\mu}}$ | $\dfrac{t^{\frac{\mu-\nu}{2}-1} M_{\frac{\mu+\nu}{2},\frac{\mu-\nu-1}{2}}(2at)}{(2a)^{\frac{\mu-\nu}{2}}\Gamma(\mu-\nu)}$ | Re(μ-ν) > o<br>Re s > \|Re a\| |
| 27 | $\dfrac{(a-s)^{\mu}}{(a+s)^{\nu}}$ | $\dfrac{t^{\frac{\nu-\mu-2}{2}} W_{\frac{\mu+\nu}{2},\frac{\nu-\mu-1}{2}}(2at)}{\Gamma(\nu)(2a)^{\frac{\nu-\mu}{2}}}$ | Re(ν-μ) > o<br>Re s > \|Re a\| |
| 28 | $\dfrac{(s-a)^{\mu}}{(s-b)^{\nu}}$ | $\dfrac{t^{\nu-\mu-1}\, e^{at}}{\Gamma(\nu-\mu)}\, {}_1F_1[\nu;\nu-\mu;(b-a)t]$<br>$= \dfrac{(a-b)^{\frac{\mu-\nu}{2}}\, t^{\frac{\nu-\mu}{2}-1}}{\Gamma(\nu-\mu)}\, e^{\frac{a+b}{2}t} M_{\frac{\mu+\nu}{2},\frac{\nu-\mu-1}{2}}[(a-b)t]$ | Re(ν-μ) > o<br>Re s > Max Re a, Re b |
| 29 | $[(s+a)^{\frac{1}{2}}-(s+b)^{\frac{1}{2}}]^{\nu}$ | $\dfrac{\nu(a-b)^{\frac{\nu}{2}} e^{-\frac{a+b}{2}t}}{2t} I_{\frac{\nu}{2}}\left(\dfrac{a-b}{2}t\right)$ | Re ν > o<br>Re s > Max - Re a, - Reb |
| 30 | $\dfrac{[(s+a)^{\frac{1}{2}}-(s+b)^{\frac{1}{2}}]^{\nu}}{(s+a)^{\frac{1}{2}}(s+b)^{\frac{1}{2}}}$ | $(a-b)^{\frac{\nu}{2}} e^{-\frac{a+b}{2}t} I_{\frac{\nu}{2}}\left(\dfrac{a-b}{2}t\right)$ | Re ν > - 2<br>Re s > Max - Re a, - Reb |
| 31 | $\dfrac{(s+a)^{\frac{1}{2}}[(s+a)^{\frac{1}{2}}-(s-a)^{\frac{1}{2}}]}{(s-a)^{\frac{1}{2}}}$ | $\dfrac{(2a)^{\frac{\nu}{2}+1}}{4}[I_{\frac{\nu}{2}-1}(at)+2I_{\frac{\nu}{2}}(at)+I_{\frac{\nu}{2}+1}(at)]$ | Re ν > o<br>Re s > Re a |

| | $g(s)$ | $f(t)$ | |
|---|---|---|---|
| 2(Contd.) | | | |
| 32 | $\dfrac{1}{(s+1)^c\left(1-2\,\dfrac{s-1}{s+1}\,b+b^2\right)^a}$ | $\dfrac{t^{c-1}e^{-t}}{\Gamma(c)(1-b)^{2a}}\,{}_1F_1\left[a;c;-\dfrac{4bt}{(1-b^2)}\right]$ | Re $c>0$<br>Re $s>$ Max $-1$, $-$Re $\left(\dfrac{1+b}{1-b}\right)^2$ |

Functions of $s,(s\pm a)$ Only

| | $g(s)$ | $f(t)$ | |
|---|---|---|---|
| 33 | $\dfrac{(s+a)^{\frac{1}{2}}}{s}$ | $\dfrac{e^{-at}}{(\pi t)^{\frac{1}{2}}}+a^{\frac{1}{2}}\mathrm{Erf}[(at)^{\frac{1}{2}}]$ | Re $s>$ Max $0$, $-$Re $a$ |
| 34 | $\dfrac{(s+a)^{\frac{1}{2}}}{s^{\frac{3}{2}}}$ | $e^{-\frac{at}{2}}[(1+at)I_0(\frac{at}{2})+atI_1(\frac{at}{2})]$ | Re $s>$ Max $0$, $-$Re $a$ |
| 35 | $\dfrac{s^{\nu-1}}{(s+a)^{\nu}}$ | $\dfrac{2e^{-\frac{at}{2}}M_{\nu-\frac{1}{4},\frac{1}{4}}(at)}{(a^3\pi^2t)^{\frac{1}{4}}}$ | Re $s>$ Max $0$, $-$Re $a$ |
| 36 | $\dfrac{s^{\nu-1}}{(s-a)^{\nu}}$ | ${}_1F_1[\nu,1;at]$ | Re $s>$ Max $0$, Re $a$ |
| 37 | $\dfrac{s^{\nu-\frac{1}{4}}}{(s+a)^{\nu+\frac{1}{4}}}$ | $\dfrac{e^{-\frac{at}{2}}M_{\nu,-\frac{1}{4}}(at)}{(a\pi^2t^3)^{\frac{1}{4}}}$ | Re $s>$ Max $0$, $-$Re $a$ |
| 38 | $\dfrac{s^c}{(s-b)^a}$ | $\dfrac{t^{a-c-1}}{\Gamma(a-c)}\,{}_1F_1[a;a-c;bt]$ | Re$(a-c)>0$<br>Re $b>0$<br>Re $s>0$ |
| 39 | $\dfrac{1}{s(s+a)^{\frac{1}{2}}}$ | $a^{-\frac{1}{2}}\mathrm{Erf}(a^{\frac{1}{2}}t^{\frac{1}{2}})$ | Re $s>$ Max $0$, $-$Re $a$ |
| 40 | $\dfrac{(s+b)^{\frac{1}{2}}}{s(s+a)^{\frac{1}{2}}}$ | $e^{-\frac{a+b}{2}t}I_0(\frac{a-b}{2}t)+b\displaystyle\int_0^t e^{-\frac{a+b}{2}u}I_0(\frac{a-b}{2}u)\,du$ | Re $s>$ Max $0$, $-$Re $a$, $-$Re $b$ |

2(Contd.)

| | g(s) | f(t) | |
|---|---|---|---|
| 41 | $\frac{1}{s}\left[1-\left(\frac{a}{a+s}\right)^{\nu}\right]$ | $\frac{\Gamma(\nu,at)}{\Gamma(\nu)}$ | Re s > − Re a<br>Re $\nu$ > − 1 |
| 42 | $\frac{1}{s^{c}\left(1-\frac{x}{s}\right)^{a}\left(1-\frac{y}{s}\right)^{b}}$ | $\frac{t^{c-1}}{\Gamma(c)}\Phi_2(a,b,c;xt,yt)$ | Re c > o<br>Re s > Max o, x,y |
| 43 | $\frac{1}{s^{c}}\left(1-\frac{b_1}{s}\right)^{-a_1}\cdots\left(1-\frac{b_n}{s}\right)^{-a_n}$ | $\frac{t^{c-1}}{\Gamma(c)}\Phi_2(a_1,\ldots,a_n;c;b_1t,\ldots,b_nt)$ | Re c > o<br>Re s > Max o, Re $b_j$ $(j=1,\ldots,n)$ |

Functions of $[(s+a)^{\frac{1}{2}} \pm b^{\frac{1}{2}}]$

| | g(s) | f(t) | |
|---|---|---|---|
| 44 | $[(s+a)^{\frac{1}{2}}+b^{\frac{1}{2}}]^{\nu}$ | $-\left(\frac{2}{\pi}\right)^{\frac{1}{2}}\nu\frac{e^{(\frac{b}{2}-a)t}}{(2t)^{\frac{\nu}{2}+1}}D_{\nu-1}[(2bt)^{\frac{1}{2}}]$ | Re $\nu$ < o<br>Re s > Max Re a, Re(a−b) |
| 45 | $\frac{[(s+a)^{\frac{1}{2}}+b^{\frac{1}{2}}]^{\nu}}{(s+a)^{\frac{1}{2}}}$ | $\frac{2^{\frac{1}{2}}e^{(\frac{b}{2}-a)t}}{\pi^{\frac{1}{2}}(2t)^{\frac{\nu+1}{2}}}D_{\nu}[(2bt)^{\frac{1}{2}}]$ | Re $\nu$ < 1<br>Re s > Max Re a, Re(a−b) |
| 46 | $\frac{(s+a)^{\frac{1}{2}}-a^{\frac{1}{2}}}{s(s+a)^{\frac{1}{2}}}$ | $\mathrm{Erfc}(a^{\frac{1}{2}}t^{\frac{1}{2}})$ | Re s > − Re a |
| 47 | $\frac{[(s+a)^{\frac{1}{2}}-a^{\frac{1}{2}}]^{\nu}}{s^{\nu}(s+a)^{\frac{1}{2}}}$ | $\left(\frac{2}{\pi}\right)^{\frac{1}{2}}(2t)^{\frac{\nu-1}{2}}e^{-\frac{at}{2}}D_{-\nu}[(2at)^{\frac{1}{2}}]$ | Re $\nu$ > − 1<br>Re s > − Re a |
| 48 | $\left[\frac{(s+a)^{\frac{1}{2}}-a^{\frac{1}{2}}}{s}\right]^{\nu}$ | $\left(\frac{2}{\pi}\right)^{\frac{1}{2}}\nu(2t)^{\frac{\nu}{2}-1}e^{-\frac{at}{2}}D_{-\nu-1}[(2at)^{\frac{1}{2}}]$ | Re $\nu$ > o<br>Re s > − Re a |

Functions of $(s^{\frac{1}{2}} \pm a)$

| | g(s) | f(t) | |
|---|---|---|---|
| 49 | $\frac{1}{s^{\frac{1}{2}}+a}$ | $\frac{1}{(\pi t)^{\frac{1}{2}}}-ae^{a^2t}\mathrm{Erfc}(at^{\frac{1}{2}})$ | Re s > o if Re a ⩾ o<br>Re s > Max o, Re $a^2$ if Re a < o |

| | $g(s)$ | $f(t)$ | |
|---|---|---|---|
| 2(Contd.) | | | |
| 50 | $(a+s^{\frac{1}{2}})^{\nu}$ | $-\dfrac{\nu e^{\frac{a^2t}{2}} D_{\nu-1}(2^{\frac{1}{2}}at^{\frac{1}{2}})}{(2\pi)^{\frac{1}{2}}2^{\frac{\nu}{2}}t^{\frac{\nu}{2}+1}}$ | $\text{Re}\,\nu < 0$<br>$\text{Re}\,s > 0$ if $\text{Re}\,a \geqslant 0$<br>$\text{Re}\,s > \text{Max}\,0, \text{Re}\,a^2$ if $\text{Re}\,a < 0$ |
| 51 | $\dfrac{1}{s^{\frac{1}{2}}(s^{\frac{1}{2}}+a)}$ | $e^{a^2t}\text{Erfc}(at^{\frac{1}{2}})$ | $\text{Re}\,s > 0$ if $\text{Re}\,a \geqslant 0$<br>$\text{Re}\,s > \text{Max}\,0, \text{Re}\,a^2$ if $\text{Re}\,a < 0$ |
| 52 | $\dfrac{1}{s(s^{\frac{1}{2}}+a)}$ | $\frac{1}{a}[1-e^{a^2t}\text{Erfc}(at^{\frac{1}{2}})]$ | $\text{Re}\,s > 0$ if $\text{Re}\,a \geqslant 0$<br>$\text{Re}\,s > \text{Max}\,0, \text{Re}\,a^2$ if $\text{Re}\,a < 0$ |
| 53 | $\dfrac{s^{\frac{1}{2}}+a}{s^{\frac{3}{2}}}$ | $\dfrac{2t^{\frac{1}{2}}}{a\pi^{\frac{1}{2}}}+\dfrac{e^{a^2t}}{a^2}\text{Erfc}(at^{\frac{1}{2}})-\dfrac{1}{a^2}$ | $\text{Re}\,s > 0$ |
| 54 | $\dfrac{(a+s^{\frac{1}{2}})^{\nu}}{s^{\frac{1}{2}}}$ | $\dfrac{e^{\frac{a^2t}{2}} D_{\nu}(2^{\frac{1}{2}}at^{\frac{1}{2}})}{2^{\frac{\nu}{2}}\pi^{\frac{1}{2}}t^{\frac{\nu+1}{2}}}$ | $\text{Re}\,\nu < 1$<br>$\text{Re}\,s > 0$ |
| 55 | $\dfrac{1}{s}\left(\dfrac{s^{\frac{1}{2}}-a}{s^{\frac{1}{2}}+a}\right)$ | $2e^{a^2t}\text{Erfc}(at^{\frac{1}{2}})-1$ | $\text{Re}\,s > 0$ if $\text{Re}\,a \geqslant 0$<br>$\text{Re}\,s > \text{Max}\,0, \text{Re}\,a^2$ if $\text{Re}\,a < 0$ |

Functions of $(s^2 \pm a^2)$ Only

| | | | |
|---|---|---|---|
| 56 | $\dfrac{1}{(s^2+a^2)^{\frac{1}{2}}}$ | $J_0(at)$ | $\text{Re}\,s > \lvert\text{Im}\,a\rvert$ |
| 57 | $\dfrac{1}{(s^2-a^2)^{\frac{1}{2}}}$ | $I_0(at)$ | $\text{Re}\,s > \lvert\text{Re}\,a\rvert$ |
| 58 | $\dfrac{1}{(s^2+a^2)^{n+\frac{1}{2}}}$ | $\dfrac{t^n J_n(at)}{1.3.5\ldots(2n-1)a^n}$ | $n = 1,2,3,\ldots$<br>$\text{Re}\,s > \lvert\text{Im}\,a\rvert$ |
| 59 | $\dfrac{1}{(s^2-a^2)^{n+\frac{1}{2}}}$ | $\dfrac{t^n I_n(at)}{1.3.5\ldots(2n-1)a^n}$ | $n = 1,2,3,\ldots$<br>$\text{Re}\,s > \lvert\text{Re}\,a\rvert$ |

| | g(s) | f(t) | |
|---|---|---|---|
| 2(Contd.) | | | |
| 60 | $\frac{1}{(s^2+a^2)^{\nu}}$ | $\frac{\pi^{\frac{1}{2}} t^{\nu-\frac{1}{2}} J_{\nu-\frac{1}{2}}(at)}{(2a)^{\nu-\frac{1}{2}}\Gamma(\nu)}$ | $\mathrm{Re}\,\nu > 0$<br>$\mathrm{Re}\,s > \lvert\mathrm{Im}\,a\rvert$ |
| 61 | $\frac{1}{(s^2-a^2)^{\nu}}$ | $\frac{\pi^{\frac{1}{2}} t^{\nu-\frac{1}{2}} I_{\nu-\frac{1}{2}}(at)}{(2a)^{\nu-\frac{1}{2}}\Gamma(\nu)}$ | $\mathrm{Re}\,\nu > 0$<br>$\mathrm{Re}\,s > \lvert\mathrm{Re}\,a\rvert$ |
| Functions of s, $(s^2 \pm a^2)$ Only | | | |
| 62 | $\frac{1}{s(s^2+a^2)^{\frac{3}{2}}}$ | $\frac{\pi t}{2a^2}[J_1(at)H_0(at)-J_0(at)H_1(at)]$ | $\mathrm{Re}\,s > \lvert\mathrm{Im}\,a\rvert$ |
| 63 | $\frac{1}{s(s^2+a^2)^{\nu}}$ | $\frac{\pi t}{2a^{2\nu-1}}[J_{\nu-\frac{1}{2}}(at)H'_{\nu-\frac{1}{2}}(at)$<br>$-J'_{\nu-\frac{1}{2}}(at)H_{\nu-\frac{1}{2}}(at)]$ | $\mathrm{Re}\,\nu > -\frac{1}{2}$<br>$\mathrm{Re}\,s > \lvert\mathrm{Im}\,a\rvert$ |
| 64 | $\frac{1}{s(s^2-a^2)^{\frac{3}{2}}}$ | $\frac{\pi t}{2a^2}[I_1(at)L_0(at)-I_0(at)L_1(at)]$ | $\mathrm{Re}\,s > \lvert\mathrm{Re}\,a\rvert$ |
| 65 | $\frac{1}{s(s^2-a^2)^{\nu}}$ | $\frac{\pi t}{2a^{2\nu-1}}[I_{\nu-\frac{1}{2}}(at)L'_{\nu-\frac{1}{2}}(at)-I'_{\nu-\frac{1}{2}}(at)L_{\nu-\frac{1}{2}}(at)]$ | $\mathrm{Re}\,\nu > -\frac{1}{2}$<br>$\mathrm{Re}\,s > \lvert\mathrm{Re}\,a\rvert$ |
| 66 | $\frac{1}{s^{2\mu}(s^2+a^2)^{\nu}}$ | $\frac{t^{2\mu+2\nu-1}}{\Gamma(2\mu+2\nu)}\,{}_1F_2\left[\begin{matrix}\nu; & -\frac{a^2t^2}{4}\\ \mu+\nu,\mu+\nu+\frac{1}{2}; & \end{matrix}\right]$ | $\mathrm{Re}(\mu+\nu) > 0$<br>$\mathrm{Re}\,s > \lvert\mathrm{Im}\,a\rvert$ |
| 67 | $\frac{s}{(s^2+a^2)^{\nu}}$ | $\frac{\pi^{\frac{1}{2}} t^{\nu-\frac{1}{2}} J_{\nu-\frac{3}{2}}(at)}{2^{\nu-\frac{1}{2}}\Gamma(\nu)a^{\nu-\frac{3}{2}}}$ | $\mathrm{Re}\,\nu > \frac{1}{2}$<br>$\mathrm{Re}\,s > \lvert\mathrm{Im}\,a\rvert$ |
| 68 | $\frac{s}{(s^2-a^2)^{\nu}}$ | $\frac{\pi^{\frac{1}{2}} t^{\nu-\frac{1}{2}} I_{\nu-\frac{3}{2}}(at)}{2^{\nu-\frac{1}{2}}\Gamma(\nu)a^{\nu-\frac{3}{2}}}$ | $\mathrm{Re}\,\nu > \frac{1}{2}$<br>$\mathrm{Re}\,s > \lvert\mathrm{Re}\,a\rvert$ |

2(Contd.)

Functions of $(s^2-a^2)$, $(s\pm a)$, $(s^2+as+b)$

| | g(s) | f(t) | |
|---|---|---|---|
| 69 | $\frac{1}{(s^2+as+b)^{\frac{1}{2}}}$ | $e^{-\frac{at}{2}} J_0[(b-\frac{a^2}{4})^{\frac{1}{2}}t]$ | $\text{Re } s > \lvert \text{Im}(b-\frac{a^2}{4})^{\frac{1}{2}} \rvert - \text{Re } \frac{a}{2}$ |
| 70 | $\frac{(s+a)^{\nu}+(s-a)^{\nu}}{(s^2-a^2)^{\nu}}$ | $\frac{2t^{\nu-1}\cosh(at)}{\Gamma(\nu)}$ | $\text{Re } \nu > 0$<br>$\text{Re } s > \lvert \text{Re } a \rvert$ |

Functions of $s,(s^3+a^3)$

| | g(s) | f(t) | |
|---|---|---|---|
| 71 | $\frac{1}{(s^3+a^3)^{\frac{1}{3}}}$ | ${}_0F_2[1,\frac{2}{3};-(\frac{at}{3})^3]$ | $\text{Re } s > \text{Max} - \text{Re } a, \frac{\text{Re } a + 3^{\frac{1}{2}}\lvert \text{Im } a \rvert}{2}$ |
| 72 | $\frac{1}{(s^3+a^3)^{\frac{1}{2}}}$ | $\frac{2(\pi t)^{\frac{1}{2}}}{3\Gamma(\frac{7}{6})\Gamma(\frac{5}{6})} {}_0F_2\left[\begin{matrix} ; -\left(\frac{at}{3}\right)^3 \\ \frac{7}{6},\frac{5}{6}; \end{matrix}\right]$ | $\text{Re } s > \text{Max} - \text{Re } a, \frac{\text{Re } a + 3^{\frac{1}{2}}\lvert \text{Im } a \rvert}{2}$ |
| 73 | $\frac{s}{(s^3+a^3)^{\frac{1}{2}}}$ | $\frac{2\pi^{\frac{1}{2}}a^{\frac{1}{3}}}{3^{\frac{1}{3}}t^{\frac{1}{6}}\Gamma(\frac{7}{6})\Gamma(\frac{1}{6})} {}_0F_2\left[\begin{matrix} ; -\left(\frac{at}{3}\right)^3 \\ \frac{7}{6},\frac{1}{6}; \end{matrix}\right]$ | $\text{Re } s > \text{Max} - \text{Re } a, \frac{\text{Re } a + 3^{\frac{1}{2}}\lvert \text{Im } a \rvert}{2}$ |
| 74 | $\frac{1}{s^{3\mu}(s^3+a^3)^{\nu}}$ | $\frac{t^{3\mu+3\nu-1}}{\Gamma(3\mu+3\nu)} {}_1F_3\left[\begin{matrix} \nu ; -\frac{a^3t^3}{27} \\ \mu+\nu,\mu+\nu+\frac{1}{3},\mu+\nu+\frac{2}{3}; \end{matrix}\right]$ | $\text{Re}(\mu+\nu) > 0$<br>$\text{Re } s > \text{Max} - \text{Re } a, \frac{\text{Re } a + 3^{\frac{1}{2}}\lvert \text{Im } a \rvert}{2}$ |

Functions of $s,(s^4+a^4)$

| | g(s) | f(t) | |
|---|---|---|---|
| 75 | $\left[\frac{1}{(s^4+a^4)^{\frac{1}{2}}} + \frac{s^2}{s^4+a^4}\right]^{\frac{1}{2}}$ | $2^{\frac{1}{2}}\text{ber}(at)$ | $\text{Re } s > \frac{\lvert \text{Re } a \rvert + \lvert \text{Im } a \rvert}{2^{\frac{1}{2}}}$ |
| 76 | $\left[\frac{1}{(s^4+a^4)^{\frac{1}{2}}} - \frac{s^2}{s^4+a^4}\right]^{\frac{1}{2}}$ | $2^{\frac{1}{2}}\text{bei}(at)$ | $\text{Re } s > \frac{\lvert \text{Re } a \rvert + \lvert \text{Im } a \rvert}{2^{\frac{1}{2}}}$ |

| | g(s) | f(t) | |
|---|---|---|---|
| 2(Contd.) | | | |
| Functions of $s, (s^2+a^2-1)$ | | | |
| 77 | $\frac{1}{s}\left[\frac{[(s^2+a^2-1)^2+4s^2]^{\frac{1}{2}}+s^2+a^2-1}{(s^2+a^2-1)^2+4s^2}\right]^{\frac{1}{2}}$ | $2^{\frac{1}{2}}\int_0^t J_0(au)\cos u\,du$ | $\mathrm{Re}\, s > \lvert \mathrm{Im}\, a \rvert$ |
| 78 | $\frac{1}{s}\left[\frac{[(s^2+a^2-1)^2+4s^2]^{\frac{1}{2}}-s^2-a^2+1}{(s^2+a^2-1)^2+4s^2}\right]^{\frac{1}{2}}$ | $-2^{\frac{1}{2}}\int_0^t J_0(au)\sin u\,du$ | $\mathrm{Re}\, s > \lvert \mathrm{Im}\, a \rvert$ |
| Functions of $s, (s\pm a), [(s\pm a)^{\frac{1}{2}}\pm s^{\frac{1}{2}}]$ | | | |
| 79 | $[(s+a)^{\frac{1}{2}}-s^{\frac{1}{2}}]^{\nu}$ | $\frac{\nu a^{\frac{\nu}{2}}}{2t} e^{-\frac{at}{2}} I_{\frac{\nu}{2}}(\frac{at}{2})$ | $\mathrm{Re}\, \nu > 0$<br>$\mathrm{Re}\, s > \mathrm{Max}\ 0, -\mathrm{Re}\, a$ |
| 80 | $\frac{s^{\frac{1}{2}}[(s+a)^{\frac{1}{2}}-s^{\frac{1}{2}}]^{\nu}}{(s+a)^{\frac{1}{2}}}$ | $\frac{a^{\frac{\nu}{2}+1} e^{-\frac{at}{2}}}{2}\left[I'_{\frac{\nu}{2}}(\frac{at}{2}) - I_{\frac{\nu}{2}}(\frac{at}{2})\right]$ | $\mathrm{Re}\, \nu > 0$<br>$\mathrm{Re}\, s > \mathrm{Max}\ 0, -\mathrm{Re}\, a$ |
| 81 | $\frac{[(s+a)^{\frac{1}{2}}-s^{\frac{1}{2}}]^{2\nu}}{s^{\frac{1}{2}}(s+a)^{\frac{1}{2}}}$ | $a^{\nu} e^{-\frac{at}{2}} I_{\nu}(\frac{at}{2})$ | $\mathrm{Re}\, \nu > -1$<br>$\mathrm{Re}\, s > \mathrm{Max}\ 0, -\mathrm{Re}\, a$ |
| 82 | $\frac{[s^{\frac{1}{2}}-(s-a)^{\frac{1}{2}}]^{2\nu}}{s^{\frac{1}{2}}(s-a)^{\frac{1}{2}}}$ | $a^{\nu} e^{\frac{at}{2}} I_{\nu}(\frac{at}{2})$ | $\mathrm{Re}\, \nu > -1$<br>$\mathrm{Re}\, s > \mathrm{Max}\ 0, \mathrm{Re}\, a$ |
| Functions of $[(s^2\pm a^2)^{\frac{1}{2}}\pm s]$ Only | | | |
| 83 | $[(s^2+a^2)^{\frac{1}{2}}-s]^{\frac{1}{2}}$ | $\frac{\sin(at)}{(2\pi)^{\frac{1}{2}} t^{\frac{3}{2}}}$ | $\mathrm{Re}\, s > \lvert \mathrm{Im}\, a \rvert$ |
| 84 | $s-(s^2-a^2)^{\frac{1}{2}}$ | $\frac{a}{t} I_1(at)$ | $\mathrm{Re}\, s > \lvert \mathrm{Re}\, a \rvert$ |
| 85 | $[(s^2+a^2)^{\frac{1}{2}}-s]^{\nu}$ | $\frac{a^{\nu}\nu J_{\nu}(at)}{t}$ | $\mathrm{Re}\, \nu > 0$<br>$\mathrm{Re}\, s \geqslant \lvert \mathrm{Im}\, a \rvert$ |

| | g(s) | f(t) | |
|---|---|---|---|
| 2(Contd.) | | | |
| 86 | $[s-(s^2-a^2)^{\frac{1}{2}}]^\nu$ | $\dfrac{\nu a^\nu I_\nu(at)}{t}$ | Re $\nu > 0$<br>Re $s >$ \|Re a\| |

Functions of $s, [(s^2 \pm a^2)^{\frac{1}{2}} \pm s]$ Only

| | g(s) | f(t) | |
|---|---|---|---|
| 87 | $s[(s^2+a^2)^{\frac{1}{2}}-s]^\nu$ | $\dfrac{a^{\nu+1}\nu}{t} J_{\nu-1}(at) - \dfrac{a^\nu \nu(\nu+1)}{t^2} J_\nu(at)$ | Re $\nu > 1$<br>Re $s >$ \|Im a\| |
| 88 | $s[s-(s^2-a^2)^{\frac{1}{2}}]^\nu$ | $\dfrac{a^{\nu+1}\nu}{t} I_{\nu-1}(at) - \dfrac{a^\nu \nu(\nu+1)}{t^2} I_\nu(at)$ | Re $\nu > 1$<br>Re $s >$ \|Re a\| |
| 89 | $\dfrac{[(s^2+a^2)^{\frac{1}{2}}-s]^\nu}{a^\nu s} - \dfrac{1}{s}$ | $\nu\, Ji_\nu(at)$ | Re $\nu > 0$<br>Re $s > 0$ |
| 90 | $\dfrac{[s+(s^2-a^2)^{\frac{1}{2}}]^\nu + [s-(s^2-a^2)^{\frac{1}{2}}]^\nu}{s}$ | $2a^\nu \left[\dfrac{\nu \sin \nu\pi}{\pi} Ki_\nu(at) + \cos \dfrac{\nu\pi}{2}\right]$ | \|Re $\nu$\| $< 1$<br>Re $s >$ \|Re a\| |
| 91 | $\dfrac{[(s^2+a^2)^{\frac{1}{2}}+s]^\nu + \cos(\nu\pi)[(s^2+a^2)^{\frac{1}{2}}-s]^\nu}{s}$ | $a^\nu[1+\cos(\nu\pi)-\nu\sin(\nu\pi) Yi_\nu(at)]$ | \|Re $\nu$\| $< 1$<br>Re $s >$ \|Im a\| |

Functions of $(s^2 \pm a^2)$, $[(s^2 \pm a^2)^{\frac{1}{2}} \pm s]$ Only

| | g(s) | f(t) | |
|---|---|---|---|
| 92 | $\dfrac{[s+(s^2+a^2)^{\frac{1}{2}}]^{\frac{1}{2}}}{(s^2+a^2)^{\frac{1}{2}}}$ | $\left(\dfrac{2}{\pi t}\right)^{\frac{1}{2}} \cos(at)$<br>$= a^{\frac{1}{2}} J_{-\frac{1}{2}}(at)$ | Re $s >$ \|Im a\| |
| 93 | $\dfrac{[(s^2+a^2)^{\frac{1}{2}}-s]^{\frac{1}{2}}}{(s^2+a^2)^{\frac{1}{2}}}$ | $\left(\dfrac{2}{\pi t}\right)^{\frac{1}{2}} \sin(at)$<br>$= a^{\frac{1}{2}} J_{\frac{1}{2}}(at)$ | Re $s >$ \|Im a\| |

| | g(s) | f(t) | |
|---|---|---|---|
| 2(Contd.) | | | |
| 94 | $\left[\dfrac{(s^2-a^2)^{\frac{1}{2}}+s}{s^2-a^2}\right]^{\frac{1}{2}}$ | $a^{\frac{1}{2}} I_{-\frac{1}{2}}(at)$ $= \left(\dfrac{2}{\pi t}\right)^{\frac{1}{2}} \cosh(at)$ | Re s > \|Re a\| |
| 95 | $\dfrac{[s-(s^2-a^2)^{\frac{1}{2}}]^{\frac{1}{2}}}{(s^2-a^2)^{\frac{1}{2}}}$ | $a^{\frac{1}{2}} I_{\frac{1}{2}}(at)$ $= \left(\dfrac{2}{\pi t}\right)^{\frac{1}{2}} \sinh(at)$ | Re s > \|Re a\| |
| 96 | $\dfrac{[(s^2+a^2)^{\frac{1}{2}}-s]^{n+\frac{1}{2}}}{(s^2+a^2)^{\frac{1}{2}}}$ | $(-1)^n a^{n+\frac{1}{2}}\, Y_{-n-\frac{1}{2}}(at)$ $= (-1)^n a^{n+\frac{1}{2}}\, \mathbf{H}_{-n-\frac{1}{2}}(at)$ | $n = 0,1,2,\ldots$ Re s > \|Im a\| |
| 97 | $\dfrac{[s-(s^2-a^2)^{\frac{1}{2}}]^{n+\frac{1}{2}}}{(s^2-a^2)^{\frac{1}{2}}}$ | $a^{n+\frac{1}{2}} \mathbf{L}_{-n-\frac{1}{2}}(at)$ | $n = 0,1,2,\ldots$ Re s > \|Re a\| |
| 98 | $\dfrac{[(s^2+a^2)^{\frac{1}{2}}-s]^{\nu}}{(s^2+a^2)^{\frac{1}{2}}}$ | $a^{\nu} J_{\nu}(at)$ | Re $\nu > -1$ Re s > \|Im a\| |
| 99 | $\dfrac{[s-(s^2-a^2)^{\frac{1}{2}}]^{\nu}}{(s^2-a^2)^{\frac{1}{2}}}$ | $a^{\nu} I_{\nu}(at)$ | Re $\nu > -1$ Re s > \|Re a\| |
| 00 | $\dfrac{[s-(s^2-ia^2)^{\frac{1}{2}}]^{\nu}}{(s^2-ia^2)^{\frac{1}{2}}}$ | $(ia)^{\nu} e^{-\frac{3i\pi\nu}{4}} [\mathrm{ber}_{\nu}(at) + i\,\mathrm{bei}_{\nu}(at)]$ | Re $\nu > -1$ Re s > $\dfrac{\|\mathrm{Re}\, a\|}{2^{\frac{1}{2}}}$ |
| 1 | $\dfrac{[(s^2+a^2)^{\frac{1}{2}}-s]^{\nu}\cos(\nu\pi)-[(s^2+a^2)^{\frac{1}{2}}+s]^{\nu}}{(s^2+a^2)^{\frac{1}{2}}}$ | $a^{\nu}\sin(\nu\pi) Y_{\nu}(at)$ | \|Re $\nu$\| < 1 Re s > \|Im a\| |

| | g(s) | f(t) | |
|---|---|---|---|
| 2(Contd.) | | | |
| 102 | $\dfrac{[(s^2+a^2)^{\frac{1}{2}}+s]^{\nu}-e^{i\nu\pi}[(s^2+a^2)^{\frac{1}{2}}-s]^{\nu}}{(s^2+a^2)^{\frac{1}{2}}}$ | $-ia^{\nu}\sin(\nu\pi)H_{\nu}^{(2)}(at)$ | $\lvert \mathrm{Re}\,\nu \rvert < 1$<br>$\mathrm{Re}\,s > \lvert \mathrm{Im}\,a \rvert$ |
| 103 | $\dfrac{e^{-i\nu\pi}[(s^2+a^2)^{\frac{1}{2}}-s]^{\nu}-[(s^2+a^2)^{\frac{1}{2}}+s]^{\nu}}{(s^2+a^2)^{\frac{1}{2}}}$ | $-ia^{\nu}\sin(\nu\pi)H_{\nu}^{(1)}(at)$ | $\lvert \mathrm{Re}\,\nu \rvert < 1$<br>$\mathrm{Re}\,s > \lvert \mathrm{Im}\,a \rvert$ |
| 104 | $\dfrac{[s+(s^2-a^2)^{\frac{1}{2}}]^{\nu}-[s-(s^2-a^2)^{\frac{1}{2}}]^{\nu}}{(s^2-a^2)^{\frac{1}{2}}}$ | $\dfrac{2a^{\nu}}{\pi}\sin(\nu\pi)K_{\nu}(at)$ | $\lvert \mathrm{Re}\,\nu \rvert < 1$<br>$\mathrm{Re}\,s > \lvert \mathrm{Re}\,a \rvert$ |
| 105 | $\dfrac{[s+(s^2-ia^2)^{\frac{1}{2}}]^{\nu}-[s-(s^2-ia^2)^{\frac{1}{2}}]^{\nu}}{(s^2-ia^2)^{\frac{1}{2}}}$ | $\dfrac{2}{\pi}a^{\nu}e^{\frac{i\pi\nu}{4}}\sin(\nu\pi)\,\cdot$<br>$\cdot\,[\mathrm{ker}_{\nu}(at)+i\,\mathrm{kei}_{\nu}(at)]$ | $\lvert \mathrm{Re}\,\nu \rvert < 1$<br>$\mathrm{Re}\,s > \dfrac{\lvert \mathrm{Re}\,a \rvert}{2^{\frac{1}{2}}}$ |

Functions of $s, (s^2 \pm a^2), [(s^2 \pm a^2)^{\frac{1}{2}} \pm s]$ Only

| | | | |
|---|---|---|---|
| 106 | $\dfrac{[(s^2+a^2)^{\frac{1}{2}}+s]^{\frac{1}{2}}}{s(s^2+a^2)^{\frac{1}{2}}}$ | $\dfrac{2}{a^{\frac{1}{2}}}C(at)$ | $\mathrm{Re}\,s > 0$ |
| 107 | $\dfrac{[(s^2+a^2)^{\frac{1}{2}}-s]^{\frac{1}{2}}}{s(s^2+a^2)^{\frac{1}{2}}}$ | $\dfrac{2}{a^{\frac{1}{2}}}S(at)$ | $\mathrm{Re}\,s > 0$ |
| 108 | $\dfrac{1}{s}\left[\dfrac{(s^2+4)^{\frac{1}{2}}+s}{s(s^2+4)}\right]^{\frac{1}{2}}$ | $2^{\frac{1}{2}}\displaystyle\int_0^t J_0(u)\cos u\,du$ | $\mathrm{Re}\,s > 0$ |
| 109 | $\dfrac{1}{s}\left[\dfrac{(s^2+4)^{\frac{1}{2}}-s}{s(s^2+4)}\right]^{\frac{1}{2}}$ | $-2^{\frac{1}{2}}\displaystyle\int_0^t J_0(u)\sin u\,du$ | $\mathrm{Re}\,s > 0$ |

| | g(s) | f(t) | |
|---|---|---|---|
| 2(Contd.) | | | |
| 110 | $\frac{s[(s^2+a^2)^{\frac{1}{2}}-s]}{(s^2+a^2)^{\frac{1}{2}}}$ | $\frac{a^{\nu+1}}{2}[J_{\nu-1}(at)-J_{\nu+1}(at)]$ | Re $\nu > 0$<br>Re $s > \|\text{Im } a\|$ |
| 111 | $\frac{s[s-(s^2-a^2)^{\frac{1}{2}}]^{\nu}}{(s^2-a^2)^{\frac{1}{2}}}$ | $\frac{a^{\nu+1}}{2}[I_{\nu-1}(at)+I_{\nu+1}(at)]$ | Re $\nu > 0$<br>Re $s > \|\text{Re } a\|$ |
| 112 | $\left(\frac{2}{s}\right)^{\frac{1}{2}} - \left[\frac{s+(s^2+a^2)^{\frac{1}{2}}}{s^2+a^2}\right]^{\frac{1}{2}}$ | $a^{\frac{1}{2}}\mathbf{H}_{\frac{1}{2}}(at)$ | Re $s > \|\text{Im } a\|$ |
| 113 | $\left[\frac{s+(s^2-a^2)^{\frac{1}{2}}}{s^2-a^2}\right]^{\frac{1}{2}} - \left(\frac{2}{s}\right)^{\frac{1}{2}}$ | $a^{\frac{1}{2}}\mathbf{L}_{\frac{1}{2}}(at)$ | Re $s > \|\text{Re } a\|$ |
| 114 | $\frac{1}{2^{\nu-\frac{1}{2}}s^{\nu+\frac{1}{2}}} - \frac{[(s^2+1)^{\frac{1}{2}}-s]^{\nu-\frac{1}{2}}}{(s^2+1)^{\frac{1}{2}}}$ | $\left(\frac{2t}{\pi}\right)^{\frac{1}{2}}\int_0^{\frac{\pi}{2}}\mathbf{H}_{\nu}(t\sin\theta)\sin^{1-\nu}\theta\,d\theta$ | Re $s > 0$ |
| 115 | $\frac{[s-(s^2-1)^{\frac{1}{2}}]^{\nu-\frac{1}{2}}}{(s^2-1)^{\frac{1}{2}}} - \frac{1}{2^{\nu-\frac{1}{2}}s^{\nu+\frac{1}{2}}}$ | $\left(\frac{2t}{\pi}\right)^{\frac{1}{2}}\int_0^{\frac{\pi}{2}}\mathbf{L}_{\nu}(t\sin\theta)\sin^{1-\nu}\theta\,d\theta$ | Re $s > 1$ |
| Functions of $[s\pm\nu(s^2\pm a^2)^{\frac{1}{2}}]$, $[(s^2\pm a^2)^{\frac{1}{2}}\pm s]$ | | | |
| 116 | $[\nu(s^2+a^2)^{\frac{1}{2}}+s][(s^2+a^2)^{\frac{1}{2}}-s]^{\nu}$ | $\frac{a^{\nu}\nu(\nu^2-1)J_{\nu}(at)}{t^2}$ | Re $\nu > 1$<br>Re $s > \|\text{Im } a\|$ |
| 117 | $[s+\nu(s^2-a^2)^{\frac{1}{2}}][s-(s^2-a^2)^{\frac{1}{2}}]^{\nu}$ | $\frac{\nu a^{\nu}(\nu^2-1)I_{\nu}(at)}{t^2}$ | Re $\nu > 1$<br>Re $s > \|\text{Re } a\|$ |
| 118 | $\frac{[\nu(s^2+a^2)^{\frac{1}{2}}+s][(s^2+a^2)^{\frac{1}{2}}-s]^{\nu}}{(s^2+a^2)^{\frac{3}{2}}}$ | $a^{\nu}t\,J_{\nu}(at)$ | Re $\nu > -2$<br>Re $s > \|\text{Im } a\|$ |

| | g(s) | f(t) | |
|---|---|---|---|

2(Contd.)

Integral Forms

| | g(s) | f(t) | |
|---|---|---|---|
| 119 | $\int_{-a}^{a} \frac{du}{[b^2+(s-u)^2]^{\frac{1}{2}}}$ | $\frac{2\sinh(at)}{t} J_0(bt)$ | Re s > Max \| Re a \|, \| Im b \| |
| 120 | $\int_{-a}^{a} \frac{du}{[b^2+(s+iu)^2]^{\frac{1}{2}}}$ | $\frac{2\sin(at)}{t} J_0(bt)$ | Re s > Max \| Im a \|, \| Im b \| |
| 121 | $\int_{-a}^{a} \frac{du}{(a^2-u^2)^{\frac{1}{2}}[b^2+(s+iu)^2]^{\frac{1}{2}}}$ | $\pi J_0(at) J_0(bt)$ | Re s > \| Im a \| + \| Im b \| |
| 122 | $\int_{-a}^{a} \left[\frac{a^2-u^2}{b^2+(s+iu)^2}\right]^{\frac{1}{2}} du$ | $\frac{\pi a}{t} J_0(bt) J_1(at)$ | Re s > \| Im a \| + \| Im b \| |
| 123 | $\int_{-1}^{1} \frac{(1-u^2)^{\nu} du}{[b^2+(s+iau)^2]^{\mu}}$ | $\frac{2^{\mu+\nu}\pi^{\frac{1}{2}}\Gamma(\nu+1)}{a^{\nu+\frac{1}{2}}b^{\mu-\frac{1}{2}}\Gamma(2\mu)} t^{\mu-\nu-1} J_{\nu+\frac{1}{2}}(at) J_{\mu-\frac{1}{2}}(bt)$ | Re $\mu$ > 0<br>Re s > \| Im a \| + \| Im b \| |
| 124 | $\int_{s}^{\infty} \frac{du}{[(u-a)(u-b)(u-c)]^{\frac{1}{2}}}$ | $\frac{1}{\pi^{\frac{1}{2}} t}\left[\frac{e^{at}}{t^{\frac{1}{2}}} * e^{\frac{b+c}{2}t} I_0\left(\frac{b-c}{2}t\right)\right]$ | Re s > Max Re a, Re b, Re c |
| 125 | $\int_{s}^{\infty} \frac{du}{(4u^3-1)^{\frac{1}{2}}}$ | $\frac{\pi^{\frac{1}{2}} {}_0F_2\left[\begin{matrix} ; & \frac{t^3}{108} \\ \frac{7}{6},\frac{5}{6} ; & \end{matrix}\right]}{3\Gamma(\frac{7}{6})\Gamma(\frac{5}{6}) t^{\frac{1}{2}}}$ | Re s > 0 |
| 126 | $\int_{s}^{\infty} \frac{u\,du}{(4u^3-1)^{\frac{1}{2}}}$ | $\frac{\pi^{\frac{1}{2}} {}_0F_2\left[\begin{matrix} ; & \frac{t^3}{108} \\ \frac{5}{6},\frac{1}{6} ; & \end{matrix}\right]}{\Gamma(\frac{5}{6})\Gamma(\frac{1}{6}) t^{\frac{3}{2}}}$ | Re s > 0 |

| | g(s) | f(t) | |
|---|---|---|---|
| 2(Contd.) | | | |
| 127 | $\int_s^\infty \frac{du}{(u^4-a^4)^{\frac{1}{2}}}$ | $\frac{1}{at}[J_0(at)*I_0(at)]$ | Re s > \|Re a\| |

Functions of $s^{\frac{1}{2}}$, $s^{\frac{3}{2}}$, $(s+a)^{\frac{1}{2}}$, $(s+b)$

| | g(s) | f(t) | |
|---|---|---|---|
| 2.1 1 | $\frac{1}{s^{\frac{1}{2}}(s-a)}$ | $a^{-\frac{1}{2}}e^{at}\mathrm{Erf}(a^{\frac{1}{2}}t^{\frac{1}{2}})$ | Re s > Max o, Re a |
| 2 | $\frac{s+a}{s^{\frac{3}{2}}}$ | $\frac{1+2at}{(\pi t)^{\frac{1}{2}}}$ | Re s > o |
| 3 | $\frac{1}{s^{\frac{3}{2}}(s-a)}$ | $a^{-\frac{3}{2}}e^{at}\mathrm{Erf}(a^{\frac{1}{2}}t^{\frac{1}{2}}) - \frac{2t^{\frac{1}{2}}}{a\pi^{\frac{1}{2}}}$ | Re s > Max o, Re a |
| 4 | $\frac{(s+a)^{\frac{1}{2}}}{s+b}$ | $\frac{e^{-at}}{(\pi t)^{\frac{1}{2}}} + (a-b)^{\frac{1}{2}}e^{-bt}\mathrm{Erf}[(a-b)^{\frac{1}{2}}t^{\frac{1}{2}}]$ | Re s > Max − Re a, − Re b |
| 5 | $\frac{1}{(s+a)(s+b)^{\frac{1}{2}}}$ | $\frac{e^{-at}\mathrm{Erf}[(b-a)^{\frac{1}{2}}t^{\frac{1}{2}}]}{(b-a)^{\frac{1}{2}}}$ | Re s > Max − Re a, − Re b |

Functions of $s^{n+\frac{1}{2}}$, $(s+a)^n$, $(s+b)^{n+\frac{1}{2}}$

| | g(s) | f(t) | |
|---|---|---|---|
| 6 | $\frac{(1-s)^n}{s^{n+\frac{1}{2}}}$ | $\frac{(2n)!}{2^n n!(\pi t)^{\frac{1}{2}}}He_{2n}[(2t)^{\frac{1}{2}}]$ | n = 0,1,2,...<br>Re s > o |
| 7 | $\frac{(\frac{1}{2}-s)^n}{s^{n+\frac{1}{2}}}$ | $\frac{2^n}{\pi^{\frac{1}{2}}}\frac{n!}{2n!}t^{-\frac{1}{2}}He_{2n}(t^{\frac{1}{2}})$ | n = 0,1,2,...<br>Re s > o |
| 8 | $\frac{(\frac{1}{2}-s)^n}{s^{n+\frac{3}{2}}}$ | $\frac{2^{n+1}}{\pi^{\frac{1}{2}}}\frac{n!}{(2n+1)!}He_{2n+1}(t^{\frac{1}{2}})$ | n = 0,1,2,...<br>Re s > o |

| | | g(s) | f(t) | |
|---|---|---|---|---|
| 2.1 (Contd.) | 9 | $\frac{(1-s)^n}{s^{n+m+\frac{1}{2}}}$ | $\frac{n!}{\pi^{\frac{1}{2}}4^m(2m+2n)!}\sum_{k=0}^{m} a_k \frac{d^k}{dt^k}\left[t^{k-\frac{1}{2}}H_{2m+2n}(t^{\frac{1}{2}})\right]$ <br> where $a_k$ is defined by <br> $H_{2m}(x) = \sum_{k=o}^{m} a_k x^{2k}$ | $n,m = 0,1,2,\ldots$ <br> $\operatorname{Re} s > o$ |
| | 10 | $\frac{(s-a)^n}{s^{\frac{1}{2}}(s+a)^{n+1}}$ | $\frac{n!}{a^{\frac{1}{2}}2\pi i}\left\{[D_{-n-1}(-i2^{\frac{1}{2}}a^{\frac{1}{2}}t^{\frac{1}{2}})]^2 - D_{-n-1}(i2^{\frac{1}{2}}a^{\frac{1}{2}}t^{\frac{1}{2}})]^2\right\}$ | $n = 0,1,2,\ldots$ <br> $\operatorname{Re} s > o$ |
| | 11 | $\frac{1}{(s+a)^{n+\frac{1}{2}}}$ | $\frac{t^{n-\frac{1}{2}}e^{-at}}{\pi^{\frac{1}{2}}\cdot\frac{1}{2}\cdot\frac{3}{2}\cdots(n-\frac{1}{2})}$ | $n = 1,2,3,\ldots$ <br> $\operatorname{Re} s > -\operatorname{Re} a$ |
| | 12 | $\frac{(s-a)^n}{(s+a)^{n+\frac{1}{2}}}$ | $\frac{D_{2n}(2a^{\frac{1}{2}}t^{\frac{1}{2}})}{(-2)^n\Gamma(n+\frac{1}{2})\,t^{\frac{1}{2}}}$ | $n = 0,1,2,\ldots$ <br> $\operatorname{Re} s > -\operatorname{Re} a$ |
| | 13 | $\frac{(s-a)^n}{(s+a)^{n+\frac{3}{2}}}$ | $\frac{D_{2n+1}(2a^{\frac{1}{2}}t^{\frac{1}{2}})}{2a^{\frac{1}{2}}(-2)^n\Gamma(n+\frac{3}{2})}$ | $n = 0,1,2,\ldots$ <br> $\operatorname{Re} s > -\operatorname{Re} a$ |
| | 14 | $\frac{(s-a)^n}{(s-b)^{n+\frac{1}{2}}}$ | $\frac{(-2)^n}{\pi^{\frac{1}{2}}}\frac{n!}{(2n)!}\frac{e^{bt}}{t^{\frac{1}{2}}}He_{2n}[2^{\frac{1}{2}}(a-b)^{\frac{1}{2}}t^{\frac{1}{2}}]$ | $n = 0,1,2,\ldots$ <br> $\operatorname{Re} s > \operatorname{Re} b$ |
| | 15 | $\frac{(s-a)^n}{(s-b)^{n+\frac{3}{2}}}$ | $(-2)^n\left[\frac{2}{\pi(a-b)}\right]^{\frac{1}{2}}\frac{n!}{(2n+1)!}e^{bt}He_{2n+1}[2^{\frac{1}{2}}(a-b)^{\frac{1}{2}}t^{\frac{1}{2}}]$ | $n = 0,1,2,\ldots$ <br> $\operatorname{Re} s > \operatorname{Re} b$ |

| | | g(s) | f(t) | |
|---|---|---|---|---|
| 2.1 (Contd.) | 16 | $\dfrac{(s-a)^n}{(s-b)^{m+n+\frac{1}{2}}}$ | $\dfrac{(-1)^n e^{bt} 2^n}{(a-b)^m \pi^{\frac{1}{2}} t^{\frac{1}{2}}} \sum_{k=1}^{m} \binom{m}{k} \dfrac{(n+k)!\, 2^k}{(2n+2k)!} \cdot He_{2n+2k}[2^{\frac{1}{2}}(a-b)^{\frac{1}{2}} t^{\frac{1}{2}}]$ | $n=0,1,2,\ldots$ <br> $m=1,2,3,\ldots$ <br> $\mathrm{Re}\, s > \mathrm{Re}\, b$ |
| 17 | 17 | $\dfrac{(s-a)^n}{(s-b)^{m+n+\frac{3}{2}}}$ | $\dfrac{(-1)^n e^{bt} 2^{n+\frac{1}{2}}}{(a-b)^m \pi^{\frac{1}{2}}} \sum_{k=1}^{m} \binom{m}{k} \dfrac{(n+k)!\, 2^k}{(2n+2k+1)!} \cdot He_{2n+2k+1}[2^{\frac{1}{2}}(a-b)^{\frac{1}{2}} t^{\frac{1}{2}}]$ | $n=0,1,2,\ldots$ <br> $m=1,2,3,\ldots$ <br> $\mathrm{Re}\, s > \mathrm{Re}\, b$ |

Functions of $s^n$, $s^{n+\nu}$, $(s+a)^n$, $(s+b)^{n+\nu}$

| | | g(s) | f(t) | |
|---|---|---|---|---|
| | 18 | $\dfrac{s^n}{(s+a)^{n+\nu}}$ | $\dfrac{n!}{\Gamma(n+\nu)} e^{-at} t^{\nu-1} L_n^{\nu-1}(at)$ | $\mathrm{Re}\, \nu > 0$ <br> $n=0,1,2,\ldots$ <br> $\mathrm{Re}\, s > -\mathrm{Re}\, a$ |
| | 19 | $\dfrac{(s-a)^n}{s^{n+\nu}}$ | $\dfrac{n!\, t^{\nu-1}}{\Gamma(n+\nu)} L_n^{\nu-1}(at)$ <br> $= (-1)^n a^{1-\nu} n!\, T_{\nu-1}^{(n)}(at)$ <br> $= \dfrac{t^{\frac{\nu}{2}-1} e^{\frac{at}{2}} M_{n+\frac{\nu}{2}, \frac{\nu-1}{2}}(at)}{a^{\frac{\nu}{2}} \Gamma(\nu)}$ | $\mathrm{Re}\, \nu > 0$ <br> $n=0,1,2,\ldots$ <br> $\mathrm{Re}\, s > 0$ |
| | 20 | $\dfrac{(s-a)^n}{(s-b)^{n+\nu}}$ | $\dfrac{n!}{\Gamma(n+\nu)} t^{\nu-1} e^{bt} L_n^{\nu-1}[(a-b)t]$ | $\mathrm{Re}\, \nu > 0$ <br> $n=0,1,2,\ldots$ <br> $\mathrm{Re}\, s > \mathrm{Re}\, b$ |
| | 21 | $\dfrac{1}{(s-b)(s+a)^{\nu}}$ | $\dfrac{e^{bt} \gamma[\nu,(a+b)t]}{\Gamma(\nu)(a+b)^{\nu}}$ | $\mathrm{Re}\, \nu > 0$ <br> $\mathrm{Re}\, s > \mathrm{Max}\ \mathrm{Re}\, b, -\mathrm{Re}\, a$ |

| | | g(s) | f(t) | |
|---|---|---|---|---|
| 2.1 (Contd.) | 22 | $\dfrac{[1+(a-1)s]^n}{s^{\mu}(1+as)^{n+\nu}}$ | $\dfrac{n!\,t^{\frac{\mu+\nu-1}{2}}}{\Gamma(n+\nu)}\displaystyle\int_0^{\infty} e^{-au} J_{\mu+\nu-1}[2(tu)^{\frac{1}{2}}] \,.$ $\cdot\, L_n^{\nu-1}(u)\, u^{\frac{\nu-\mu-1}{2}}\, du$ | $Re(\mu+\nu) > o$<br>$Re\,\nu > o$<br>$Re\, s > Max\, o,\ -Re\,\frac{1}{a}$ |

Functions of $s^{\frac{1}{2}}$, s, $(s+a)^{\frac{1}{2}}$, (s+b)

| | | | |
|---|---|---|---|
| 23 | $\dfrac{1}{(s^{\frac{1}{2}}+a)^2}$ | $1-\dfrac{2at^{\frac{1}{2}}}{\pi^{\frac{1}{2}}}+(1-2a^2t)e^{a^2t}[Erf(at^{\frac{1}{2}})-1]$ | Re s > o if Re a ⩾ o<br>Re s > Max o, Re $a^2$ if Re a < |
| 24 | $\dfrac{1}{(s^{\frac{1}{2}}+a)^3}$ | $\dfrac{2(a^2t+1)t^{\frac{1}{2}}}{\pi^{\frac{1}{2}}} - at\,e^{a^2t}(2a^2t+3)\,.$ $Erfc(at^{\frac{1}{2}})$ | Re s > o if Re a ⩾ o<br>Re s > Max o, Re $a^2$ if Re a < |
| 25 | $\dfrac{1}{(s^{\frac{1}{2}}+a)^4}$ | $\frac{t}{3}(4a^4t^2+12a^2t+3)e^{a^2t}Erfc(at^{\frac{1}{2}})$ $-\dfrac{2a^3}{3\pi^{\frac{1}{2}}}\,t^{\frac{5}{2}}(2a^2t+5)$ | Re s > o if Re a ⩾ o<br>Re s > Max o, Re $a^2$ if Re a < |
| 26 | $\dfrac{1}{s^{\frac{1}{2}}(s^{\frac{1}{2}}+a)^2}$ | $\dfrac{2t^{\frac{1}{2}}}{\pi^{\frac{1}{2}}}-2at\,e^{a^2t}Erfc(at^{\frac{1}{2}})$ | Re s > o if Re a ⩾ o<br>Re s > Max o, Re $a^2$ if Re a < |
| 27 | $\dfrac{1}{s(s^{\frac{1}{2}}+a)^2}$ | $\dfrac{1}{a^2}+(2t-\dfrac{1}{a^2})e^{a^2t}Erfc(at^{\frac{1}{2}})$ $-\dfrac{2t^{\frac{1}{2}}}{\pi^{\frac{1}{2}}a}$ | Re s > o if Re a ⩾ o<br>Re s > Max o, Re $a^2$ if Re a < |
| 28 | $\dfrac{1}{s^{\frac{1}{2}}(s^{\frac{1}{2}}+a)^3}$ | $(2at^2+1)t\,e^{a^2t}Erfc(at^{\frac{1}{2}})-\dfrac{2at^{\frac{3}{2}}}{\pi^{\frac{1}{2}}}$ | Re s > o if Re a ⩾ o<br>Re s > Max o, Re $a^2$ if Re a < |

| | | g(s) | f(t) | |
|---|---|---|---|---|
| 2.1 (Contd.) | 29 | $\frac{1}{s(s^{\frac{1}{2}}+a)^3}$ | $\frac{1}{a^3} - (2at^2 - \frac{t}{a} + \frac{1}{a^3})e^{a^2 t}\text{Erfc}(at^{\frac{1}{2}}) + 2(\frac{t}{\pi})^{\frac{1}{2}}(t - \frac{1}{a^2})$ | Re s > o if Re a ⩾ o<br>Re s > Max o, Re $a^2$ if Re a < o |
| | 30 | $\frac{s^{\frac{1}{2}}}{(s^{\frac{1}{2}}+a)^3}$ | $(2a^4 t^2 + 5a^2 t+1)e^{a^2 t}\text{Erfc}(at^{\frac{1}{2}}) - \frac{2at^{\frac{1}{2}}}{\pi^{\frac{1}{2}}}(a^2 t+2)$ | Re s > o if Re a ⩾ o<br>Re s > Max o, Re $a^2$ if Re a < o |
| | 31 | $\frac{1}{s}\left(\frac{s^{\frac{1}{2}}-a}{s^{\frac{1}{2}}+a}\right)^2$ | $1+8a^2 t\, e^{a^2 t}\text{Erfc}(at^{\frac{1}{2}}) - \frac{8at^{\frac{1}{2}}}{\pi^{\frac{1}{2}}}$ | Re s > o if Re a ⩾ o<br>Re s > Max o, Re $a^2$ if Re a < o |
| | 32 | $\frac{1}{s}\left(\frac{s^{\frac{1}{2}}-a}{s^{\frac{1}{2}}+a}\right)^3$ | $2(8a^4 t^2 + 8a^2 t+1)e^{a^2 t}\text{Erfc}(at^{\frac{1}{2}}) - \frac{8at^{\frac{1}{2}}}{\pi^{\frac{1}{2}}}(2a^2 t+1)-1$ | Re s > o if Re a ⩾ o<br>Re s > Max o, Re $a^2$ if Re a < o |
| | 33 | $\frac{1}{s^{\frac{1}{2}}(s^{\frac{1}{2}}+a)(s-b^2)}$ | $\frac{e^{a^2 t}\text{Erfc}(at^{\frac{1}{2}})}{a^2-b^2} + \frac{a\, e^{b^2 t}\text{Erf}(bt^{\frac{1}{2}})}{b(a^2-b^2)} - \frac{e^{b^2 t}}{a^2-b^2}$ | Re s > Max o, Re $b^2$ if Re a ⩾ o<br>Re s > Max o, Re $b^2$, Re $a^2$ if Re a < o |
| | 34 | $\frac{s^{\frac{1}{2}}}{(s^{\frac{1}{2}}+a)(s-b^2)}$ | $\frac{a^2}{a^2-b^2}e^{a^2 t}\text{Erfc}(at^{\frac{1}{2}}) + \frac{ab}{a^2-b^2}e^{b^2 t}\text{Erfc}(bt^{\frac{1}{2}}) - \frac{b^2}{a^2-b^2}e^{b^2 t}$ | Re s > Max o, Re $b^2$ if Re a ⩾ o<br>Re s > Max o, Re $b^2$, Re $a^2$ if Re a < o |

Functions Involving $[(s^2 \pm a^2)^{\frac{1}{2}} \pm s]$

| | | | |
|---|---|---|---|
| 35 | $[(s^2+a^2)^{\frac{1}{2}}-s]^n$ | $\frac{a^n n}{t} J_n(at)$ | n = 1,2,3,...<br>Re s > \|Im a\| |

| | | g(s) | f(t) | |
|---|---|---|---|---|
| 2.1 (Contd.) | 36 | $[s-(s^2-a^2)^{\frac{1}{2}}]^n$ | $\frac{n a^n I_n(at)}{t}$ | $n=1,2,3,\ldots$ <br> $\text{Re } s > \lvert \text{Re } a \rvert$ |
| | 37 | $(s^2+a^2)^{\frac{m-1}{2}}[(s^2+a^2)^{\frac{1}{2}}-s]^n$ | $\frac{1}{\pi} a^{m+n}\int_0^{\pi}(\cos u)^m \cos(nu-at\sin u)\,du$ | $n>m-1$ <br> $n,m=0,1,2,\ldots$ <br> $\text{Re } s > \lvert \text{Im } a \rvert$ |
| | 38 | $\frac{[s+\nu(s^2-a^2)^{\frac{1}{2}}][s-(s^2-a^2)^{\frac{1}{2}}]^{\nu}}{(s^2-a^2)^{\frac{3}{2}}}$ | $a^{\nu} t I_{\nu}(at)$ | $\text{Re } \nu > -2$ <br> $\text{Re } s > \lvert \text{Re } a \rvert$ |
| | 39 | $\left\{\nu^2-1+\frac{3s[s+\nu(s^2+a^2)^{\frac{1}{2}}]}{s^2+a^2}\right\}\frac{[(s^2+a^2)^{\frac{1}{2}}-s]^{\nu}}{(s^2+a^2)^{\frac{3}{2}}}$ | $a^{\nu} t^2 J_{\nu}(at)$ | $\text{Re } \nu > -3$ <br> $\text{Re } s > \lvert \text{Im } a \rvert$ |
| Miscellaneous | | | | |
| | 40 | $\frac{1-(\frac{a}{s})^{\nu}}{s-a}$ | $e^{at}\frac{\Gamma(\nu,at)}{\Gamma(\nu)}$ | $\text{Re } \nu > -1$ <br> $\text{Re } s > 0$ |
| | 41 | $\frac{s+a}{(s^2-b^2)(s+c)^{\nu}}$ | $\frac{1}{2\Gamma(\nu)}\left\{(1+\frac{a}{b})\, e^{bt}\frac{\gamma[\nu,(b+c)t]}{(b+c)^{\nu}} + (1-\frac{a}{b})\, e^{-bt}\frac{\gamma[\nu,(c-b)t]}{(c-b)^{\nu}}\right\}$ | $\text{Re } \nu > 0$ <br> $\text{Re } s > \text{Max} - \text{Re } c, \lvert \text{Re } b \rvert$ |
| | 42 | $\frac{1}{s^{\nu}(2s^2-2as+a^2)}$ | $t^{\nu+1}\sum_{k=0}^{\infty}\frac{(-1)^k (2k)!\, L_{2k}^{(\nu+1)}(2at)}{\Gamma(2k+\nu+2)}$ | $\text{Re } \nu > -2$ <br> $\text{Re } s > \text{Max } 0, \text{Re } \frac{a}{2} + \lvert \text{Im } \frac{a}{2} \rvert$ |
| Functions of $e^{-as}$ and s Only | | | | |
| 3 | 1 | $e^{-as}$ | $\delta(t-a)$ | $a \geq 0$ <br> $\text{Re } s > 0$ |

| | | $g(s)$ | $f(t)$ | |
|---|---|---|---|---|
| 3(Contd.) | 2 | $\frac{e^{-as}}{s}$ | $0 \quad 0 < t < a$<br>$1 \quad t > a$ | $a \geq 0$<br>$\text{Re } s > 0$ |

Functions Containing s and One Term Only of the Type $(e^{\pm as} \pm b)$ or $(e^{-as} - e^{-bs})$

| | | $g(s)$ | $f(t)$ | |
|---|---|---|---|---|
| | 3 | $\frac{1}{s(e^{as}+1)}$ | $0 \quad 2na < t < (2n+1)a$<br>$1 \quad (2n+1)a < t < (2n+2)a$ | $a \geq 0$<br>$\text{Re } s > 0$<br>$n = 0, 1, 2, \ldots$ |
| | 4 | $\frac{1}{s(1+e^{-as})}$ | $1 \quad 2na < t < (2n+1)a$<br>$0 \quad (2n+1)a < t < (2n+2)a$ | $a \geq 0$<br>$\text{Re } s > 0$<br>$n = 0, 1, 2, \ldots$ |
| | 5 | $\frac{1}{s(e^{s}-1)}$ | $[t]$ | $\text{Re } s > 0$ |
| | 6 | $\frac{1}{s(e^{as}-1)}$ | $n \quad na < t < (n+1)a$ | $a > 0$<br>$\text{Re } s > 0$<br>$n = 0, 1, 2, \ldots$ |
| | 7 | $\frac{1}{s(e^{bs}-a)}$ | $\frac{1-a^{n}}{1-a} \quad nb < t < (n+1)b$ | $b > 0$<br>$\text{Re } s > \text{Max } 0, \frac{1}{b} \text{Re}(\log a)$<br>$n = 0, 1, 2, \ldots$ |
| | 8 | $\frac{1}{s(1-e^{-as})}$ | $n+1 \quad na < t < (n+1)a$ | $a > 0$<br>$\text{Re } s > 0$<br>$n = 0, 1, 2, \ldots$ |
| | 9 | $\frac{1-e^{-as}}{s}$ | $1 \quad 0 < t < a$<br>$0 \quad t > a$ | $a > 0$<br>$\text{Re } s > -\infty$ |
| | 10 | $\frac{e^{-as}-e^{-bs}}{s}$ | $0 \quad 0 < t < a$<br>$1 \quad a < t < b$<br>$0 \quad t > b$ | $0 \leq a < b$<br>$\text{Re } s > -\infty$ |

| | $g(s)$ | $f(t)$ | |
|---|---|---|---|

3(Contd.)

Functions Containing s and Two Terms of the Type $(e^{\pm as} \pm b)$ or $(e^{\pm as} - e^{-bs})$

| | $g(s)$ | $f(t)$ | |
|---|---|---|---|
| 11 | $\frac{1}{s(e^{s}-1)(e^{s}-a)}$ | $\left[\frac{a^{t}-1}{(a-1)^2}\right] - \left[\frac{t}{a-1}\right]$ | Re s > Max o, Re(log a) |
| 12 | $\frac{e^{s}-1}{s(e^{s}-a)}$ | $[a^{t}]$ | Re s > Re(log a) |
| 13 | $\frac{1-e^{-bs}}{s(1-e^{-as})}$ | 1   $na < t < na+b$<br>0   $na+b < t < (n+1)a$ | $o < b < a$<br>Re s > −∞<br>$n = 0,1,2,\ldots$ |
| 14 | $\frac{1-e^{-as}}{s(1+e^{-as})}$ | 1   $2n\,a < t < (2n+1)a$<br>−1   $(2n+1)a < t < (2n+2)a$ | $a > o$<br>Re s > o<br>$n = 0,1,2,\ldots$ |
| 15 | $\frac{1-e^{-as}}{s(1+e^{as})}$ | 0   $0 < t < a$<br>1   $(2n+1)a < t < (2n+2)a$<br>−1   $(2n+2)a < t < (2n+3)a$ | $a > o$<br>Re s > o<br>$n = 0,1,2,\ldots$ |
| 16 | $\frac{1-e^{-as}}{s(e^{as}-e^{-as})}$ | 0   $2na < t < (2n+1)a$<br>1   $(4n+1)a < t < (4n+2)a$<br>−1   $(4n+3)a < t < (4n+4)a$ | $a > o$<br>Re s > o<br>$n = 0,1,2,\ldots$ |
| 17 | $\frac{4-e^{-as}}{s(2+e^{-as})}$ | $1+(-1)^n 2^{-n}$   $na < t < (n+1)a$ | $a > o$<br>Re s > o<br>$n = 0,1,2,\ldots$ |
| 18 | $\frac{(1-e^{-as})^2}{s}$ | 1   $0 < t < a$<br>−1   $a < t < 2a$<br>0   $t > 2a$ | $a > o$<br>Re s > −∞ |

| | | g(s) | f(t) | |
|---|---|---|---|---|
| 3(Contd.) | 19 | $\frac{(e^{-as}-e^{-bs})^2}{s}$ | $0 \quad 0 < t < 2a$<br>$1 \quad 2a < t < a+b$<br>$-1 \quad a+b < t < 2b$<br>$0 \quad t > 2b$ | $0 \leqslant a < b$<br>Re $s > -\infty$ |

Functions Containing s and Three Terms of the Type $(e^s \pm a)$

| | | | | |
|---|---|---|---|---|
| | 20 | $\frac{e^s+1}{s(e^s-1)^2}$ | $\left[ t^2 \right.$ | Re $s > 0$ |
| | 21 | $\frac{e^s-1}{s(e^s-a)^2}$ | $\left[ t\,a^{t-1} \right.$ | Re $s >$ Re(log a) |
| | 22 | $\frac{e^s-1}{s(e^s-a)(e^s-b)}$ | $\left[ \frac{a^t-b^t}{a-b} \right.$ | $a \neq b$<br>Re $s >$ Max Re(log a), Re(log b ) |

Functions Containing s and Four or Five Terms of the Type $(e^s \pm a)$

| | | | | |
|---|---|---|---|---|
| | 23 | $\frac{e^s-1}{s(e^s-a)^3}$ | $\frac{1}{2}\left[ t(t-1)a^{t-2} \right.$ | Re $s >$ Re(log a) |
| | 24 | $\frac{c^s-1}{s} \cdot \frac{e^s-(a+b)}{(e^s-a)(e^s-b)}$ | $-\frac{ab}{a-b}\left[ a^{t-1}-b^{t-1} \right.$ | $a \neq b$<br>Re $s >$ Max Re(log a), Re(log b) |
| | 25 | $\frac{(e^s-1)[(c-d)e^s-cb+da]}{s(e^s-a)(e^s-b)}$ | $\left[ c a^t - d b^t \right.$ | Re $s >$ Max Re(log a), Re(log b) |
| | 26 | $\frac{(e^s-1)(e^s+a)}{s(e^s-a)^3}$ | $\left[ t^2 a^{t-1} \right.$ | Re $s >$ Re(log a) |

Functions Containing a Term of the Type $(e^{as}-b)^n$

| | | | | |
|---|---|---|---|---|
| | 27 | $\frac{1}{s(e^s-1)^n}$ | $\left[ \binom{t}{n} \right.$ | $n = 0,1,2,\ldots$<br>Re $s > 0$ |

| | | g(s) | f(t) | |
|---|---|---|---|---|
| 3(Contd.) | 28 | $\frac{e^{as}}{s(e^{s}-1)^{n}}$ | $\left[\frac{\Gamma(t+a+1)}{n!\,\Gamma(t+a+1-n)}\right.$ | $n=0,1,2,\ldots$<br>$a \leqslant n$<br>$\mathrm{Re}\, s > 0$ |
| | 29 | $\frac{e^{-as}}{s(e^{as}-1)^{m}}$ | $\binom{n}{m}$  $na < t < (n+1)a$ | $a > 0$<br>$m=0,1,2,\ldots$<br>$\mathrm{Re}\, s > 0$<br>$n=0,1,2,\ldots$ |
| | 30 | $\frac{e^{s}-1}{s(e^{s}-a)^{n+1}}$ | $\left[\binom{t}{n} n^{t-n}\right.$ | $n=0,1,2,\ldots$<br>$\mathrm{Re}\, s > \mathrm{Re}(\log a)$ |

Functions Containing $e^{\pm\frac{a}{s}}$

| | | | | |
|---|---|---|---|---|
| | 31 | $\frac{e^{\frac{a}{s}}}{s}$ | $I_0(2a^{\frac{1}{2}}t^{\frac{1}{2}})$ | $\mathrm{Re}\, s > 0$ |
| | 32 | $\frac{e^{-\frac{a}{s}}}{s}$ | $J_0(2a^{\frac{1}{2}}t^{\frac{1}{2}})$ | $\mathrm{Re}\, s > 0$ |
| | 33 | $e^{\frac{a}{s}}-1$ | $(\frac{a}{t})^{\frac{1}{2}} I_1(2a^{\frac{1}{2}}t^{\frac{1}{2}})$ | $\mathrm{Re}\, s > 0$ |
| | 34 | $1-e^{-\frac{a}{s}}$ | $(\frac{a}{t})^{\frac{1}{2}} J_1(2a^{\frac{1}{2}}t^{\frac{1}{2}})$ | $\mathrm{Re}\, s > 0$ |
| | 35 | $\frac{1}{s(1-e^{-\frac{1}{s}})}$ | $\sum_{n=0}^{\infty} J_0(2n^{\frac{1}{2}}t^{\frac{1}{2}})$ | $\mathrm{Re}\, s > 0$ |

Miscellaneous

| | | | | |
|---|---|---|---|---|
| | 36 | $\frac{e^{-bs}-e^{-cs}+e^{-as}-e^{-ds}}{s(1-e^{-as})}$ | $0$  $na < t < na+b$ and $na+c < t < na+d$<br>$1$  $na+b < t < na+c$<br>$-1$  $na+d < t < (n+1)a$ | $a > d > c > b \geqslant 0$<br>$\mathrm{Re}\, s > 0$<br>$n=0,1,2,\ldots$ |

| | | g(s) | f(t) | | |
|---|---|---|---|---|---|
| 3(Contd.) | 37 | $\dfrac{e^{2s}+4e^{s}+1}{s(e^{s}-1)^{3}}$ | $\Big\lceil t^{3}$ | | Re s > o |
| | 38 | $\dfrac{e^{3s}+11e^{2s}+11e^{s}+1}{s(e^{s}-1)^{4}}$ | $\Big\lceil t^{4}$ | | Re s > o |
| | 39 | $\dfrac{e^{s}-1}{s(e^{2s}-2e^{s}\cos a+1)}$ | $\Big\lceil \dfrac{\sin(at)}{\sin a}$ | | Re s > \|Im a\| |
| | 40 | $\dfrac{e^{s}-1}{s(e^{2s}-2ae^{s}\cos b+a^{2})}$ | $\dfrac{1}{a\sin b}\Big\lceil a^{t}\sin(bt)$ | | Re s > Re(log a) + \|Im b\| |
| | 41 | $\dfrac{(e^{s}-1)(e^{s}-\cos a)}{s(e^{2s}-2e^{s}\cos a+1)}$ | $\Big\lceil \cos(at)$ | | Re s > \|Im a\| |
| | 42 | $\dfrac{(e^{s}-1)(e^{s}-a\cos b)}{s(e^{2s}-2ae^{s}\cos b+a^{2})}$ | $\Big\lceil a^{t}\cos(bt)$ | | Re s > Re(log a) + \|Im b\| |
| | 43 | $\dfrac{1-e^{-bs}}{(-b)^{m}s}\dfrac{d^{m}}{ds^{m}}\left(\dfrac{1}{1-e^{-bs}}\right)$ | $n^{m}$ | $nb < t < (n+1)b$ | b > o<br>m = 0,1,2,...<br>Re s > o<br>n = 0,1,2,... |

Functions Containing $e^{-as}$ Only

| | | | | | |
|---|---|---|---|---|---|
| 3.1 | 1 | $\dfrac{e^{-as}}{s+b}$ | 0<br>$e^{-b(t-a)}$ | $0 < t < a$<br>$t > a$ | a > o<br>Re s > - Re b |
| | 2 | $\dfrac{e^{-as}}{s(s+b)}$ | 0<br>$\dfrac{1-e^{-b(t-a)}}{b}$ | $0 < t < a$<br>$t > a$ | Re s > Max o, - Re b |

3.1 (Contd.)

| | g(s) | f(t) | | |
|---|---|---|---|---|
| 3 | $\frac{s+c}{s^2+b^2}e^{-as}$ | $0$ <br> $\cos[b(t-a)]+\frac{c}{b}\sin[b(t-a)]$ | $0<t<a$ <br> $t>a$ | $a>0$ <br> $\mathrm{Re}\, s>\lvert\mathrm{Im}\, b\rvert$ |
| 4 | $\frac{s+c}{s^2-b^2}e^{-as}$ | $0$ <br> $\cosh[b(t-a)]+\frac{c}{b}\sinh[b(t-a)]$ | $0<t<a$ <br> $t>a$ | $a>0$ <br> $\mathrm{Re}\, s>\lvert\mathrm{Re}\, b\rvert$ |
| 5 | $\left(\frac{a}{s}+\frac{1}{s^2}\right)e^{-as}$ | $0$ <br> $t$ | $0<t<a$ <br> $t>a$ | $a\geqslant 0$ <br> $\mathrm{Re}\, s>0$ |
| 6 | $\left(\frac{2}{s^3}+\frac{2a}{s^2}+\frac{a^2}{s}\right)e^{-as}$ | $0$ <br> $t^2$ | $0<t<a$ <br> $t>a$ | $a>0$ <br> $\mathrm{Re}\, s>0$ |
| 7 | $\frac{e^{-as}+as-1}{s^2}$ | $a-t$ <br> $0$ | $0<t<a$ <br> $t>a$ | $a>0$ <br> $\mathrm{Re}\, s>-\infty$ |
| 8 | $e^{-\frac{\pi}{2}s}\frac{\frac{\pi}{2}(s^2+1)+2s}{(s^2+1)^2}$ | $0$ <br> $-t\cos t$ | $0<t<\frac{\pi}{2}$ <br> $t>\frac{\pi}{2}$ | $\mathrm{Re}\, s>0$ |
| 9 | $\frac{e^{-\frac{\pi}{2}s}}{(1+s^2)^2}\left[\frac{\pi}{2}s(1+s^2)+s^2-1\right]$ | $0$ <br> $t\sin t$ | $0<t<\frac{\pi}{2}$ <br> $t>\frac{\pi}{2}$ | $\mathrm{Re}\, s>0$ |
| 10 | $\frac{2s-e^{-\frac{\pi}{2}s}\left[\frac{\pi}{2}s(1+s^2)+s^2-1\right]}{(1+s^2)^2}$ | $t\sin t$ <br> $0$ | $0<t<\frac{\pi}{2}$ <br> $t>\frac{\pi}{2}$ | $\mathrm{Re}\, s>-\infty$ |
| 11 | $\frac{s^2-1+e^{-\frac{\pi}{2}s}\left[\frac{\pi}{2}(s^2+1)+2s\right]}{(s^2+1)^2}$ | $t\cos t$ <br> $0$ | $0<t<\frac{\pi}{2}$ <br> $t>\frac{\pi}{2}$ | $\mathrm{Re}\, s>-\infty$ |

| | | $g(s)$ | $f(t)$ | | |
|---|---|---|---|---|---|
| 3.1 (Contd.) | 12 | $\dfrac{e^{-\frac{\pi}{2}s}}{s(s^2+2^2)(s^2+4^2)\ldots(s^2+4n^2)}$ | $0$ | $0<t<\frac{\pi}{2}$ | $n=1,2,3,\ldots$ Re $s>0$ |
| | | | $\dfrac{\cos^{2n}t}{(2n)!}$ | $t>\frac{\pi}{2}$ | |
| | 13 | $\dfrac{e^{-\frac{\pi}{2}s}}{[s^2+1^2][s^2+3^2]\ldots[s^2+(2n+1)^2]}$ | $0$ | $0<t<\frac{\pi}{2}$ | $n=0,1,2,\ldots$ Re $s>0$ |
| | | | $-\dfrac{\cos^{2n+1}t}{(2n+1)!}$ | $t>\frac{\pi}{2}$ | |
| | 14 | $\dfrac{1-e^{-\frac{\pi}{2}s}\left\{1+\frac{s^2}{2!}+\ldots+\frac{s^2[s^2+2^2]\ldots[s^2+(2n-2)^2]}{(2n)!}\right\}}{s[s^2+2^2][s^2+4^2]\ldots[s^2+(2n)^2]}$ | $\dfrac{\sin^{2n}t}{(2n)!}$ | $0<t<\frac{\pi}{2}$ | $n=1,2,3,\ldots$ Re $s>-\infty$ |
| | | | $0$ | $t>\frac{\pi}{2}$ | |
| | 15 | $\dfrac{1-se^{-\frac{\pi}{2}s}\left\{1+\frac{s^2+1^2}{3!}+\ldots+\frac{[s^2+1^2][s^2+3^2]\ldots[s^2+(2n-1)^2]}{(2n+1)!}\right\}}{[s^2+1^2][s^2+3^2]\ldots[s^2+(2n+1)^2]}$ | $\dfrac{\sin^{2n+1}t}{(2n+1)!}$ | $0<t<\frac{\pi}{2}$ | $n=1,2,3,\ldots$ Re $s>-\infty$ |
| | | | $0$ | $t>\frac{\pi}{2}$ | |
| | 16 | $\dfrac{e^{-\frac{\pi}{2}s}+s\left\{1+\frac{s^2+1^2}{3!}+\ldots+\frac{[s^2+1^2][s^2+3^2]\ldots[s^2+(2n-1)^2]}{(2n+1)!}\right\}}{[s^2+1^2][s^2+3^2]\ldots[s^2+(2n+1)^2]}$ | $\dfrac{\cos^{2n+1}t}{(2n+1)!}$ | $0<t<\frac{\pi}{2}$ | $n=1,2,3,\ldots$ Re $s>-\infty$ |
| | | | $0$ | $t>\frac{\pi}{2}$ | |
| | 17 | $\dfrac{-e^{-\frac{\pi}{2}s}+1+\frac{s^2}{2!}+\ldots+\frac{s^2[s^2+2^2]\ldots[s^2+4(n-1)^2]}{(2n)!}}{s(s^2+2^2)(s^2+4^2)\ldots(s^2+4n^2)}$ | $\cos^{2n}t$ | $0<t<\frac{\pi}{2}$ | $n=1,2,3,\ldots$ Re $s>-\infty$ |
| | | | $0$ | $t>\frac{\pi}{2}$ | |
| | 18 | $\dfrac{1+\frac{s^2}{2!}+\frac{s^2[s+2^2]}{4!}+\ldots+\frac{s^2[s^2+2]\ldots[s^2+(2n-2)^2]}{(2n)!}}{e^{\frac{\pi}{2}s}s[s^2+2^2][s^2+4^2]\ldots[s^2+(2n)^2]}$ | $0$ | $0<t<\frac{\pi}{2}$ | $n=1,2,3,\ldots$ Re $s>0$ |
| | | | $\dfrac{\sin^{2n}t}{(2n)!}$ | $t>\frac{\pi}{2}$ | |

| | | g(s) | f(t) | | |
|---|---|---|---|---|---|
| 3.1 (Contd.) | 19 | $\dfrac{se^{-\frac{\pi}{2}s}\left\{1+\dfrac{s^2+1^2}{3!}+\dots+\dfrac{(s^2+1^2)(s^2+3^2)\dots[s^2+(2n-1)^2]}{(2n+1)!}\right\}}{[s^2+1^2][s^2+3^2]\dots[s^2+(2n+1)^2]}$ | $0$ | $0<t<\frac{\pi}{2}$ | $n=0,1,2,\dots$ Re $s>0$ |
| | | | $\dfrac{\sin^{2n+1}t}{(2n+1)!}$ | $t>\frac{\pi}{2}$ | |
| | 20 | $e^{-as}\sum_{m=0}^{n}\dfrac{1}{m!}\dfrac{a^m}{s^{n-m+1}}$ | $0$ | $0<t<a$ | $a>0$ $n=0,1,2,\dots$ |
| | | | $\dfrac{t^n}{n!}$ | $t>a$ | Re $s>0$ |
| | 21 | $\dfrac{1}{s^{n+1}}-e^{-as}\sum_{m=0}^{n}\dfrac{1}{m!}\dfrac{a^m}{s^{n-m+1}}$ | $\dfrac{t^n}{n!}$ | $0<t<a$ | $a>0$ $n=0,1,2,\dots$ |
| | | | $0$ | $t>a$ | Re $s>-\infty$ |
| | 22 | $\dfrac{e^{-as}[c\cos(ac)+s\sin(ac)]-e^{-bs}[c\cos(bc)+s\sin(bc)]}{s^2+c^2}$ | $0$ | $0<t<a$ | $0\leqslant a<b$ Re $s>-\infty$ |
| | | | $\sin(ct)$ | $a<t<b$ | |
| | | | $0$ | $t>b$ | |
| | 23 | $\dfrac{e^{-as}[s\cos(ac)-c\sin(ac)]-e^{-bs}[s\cos(bc)-c\cos(bc)]}{s^2+c^2}$ | $0$ | $0<t<a$ | $0\leqslant a<b$ Re $s>-\infty$ |
| | | | $\cos(ct)$ | $a<t<b$ | |
| | | | $0$ | $t>b$ | |
| | 24 | $\dfrac{e^{-as}[c\cosh(ac)+s\sinh(ac)]-e^{-bs}[c\cosh(bc)+s\sinh(bc)]}{s^2-c^2}$ | $0$ | $0<t<a$ | $0\leqslant a<b$ Re $s>-\infty$ |
| | | | $\sinh(ct)$ | $a<t<b$ | |
| | | | $0$ | $t>b$ | |
| | 25 | $\dfrac{e^{-as}[s\cosh(ac)+c\sinh(ac)]-e^{-bs}[s\cosh(bc)+c\sinh(bc)]}{s^2-c^2}$ | $0$ | $0<t<a$ | $0\leqslant a<b$ Re $s>-\infty$ |
| | | | $\cosh(ct)$ | $a<t<b$ | |
| | | | $0$ | $t>b$ | |

3.1 (Contd.)

| | g(s) | f(t) | | |
|---|---|---|---|---|
| 26 | $\frac{e^{-as}}{s^2+4c^2}\left[\frac{2c^2}{s}+s\sin^2(ac)+c\sin(2ac)\right] - \frac{e^{-bs}}{s^2+4c^2}\left[\frac{2c^2}{s}+s\sin^2(bc)+c\sin(2bc)\right]$ | $0$<br>$\sin^2(ct)$<br>$0$ | $0<t<a$<br>$a<t<b$<br>$t>b$ | $0\leq a<b$<br>$\text{Re } s>-\infty$ |
| 27 | $\frac{e^{-as}}{s^2+4c^2}\left[\frac{2c^2}{s}+s\cos^2(ac)-c\sin(2ac)\right] - \frac{e^{-bs}}{s^2+4c^2}\left[\frac{2c^2}{s}+s\cos^2(bc)-c\sin(2bc)\right]$ | $0$<br>$\cos^2(ct)$<br>$0$ | $0<t<a$<br>$a<t<b$<br>$t>b$ | $0\leq a<b$<br>$\text{Re } s>-\infty$ |
| 28 | $\frac{e^{-as}}{s^2-4c^2}\left[s\sinh^2(ac)+\frac{2c^2}{s}+c\sinh(2ac)\right] - \frac{e^{-bs}}{s^2-4c^2}\left[s\sinh^2(bc)+\frac{2c^2}{s}+c\sinh(2bc)\right]$ | $0$<br>$\sinh^2(ct)$<br>$0$ | $0<t<a$<br>$a<t<b$<br>$t>b$ | $0\leq a<b$<br>$\text{Re } s>-\infty$ |
| 29 | $\frac{e^{-as}}{s^2-4c^2}\left[s\cosh^2(ac)-\frac{2c^2}{s}+c\sinh(2ac)\right] - \frac{e^{-bs}}{s^2-4c^2}\left[s\cosh^2(bc)-\frac{2c^2}{s}+c\sinh(2bc)\right]$ | $0$<br>$\cosh^2(ct)$<br>$0$ | $0<t<a$<br>$a<t<b$<br>$t>b$ | $0\leq a<b$<br>$\text{Re } s>-\infty$ |

unctions Containing One Term Only of the Type $(e^{\pm as}\pm b)$

| | g(s) | f(t) | | |
|---|---|---|---|---|
| 30 | $\frac{1-e^{-2n\pi s}}{s-i}$ | $e^{it}$<br>$0$ | $0<t<2n\pi$<br>$t>2n\pi$ | $n=1,2,3,\ldots$<br>$\text{Re } s>-\infty$ |
| 31 | $\frac{1-e^{-as}}{s^2}$ | $t$<br>$a$ | $0<t<a$<br>$t>a$ | $a>0$<br>$\text{Re } s>0$ |
| 32 | $\frac{1+e^{-\pi s}}{s^2+1}$ | $\sin t$<br>$0$ | $0<t<\pi$<br>$t>\pi$ | $\text{Re } s>-\infty$ |

| | | g(s) | f(t) | | |
|---|---|---|---|---|---|
| 3.1 (Contd.) | 33 | $\dfrac{1-e^{-b\pi s}}{s^2+a^2}$ | $\dfrac{\sin(at)}{a}$<br>0 | $0 < t < b\pi$<br>$t > b\pi$ | $a > 0$<br>$b > 0$<br>$\text{Re } s > -\infty$ |
| | 34 | $\dfrac{s(1+e^{-\pi s})}{s^2+1}$ | $\cos t$<br>0 | $0 < t < \pi$<br>$t > \pi$ | $\text{Re } s > -\infty$ |
| | 35 | $\dfrac{s}{s^2+a^2}(1-e^{-b\pi s})$ | $\cos(at)$<br>0 | $0 < t < b\pi$<br>$t > b\pi$ | $a > 0$<br>$b > 0$<br>$\text{Re } s > -\infty$ |
| | 36 | $\dfrac{1-e^{-b\pi s}}{s(s^2+a^2)}$ | $\dfrac{2\sin^2(\frac{at}{2})}{a^2}$<br>0 | $0 < t < b\pi$<br>$t > b\pi$ | $b > 0$<br>$\text{Re } s > -\infty$ |
| | 37 | $\dfrac{2s^2+a^2}{s(s^2+a^2)}(1-e^{-\frac{2n\pi s}{a}})$ | $2\cos^2\frac{at}{2}$<br>0 | $0 < t < \frac{2n\pi}{a}$<br>$t > \frac{2n\pi}{a}$ | $a > 0$<br>$n = 1, 2, 3, \ldots$<br>$\text{Re } s > -\infty$ |
| | 38 | $\dfrac{(1-e^{-\frac{2n\pi s}{b}})(b\cos a + s\sin a)}{s^2+b^2}$ | $\sin(bt+a)$<br>0 | $0 < t < \frac{2n\pi}{b}$<br>$t > \frac{2n\pi}{b}$ | $b > 0$<br>$n = 1, 2, 3, \ldots$<br>$\text{Re } s > -\infty$ |
| | 39 | $\dfrac{(1-e^{-\frac{2n\pi s}{b}})(s\cos a - b\sin a)}{s^2+b^2}$ | $\cos(bt+a)$<br>0 | $0 < t < \frac{2n\pi}{b}$<br>$t > \frac{2n\pi}{b}$ | $b > 0$<br>$n = 1, 2, 3, \ldots$<br>$\text{Re } s > -\infty$ |
| | 40 | $\dfrac{1-e^{-m\pi s}}{s(s^2+2^2)(s^2+4^2)\ldots(s^2+4n^2)}$ | $\dfrac{\sin^{2n} t}{(2n)!}$<br>0 | $0 < t < m\pi$<br>$t > m\pi$ | $n, m = 1, 2, 3, \ldots$<br>$\text{Re } s > -\infty$ |

| | | g(s) | f(t) | | |
|---|---|---|---|---|---|
| 3.1 (Contd.) | 41 | $\frac{1-(-1)^m e^{-m\pi s}}{[s^2+1^2][s^2+3^2]\ldots[s^2+(2n+1)^2]}$ | $\frac{\sin^{2n+1} t}{(2n+1)!}$ | $0 < t < m\pi$ | $n = 0,1,2,\ldots$ |
| | | | $0$ | $t > m\pi$ | $m = 1,2,3,\ldots$ <br> $\text{Re } s > -\infty$ |
| | 42 | $\frac{1}{s^2(e^s-1)}$ | $\frac{1}{2}\left[t(t-1)\right]$ | | $\text{Re } s > 0$ |
| | 43 | $\frac{1}{s^2(e^{as}+1)}$ | $\frac{1}{4}[1-(-1)^n](2t-a)+\frac{1}{2}(-1)^n an$ | $na < t < (n+1)a$ | $a > 0$ <br> $\text{Re } s > 0$ <br> $n = 0,1,2,\ldots$ |
| | 44 | $\frac{1}{s^2(e^{as}-1)}$ | $nt-\frac{1}{2}an(n+1)$ | $na < t < (n+1)a$ | $a > 0$ <br> $\text{Re } s > 0$ <br> $n = 0,1,2,\ldots$ |
| | 45 | $\frac{1}{s^2(e^{bs}-a)}$ | $\frac{1-a^n}{1-a}t-b\,\frac{1-(n+1)a^n+na^{n+1}}{(1-a)^2}$ | $nb < t < (n+1)b$ | $b > 0$ <br> $\text{Re } s > \text{Max } o, \frac{1}{b}\text{ Re}(\log a)$ <br> $n = 0,1,2,\ldots$ |
| | 46 | $\frac{1}{s^2+a^2}\cdot\frac{1}{e^{\frac{\pi}{a}s}-1}$ | $0$ | $\frac{2n\pi}{a} < t < \frac{(2n+1)\pi}{a}$ | $a > 0$ |
| | | | $-\frac{1}{a}\sin at$ | $\frac{(2n+1)\pi}{a} < t < \frac{(2n+2)\pi}{a}$ | $\text{Re } s > 0$ <br> $n = 0,1,2,\ldots$ |
| | 47 | $\frac{1}{s^2+a^2}\cdot\frac{1}{1-e^{-\frac{\pi}{a}s}}$ | $\frac{1}{a}\sin at$ | $\frac{2n\pi}{a} < t < \frac{(2n+1)\pi}{a}$ | $a > 0$ |
| | | | $0$ | $\frac{(2n+1)\pi}{a} < t < \frac{(2n+2)\pi}{a}$ | $\text{Re } s > 0$ <br> $n = 0,1,2,\ldots$ |
| | 48 | $\frac{1}{(s^2+a^2)(1+e^{-b\pi s})}$ | $\frac{\sin(at)}{a}$ | $2nb\pi < t < (2n+1)b\pi$ | $b > 0$ <br> $\text{Re } s > \lvert \text{Im } a \rvert$ |
| | | | $0$ | $(2n+1)b\pi < t < (2n+2)b\pi$ | $n = 0,1,2,\ldots$ |

| | | g(s) | f(t) | | |
|---|---|---|---|---|---|
| 3.1 (Contd.) | 49 | $\frac{1}{s(s^2+a^2)(1+e^{-b\pi s})}$ | $\frac{2\sin^2\frac{at}{2}}{a^2}$ | $2nb\pi < t < (2n+1)b\pi$ | $b>0$ |
| | | | $0$ | $(2n+1)b\pi < t < (2n+2)b\pi$ | Re $s > \lvert \text{Im}\, a$; $n=0,1,2,\ldots$ |
| | 50 | $\frac{s}{(s^2+a^2)(1+e^{-b\pi s})}$ | $\cos(at)$ | $2nb\pi < t < (2n+1)b\pi$ | $b>0$ |
| | | | $0$ | $(2n+1)b\pi < t < (2n+2)b\pi$ | Re $s > \lvert \text{Im}\, a$; $n=0,1,2,\ldots$ |
| | 51 | $\frac{2s^2+a^2}{s(s^2+a^2)(1+e^{-b\pi s})}$ | $2\cos^2\frac{at}{2}$ | $2nb\pi < t < (2n+1)b\pi$ | $b>0$ |
| | | | $0$ | $(2n+1)b\pi < t < (2n+2)b\pi$ | Re $s > \lvert \text{Im}\, a$; $n=0,1,2,\ldots$ |
| | 52 | $\frac{2}{s^3} - \frac{a(a+2s)}{s^2(e^{as}-1)}$ | $(t-na)^2$ | $na < t < (n+1)a$ | $a>0$; Re $s>0$; $n=0,1,2,\ldots$ |

Functions Containing $e^{\pm as}$ and One Term Only of the Type $(e^{\pm as} \pm b)$

| | | | | |
|---|---|---|---|---|
| 53 | $\frac{e^{-as}+as-1}{s^2(1-e^{-as})}$ | $a(n+1)-t$ | $na < t < (n+1)a$ | $a>0$; Re $s>0$; $n=0,1,2,\ldots$ |
| 54 | $\frac{as+1-e^{as}}{s^2(1-e^{as})}$ | $t-na$ | $na < t < (n+1)a$ | $a>0$; Re $s>0$; $n=0,1,2,\ldots$ |
| 55 | $\frac{1-(1+as)e^{-as}}{s^2(1-e^{-2as})}$ | $t-2na$ | $2na < t < (2n+1)a$ | $a>0$ |
| | | $0$ | $(2n+1)a < t < (2n+2)a$ | Re $s>0$; $n=0,1,2,\ldots$ |

| | | g(s) | f(t) | | |
|---|---|---|---|---|---|
| 3.1 (Contd.) | 56 | $\dfrac{1-(1+bs)e^{-bs}}{s^2(1-e^{-as})}$ | $\frac{a}{b}(t-na)$ | $na < t < na+b$ | $0 < b \leqslant a$ |
| | | | 0 | $na+b < t < (n+1)a$ | Re $s > 0$ |
| | | | | | $n = 0, 1, 2, \ldots$ |
| | 57 | $\dfrac{1-e^{-bs}-bse^{-as}}{s^2(1-e^{-as})}$ | $t-na$ | $na < t < na+b$ | $0 < b \leqslant a$ |
| | | | b | $na+b < t < (n+1)a$ | Re $s > 0$ |
| | | | | | $n = 0, 1, 2, \ldots$ |
| | 58 | $\dfrac{1-e^{-bs}-bse^{-as}}{s^2(1-e^{-2as})}$ | $t-2na$ | $2na < t < 2na+b$ | $0 < b \leqslant a$ |
| | | | b | $2na+b < t < (2n+1)a$ | Re $s > 0$ |
| | | | 0 | $(2n+1)a < t < (2n+2)a$ | $n = 0, 1, 2, \ldots$ |
| | 59 | $\dfrac{1-e^{-cs}-cse^{-bs}}{s^2(1-e^{-as})}$ | $t-na$ | $na < t < na+c$ | $0 < c \leqslant b \leqslant a$ |
| | | | c | $na+c < t < na+b$ | Re $s > 0$ |
| | | | 0 | $na+b < t < (n+1)a$ | $n = 0, 1, 2, \ldots$ |
| | 60 | $\dfrac{1-e^{-cs}-e^{-(b-c)s}+e^{-bs}}{s^2(1-e^{-as})}$ | $t-na$ | $na < t < na+c$ | $0 < c < b < a$ |
| | | | c | $na+c < t < na+b-c$ | Re $s > 0$ |
| | | | $b+na-t$ | $na+b-c < t < na+b$ | $n = 0, 1, 2, \ldots$ |
| | | | 0 | $na+b < t < (n+1)a$ | |
| | 61 | $\dfrac{1}{s^2+a^2}\left(\dfrac{s}{a}+\dfrac{2e^{-\frac{\pi s}{2a}}}{1-e^{-\frac{\pi s}{a}}}\right)$ | $\frac{1}{a}\lvert\cos at\rvert$ | | Re $s > \lvert \text{Im } a \rvert$ |
| | 62 | $\dfrac{se^{-as}(1-e^{-2n\pi s})}{s^2+1}$ | 0 | $0 < t < a$ | $n = 1, 2, 3, \ldots$ |
| | | | $\cos(t-a)$ | $a < t < a+2n\pi$ | $a \geqslant 0$ |
| | | | 0 | $t > a+2n\pi$ | Re $s > -\infty$ |

| | | g(s) | f(t) | | |
|---|---|---|---|---|---|
| 3.1 (Contd.) | 63 | $\dfrac{e^{-\frac{2n\pi s}{a}}\left(1-e^{-\frac{\pi s}{a}}\right)}{s(s^2+a^2)}$ | $0$ | $0<t<\dfrac{2n\pi}{a}$ | $a>0$ |
| | | | $\dfrac{2}{a^2}\sin^2\dfrac{at}{2}$ | $\dfrac{2n\pi}{a}<t<\dfrac{(2n+1)\pi}{a}$ | $n=1,2,3,\ldots$ |
| | | | $0$ | $t>\dfrac{(2n+1)\pi}{a}$ | Re $s>-\infty$ |
| | 64 | $\dfrac{2s^2+a^2}{s(s^2+a^2)}e^{-\frac{2n\pi s}{a}}\left(1-e^{-\frac{\pi s}{a}}\right)$ | $0$ | $0<t<\dfrac{2n\pi}{a}$ | $a>0$ |
| | | | $2\cos^2\dfrac{at}{2}$ | $\dfrac{2n\pi}{a}<t<\dfrac{(2n+1)\pi}{a}$ | $n=1,2,3,\ldots$ |
| | | | $0$ | $t>\dfrac{(2n+1)\pi}{a}$ | Re $s>-\infty$ |
| | 65 | $\dfrac{e^{-\frac{\pi}{2}s}(1-e^{-m\pi s})}{s(s^2+2^2)(s^2+4^2)\ldots(s^2+4n^2)}$ | $0$ | $0<t<\dfrac{\pi}{2}$ | $n,m=1,2,3,\ldots$ |
| | | | $\dfrac{\cos^{2n}t}{(2n)!}$ | $\dfrac{\pi}{2}<t<(m+\dfrac{1}{2})\pi$ | Re $s>-\infty$ |
| | | | $0$ | $t>(m+\dfrac{1}{2})\pi$ | |

Functions Containing Two Terms of the Type $(1\pm e^{-as})$

| | | | | | |
|---|---|---|---|---|---|
| | 66 | $\dfrac{(1-e^{-as})^2}{s^2}$ | $t$ | $0<t<a$ | $a>0$ |
| | | | $2a-t$ | $a<t<2a$ | Re $s>-\infty$ |
| | | | $0$ | $t>2a$ | |
| | 67 | $\dfrac{1-e^{-as}}{s^2(1+e^{-as})}$ | $t-2na$ | $2na<t<(2n+1)a$ | $a>0$ |
| | | | $2a(n+1)-t$ | $(2n+1)a<t<(2n+2)a$ | Re $s>0$ |
| | | | | | $n=0,1,2,\ldots$ |
| | 68 | $\dfrac{1}{s^2}\left[\dfrac{a(1-e^{-bs})}{b(1-e^{-as})}-1\right]$ | $\dfrac{a-b}{b}(t-na)$ | $na<t<na+b$ | $0<b\leqslant a$ |
| | | | $(n+1)a-t$ | $na+b<t<(n+1)a$ | Re $s>0$ |
| | | | | | $n=0,1,2,\ldots$ |

| | | g(s) | f(t) | | |
|---|---|---|---|---|---|
| 3.1 (Contd.) | 69 | $\frac{2(1-e^{-as})}{s^2(1+e^{-as})} - \frac{a}{s}$ | $2t-a(4n+1)$<br>$a(4n+3)-2t$ | $2na < t < (2n+1)a$<br>$(2n+1)a < t < (2n+2)a$ | $a > 0$<br>$\text{Re } s > 0$<br>$n = 0,1,2,\ldots$ |
| | 70 | $\frac{2}{as^2} - \frac{1+e^{-as}}{s(1-e^{-as})}$ | $\frac{2t}{a} - 2n-1$ | $na < t < (n+1)a$ | $a > 0$<br>$\text{Re } s > 0$<br>$n = 0,1,2,\ldots$ |
| | 71 | $\frac{1}{s^2+a^2} \cdot \frac{1+e^{-\frac{\pi s}{a}}}{1-e^{-\frac{\pi s}{a}}}$ | $\frac{\lvert\sin(at)\rvert}{a}$ | | $\text{Re } s > \lvert \text{Im } a \rvert$ |
| | 72 | $\frac{s}{s^2+a^2} \cdot \frac{1+e^{-\frac{\pi s}{a}}}{1-e^{-\frac{\pi s}{a}}}$ | $\cos(at)$<br>$-\cos(at)$ | $2n\pi < at < (2n+1)\pi$<br>$(2n+1)\pi < at < (2n+2)\pi$ | $a > 0$<br>$\text{Re } s > 0$<br>$n = 0,1,2,\ldots$ |

Functions Containing Three Terms of the Type $(1-e^{-as})$

| | | | | |
|---|---|---|---|---|
| 73 | $\frac{(1-e^{-as})^2}{s^2(1-e^{-4as})}$ | $t-4na$<br>$4na+2a-t$<br>$0$ | $4na < t < (4n+1)a$<br>$(4n+1)a < t < (4n+2)a$<br>$(4n+2)a < t < (4n+4)a$ | $a > 0$<br>$\text{Re } s > 0$<br>$n = 0,1,2,\ldots$ |
| 74 | $\frac{(1-e^{-\frac{bs}{2}})^2}{s^2(1-e^{-as})}$ | $t-na$<br>$b+na-t$<br>$0$ | $na < t < na+\frac{b}{2}$<br>$na+\frac{b}{2} < t < na+b$<br>$na+b < t < (n+1)a$ | $0 < b \leq a$<br>$\text{Re } s > 0$<br>$n = 0,1,2,\ldots$ |
| 75 | $\frac{(1-e^{-bs})[1-e^{-(2-\frac{b}{a})as}]}{s^2(1-e^{-4as})}$ | $t-4na$<br>$b$<br>$(4n+2)a-t$<br>$0$ | $4na < t < 4na+b$<br>$4na+b < t < (4n+2)a-b$<br>$(4n+2)a-b < t < (4n+2)a$<br>$(4n+2)a < t < (4n+4)a$ | $0 < b \leq a$<br>$\text{Re } s > 0$<br>$n = 0,1,2,\ldots$ |

| | | g(s) | f(t) | | |
|---|---|---|---|---|---|
| 3.1 (Contd.) | 76 | $\dfrac{(1-e^{-bs})[1-e^{-(2-\frac{b}{a})as}]}{s^2(1-e^{-2as})}$ | $\dfrac{t-2na}{a}$ | $2na < t < 2na+b$ | $0 < b \leqslant a$ |
| | | | $\dfrac{b}{a}$ | $2na+b < t < (2n+2)a-b$ | Re $s > 0$ |
| | | | $\dfrac{(2n+2)a-t}{a}$ | $(2n+2)a-b < t < (2n+2)a$ | $n = 0,1,2,\ldots$ |
| | 77 | $\dfrac{a(1-e^{-bs})-b(1-e^{-as})}{s^2(1-e^{-2as})}$ | $(a-b)(t-2na)$ | $2na < t < 2na+b$ | $0 < b \leqslant a$ |
| | | | $b[(2n+1)a-t]$ | $2na+b < t < (2n+1)a$ | Re $s > 0$ |
| | | | $0$ | $(2n+1)a < t < (2n+2)a$ | $n = 0,1,2,\ldots$ |
| | 78 | $\dfrac{b(1-e^{-cs})-c(1-e^{-bs})}{s^2(1-e^{-as})}$ | $(b-c)(t-na)$ | $na < t < na+c$ | $0 < c \leqslant b \leqslant a$ |
| | | | $c(b+na-t)$ | $na+c < t < na+b$ | Re $s > 0$ |
| | | | $0$ | $na+b < t < (n+1)a$ | $n = 0,1,2,\ldots$ |

Functions Containing Terms of the Type $(e^{-as}-e^{-bs})$

| | | | | |
|---|---|---|---|---|
| 79 | $\dfrac{e^{-as}-e^{-bs}}{s^2}$ | $0$ | $0 < t < a$ | $0 \leqslant a < b$ |
| | | $t-a$ | $a < t < b$ | Re $s > 0$ |
| | | $b-a$ | $t > b$ | |
| 80 | $\dfrac{e^{-as}-e^{-bs}}{s^3}$ | $0$ | $0 < t < a$ | $0 \leqslant a < b$ |
| | | $\frac{1}{2}(t-a)^2$ | $a < t < b$ | Re $s > 0$ |
| | | $t(b-a)+\frac{1}{2}(a^2-b^2)$ | $t > b$ | |
| 81 | $\dfrac{(e^{-as}-e^{-bs})^2}{s^2}$ | $0$ | $0 < t < 2a$ | $0 \leqslant a < b$ |
| | | $t-2a$ | $2a < t < a+b$ | Re $s > -\infty$ |
| | | $2b-t$ | $a+b < t < 2b$ | |
| | | $0$ | $t > 2b$ | |

| | | $g(s)$ | $f(t)$ | | |
|---|---|---|---|---|---|
| **3.1 (Contd.)** | 82 | $\dfrac{(e^{-as}-e^{-bs})^2}{s^3}$ | $0$ | $0 < t < 2a$ | $0 \leqslant a < b$ |
| | | | $\frac{1}{2}(t-2a)^2$ | $2a < t < a+b$ | Re $s > 0$ |
| | | | $(b-a)^2 - \frac{1}{2}(t-2b)^2$ | $a+b < t < 2b$ | |
| | | | $(b-a)^2$ | $t > 2b$ | |
| | 83 | $\dfrac{(e^{-as}-e^{-bs})^3}{s^3}$ | $0$ | $0 < t < 3a$ | $0 \leqslant a < b$ |
| | | | $\frac{1}{2}(t-3a)^2$ | $3a < t < 2a+b$ | Re $s > -\infty$ |
| | | | $\frac{3}{4}(b-a)^2 - [t - \frac{3}{2}(a+b)]^2$ | $2a+b < t < a+2b$ | |
| | | | $\frac{1}{2}(3b-t)^2$ | $a+2b < t < 3b$ | |
| | | | $0$ | $t > 3b$ | |
| | 84 | $\dfrac{2\left(e^{-\frac{a-b}{2}s}-e^{-\frac{a+b}{2}s}\right)}{s^2(1+e^{-as})} - \dfrac{b}{s}$ | $-b$ | $0 < t < \frac{a-b}{2}$ | $0 < b < a$ |
| | | | $2t-(4n+1)a$ | $\frac{(4n+1)a-b}{2} < t < \frac{(4n+1)a+b}{2}$ | Re $s > 0$ |
| | | | $b$ | $\frac{(4n+1)a+b}{2} < t < \frac{(4n+3)a-b}{2}$ | $n = 0,1,2,\ldots$ |
| | | | $-2t+(4n+3)a$ | $\frac{(4n+3)a-b}{2} < t < \frac{(4n+3)a+b}{2}$ | |
| | | | $-b$ | $\frac{(4n+3)a+b}{2} < t < \frac{(4n+5)a-b}{2}$ | |
| | 85 | $\dfrac{2e^{-\frac{as}{2}}\left(e^{\frac{bs}{2}}-e^{-\frac{bs}{2}}\right)-bs(1+e^{-as})}{s^2(1-e^{-as})}$ | $-\frac{b}{a}$ | $na < t < \frac{(2n+1)a-b}{2}$ | $0 < b < a$ |
| | | | $\frac{2t}{a}-(2n+1)$ | $\frac{(2n+1)a-b}{2} < t < \frac{(2n+1)a+b}{2}$ | Re $s > 0$ |
| | | | $\frac{b}{a}$ | $\frac{(2n+1)a+b}{2} < t < (n+1)a$ | $n = 0,1,2,\ldots$ |
| **Miscellaneous** | | | | | |
| | 86 | $\dfrac{e^{-\frac{a}{s}}}{s^2}$ | $(\frac{t}{a})^{\frac{1}{2}} J_1(2a^{\frac{1}{2}}t^{\frac{1}{2}})$ | | Re $s > 0$ |

| | | g(s) | f(t) | |
|---|---|---|---|---|
| 3.1 (Contd.) | 87 | $\frac{1}{s} e^{s^{-n}}$ | ${}_0F_n\left[\frac{1}{n},\frac{2}{n},\ldots,\frac{n-1}{n},1;\ \left(\frac{t}{n}\right)^n\right]$ | $n = 1,2,3,\ldots$ <br> $\mathrm{Re}\, s > 0$ |
| | 88 | $\frac{e^{-as^{\frac{1}{2}}}}{s+b}$ | $\frac{1}{2} e^{-bt}\left[e^{-iab^{\frac{1}{2}}}\mathrm{Erfc}\left(\frac{a}{2t^{\frac{1}{2}}} - ib^{\frac{1}{2}}t^{\frac{1}{2}}\right) + e^{iab^{\frac{1}{2}}}\mathrm{Erfc}\left(\frac{a}{2t^{\frac{1}{2}}} + ib^{\frac{1}{2}}t^{\frac{1}{2}}\right)\right]$ | $\mathrm{Re}\, a^2 \geq 0$ <br> $\mathrm{Re}\, s > -\mathrm{Re}\, b$ |
| | 89 | $\frac{e^{-\frac{as}{s^2+1}}}{s^2+1}$ | $\int_0^t J_0[2u^{\frac{1}{2}}(t-u)^{\frac{1}{2}}]J_0(2a^{\frac{1}{2}}u^{\frac{1}{2}})\,du$ | $\mathrm{Re}\, s > 0$ |
| | 90 | $\frac{e^{-b(s^2-a^2)^{\frac{1}{2}}}}{(s^2-a^2)^{\frac{1}{2}}}$ | $0 \quad 0 < t < b$ <br> $I_0[a(t^2-b^2)^{\frac{1}{2}}] \quad t > b$ | $b > 0$ <br> $\mathrm{Re}\, s > \lvert\mathrm{Re}\, a\rvert$ |
| | 91 | $e^{-b(s^2-a^2)^{\frac{1}{2}}} - e^{-bs}$ | $0 \quad 0 < t < b$ <br> $\frac{abI_1[a(t^2-b^2)^{\frac{1}{2}}]}{(t^2-b^2)^{\frac{1}{2}}} \quad t > b$ | $b > 0$ <br> $\mathrm{Re}\, s > \lvert\mathrm{Re}\, a\rvert$ |
| | 92 | $e^{-s}s^n\left(\frac{1}{s}\frac{d}{ds}\right)^n\left(\frac{e^s}{s}\right)$ | $P_n(1-t)$ | $n = 0,1,2,\ldots$ <br> $\mathrm{Re}\, s > 0$ |

Functions of $e^{-bs}$

| | | | | |
|---|---|---|---|---|
| 3.2 | 1 | $\frac{e^{-bs}}{s^{\nu}}$ | $0 \quad 0 < t < b$ <br> $(t-b)^{\nu-1} \quad t > b$ | $b > 0$ <br> $\mathrm{Re}\, \nu > 0$ <br> $\mathrm{Re}\, s > 0$ |

| | g(s) | f(t) | | |
|---|---|---|---|---|
| 3.2 (Contd.) | $2\frac{e^{-bs}}{(s^2-ia^2)^{\frac{1}{2}}}\left\{\left[\frac{s+(s^2-ia^2)^{\frac{1}{2}}}{ai^{\frac{1}{2}}}\right]^{\nu}-\left[\frac{ai^{\frac{1}{2}}}{s+(s^2-ia^2)^{\frac{1}{2}}}\right]^{\nu}\right\}$ | $0$ | $0<t<b$ | $\lvert\mathrm{Re}\,\nu\rvert<1$ |
| | | $\frac{2}{\pi}e^{\frac{i\nu\pi}{2}}\left(\frac{t-b}{t+b}\right)^{\frac{\nu}{2}}\left\{\mathrm{ker}_{\nu}[a(t^2-b^2)^{\frac{1}{2}}]\right.$ | | $b>0$ |
| | | $\left.+\,i\,\mathrm{kei}_{\nu}[a(t^2-b^2)^{\frac{1}{2}}]\right\}$ | $t>b$ | $\mathrm{Re}(s+ai^{\frac{1}{2}})>0$ |

Functions of $e^{\pm\frac{a}{s}}$

| | g(s) | f(t) | |
|---|---|---|---|
| 3 | $\frac{e^{\frac{a}{s}}}{s^{\frac{1}{2}}}$ | $\frac{\cosh(2a^{\frac{1}{2}}t^{\frac{1}{2}})}{(\pi t)^{\frac{1}{2}}}$ | $\mathrm{Re}\,s>0$ |
| 4 | $\frac{e^{-\frac{a}{s}}}{s^{\frac{1}{2}}}$ | $\frac{\cos(2a^{\frac{1}{2}}t^{\frac{1}{2}})}{(\pi t)^{\frac{1}{2}}}$ | $\mathrm{Re}\,s>0$ |
| 5 | $\frac{e^{\frac{a}{s}}}{s^{\frac{3}{2}}}$ | $\frac{\sinh(2a^{\frac{1}{2}}t^{\frac{1}{2}})}{(\pi a)^{\frac{1}{2}}}$ | $\mathrm{Re}\,s>0$ |
| 6 | $\frac{e^{-\frac{a}{s}}}{s^{\frac{3}{2}}}$ | $\frac{\sin(2a^{\frac{1}{2}}t^{\frac{1}{2}})}{(\pi a)^{\frac{1}{2}}}$ | $\mathrm{Re}\,a^{\frac{1}{2}}\geq 0$<br>$\mathrm{Re}\,s>0$ |
| 7 | $\frac{e^{\frac{a}{s}}}{s^{\frac{5}{2}}}$ | $\frac{t^{\frac{1}{2}}}{a\pi^{\frac{1}{2}}}\cosh(2a^{\frac{1}{2}}t^{\frac{1}{2}})-\frac{1}{2a^{\frac{3}{2}}\pi^{\frac{1}{2}}}\sinh(2a^{\frac{1}{2}}t^{\frac{1}{2}})$ | $\mathrm{Re}\,s>0$ |
| 8 | $\frac{e^{-\frac{a}{s}}}{s^{\frac{5}{2}}}$ | $\frac{1}{\pi^{\frac{1}{2}}a}\left[\frac{\sin(2a^{\frac{1}{2}}t^{\frac{1}{2}})}{2a^{\frac{1}{2}}}-t^{\frac{1}{2}}\cos(2a^{\frac{1}{2}}t^{\frac{1}{2}})\right]$ | $\mathrm{Re}\,a^{\frac{1}{2}}>0$<br>$\mathrm{Re}\,s>0$ |
| 9 | $\frac{e^{\frac{a}{s}}}{s^{\nu}}$ | $\left(\frac{t}{a}\right)^{\frac{\nu-1}{2}}I_{\nu-1}(2a^{\frac{1}{2}}t^{\frac{1}{2}})$ | $\mathrm{Re}\,\nu>0$<br>$\mathrm{Re}\,s>0$ |

| | | $g(s)$ | $f(t)$ | |
|---|---|---|---|---|
| 3.2 (Contd.) | 10 | $\frac{e^{-\frac{a}{s}}}{s^{\nu}}$ | $\left(\frac{t}{a}\right)^{\frac{\nu-1}{2}} J_{\nu-1}(2a^{\frac{1}{2}}t^{\frac{1}{2}})$ | Re $\nu > 0$<br>Re $s > 0$ |
| | 11 | $\frac{e^{\frac{a}{s}}+1}{s^{\frac{1}{2}}}$ | $\frac{2}{(\pi t)^{\frac{1}{2}}}\cosh^2(a^{\frac{1}{2}}t^{\frac{1}{2}})$ | Re $s > 0$ |
| | 12 | $\frac{e^{\frac{a}{s}}-1}{s^{\frac{1}{2}}}$ | $\frac{2}{(\pi t)^{\frac{1}{2}}}\sinh^2(a^{\frac{1}{2}}t^{\frac{1}{2}})$ | Re $s > 0$ |
| | 13 | $\frac{e^{\frac{y}{s}}}{s^c(1-\frac{x}{s})^b}$ | $\frac{t^{c-1}}{\Gamma(c)}\Phi_3(b,c;xt,yt)$ | Re $c > 0$<br>Re $s >$ Max o, Re $x$ |

Functions of $e^{-as^{\frac{1}{2}}}$ and $e^{-\frac{a}{s^{\frac{1}{2}}}}$

| | | | | |
|---|---|---|---|---|
| | 14 | $e^{-as^{\frac{1}{2}}}$ | $\frac{a\,e^{-\frac{a^2}{4t}}}{2\pi^{\frac{1}{2}}t^{\frac{3}{2}}}$ | Re $a^2 > 0$<br>Re $s > 0$ |
| | 15 | $s^{\frac{1}{2}}e^{-as^{\frac{1}{2}}}$ | $\frac{(a^2-2t)\,e^{-\frac{a^2}{4t}}}{4\pi^{\frac{1}{2}}t^{\frac{5}{2}}}$ | Re $a^2 \geqslant 0$<br>Re $s > 0$ |
| | 16 | $\frac{e^{-as^{\frac{1}{2}}}}{s^{\frac{1}{2}}}$ | $\frac{e^{-\frac{a^2}{4t}}}{(\pi t)^{\frac{1}{2}}}$ | Re $a^2 \geqslant 0$<br>Re $s > 0$ |
| | 17 | $\frac{e^{-as^{\frac{1}{2}}}-1}{s^{\frac{1}{2}}}$ | $\frac{e^{-\frac{a^2}{4t}}-1}{(\pi t)^{\frac{1}{2}}}$ | Re $a^2 \geqslant 0$<br>Re $s \geqslant 0$ |
| | 18 | $s\,e^{-as^{\frac{1}{2}}}$ | $\frac{a\left(\frac{a^2}{2t}-3\right)e^{-\frac{a^2}{4t}}}{4\pi^{\frac{1}{2}}t^{\frac{5}{2}}}$ | Re $a^2 \geqslant 0$<br>Re $s > 0$ |

| | | g(s) | f(t) | |
|---|---|---|---|---|
| 3.2 (Contd.) | 19 | $\frac{e^{-as^{\frac{1}{2}}}}{s}$ | $\mathrm{Erfc}\left(\frac{a}{2t^{\frac{1}{2}}}\right)$ | Re $a^2 \geqslant 0$<br>Re $s > 0$ |
| | 20 | $\frac{1-e^{-as^{\frac{1}{2}}}}{s}$ | $\mathrm{Erf}\left(\frac{a}{2t^{\frac{1}{2}}}\right)$ | Re $a^2 > 0$<br>Re $s > 0$ |
| | 21 | $s^{\frac{3}{2}}e^{-as^{\frac{1}{2}}}$ | $\frac{1}{4\pi^{\frac{1}{2}}t^{\frac{5}{2}}}e^{-\frac{a^2}{4t}}\left[\frac{a^4}{4t^2}-\frac{3a^2}{2t}+3\right]$ | Re $a > 0$<br>Re $s > 0$ |
| | 22 | $\frac{e^{-as^{\frac{1}{2}}}}{s^{\frac{3}{2}}}$ | $\frac{2t^{\frac{1}{2}}}{\pi^{\frac{1}{2}}}e^{-\frac{a^2}{4t}}-a\mathrm{Erfc}\frac{a}{2t^{\frac{1}{2}}}$ | Re $a^2 \geqslant 0$<br>Re $s > 0$ |
| | 23 | $s^{\frac{n-1}{2}}e^{-(2as)^{\frac{1}{2}}}$ | $\frac{He_n\left(\frac{a^{\frac{1}{2}}}{t^{\frac{1}{2}}}\right)}{2^{\frac{n}{2}}\pi^{\frac{1}{2}}t^{\frac{n+1}{2}}e^{\frac{a}{2t}}}$ | $n = 0, 1, 2, \ldots$<br>Re $a > 0$<br>Re $s > 0$ |
| | 24 | $s^{\nu}e^{-as^{\frac{1}{2}}}$ | $\frac{e^{-\frac{a^2}{8t}}D_{2\nu+1}\left(\frac{a}{2^{\frac{1}{2}}t^{\frac{1}{2}}}\right)}{2^{\nu+\frac{1}{2}}\pi^{\frac{1}{2}}t^{\nu+1}}$ | Re $a^2 > 0$<br>Re $s > 0$ |
| | 25 | $\frac{e^{-as^{\frac{1}{2}}}}{(s-1)^{\frac{1}{2}}}$ | $\frac{e^t}{(\pi t)^{\frac{1}{2}}}\left\{e^{-\frac{a^2}{4t}}-a\int_0^{\infty}e^{-\frac{u^2}{4t}}(u^2-a^2)^{-\frac{1}{2}}\cdot J_1[(u^2-a^2)^{\frac{1}{2}}]du\right\}$ | Re $a^2 > 0$<br>Re $s > 1$ |
| | 26 | $\frac{e^{-as^{\frac{1}{2}}}}{s^{\frac{1}{2}}+b}$ | $\frac{e^{-\frac{a^2}{4t}}}{(\pi t)^{\frac{1}{2}}}-be^{ab+b^2t}\mathrm{Erfc}\left(\frac{a}{2t^{\frac{1}{2}}}+bt^{\frac{1}{2}}\right)$ | Re $a^2 \geqslant 0$<br>Re $s > 0$ if Re $b \geqslant 0$<br>Re $s >$ Max $0$, Re $b^2$ if Re $b < 0$ |

| | | $g(s)$ | $f(t)$ | |
|---|---|---|---|---|
| 3.2 (Contd.) | 27 | $\dfrac{s^{\frac{1}{2}}e^{-as^{\frac{1}{2}}}}{s^{\frac{1}{2}}+b}$ | $\pi^{-\frac{1}{2}}\left(\dfrac{a}{2t^{\frac{3}{2}}}-\dfrac{b}{t^{\frac{1}{2}}}\right)e^{-\frac{a^2}{4t}} + b^2e^{ab+b^2t}\text{Erfc}\left(\dfrac{a}{2t^{\frac{1}{2}}}+bt^{\frac{1}{2}}\right)$ | Re $a^2 \geqslant 0$<br>Re $s > 0$ if Re $b \geqslant 0$<br>Re $s >$ Max $0$, Re $b^2$ if Re $b < 0$ |
| | 28 | $\dfrac{e^{-bs^{\frac{1}{2}}}}{s^{\frac{1}{2}}(s^{\frac{1}{2}}+a)}$ | $e^{a^2t+ab}\text{Erfc}\left(at^{\frac{1}{2}}+\dfrac{b}{2t^{\frac{1}{2}}}\right)$ | Re $b^2 \geqslant 0$<br>Re $s > 0$ if Re $a \geqslant 0$<br>Re $s >$ Max $0$, Re $a^2$ if Re $a < 0$ |
| | 29 | $\dfrac{s}{s^{\frac{1}{2}}+b}e^{-as^{\frac{1}{2}}}$ | $\pi^{-\frac{1}{2}}t^{-\frac{3}{2}}\left(\dfrac{a^2}{4}t^{-1}-\dfrac{1}{2}-\dfrac{ab}{2}+b^2t\right)e^{-\frac{a^2}{4t}} - b^3e^{ab+b^2t}\text{Erfc}\left(\frac{a}{2}t^{-\frac{1}{2}}+bt^{\frac{1}{2}}\right)$ | Re $a^2 > 0$<br>Re $s > 0$ if Re $b \geqslant 0$<br>Re $s >$ Max $0$, Re $b^2$ if Re $b < 0$ |
| | 30 | $\dfrac{e^{-as^{\frac{1}{2}}}}{s(s^{\frac{1}{2}}+b)}$ | $\dfrac{1}{b}\text{Erfc}\dfrac{a}{2t^{\frac{1}{2}}}-\dfrac{1}{b}e^{ab+b^2t}\text{Erfc}\left(\dfrac{a}{2t^{\frac{1}{2}}}+bt^{\frac{1}{2}}\right)$ | Re $a^2 \geqslant 0$<br>Re $s > 0$ if Re $b \geqslant 0$<br>Re $s >$ Max $0$, Re $b^2$ if Re $b < 0$ |
| | 31 | $\dfrac{e^{-as^{\frac{1}{2}}}}{s^{\frac{3}{2}}(s^{\frac{1}{2}}+b)}$ | $\dfrac{2t^{\frac{1}{2}}e^{-\frac{a^2}{4t}}}{\pi^{\frac{1}{2}}b}-\left(\dfrac{1}{b^2}+\dfrac{a}{b}\right)\text{Erfc}\dfrac{a}{2t^{\frac{1}{2}}} + \dfrac{e^{ab+b^2t}}{b^2}\text{Erfc}\left(\dfrac{a}{2t^{\frac{1}{2}}}+bt^{\frac{1}{2}}\right)$ | Re $a^2 \geqslant 0$<br>Re $s > 0$ if Re $b \geqslant 0$<br>Re $s >$ Max $0$, Re $b^2$ if Re $b < 0$ |
| | 32 | $\dfrac{1+as^{\frac{1}{2}}}{s^{\frac{3}{2}}e^{as^{\frac{1}{2}}}}$ | $2\left(\frac{t}{\pi}\right)^{\frac{1}{2}}e^{-\frac{a^2}{4t}}$ | Re $a^2 \geqslant 0$<br>Re $s > 0$ |
| | 33 | $\dfrac{e^{-\frac{a}{s^{\frac{1}{2}}}}}{s^{\frac{1}{2}}}$ | $\dfrac{1}{2\pi^{\frac{1}{2}}t^{\frac{3}{2}}}\displaystyle\int_0^\infty ue^{-\frac{u^2}{4t}}J_0(2a^{\frac{1}{2}}u^{\frac{1}{2}})\,du$ | Re $a > 0$<br>Re $s > 0$ |

| | | g(s) | f(t) | |
|---|---|---|---|---|
| 3.2 (Contd.) | 34 | $\dfrac{e^{-\frac{a}{s^{\frac{1}{2}}}}}{s^{\nu}}$ | $\dfrac{\int_0^{\infty} u^{\nu+\frac{1}{2}} e^{-\frac{u^2}{4t}} J_{2\nu-1}(2a^{\frac{1}{2}}u^{\frac{1}{2}})\,du}{2\pi^{\frac{1}{2}} a^{\nu-\frac{1}{2}} t^{\frac{3}{2}}}$ | Re a > o<br>Re $\nu$ > o<br>Re s > o |
| Functions of $e^{-as^{\frac{1}{3}}}$ | | | | |
| | 35 | $e^{-3s^{\frac{1}{3}}}$ | $\dfrac{3^{\frac{1}{2}}}{\pi t^{\frac{3}{2}}} K_{\frac{1}{3}}\left(\dfrac{2}{t^{\frac{1}{2}}}\right)$ | Re s > o |
| | 36 | $\dfrac{e^{-3s^{\frac{1}{3}}}}{s^{\frac{1}{3}}}$ | $\dfrac{3^{\frac{1}{2}}}{\pi t} K_{\frac{2}{3}}\left(\dfrac{2}{t^{\frac{1}{2}}}\right)$ | Re s > o |
| | 37 | $\dfrac{e^{-3s^{\frac{1}{3}}}}{s^{\frac{2}{3}}}$ | $\dfrac{3^{\frac{1}{2}}}{\pi t^{\frac{1}{2}}} K_{\frac{1}{3}}\left(\dfrac{2}{t^{\frac{1}{2}}}\right)$ | Re s > o |
| | 38 | $\dfrac{e^{s^{\frac{1}{3}}} + \omega^2 e^{\omega s^{\frac{1}{3}}} + \omega e^{\omega^2 s^{\frac{1}{3}}}}{s^{\frac{2}{3}}}$<br>where $\omega = -\frac{1}{2} + i\dfrac{3^{\frac{1}{2}}}{2}$ | $\left(\dfrac{3}{t}\right)^{\frac{1}{2}} J_{\frac{1}{3}}\left(\dfrac{2}{3^{\frac{4}{3}} t^{\frac{1}{3}}}\right)$ | Re s > o |
| | 39 | $\dfrac{e^{s^{\frac{1}{3}}} + e^{\omega s^{\frac{1}{3}}} + e^{\omega^2 s^{\frac{1}{3}}}}{s^{\frac{2}{3}}}$<br>where $\omega = -\frac{1}{2} + i\dfrac{3^{\frac{1}{2}}}{2}$ | $\left(\dfrac{3}{t}\right)^{\frac{1}{2}} J_{-\frac{1}{3}}\left(\dfrac{2}{3^{\frac{4}{3}} t^{\frac{1}{3}}}\right)$ | Re s > o |
| Functions of $e^{as^{\pm b}}$ | | | | |
| | 40 | $\dfrac{e^{as^{-b}}}{s^{b}}$ | $t^{b-1} \sum_{n=o}^{\infty} \dfrac{(at^b)^n}{n!\Gamma[b(n+1)]}$ | Re b > o<br>Re s > o |

| | | g(s) | f(t) | | |
|---|---|---|---|---|---|
| 3.2 (Contd.) | 41 | $s^{a-1} e^{-(bs)^{\frac{1}{m}}}$ | $\frac{m^{\frac{1}{2}+ma}}{(2\pi)^{\frac{1+m}{2}} b^a} \sum_{i,-i} \frac{1}{i} E\left(a, a+\frac{1}{m}, \ldots, a+\frac{m-1}{m} :: \frac{be^{i\pi}}{m^m t}\right)$ <br> $\sum_{i,-i}$ denotes that in the expression following the $\Sigma$ sign i is to be replaced by -i and the two expressions are to be added. | | Re a > o <br> Re b > o <br> m = 2,3,4,... <br> Re s > o |

Functions of $e^{-b(s^2 \pm a^2)^{\frac{1}{2}}}$

| | g(s) | f(t) | | |
|---|---|---|---|---|
| 42 | $\frac{[(s^2+a^2)^{\frac{1}{2}}-s]^{\frac{1}{2}}}{(s^2+a^2)^{\frac{1}{2}}} e^{-b(s^2+a^2)^{\frac{1}{2}}}$ | 0 <br> $\frac{2^{\frac{1}{2}} \sin[a(t^2-b^2)^{\frac{1}{2}}]}{\pi^{\frac{1}{2}}(t+b)^{\frac{1}{2}}}$ | $0 < t < b$ <br> $t > b$ | b > o <br> Re s > \|Im a\| |
| 43 | $\frac{[s+(s^2+a^2)^{\frac{1}{2}}]^{\frac{1}{2}}}{(s^2+a^2)^{\frac{1}{2}}} e^{-b(s^2+a^2)^{\frac{1}{2}}}$ | 0 <br> $(\frac{2}{\pi})^{\frac{1}{2}} \frac{\cos[a(t^2-b^2)^{\frac{1}{2}}]}{(t+b)^{\frac{1}{2}}}$ | $0 < t < b$ <br> $t > b$ | b > o <br> Re s > \|Im a\| |
| 44 | $e^{-b(s^2-a^2)^{\frac{1}{2}}} \left[\frac{s-(s^2-a^2)^{\frac{1}{2}}}{s^2-a^2}\right]^{\frac{1}{2}}$ | 0 <br> $(\frac{2}{\pi})^{\frac{1}{2}} \frac{\sinh[a(t^2-b^2)^{\frac{1}{2}}]}{(t+b)^{\frac{1}{2}}}$ | $0 < t < b$ <br> $t > b$ | Re s > \|Re a\| |
| 45 | $e^{-b(s^2-a^2)^{\frac{1}{2}}} \left[\frac{(s^2-a^2)^{\frac{1}{2}}+s}{s^2-a^2}\right]^{\frac{1}{2}}$ | 0 <br> $(\frac{2}{\pi})^{\frac{1}{2}} \frac{\cosh[a(t^2-b^2)^{\frac{1}{2}}]}{(t+b)^{\frac{1}{2}}}$ | $0 < t < b$ <br> $t > b$ | Re s > \|Re a\| |
| 46 | $\frac{e^{-b(s^2+a^2)^{\frac{1}{2}}}}{(s^2+a^2)^{\frac{1}{2}}}$ | 0 <br> $J_0[a(t^2-b^2)^{\frac{1}{2}}]$ | $0 < t < b$ <br> $t > b$ | b > o <br> Re s > \|Im a\| |

| | | g(s) | f(t) | | |
|---|---|---|---|---|---|
| 3.2 (Contd.) | 47 | $\frac{s[b(s^2+a^2)^{\frac{1}{2}}+1]}{(s^2+a^2)^{\frac{3}{2}}} e^{-b(s^2+a^2)^{\frac{1}{2}}}$ | $0$ | $0 < t < b$ | $b > 0$ |
| | | | $t J_0[a(t^2-b^2)^{\frac{1}{2}}]$ | $t > b$ | $\mathrm{Re}\, s > \lvert \mathrm{Im}\, a \rvert$ |
| | 48 | $e^{-bs} - e^{-b(s^2+a^2)^{\frac{1}{2}}}$ | $0$ | $0 < t < b$ | $b > 0$ |
| | | | $\frac{ab J_1[a(t^2-b^2)^{\frac{1}{2}}]}{(t^2-b^2)^{\frac{1}{2}}}$ | $t > b$ | $\mathrm{Re}\, s > \lvert \mathrm{Im}\, a \rvert$ |
| | 49 | $e^{-bs} - \frac{s}{(s^2+a^2)^{\frac{1}{2}}} e^{-b(s^2+a^2)^{\frac{1}{2}}}$ | $0$ | $0 < t < b$ | $b > 0$ |
| | | | $\frac{at J_1[a(t^2-b^2)^{\frac{1}{2}}]}{(t^2-b^2)^{\frac{1}{2}}}$ | $t > b$ | $\mathrm{Re}\, s > \lvert \mathrm{Im}\, a \rvert$ |
| | 50 | $\frac{s e^{-b(s^2-a^2)^{\frac{1}{2}}}}{(s^2-a^2)^{\frac{1}{2}}} - e^{-bs}$ | $0$ | $0 < t < b$ | $b > 0$ |
| | | | $\frac{at I_1[a(t^2-b^2)^{\frac{1}{2}}]}{(t^2-b^2)^{\frac{1}{2}}}$ | $t > b$ | $\mathrm{Re}\, s > \lvert \mathrm{Re}\, a \rvert$ |
| | 51 | $\left[1 - \frac{s}{(s^2+a^2)^{\frac{1}{2}}}\right] e^{-b(s^2+a^2)^{\frac{1}{2}}}$ | $0$ | $0 < t < b$ | $b > 0$ |
| | | | $a\left(\frac{t-b}{t+b}\right)^{\frac{1}{2}} J_1[a(t^2-b^2)^{\frac{1}{2}}]$ | $t > b$ | $\mathrm{Re}\, s > \lvert \mathrm{Im}\, a \rvert$ |
| | 52 | $\left[\frac{s}{(s^2-a^2)^{\frac{1}{2}}} - 1\right] e^{-b(s^2-a^2)^{\frac{1}{2}}}$ | $0$ | $0 < t < b$ | $b > 0$ |
| | | | $a\left(\frac{t-b}{t+b}\right)^{\frac{1}{2}} I_1[a(t^2-b^2)^{\frac{1}{2}}]$ | $t > b$ | $\mathrm{Re}\, s > \lvert \mathrm{Re}\, a \rvert$ |
| | 53 | $\frac{b(s^2+a^2)^{\frac{1}{2}}+1}{(s^2+a^2)^{\frac{3}{2}}} e^{-b(s^2+a^2)^{\frac{1}{2}}}$ | $0$ | $0 < t < b$ | $b > 0$ |
| | | | $a^{-1}(t^2-b^2)^{\frac{1}{2}} J_1[a(t^2-b^2)^{\frac{1}{2}}]$ | $t > b$ | $\mathrm{Re}\, s > \lvert \mathrm{Im}\, a \rvert$ |

| | | g(s) | f(t) | | |
|---|---|---|---|---|---|
| 3.2 (Contd.) | 54 | $\dfrac{[(s^2+a^2)^{\frac{1}{2}}-s]^{\nu} e^{-b(s^2+a^2)^{\frac{1}{2}}}}{(s^2+a^2)^{\frac{1}{2}}}$ | $0$ | $0 < t < b$ | $b > 0$ |
| | | | $a^{\nu}\left(\dfrac{t-b}{t+b}\right)^{\frac{\nu}{2}} J_{\nu}[a(t^2-b^2)^{\frac{1}{2}}]$ | $t > b$ | $\operatorname{Re}\nu > -1$<br>$\operatorname{Re} s > \lvert\operatorname{Im} a\rvert$ |
| | 55 | $\dfrac{[s-(s^2-a^2)^{\frac{1}{2}}]^{\nu} e^{-b(s^2-a^2)^{\frac{1}{2}}}}{(s^2-a^2)^{\frac{1}{2}}}$ | $0$ | $0 < t < b$ | $b > 0$ |
| | | | $a^{\nu}\left(\dfrac{t-b}{t+b}\right)^{\frac{\nu}{2}} I_{\nu}[a(t^2-b^2)^{\frac{1}{2}}]$ | $t > b$ | $\operatorname{Re}\nu > -1$<br>$\operatorname{Re} s > \lvert\operatorname{Re} a\rvert$ |
| | 56 | $\dfrac{[\{s+(s^2-a^2)^{\frac{1}{2}}\}^{\nu}-\{s-(s^2-a^2)^{\frac{1}{2}}\}^{\nu}] e^{-b(s^2-a^2)^{\frac{1}{2}}}}{(s^2-a^2)^{\frac{1}{2}}}$ | $0$ | $0 < t < b$ | $\lvert\operatorname{Re}\nu\rvert < 1$ |
| | | | $\dfrac{2}{\pi}a^{\nu}\sin(\nu\pi)\left(\dfrac{t-b}{t+b}\right)^{\frac{\nu}{2}} K_{\nu}[a(t^2-b^2)^{\frac{1}{2}}]$ | $t > b$ | $\operatorname{Re} s > \lvert\operatorname{Re} a\rvert$<br>$b > 0$ |
| | 57 | $e^{-bs}-e^{-b(s^2-ia^2)^{\frac{1}{2}}}$ | $0$ | $0 < t < b$ | $b > 0$<br>$\operatorname{Re}(s \pm a i^{\frac{1}{2}}) > 0$ |
| | | | $ab\, e^{\frac{3\pi}{4}i} \dfrac{\operatorname{ber}_1[a(t^2-b^2)^{\frac{1}{2}}]+i\operatorname{bei}_1[a(t^2-b^2)^{\frac{1}{2}}]}{(t^2-b^2)^{\frac{1}{2}}}$ | $t > b$ | |
| | 58 | $e^{-bs}-\dfrac{s}{(s^2-ia^2)^{\frac{1}{2}}} e^{-b(s^2-ia^2)^{\frac{1}{2}}}$ | $0$ | $0 < t < b$ | $b > 0$<br>$\operatorname{Re}(s \pm a i^{\frac{1}{2}}) > 0$ |
| | | | $\dfrac{a e^{\frac{3}{4}\pi i}\, t\{\operatorname{ber}_1[a(t^2-b^2)^{\frac{1}{2}}]+i\operatorname{bei}_1[a(t^2-b^2)^{\frac{1}{2}}]\}}{(t^2-b^2)^{\frac{1}{2}}}$ | $t > b$ | |
| | 59 | $\dfrac{e^{-b(s^2-ia^2)^{\frac{1}{2}}}}{(s^2-ia^2)^{\frac{1}{2}}}$ | $0$ | $0 < t < b$ | $b > 0$<br>$\operatorname{Re}(s \pm a i^{\frac{1}{2}}) > 0$ |
| | | | $\operatorname{ber}[a(t^2-b^2)^{\frac{1}{2}}]+i\operatorname{bei}[a(t^2-b^2)^{\frac{1}{2}}]$ | $t > b$ | |

| | | g(s) | f(t) | | |
|---|---|---|---|---|---|
| 3.2 (Contd.) | 60 | $\frac{b(s^2-ia^2)^{\frac{1}{2}}+1}{(s^2-ia^2)^{\frac{3}{2}}} e^{-b(s^2-ia^2)^{\frac{1}{2}}}$ | $0$ | $0<t<b$ | $b>0$ |
| | | | $a^{-1} e^{-\frac{3\pi}{4}i} (t^2-b^2)^{\frac{1}{2}} \{ber_1[a(t^2-b^2)^{\frac{1}{2}}] + i\, bei_1[a(t^2-b^2)^{\frac{1}{2}}]\}$ | $t>b$ | $Re(s \pm ai^{\frac{1}{2}})>0$ |
| | 61 | $\frac{s[b(s^2-ia^2)^{\frac{1}{2}}+1]}{(s^2-ia^2)^{\frac{3}{2}}} e^{-b(s^2-ia^2)^{\frac{1}{2}}}$ | $0$ | $0<t<b$ | $b>0$ |
| | | | $t\{ber[a(t^2-b^2)^{\frac{1}{2}}] + i\, bei[a(t^2-b^2)^{\frac{1}{2}}]\}$ | $t>b$ | $Re(s \pm ai^{\frac{1}{2}})>0$ |
| | 62 | $\frac{[s-(s^2-ia^2)^{\frac{1}{2}}]^{\nu}}{(s^2-ia^2)^{\frac{1}{2}}} e^{-b(s^2-ia^2)^{\frac{1}{2}}}$ | $0$ | $0<t<b$ | $b>0$ |
| | | | $(ia)^{\nu} e^{-\frac{3}{4}\nu\pi i} \left(\frac{t-b}{t+b}\right)^{\frac{\nu}{2}} \{ber_{\nu}[a(t^2-b^2)^{\frac{1}{2}}] + i\, bei_{\nu}[a(t -b^2)^{\frac{1}{2}}]\}$ | $t>b$ | $Re\,\nu>-1$, $Re(s \pm ai^{\frac{1}{2}})>0$ |

Functions of $e^{-c[(s+a)(s+b)]^{\frac{1}{2}}}$

| | | | | |
|---|---|---|---|---|
| 63 | $\frac{e^{-c[(s+a)(s+b)]^{\frac{1}{2}}}}{(s+a)^{\frac{1}{2}}(s+b)^{\frac{1}{2}}}$ | $0$ | $0<t<c$ | $Re\, s > Max - Re\, a, - Re\, b$ |
| | | $e^{-\frac{a+b}{2}t} I_0[\frac{a-b}{2}(t^2-c^2)^{\frac{1}{2}}]$ | $t>c$ | $c>0$ |
| 64 | $\frac{1}{s}\left(\frac{s+b}{s+a}\right)^{\frac{1}{2}} e^{-c[(s+a)(s+b)]^{\frac{1}{2}}}$ | $0$ | $0<t<c$ | $Re\, s > Max - Re\, a, - Re\, b, 0$ |
| | | $e^{-\frac{a+b}{2}t} I_0[\frac{a-b}{2}(t^2-c^2)^{\frac{1}{2}}] + b\int_0^t e^{-\frac{a+b}{2}u} I_0[\frac{a-b}{2}(u^2-c^2)^{\frac{1}{2}}]du$ | $t>c$ | $c>0$ |

| | | g(s) | f(t) | | |
|---|---|---|---|---|---|
| 3.2 (Contd.) | 65 | $\dfrac{e^{-b(s+a)^{\frac{1}{2}}(s+b)^{\frac{1}{2}}}}{(s+a)^{\frac{1}{2}}(s+b)^{\frac{1}{2}}[s+\frac{a+b}{2}+(s+a)^{\frac{1}{2}}(s+b)^{\frac{1}{2}}]^{\nu}}$ | $0$ | $0<t<b$ | $\mathrm{Re}\,\nu>-1$ |
| | | | $\left(\dfrac{t-b}{t+b}\right)^{\frac{\nu}{2}}\dfrac{e^{-\frac{a+b}{2}t}}{(a-b)^{\nu}}2^{\nu}I_{\nu}[\frac{a-b}{2}(t^2-b^2)^{\frac{1}{2}}]$ | $t>b$ | $b>0$<br>$\mathrm{Re}\,s>\frac{1}{2}\lvert\mathrm{Re}(a-b)\rvert-\frac{1}{2}\mathrm{Re}(a+b)$ |

Functions of $e^{b[s-(s^2\pm a^2)^{\frac{1}{2}}]}$

| | g(s) | f(t) | |
|---|---|---|---|
| 66 | $\dfrac{[(s^2+a^2)^{\frac{1}{2}}-s]^{\frac{1}{2}}}{(s^2+a^2)^{\frac{1}{2}}}e^{b[s-(s^2+a^2)^{\frac{1}{2}}]}$ | $\dfrac{2^{\frac{1}{2}}\sin[a(t^2+2bt)^{\frac{1}{2}}]}{\pi^{\frac{1}{2}}(t+2b)^{\frac{1}{2}}}$ | $\mathrm{Re}\,s>\lvert\mathrm{Im}\,a\rvert$ |
| 67 | $\dfrac{[s+(s^2+a^2)^{\frac{1}{2}}]^{\frac{1}{2}}}{(s^2+a^2)^{\frac{1}{2}}}e^{b[s-(s^2+a^2)^{\frac{1}{2}}]}$ | $\dfrac{2^{\frac{1}{2}}\cos[a(t^2+2bt)^{\frac{1}{2}}]}{\pi^{\frac{1}{2}}(t+2b)^{\frac{1}{2}}}$ | $\mathrm{Re}\,s>\lvert\mathrm{Im}\,a\rvert$ |
| 68 | $\left[\dfrac{s-(s^2-a^2)^{\frac{1}{2}}}{s^2-a^2}\right]^{\frac{1}{2}}e^{b[s-(s^2-a^2)^{\frac{1}{2}}]}$ | $(\frac{2}{\pi})^{\frac{1}{2}}\dfrac{\sinh[a(t^2+2bt)^{\frac{1}{2}}]}{(t+2b)^{\frac{1}{2}}}$ | $\mathrm{Re}\,s>\lvert\mathrm{Re}\,a\rvert$ |
| 69 | $\left[\dfrac{(s^2-a^2)^{\frac{1}{2}}+s}{s^2-a^2}\right]^{\frac{1}{2}}e^{b[s-(s^2-a^2)^{\frac{1}{2}}]}$ | $(\frac{2}{\pi})^{\frac{1}{2}}\dfrac{\cosh[a(t^2+2bt)^{\frac{1}{2}}]}{(t+2b)^{\frac{1}{2}}}$ | $\mathrm{Re}\,s>\lvert\mathrm{Re}\,a\rvert$ |
| 70 | $\dfrac{e^{b[s-(s^2+a^2)^{\frac{1}{2}}]}}{(s^2+a^2)^{\frac{1}{2}}}$ | $J_0[a(t^2+2bt)^{\frac{1}{2}}]$ | $\lvert\arg b\rvert<\pi$<br>$\mathrm{Re}\,s>\lvert\mathrm{Im}\,a\rvert$ |
| 71 | $\dfrac{e^{b[s-(s^2-a^2)^{\frac{1}{2}}]}}{(s^2-a^2)^{\frac{1}{2}}}$ | $I_0[a(t^2+2bt)^{\frac{1}{2}}]$ | $\lvert\arg b\rvert<\pi$<br>$\mathrm{Re}\,s>\lvert\mathrm{Re}\,a\rvert$ |
| 72 | $1-e^{-b[(s^2+a^2)^{\frac{1}{2}}-s]}$ | $\dfrac{ab\,J_1[a(t^2+2bt)^{\frac{1}{2}}]}{(t^2+2bt)^{\frac{1}{2}}}$ | $\mathrm{Re}\,s>\lvert\mathrm{Im}\,a\rvert$ |

| | | $g(s)$ | $f(t)$ | |
|---|---|---|---|---|
| 3.2 (Contd.) | 73 | $e^{b[s-(s^2-a^2)^{\frac{1}{2}}]}-1$ | $\dfrac{ab\,I_1[a(t^2+2bt)^{\frac{1}{2}}]}{(t^2+2bt)^{\frac{1}{2}}}$ | $\text{Re } s > \lvert \text{Re } a \rvert$ |
| | 74 | $1-\dfrac{s e^{b[s-(s^2+a^2)^{\frac{1}{2}}]}}{(s^2+a^2)^{\frac{1}{2}}}$ | $\dfrac{a(t+b)}{(t^2+2bt)^{\frac{1}{2}}} J_1[a(t^2+2bt)^{\frac{1}{2}}]$ | $\text{Re } s > \lvert \text{Im } a \rvert$ |
| | 75 | $1-\dfrac{s}{(s^2-a^2)^{\frac{1}{2}}} e^{b[s-(s^2-a^2)^{\frac{1}{2}}]}$ | $-\dfrac{a(t+b)}{(t^2+2bt)^{\frac{1}{2}}} I_1[a(t^2+2bt)^{\frac{1}{2}}]$ | $\text{Re } s > \lvert \text{Re } a \rvert$ |
| | 76 | $\dfrac{[(s^2+a^2)^{\frac{1}{2}}-s]^{\nu}}{(s^2+a^2)^{\frac{1}{2}}} e^{b[s-(s^2+a^2)^{\frac{1}{2}}]}$ | $a^{\nu}\left(\dfrac{t}{t+2b}\right)^{\frac{\nu}{2}} J_{\nu}[a(t^2+2bt)^{\frac{1}{2}}]$ | $\text{Re } \nu > -1$<br>$\lvert \arg b \rvert < \pi$<br>$\text{Re } s > \lvert \text{Im } a \rvert$ |
| | 77 | $\dfrac{[s-(s^2-a^2)^{\frac{1}{2}}]^{\nu}}{(s^2-a^2)^{\frac{1}{2}}} e^{b[s-(s^2-a^2)^{\frac{1}{2}}]}$ | $a^{\nu}\left(\dfrac{t}{t+2b}\right)^{\frac{\nu}{2}} I_{\nu}[a(t^2+2bt)^{\frac{1}{2}}]$ | $\text{Re } \nu > -1$<br>$\lvert \arg b \rvert < \pi$<br>$\text{Re } s > \lvert \text{Re } a \rvert$ |

Functions of $e^{c[s-(s+a)^{\frac{1}{2}}(s+b)^{\frac{1}{2}}]}$

| | | | |
|---|---|---|---|
| 78 | $\dfrac{e^{c[s-(s+a)^{\frac{1}{2}}(s+b)^{\frac{1}{2}}]}}{(s+a)^{\frac{1}{2}}(s+b)^{\frac{1}{2}}}$ | $e^{-\frac{a+b}{2}(t+c)} I_0[\frac{a-b}{2}(t^2+2ct)^{\frac{1}{2}}]$ | $\text{Re } s > \text{Max } -\text{Re } a, -\text{Re } b$ |
| 79 | $\dfrac{e^{c[s-(s+a)^{\frac{1}{2}}(s+b)^{\frac{1}{2}}]}}{(s+a)^{\frac{1}{2}}(s+b)^{\frac{1}{2}}[s+\frac{a+b}{2}+(s+a)^{\frac{1}{2}}(s+b)^{\frac{1}{2}}]^{\nu}}$ | $\dfrac{2^{\nu} t^{\frac{\nu}{2}} e^{-\frac{a+b}{2}(t+c)} I_{\nu}[\frac{a-b}{2}(t^2+2ct)^{\frac{1}{2}}]}{(a-b)^{\nu}(t+2c)^{\frac{\nu}{2}}}$ | $\text{Re } \nu > -1$<br>$\text{Re } s > \frac{1}{2}\lvert \text{Re}(a-b) \rvert - \frac{1}{2}\text{Re}(a+b)$ |

Miscellaneous

| | | | |
|---|---|---|---|
| 80 | $\dfrac{e^{-a(s+b^2)^{\frac{1}{2}}}}{s}$ | $\dfrac{e^{-ab}}{2}\text{Erfc}\left(\dfrac{a}{2t^{\frac{1}{2}}}-bt^{\frac{1}{2}}\right)+\dfrac{e^{ab}}{2}\text{Erfc}\left(\dfrac{a}{2t^{\frac{1}{2}}}+bt^{\frac{1}{2}}\right)$ | $\text{Re } s > 0$ |

| | | $g(s)$ | $f(t)$ | |
|---|---|---|---|---|
| 3.2 (Contd.) | 81 | $\dfrac{e^{-\frac{(s^2+1)^{\frac{1}{2}}}{as}}}{s^{\nu}}$ | $\left(\dfrac{t}{a}\right)^{\frac{\nu-1}{2}}\left\{J_{\nu-1}(2a^{\frac{1}{2}}t^{\frac{1}{2}}) - a\,J_{\nu-1}(2a^{\frac{1}{2}}t^{\frac{1}{2}})\displaystyle\int_0^{\infty}\dfrac{J_1[(u^2-a^2)^{\frac{1}{2}}]}{(u^2-a^2)^{\frac{1}{2}}}du\right\}$ | $\mathrm{Re}\,\nu > 0$<br>$\mathrm{Re}\,s > 0$ |
| | 82 | $\displaystyle\int_0^h e^{-u}u^b\left(\frac{a^2}{4}-su-u^2\right)^{\nu}du$<br>where $h = \dfrac{(s^2+a^2)^{\frac{1}{2}}-s}{2}$ | $\left(\frac{a}{2}\right)^{\nu}\Gamma(\nu+1)\,\dfrac{t^{\frac{b-\nu-1}{2}}}{(t+1)^{\frac{b+\nu+1}{2}}}$<br>$\cdot\, J_{b+\nu+1}[a(t^2+t)^{\frac{1}{2}}]$ | $\mathrm{Re}(\nu+b+1) > \mathrm{Re}\,b > -1$<br>$\mathrm{Re}\,s > \lvert\mathrm{Im}\,a\rvert$ |
| | 83 | $e^{-b(s^2+a^2)^{\frac{1}{2}}}\displaystyle\int_0^{\infty}e^{-u}\{u^2-2[cs-b(s^2+a^2)^{\frac{1}{2}}]u$<br>$+\, c^2[(s^2+a^2)^{\frac{1}{2}}-s]^2\}^{-\frac{1}{2}}du$ | $0 \qquad 0 < t < b$<br>$\dfrac{J_0[a(t -b^2)^{\frac{1}{2}}]}{c-t} \qquad t > b$ | $b > 0$<br>$\lvert\arg(b-c)\rvert < \pi$<br>$\mathrm{Re}\,s > \lvert\mathrm{Im}\,a\rvert$ |

Functions of $e^{\pm\frac{a}{2s}}$

| | | | | |
|---|---|---|---|---|
| 3.2.1 | 1 | $\dfrac{(s+a)e^{\frac{a}{2s}}}{s^{\frac{5}{2}}}$ | $\dfrac{2}{\pi^{\frac{1}{2}}}t^{\frac{1}{2}}\cosh(2^{\frac{1}{2}}a^{\frac{1}{2}}t^{\frac{1}{2}})$ | $\mathrm{Re}\,s > 0$ |
| | 2 | $\dfrac{(s-a)e^{-\frac{a}{2s}}}{s^{\frac{5}{2}}}$ | $\dfrac{2}{\pi^{\frac{1}{2}}}t^{\frac{1}{2}}\cos(2^{\frac{1}{2}}a^{\frac{1}{2}}t^{\frac{1}{2}})$ | $\mathrm{Re}\,s > 0$ |

Functions of $e^{-as^{\frac{1}{2}}}$

| | | | | |
|---|---|---|---|---|
| | 3 | $\dfrac{e^{-as^{\frac{1}{2}}}}{s^2}$ | $\left(t+\dfrac{a^2}{2}\right)\mathrm{Erfc}\,\dfrac{a}{2t^{\frac{1}{2}}} - \dfrac{at^{\frac{1}{2}}}{\pi^{\frac{1}{2}}}e^{-\frac{a^2}{4t}}$ | $\mathrm{Re}\,a^2 \geqslant 0$<br>$\mathrm{Re}\,s > 0$ |
| | 4 | $\dfrac{s}{s^2+b^2}e^{-as^{\frac{1}{2}}}$ | $e^{-\frac{ab^{\frac{1}{2}}}{2^{\frac{1}{2}}}}\cos\left[bt-\left(\dfrac{a^2b}{2}\right)^{\frac{1}{2}}\right]$<br>$-\dfrac{1}{\pi}\displaystyle\int_0^{\infty}e^{-ut}\sin(au^{\frac{1}{2}})\dfrac{u}{u^2+b^2}du$ | $\mathrm{Re}\,a^2 \geqslant 0$<br>$\mathrm{Re}\,b \geqslant 0$<br>$\mathrm{Re}\,s > \lvert\mathrm{Im}\,b\rvert$ |

| | | $g(s)$ | $f(t)$ | |
|---|---|---|---|---|
| 3.2.1 (Contd.) | 5 | $\dfrac{e^{-as^{\frac{1}{2}}}}{(s^{\frac{1}{2}}+b)^2}$ | $(2bt^2+ab+1)e^{ab+b^2t}\text{Erfc}\left(\dfrac{a}{2t^{\frac{1}{2}}}+bt^{\frac{1}{2}}\right) - \dfrac{2bt^{\frac{1}{2}}}{\pi^{\frac{1}{2}}}e^{-\frac{a^2}{4t}}$ | Re $a^2 > 0$<br>Re $s > 0$ if Re $b \geq 0$<br>Re $s >$ Max $0$, Re $b^2$ if Re $b < 0$ |
| | 6 | $\dfrac{e^{-as^{\frac{1}{2}}}}{s^{\frac{1}{2}}(s^{\frac{1}{2}}+b)^2}$ | $2(\frac{t}{\pi})^{\frac{1}{2}}e^{-\frac{a^2}{4t}}-(2bt+a)e^{ab+b^2t}\cdot \text{Erfc}\left(\dfrac{a}{2t^{\frac{1}{2}}}+bt^{\frac{1}{2}}\right)$ | Re $a^2 > 0$<br>Re $s > 0$ if Re $b \geq 0$<br>Re $s >$ Max $0$, Re $b^2$ if Re $b < 0$ |
| | 7 | $\dfrac{e^{-as^{\frac{1}{2}}}}{s(s^{\frac{1}{2}}+b)^2}$ | $\dfrac{1}{b^2}\text{Erfc}\dfrac{a}{2t^{\frac{1}{2}}} - \dfrac{2t^{\frac{1}{2}}e^{-\frac{a^2}{4t}}}{\pi^{\frac{1}{2}}b} + (2t+\frac{a}{b}-\frac{1}{b^2})e^{ab+b^2t}\text{Erfc}\left(\dfrac{a}{2t^{\frac{1}{2}}}+bt^{\frac{1}{2}}\right)$ | Re $a^2 > 0$<br>Re $s > 0$ if Re $b \geq 0$<br>Re $s >$ Max $0$, Re $b^2$ if Re $b < 0$ |

Functions of $e^{-b(s^2 \pm a^2)^{\frac{1}{2}}}$

| | $g(s)$ | $f(t)$ | | |
|---|---|---|---|---|
| 8 | $\dfrac{e^{-b(s^2+a^2)^{\frac{1}{2}}}}{s^2+a^2}$ | $0$ | $0 < t < b$ | $b > 0$ |
| | | $\int_b^t J_0[a(t-u)]J_0[a(u^2-b^2)^{\frac{1}{2}}]du$ | $t > b$ | Re $s > \lvert \text{Im } a \rvert$ |
| 9 | $\dfrac{e^{-b(s^2-a^2)^{\frac{1}{2}}}}{s^2-a^2}$ | $0$ | $0 < t < b$ | $b > 0$ |
| | | $\int_b^t I_0[a(t-u)]I_0[a(u^2-b^2)]du$ | $t > b$ | Re $s > \lvert \text{Re } a \rvert$ |
| 10 | $\dfrac{se^{-b(s^2+a^2)^{\frac{1}{2}}}}{s^2+a^2}$ | $0$ | $0 < t < b$ | $b > 0$ |
| | | $\frac{\pi a}{2}Y_0[a(t^2-b^2)^{\frac{1}{2}}]*[ab\, J_0(at)+\sin at] - \frac{\pi a}{2}(t^2-b^2)^{\frac{1}{2}}Y_0[a(t^2-b^2)^{\frac{1}{2}}]$ | $t > b$ | Re $s > \lvert \text{Im } a \rvert$ |

| | | $g(s)$ | $f(t)$ | | |
|---|---|---|---|---|---|
| 3.2.1 (Contd.) | 11 | $s\,e^{-b(s^2-a^2)^{\frac{1}{2}}}\left[\frac{b}{s^2-a^2}+\frac{1}{(s^2-a^2)^{\frac{3}{2}}}\right]$ | $0$ | $0<t<b$ | $b>0$ <br> $\mathrm{Re}\, s>\lvert\mathrm{Re}\, a\rvert$ |
| | | | $t\,I_0[a(t^2-b^2)^{\frac{1}{2}}]$ | $t>b$ | |
| | 12 | $e^{-b(s^2-a^2)^{\frac{1}{2}}}\left[\frac{b}{s^2-a^2}-\frac{1}{(s^2-a^2)^{\frac{3}{2}}}\right]$ | $0$ | $0<t<b$ | $b>0$ <br> $\mathrm{Re}\, s>\lvert\mathrm{Re}\, a\rvert$ |
| | | | $\frac{1}{a}(t^2-b^2)^{\frac{1}{2}}I_1[a(t^2-b^2)^{\frac{1}{2}}]$ | $t>b$ | |
| **Miscellaneous** | | | | | |
| | 13 | $\int_0^\infty \frac{u^\mu}{(s+au)^\nu}e^{-\frac{u^2}{2}}du$ | $\frac{\Gamma(\mu+1)}{\Gamma(\nu)}t^{\nu-1}e^{\frac{a^2t^2}{4}}D_{-\mu-1}(at)$ | | $\mathrm{Re}\,\nu>0$ <br> $\mathrm{Re}\, s>0$ |
| 4 | 1 | $\frac{\log s}{s}$ | $-\log(\gamma t)$ | | $\mathrm{Re}\, s>0$ |
| | 2 | $\frac{1}{\log s}$ | $\int_0^\infty \frac{t^{u-1}}{\Gamma(u)}du$ | | $\mathrm{Re}\, s>0$ |
| | 3 | $\frac{1}{s\log\frac{s}{a}}$ | $\nu(at)$ | | $\mathrm{Re}\, s>0$ |
| | 4 | $\frac{1}{s(\log\frac{s}{a})^b}$ | $\frac{\mu(at,b-1)}{\Gamma(b)}$ | | $\mathrm{Re}\, b>0$ <br> $\mathrm{Re}\, s>\mathrm{Re}\, a$ |
| | 5 | $\frac{(\log s)^2}{s}$ | $[\log(\gamma t)]^2-\frac{\pi^2}{6}$ | | $\mathrm{Re}\, s>0$ |
| | 6 | $\frac{1}{s}\left\{\frac{\pi^2}{6}+[\log(\gamma s)]^2\right\}$ | $(\log t)^2$ | | $\mathrm{Re}\, s>0$ |

| | | g(s) | f(t) | |
|---|---|---|---|---|
| 4 (Contd.) | 7 | $\frac{\log^3 s}{s}$ | $\frac{\pi^2}{2}\log \gamma t-\log^3\gamma t+\psi''(1)$ | Re s > 0 |
| 4.1 | 1 | $\frac{\log s}{s^{n+1}}$ | $[1+\frac{1}{2}+\frac{1}{3}+\dots+\frac{1}{n}-\log(\gamma t)]\frac{t^n}{n!}$ | n = 1,2,3,... Re s > 0 |
| | 2 | $\left(\frac{\log s}{s}\right)^2$ | $t\left\{[1-\log(\gamma t)]^2+1-\frac{\pi^2}{6}\right\}$ | Re s > 0 |
| | 3 | $\frac{\log^3 s}{s^2}$ | $t[(1-\log\gamma t)^3-3(1-\frac{\pi^2}{6})\log\gamma t+5-\frac{\pi^2}{2}+\psi''(1)]$ | Re s > 0 |
| | 4 | $\frac{1}{s^{n+1}}[1+\frac{1}{2}+\frac{1}{3}+\dots+\frac{1}{n}-\log(\gamma s)]$ | $\frac{t^n}{n!}\log t$ | n = 1,2,3,... Re s > 0 |
| | 5 | $\frac{\log s}{s^2+a^2}$ | $a^{-1}\{\cos(at)\mathrm{Si}(at)+\sin(at)[\log a-\mathrm{Ci}(at)]\}$ | Re s > 0 |
| | 6 | $\frac{s\log s}{s^2+a^2}$ | $\cos(at)[\log a-\mathrm{Ci}(at)]-\sin(at)\mathrm{Si}(at)$ | Re s > 0 |
| | 7 | $\frac{\log\frac{s}{a}}{s^2+a^2}$ | $\frac{\cos(at)\mathrm{Si}(at)-\sin(at)\mathrm{Ci}(at)}{a}$ | Re s > 0 |
| | 8 | $\frac{s\log\frac{s}{a}}{s^2+a^2}$ | $-\sin(at)\mathrm{Si}(at)-\cos(at)\mathrm{Ci}(at)$ | Re s > 0 |
| | 9 | $\frac{\log(s+b)}{s+a}$ | $e^{-at}\{\log(b-a)-\mathrm{Ei}[(a-b)t]\}$ | Re s > - Re a |

| | | g(s) | t(f) | |
|---|---|---|---|---|
| 4.1 (Contd.) | 10 | $(s+2a)\log(s+2a) + s\log s - 2(s+a)\log(s+a)$ | $\frac{(1-e^{-at})^2}{t^2}$ | Re s > Max o, - Re 2a |
| | 11 | $\frac{1}{s}\log(\frac{s}{a}+1)$ | $-\mathrm{Ei}(-at)$ $= -\mathrm{li}(e^{-at})$ | $\lvert \arg a \rvert < \pi$ Re s > o |
| | 12 | $\frac{1}{s}\log(\frac{s}{a}-1)$ | $-\overline{\mathrm{Ei}}(at)$ $= -\mathrm{li}(e^{at})$ | Re a > o Re s > Re a |
| | 13 | $\log\frac{s-a}{s}$ | $\frac{1-e^{at}}{t}$ | Re s > Max o, Re a |
| | 14 | $s\log(1+\frac{a}{s})-a$ | $\frac{(at+1)e^{-at}-1}{t^2}$ | Re s > - Re a |
| | 15 | $(s+\frac{a}{2})\log(1+\frac{a}{s})-a$ | $\frac{a}{t}-\frac{(at+2)(1-e^{-at})}{2t^2}$ | Re s > - Re a |
| | 16 | $\log\frac{s+a}{s-a}$ | $\frac{2\sinh(at)}{t}$ | Re s > $\lvert$Re a$\rvert$ |
| | 17 | $\frac{1}{s}\log\frac{s+a}{s-a}$ | $2\sinh(at)$ | Re s > $\lvert$Re a$\rvert$ |
| | 18 | $\log\frac{s+b}{s+a}$ | $\frac{e^{-at}-e^{-bt}}{t}$ | Re s > Max - Re a, - Re b |
| | 19 | $s\log\frac{s+a}{s+b}+b-a$ | $e^{-at}\left(\frac{a}{t}+\frac{1}{t^2}\right)-e^{-bt}\left(\frac{b}{t}+\frac{1}{t^2}\right)$ | Re s > Max - Re a, - Re b |

| | | g(s) | f(t) | |
|---|---|---|---|---|
| 4.1 (Contd.) | 20 | $\frac{\log(s^2+a^2)}{s}$ | $2\,\mathrm{ci}(at) + 2\log a$ | Re s > \|Im a\| |
| | 21 | $\frac{\log(s^2+a^2)}{s^2}$ | $2t\left[\log a + \frac{\sin(at)}{at} + \mathrm{ci}(at)\right]$ | Re a > o<br>Re s > \|Im a\| |
| | 22 | $\frac{1}{s}\log(s^2-a^2)$ | $2\log a - 2\,\mathrm{Cih}(at)$ | Re s > \|Re a\| |
| | 23 | $\frac{1}{s^2}\log(s^2-a^2)$ | $-2t\,\mathrm{Cih}(at) + \frac{2}{a}\sinh(at) + 2t\log a$ | Re a > o<br>Re s > Re a |
| | 24 | $\log(1+\frac{a^2}{s^2})$ | $\left(\frac{2\pi a}{t}\right)^{\frac{1}{2}} \mathbf{H}_{\frac{1}{2}}(at)$<br>$= 2\,\frac{1-\cos(at)}{t}$ | Re s > \|Im a\| |
| | 25 | $\log\left(1-\frac{a^2}{s^2}\right)$ | $-\left(\frac{2\pi a}{t}\right)^{\frac{1}{2}} \mathbf{L}_{\frac{1}{2}}(at)$<br>$= \frac{2[1-\cosh(at)]}{t}$ | Re s > \|Re a\| |
| | 26 | $s\log\left(1+\frac{a^2}{s^2}\right)$ | $\frac{2[\cos(at)-1]}{t^2} + \frac{2a\sin(at)}{t}$ | Re s > \|Im a\| |
| | 27 | $s\log\left(1-\frac{a^2}{s^2}\right)$ | $\frac{3}{t^2}\,[\cosh(at)-1] - \frac{2a}{t}\sinh(at)$ | Re s > \|Re a\| |
| | 28 | $\frac{1}{s}\log\left(1+\frac{s^2}{a^2}\right)$ | $-2\,\mathrm{Ci}(at)$<br>$= 2\,\mathrm{ci}(at)$ | Re s > \|Im a\| |

| | | g(s) | f(t) | |
|---|---|---|---|---|
| 4.1 (Contd.) | 29 | $\frac{a}{s}-\frac{s}{a}\log\left(1+\frac{a^2}{s^2}\right)$ | $\left(\frac{2\pi a}{t}\right)^{\frac{1}{2}}\mathbf{H}_{\frac{3}{2}}(at)$ | Re s > \|Im a\| |
| | 30 | $\frac{s}{a}\log\left(1-\frac{a^2}{s^2}\right)-\frac{a}{s}$ | $\left(\frac{2\pi a}{t}\right)^{\frac{1}{2}}\mathbf{L}_{\frac{3}{2}}(at)$ | Re s > \|Re a\| |
| | 31 | $\frac{a^2-s^2}{s^2(a^2+s^2)}+\frac{\log\left(1+\frac{a^2}{s^2}\right)}{a^2}$ | $\left(\frac{2\pi t}{a}\right)^{\frac{1}{2}}\mathbf{H}_{\frac{3}{2}}(at)$ | Re s > \|Im a\| |
| | 32 | $\frac{s^2+a^2}{s^2(s^2-a^2)}-\frac{1}{a^2}\log\left(1-\frac{a^2}{s^2}\right)$ | $\left(\frac{2\pi t}{a}\right)^{\frac{1}{2}}\mathbf{L}_{\frac{3}{2}}(at)$ | Re s > \|Re a\| |
| | 33 | $\frac{\log(s^2+a^2)}{s^2+a^2}$ | $\frac{\sin(at)}{a}\left[\log\frac{2a}{\gamma t}-\mathrm{Ci}(2at)\right]+\frac{\cos(at)\mathrm{Si}(2at)}{a}$ | Re s > \|Im a\| |
| | 34 | $\frac{s\log(s^2+a^2)}{s^2+a^2}$ | $\cos(at)\left[\log\frac{2a}{\gamma t}-\mathrm{Ci}(2at)\right]-\sin(at)\mathrm{Si}(2at)$ | Re s > \|Im a\| |
| | 35 | $\frac{\log(s^2-a^2)}{s^2-a^2}$ | $\frac{2}{a}\left[-\log\gamma t\sinh(at)+\cosh(at)*\frac{\sinh(at)}{t}\right]$ | Re s > \|Re a\| |
| | 36 | $\frac{s\log(s^2-a^2)}{s^2-a^2}$ | $2\left[-\log\gamma t\cosh(at)+\sinh(at)*\frac{\sinh(at)}{t}\right]$ | Re s > \|Re a\| |
| | 37 | $\log\frac{s^2+b^2}{s^2+a^2}$ | $2\,\frac{\cos(at)-\cos(bt)}{t}$ | Re s > Max \|Im a\|,\|Im b\| |
| | 38 | $s\log\frac{s^2+b^2}{s^2+a^2}$ | $\frac{2}{t^2}[\cos(bt)+bt\sin(bt)-\cos(at)-at\sin(at)]$ | Re s > Max \|Im a\|,\|Im b\| |

| | | g(s) | f(t) | |
|---|---|---|---|---|
| 4.1 (Contd.) | 39 | $\log \frac{(s+a)^2+c^2}{(s+b)^2+c^2}$ | $\frac{2\cos(ct)}{t}(e^{-bt}-e^{-at})$ | Re $s > \lvert \text{Im } c \rvert$ - Min Re $a$, Re $b$ |
| | 40 | $2\log \frac{(s^2+a^2)^2}{s^3} - \log(s^2+4a^2)$ | $\frac{16}{t}\sin^4(\frac{at}{2})$ | Re $s > 2\lvert \text{Im } a \rvert$ |
| | 41 | $\log \frac{s^2+as+b}{s^2-as+b}$ | $\frac{4\cos[t(b-\frac{a^2}{4})^{\frac{1}{2}}]\sinh\frac{at}{2}}{t}$ | Re $s > \lvert \text{Im}(b-\frac{a^2}{4})^{\frac{1}{2}} \rvert + \lvert \text{Re } \frac{a}{2} \rvert$ |
| | 42 | $\log \frac{(s^2+a^2)(s^2+b^2)}{[s^2+(\frac{a-b}{2})^2]^2}$ | $\frac{8\sin^2\left(\frac{a+b}{4}t\right)\cos\left(\frac{a-b}{2}t\right)}{t}$ | Re $s >$ Max $\lvert \text{Im } a \rvert, \lvert \text{Im } b \rvert, \lvert \text{Im } \frac{a-b}{2} \rvert$ |
| 4.2 | 1 | $\frac{1}{s^{\frac{1}{2}}}\log(4\gamma s)$ | $-\frac{\log t}{(\pi t)^{\frac{1}{2}}}$ | Re $s > 0$ |
| | 2 | $\frac{\log s}{s^{n+\frac{1}{2}}}$ | $\frac{2^n t^{n-\frac{1}{2}}}{1.3.5\ldots(2n-1)\pi^{\frac{1}{2}}}\left[2(1+\frac{1}{3}+\ldots+\frac{1}{2n-1}) - \log(4\gamma t)\right]$ | $n = 1,2,3,\ldots$ Re $s > 0$ |
| | 3 | $\frac{\log s}{s^{\nu}}$ | $\frac{t^{\nu-1}}{\Gamma(\nu)}[\psi(\nu)-\log t]$ | Re $\nu > 0$ Re $s > 0$ |
| | 4 | $\frac{1}{s^b \log \frac{s}{a}}$ | $a^{-b+1}\nu(at,b-1)$ | Re $b > 0$ Re $s >$ Re $a$ |
| | 5 | $\frac{1}{s^{n+\frac{1}{2}}}[2(1+\frac{1}{3}+\frac{1}{5}+\ldots+\frac{1}{2n-1})-\log(4\gamma s)]$ | $\frac{2^n}{\pi^{\frac{1}{2}}.1.3.5\ldots(2n-1)}t^{n-\frac{1}{2}}\log t$ | $n = 1,2,3,\ldots$ Re $s > 0$ |

| | | g(s) | f(t) | |
|---|---|---|---|---|
| 4.2 (Contd.) | 6 | $\dfrac{1}{s^{\nu}\log s}$ | $\displaystyle\int_{\nu}^{\infty}\frac{t^{u-1}}{\Gamma(u)}\,du$ | Re s > o |
| | 7 | $\dfrac{s^{\nu}-1}{(s^{\nu}+1)\log s}$ | $\displaystyle\sum_{n=1}^{\infty}\left[\int_{(2n-2)\nu}^{(2n-1)\nu}\frac{t^{u-1}}{\Gamma(u)}\,du-\int_{(2n-1)\nu}^{2n\nu}\frac{t^{u-1}}{\Gamma(u)}\,du\right]$ | Re s > o |
| | 8 | $\dfrac{s^{\nu}+1}{(s^{\nu}-1)\log s}$ | $\displaystyle\sum_{n=1}^{\infty}(2n-1)\int_{(n-1)\nu}^{n\nu}\frac{t^{u-1}}{\Gamma(u)}\,du$ | Re s > o |
| | 9 | $\dfrac{s^{\nu}}{(s^{2\nu}+1)\log s}$ | $\displaystyle\sum_{n=1}^{\infty}\int_{(4n-3)\nu}^{(4n-1)\nu}\frac{t^{u-1}}{\Gamma(u)}\,du$ | Re s > o |
| | 10 | $\dfrac{s^{\nu}}{(s^{2\nu}-1)\log s}$ | $\displaystyle\sum_{n=1}^{\infty}n\int_{(2n-1)\nu}^{(2n+1)\nu}\frac{t^{u-1}}{\Gamma(u)}\,du$ | Re s > o |
| | 11 | $\dfrac{s^{\nu}(s^{2\nu}-1)}{(s^{4\nu}+1)\log s}$ | $\displaystyle\sum_{n=1}^{\infty}\left[\int_{(8n-7)\nu}^{(8n-5)\nu}\frac{t^{u-1}}{\Gamma(u)}du-\int_{(8n-3)\nu}^{(8n-1)\nu}\frac{t^{u-1}}{\Gamma(u)}du\right]$ | Re s > o |
| | 12 | $\dfrac{\log\left[\dfrac{(s^2+a^2)^{\frac{1}{2}}+a}{s}\right]}{(s^2+a^2)^{\frac{1}{2}}}$ | $\frac{\pi}{2}\,\mathbf{H}_0(at)$ | Re s > \|Im a\| |
| | 13 | $\dfrac{1}{s}-\dfrac{s}{a(s^2+a^2)^{\frac{1}{2}}}\log\dfrac{(s^2+a^2)^{\frac{1}{2}}+a}{s}$ | $\frac{\pi}{2}\,\mathbf{H}_1(at)$ | Re s > \|Im a\| |
| | 14 | $\dfrac{1}{s^{\frac{1}{2}}}\log\left[\left(\dfrac{s}{a}\right)^{\frac{1}{2}}+\left(\dfrac{s}{a}+1\right)^{\frac{1}{2}}\right]$ | $-\dfrac{Ei(-at)}{2(\pi t)^{\frac{1}{2}}}$ | Re s > o |

| | | g(s) | f(t) | |
|---|---|---|---|---|
| 4.2 (Contd.) | 15 | $\dfrac{\log[(s+a)^{\frac{1}{2}}+(s+b)^{\frac{1}{2}}]}{(s+b)^{\frac{1}{2}}}$ | $\dfrac{e^{-bt}}{2\pi^{\frac{1}{2}}t^{\frac{1}{2}}}\{\log(a-b)-\mathrm{Ei}[(b-a)t]\}$ | $\lvert\arg(b-a)\rvert<\pi$<br>$\mathrm{Re}\, s > -\mathrm{Re}\, b$ |
| | 16 | $\dfrac{1}{s}\log[s+(s^2+a^2)^{\frac{1}{2}}]$ | $\mathrm{Ji}_0(at)+\log a$ | $\mathrm{Re}\, s > 0$ |
| | 17 | $\dfrac{1}{s}\log[s+(s^2-a^2)^{\frac{1}{2}}]$ | $\mathrm{Ii}_0(at)+\log a+\dfrac{\pi i}{2}$ | $\mathrm{Re}\, s > \lvert\mathrm{Re}\, a\rvert$ |
| | 18 | $\dfrac{1}{s}\log^2[s+(s^2+a^2)^{\frac{1}{2}}]$ | $\log a[\log a+2\,\mathrm{Ji}_0(at)]-\pi\,\mathrm{Yi}_0(at)$ | $\mathrm{Re}\, s > \lvert\mathrm{Im}\, a\rvert$ |
| | 19 | $\dfrac{1}{s}\log^2[s+(s^2-a^2)^{\frac{1}{2}}]$ | $\log a[\log a+i\pi+2\,\mathrm{Ii}_0(at)]+2\,\mathrm{Ki}_0(at)-\dfrac{\pi^2}{4}$ | $\mathrm{Re}\, s > \lvert\mathrm{Re}\, a\rvert$ |
| | 20 | $\dfrac{\log[s+(s^2+a^2)^{\frac{1}{2}}]}{(s^2+a^2)^{\frac{1}{2}}}$ | $\log a\, J_0(at)-\dfrac{\pi}{2}Y_0(at)$ | $\mathrm{Re}\, s > \lvert\mathrm{Im}\, a\rvert$ |
| | 21 | $\dfrac{\log\dfrac{s+(s^2+a^2)^{\frac{1}{2}}}{a}}{(s^2+a^2)^{\frac{1}{2}}}$ | $-\dfrac{\pi}{2}Y_0(at)$ | $\mathrm{Re}\, s > \lvert\mathrm{Im}\, a\rvert$ |
| | 22 | $\dfrac{1+\dfrac{2i}{\pi}\log\dfrac{s+(s^2+a^2)^{\frac{1}{2}}}{a}}{(s^2+a^2)^{\frac{1}{2}}}$ | $H_0^{(2)}(at)$ | $\mathrm{Re}\, s > \lvert\mathrm{Im}\, a\rvert$ |
| | 23 | $\dfrac{1-\dfrac{2i}{\pi}\log\dfrac{s+(s^2+a^2)^{\frac{1}{2}}}{a}}{(s^2+a^2)^{\frac{1}{2}}}$ | $H_0^{(1)}(at)$ | $\mathrm{Re}\, s > \lvert\mathrm{Im}\, a\rvert$ |
| | 24 | $\dfrac{\log[s+(s^2+a^2)^{\frac{1}{2}}]}{(s^2+a^2)^{\frac{3}{2}}}$ | $\dfrac{t}{a}[J_1(at)\log a-\dfrac{\pi}{2}Y_1(at)]-\dfrac{\cos(at)}{a^2}$ | $\mathrm{Re}\, s > \lvert\mathrm{Im}\, a\rvert$ |

| | | $g(s)$ | $f(t)$ | |
|---|---|---|---|---|
| 4.2 (Contd.) | 25 | $\dfrac{s}{(s^2+a^2)^{\frac{3}{2}}}\log[s+(s^2+a^2)^{\frac{1}{2}}]$ | $t[J_0(at)\log a-\frac{\pi}{2}Y_0(at)]+\dfrac{\sin(at)}{a}$ | $\mathrm{Re}\, s>\lvert\mathrm{Im}\, a\rvert$ |
| | 26 | $\dfrac{\log[s+(s^2-a^2)^{\frac{1}{2}}]}{(s^2-a^2)^{\frac{1}{2}}}$ | $I_0(at)\log a+K_0(at)$ | $\mathrm{Re}\, s>\lvert\mathrm{Re}\, a\rvert$ |
| | 27 | $\dfrac{\log\dfrac{s+(s^2-a^2)^{\frac{1}{2}}}{a}}{(s^2-a^2)^{\frac{1}{2}}}$ | $K_0(at)$ | $\mathrm{Re}\, s>-\mathrm{Re}\, a$ |
| | 28 | $\dfrac{\log[s+(s^2-ia^2)^{\frac{1}{2}}]}{(s^2-ia^2)^{\frac{1}{2}}}$ | $\mathrm{ker}(at)+i\,\mathrm{kei}(at)+\frac{\pi}{4}[\mathrm{ber}(at)+i\,\mathrm{bei}(at)]$ $+\log a\, I_0(ai^{\frac{1}{2}}t)$ | $\mathrm{Re}\, s>\dfrac{\lvert\mathrm{Re}\, a\rvert+\lvert\mathrm{Im}\, a\rvert}{2^{\frac{1}{2}}}$ |
| | 29 | $\dfrac{\log[s+(s^2-a^2)^{\frac{1}{2}}]}{(s^2-a^2)^{\frac{3}{2}}}$ | $\frac{t}{a}[I_1(at)\log a-K_1(at)]+\dfrac{\cosh(at)}{a^2}$ | $\mathrm{Re}\, s>\lvert\mathrm{Re}\, a\rvert$ |
| | 30 | $\dfrac{s\log[s+(s^2-a^2)^{\frac{1}{2}}]}{(s^2-a^2)^{\frac{3}{2}}}$ | $t[I_0(at)\log a+K_0(at)]+\dfrac{\sinh(at)}{a}$ | $\mathrm{Re}\, s>\lvert\mathrm{Re}\, a\rvert$ |
| | 31 | $\dfrac{s}{(s^2+a^2)^{\frac{1}{2}}}\log\dfrac{a+(s^2+a^2)^{\frac{1}{2}}}{s}$ | $a-\frac{\pi a}{2}\mathbf{H}_1(at)$ | $\mathrm{Re}\, s>\lvert\mathrm{Im}\, a\rvert$ |
| | 32 | $1-\dfrac{(s^2+a^2)^{\frac{1}{2}}}{a}\log\dfrac{(s^2+a^2)^{\frac{1}{2}}+a}{s}$ | $-\dfrac{\pi}{2t}\mathbf{H}_1(at)$ | $\mathrm{Re}\, s>\lvert\mathrm{Im}\, a\rvert$ |
| | 33 | $\dfrac{1}{(s^2+1)^{\frac{1}{2}}}\log\dfrac{[s+(s^2+1)^{\frac{1}{2}}][1+(s^2+1)^{\frac{1}{2}}]}{s}$ | $\frac{\pi}{2}[\mathbf{H}_0(t)-Y_0(t)]$ | $\mathrm{Re}\, s>0$ |

| | | g(s) | f(t) | |
|---|---|---|---|---|
| 4.2 (Contd.) | 34 | $\dfrac{\log \dfrac{[(s+b)^{\frac{1}{2}}+1][(s-b)^{\frac{1}{2}}+1]+(s+b-1)^{\frac{1}{2}}(s-b-1)^{\frac{1}{2}}}{[(s+b)^{\frac{1}{2}}+1][(s-b)^{\frac{1}{2}}+1]-(s+b-1)^{\frac{1}{2}}(s-b-1)^{\frac{1}{2}}}}{(s+b-1)^{\frac{1}{2}}(s-b-1)^{\frac{1}{2}}}$ | $-\frac{1}{2}e^{t}I_0(bt)Ei(-t)$ | Re $s > 1+\lvert \text{Re } b\rvert$ |
| 4.2.1 | 1 | $\dfrac{a}{(s^2+a^2)^{\frac{3}{2}}}\left(\dfrac{\pi}{2}+i\log\dfrac{s+(s^2+a^2)^{\frac{1}{2}}}{a}\right)+\dfrac{is}{a(s^2+a^2)}$ | $\frac{\pi}{2}tH_1^{(2)}(at)$ | Re $s > \lvert \text{Im } a\rvert$ |
| | 2 | $\dfrac{a}{(s^2+a^2)^{\frac{3}{2}}}\left(\dfrac{\pi}{2}-i\log\dfrac{s+(s^2+a^2)^{\frac{1}{2}}}{a}\right)-\dfrac{is}{a(s^2+a^2)}$ | $\frac{\pi}{2}tH_1^{(1)}(at)$ | Re $s > \lvert \text{Im } a\rvert$ |
| | 3 | $\dfrac{s}{(s^2+a^2)^{\frac{3}{2}}}\left(\dfrac{\pi}{2}+i\log\dfrac{s+(s^2+a^2)^{\frac{1}{2}}}{a}\right)-\dfrac{i}{s^2+a^2}$ | $\frac{\pi}{2}tH_0^{(2)}(at)$ | Re $s > \lvert \text{Im } a\rvert$ |
| | 4 | $\dfrac{s}{(s^2+a^2)^{\frac{3}{2}}}\left(\dfrac{\pi}{2}-i\log\dfrac{s+(s^2+a^2)^{\frac{1}{2}}}{a}\right)+\dfrac{i}{s^2+a^2}$ | $\frac{\pi}{2}tH_0^{(1)}(at)$ | Re $s > \lvert \text{Im } a\rvert$ |
| | 5 | $\dfrac{1-\dfrac{s}{(s^2+a^2)^{\frac{1}{2}}}\log\dfrac{s+(s^2+a^2)^{\frac{1}{2}}}{a}}{s^2+a^2}$ | $\frac{\pi}{2}tY_0(at)$ | Re $s > \lvert \text{Im } a\rvert$ |
| | 6 | $\dfrac{s}{a(s^2+a^2)}+\dfrac{a\log\dfrac{s+(s^2+a^2)^{\frac{1}{2}}}{a}}{(s^2+a^2)^{\frac{3}{2}}}$ | $-\frac{\pi}{2}tY_1(at)$ | Re $s > \lvert \text{Im } a\rvert$ |
| | 7 | $\dfrac{s}{a(s^2-a^2)}-\dfrac{a\log\dfrac{s+(s^2-a^2)^{\frac{1}{2}}}{a}}{(s^2-a^2)^{\frac{3}{2}}}$ | $tK_1(at)$ | Re $s > -$ Re $a$ |
| | 8 | $\dfrac{s\log\dfrac{s+(s^2-a^2)^{\frac{1}{2}}}{a}}{(s^2-a^2)^{\frac{3}{2}}}-\dfrac{1}{s^2-a^2}$ | $tK_0(at)$ | Re $s > -$ Re $a$ |

| | | g(s) | f(t) | | |
|---|---|---|---|---|---|
| 4.2.1 (Contd.) | 9 | $\frac{s}{(s^2-ia^2)^{\frac{3}{2}}}\log\frac{i^{-\frac{1}{2}}[s+(s^2-ia^2)^{\frac{1}{2}}]}{a}-\frac{1}{s^2-ia^2}$ | $t[\mathrm{ker}(at)+i\,\mathrm{kei}(at)]$ | | $\mathrm{Re}(s\pm ai^{\frac{1}{2}})>0$ |
| | 10 | $\frac{s}{ai^{\frac{1}{2}}(s^2-ia^2)}-\frac{ai^{\frac{1}{2}}}{(s^2-ia^2)^{\frac{3}{2}}}\log\frac{s+(s^2-ia^2)^{\frac{1}{2}}}{ai^{\frac{1}{2}}}$ | $t[\mathrm{ker}_1(at)+i\,\mathrm{kei}_1(at)]$ | | $\mathrm{Re}(s\pm ai^{\frac{1}{2}})>0$ |
| | 11 | $\frac{3s^2+a^2}{3s}-(s^2+a^2)^{\frac{1}{2}}\log\frac{(s^2+a^2)^{\frac{1}{2}}+a}{s}$ | $\frac{\pi a}{2t}\mathbf{H}_2(at)$ | | $\mathrm{Re}\,s>\lvert\mathrm{Im}\,a\rvert$ |
| | 12 | $\frac{a^2-6s^2}{3s^2}+\frac{a^2+2s^2}{a(s^2+a^2)^{\frac{1}{2}}}\log\frac{(s^2+a^2)^{\frac{1}{2}}+a}{s}$ | $\frac{\pi a}{2}\mathbf{H}_2(at)$ | | $\mathrm{Re}\,s>\lvert\mathrm{Im}\,a\rvert$ |
| | 13 | $\frac{5a^2s^2+60s^4+2a^4}{15s^3}-\frac{s(3a^2+4s^2)}{a(s^2+a^2)^{\frac{1}{2}}}\log\frac{(s^2+a^2)^{\frac{1}{2}}+a}{s}$ | $\frac{\pi a^2}{2}\mathbf{H}_3(at)$ | | $\mathrm{Re}\,s>\lvert\mathrm{Im}\,a\rvert$ |
| | 14 | $\frac{3a^4-60s^4-35a^2s^2}{15s^2}+\frac{1}{a}(4s^2+a^2)(s^2+a^2)^{\frac{1}{2}}\cdot\log\frac{(s^2+a^2)^{\frac{1}{2}}+a}{s}$ | $\frac{3\pi a^2}{2t}\mathbf{H}_3(at)$ | | $\mathrm{Re}\,s>\lvert\mathrm{Im}\,a\rvert$ |
| 4.3.2 | 1 | $\frac{e^{-b(s^2-ia^2)^{\frac{1}{2}}}}{(s^2-ia^2)^{\frac{1}{2}}}\log\frac{i^{-\frac{1}{2}}[s+(s^2-ia^2)^{\frac{1}{2}}]}{a}$ | $0$ | $0<t<b$ | $b>0$ |
| | | | $\mathrm{ker}[a(t^2-b^2)^{\frac{1}{2}}]+i\,\mathrm{kei}[a(t^2-b^2)^{\frac{1}{2}}]$ | $t>b$ | $\mathrm{Re}(s+ai^{\frac{1}{2}})>0$ |
| | 2 | $\frac{e^{-b(s^2+a^2)^{\frac{1}{2}}}\log[s+(s^2+a^2)^{\frac{1}{2}}]}{(s^2+a^2)^{\frac{1}{2}}}$ | $0$ | $0<t<b$ | $b>0$ |
| | | | $\log a\,J_0[a(t^2-b^2)^{\frac{1}{2}}]-\frac{\pi}{2}Y_0[a(t^2-b^2)^{\frac{1}{2}}]$ | $t>b$ | $\mathrm{Re}\,s>\lvert\mathrm{Im}\,a\rvert$ |

| | | g(s) | f(t) | | |
|---|---|---|---|---|---|
| 4.3.2 (Contd.) | 3 | $\dfrac{e^{-b(s^2-a^2)^{\frac{1}{2}}}\log[s+(s^2-a^2)^{\frac{1}{2}}]}{(s^2-a^2)^{\frac{1}{2}}}$ | $0$ | $0<t<b$ | $b>0$ <br> $\mathrm{Re}\, s>\lvert\mathrm{Re}\, a\rvert$ |
| | | | $K_0[a(t^2-b^2)^{\frac{1}{2}}]$ $+\log a\, I_0[a(t^2-b^2)^{\frac{1}{2}}]$ | $t>b$ | |
| | 4 | $\dfrac{e^{b[s-(s^2+a^2)^{\frac{1}{2}}]}\log[s+(s^2+a^2)^{\frac{1}{2}}]}{(s^2+a^2)^{\frac{1}{2}}}$ | $\log a J_0[a(t^2+2bt)^{\frac{1}{2}}]-\frac{\pi}{2}Y_0[a(t^2+2bt)^{\frac{1}{2}}]$ | | $\mathrm{Re}\, s>\lvert\mathrm{Im}\, a\rvert$ |
| | 5 | $\dfrac{e^{-b(s^2-ia^2)^{\frac{1}{2}}}}{(s^2-ia^2)^{\frac{1}{2}}}\left\{\dfrac{is}{a}-a\left[b+\dfrac{1}{(s^2-ia^2)^{\frac{1}{2}}}\right]\cdot\log\dfrac{i^{-\frac{1}{2}}[s+(s^2-ia^2)^{\frac{1}{2}}]}{a}\right\}$ | $0$ | $0<t<b$ | $b>0$ <br> $\mathrm{Re}(s+ai^{\frac{1}{2}})>0$ |
| | | | $i^{\frac{1}{2}}(t^2-b^2)^{\frac{1}{2}}\{\mathrm{ker}_1[a(t^2-b^2)^{\frac{1}{2}}]$ $+i\,\mathrm{kei}_1[a(t^2-b^2)^{\frac{1}{2}}]\}$ | $t>b$ | |
| 4.3.2.1 | 1 | $\dfrac{e^{-b(s^2-ia^2)^{\frac{1}{2}}}}{s^2-ia^2}\left\{1+\left[bs-\dfrac{s}{(s^2-ia^2)^{\frac{1}{2}}}\right]\cdot\log\dfrac{i^{-\frac{1}{2}}[s+(s^2-ia^2)^{\frac{1}{2}}]}{a}\right\}$ | $0$ | $0<t<b$ | $b>0$ <br> $\mathrm{Re}(s+ai^{\frac{1}{2}})>0$ |
| | | | $-t\{\mathrm{ker}[a(t^2-b^2)^{\frac{1}{2}}]$ $+i\,\mathrm{kei}[a(t^2-b^2)^{\frac{1}{2}}]\}$ | $t>b$ | |
| 5 | 1 | $\dfrac{1}{s}\sin\dfrac{a}{s}$ | $\mathrm{bei}(2a^{\frac{1}{2}}t^{\frac{1}{2}})$ | | $\mathrm{Re}\, s>0$ |
| | 2 | $\dfrac{1}{s}\cos\dfrac{a}{s}$ | $\mathrm{ber}(2a^{\frac{1}{2}}t^{\frac{1}{2}})$ | | $\mathrm{Re}\, s>0$ |
| | 3 | $\displaystyle\int_0^{\frac{\pi}{2}}\frac{\sin\theta\, d\theta}{(s^2+\sin^2\theta)^{\frac{1}{2}}[s+(s^2+\sin^2\theta)^{\frac{1}{2}}]^{\nu}}$ | $\left(\dfrac{\pi}{2t}\right)^{\frac{1}{2}}\mathbf{H}_{\nu-\frac{1}{2}}(t)$ | | $\mathrm{Re}\,\nu>-1$ <br> $\mathrm{Re}\, s>0$ |
| | 4 | $\displaystyle\int_0^{\frac{\pi}{2}}\frac{\sin\theta\, d\theta}{(s^2-\sin^2\theta)^{\frac{1}{2}}[s+(s^2-\sin^2\theta)^{\frac{1}{2}}]^{\nu}}$ | $\left(\dfrac{\pi}{2t}\right)^{\frac{1}{2}}\mathbf{L}_{\nu}(t)$ | | $\mathrm{Re}\,\nu>-1$ <br> $\mathrm{Re}\, s>1$ |

| | | g(s) | f(t) | |
|---|---|---|---|---|
| 5(Contd.) | 5 | $\int_0^{\frac{\pi}{2}} \frac{\cos(2n\theta)\,d\theta}{(s^2+a^2\cos^2\theta)^{\frac{1}{2}}}$ | $\frac{(-1)^n\pi}{2} J_n^2(\frac{at}{2})$ | Re s > \| Im a \| |
| | 6 | $\int_0^{\pi} \left[\left(\frac{s^2}{a^2}+2-2\cos\theta\right)^{\frac{1}{2}} - \frac{s}{a}\right](1+\cos\theta)\,d\theta$ | $\frac{2\pi}{at^2} J_1^2(at)$ | Re s > o |
| | 7 | $\int_0^{\frac{\pi}{2}} \frac{\cos^{\mu}\theta\cos(\nu\theta)\,d\theta}{(s^2+a^2\cos^2\theta)^{\mu+\frac{1}{2}}}$ | $\frac{\pi^{\frac{3}{2}}t^{\mu}}{2(2a)^{\mu}\Gamma(\mu+\frac{1}{2})} J_{\frac{\mu+\nu}{2}}\left(\frac{at}{2}\right) J_{\frac{\mu-\nu}{2}}\left(\frac{at}{2}\right)$ | Re s > \| Im a \|<br>Re $\mu > -\frac{1}{2}$ |
| | 8 | $\int_0^{\frac{\pi}{2}} \frac{\cos^{\mu+\frac{1}{2}}\theta\cos[(\mu-\frac{1}{2})\theta]\,d\theta}{(\frac{s^2}{4}+a^2\cos^2\theta)^{\mu+1}}$ | $\frac{2^{\frac{1}{2}}\pi}{\Gamma(\mu+1)a^{\mu+1}} t^{\mu}\sin(at)J_{\mu}(at)$ | a > o<br>Re $\mu > -1$<br>Re s > o |
| | 9 | $\int_0^{\frac{\pi}{2}} \frac{\cos^{\mu-\frac{1}{2}}\theta\cos[(\mu+\frac{1}{2})\theta]\,d\theta}{(\frac{s^2}{4}+a^2\cos^2\theta)^{\mu}}$ | $\frac{2^{\frac{1}{2}}\pi}{\Gamma(\mu)a^{\mu}} t^{\mu-1}\cos(at)J_{\mu}(at)$ | a > o<br>Re $\mu$ > o<br>Re s > o |
| | 10 | $\int_0^{\pi} \frac{\sin^{2\nu}\theta\,d\theta}{[b^2+(s+ia\cos\theta)^2]^{\nu+\frac{1}{2}}}$ | $\frac{\pi}{(ab)^{\nu}\Gamma(\nu+1)} J_{\nu}(at)J_{\nu}(bt)$ | Re $\nu > -\frac{1}{2}$<br>Re s > \| Im a \| + \| Im b |
| | 11 | $\int_0^{\pi} \frac{\sin^{2\nu}\theta\,d\theta}{[b^2+(s+ia\cos\theta)^2]^{\mu}}$ | $\frac{2^{\mu+\nu-\frac{1}{2}}\pi^{\frac{1}{2}}\Gamma(\nu+\frac{1}{2})}{a^{\nu}b^{\mu-\frac{1}{2}}\Gamma(2\mu)} t^{\mu-\nu-\frac{1}{2}} J_{\nu}(at)J_{\mu-\frac{1}{2}}(bt)$ | Re $\mu$ > o<br>Re s > \| Im a \| + \| Im b |
| 5.2 | 1 | $\frac{1}{s^{\frac{1}{2}}}\sin\frac{a}{s}$ | $\frac{\sinh[(2at)^{\frac{1}{2}}]\sin[(2at)^{\frac{1}{2}}]}{(\pi t)^{\frac{1}{2}}}$ | Re s > o |
| | 2 | $\frac{1}{s^{\frac{3}{2}}}\sin\frac{a}{s}$ | $\frac{\cosh[(2at)^{\frac{1}{2}}]\sin[(2at)^{\frac{1}{2}}]}{(\pi a)^{\frac{1}{2}}}$ | Re s > o |

| | | g(s) | f(t) | |
|---|---|---|---|---|
| 5.2 (Contd.) | 3 | $\frac{1}{s^{\nu}}\sin\frac{a}{s}$ | $\left(\frac{t}{a}\right)^{\frac{\nu-1}{2}}\left[\cos\frac{3\pi(\nu-1)}{4}\mathrm{bei}_{\nu-1}[(4at)^{\frac{1}{2}}] - \sin\frac{3\pi(\nu-1)}{4}\mathrm{ber}_{\nu-1}[(4at)^{\frac{1}{2}}]\right]$ | Re $\nu > -1$<br>Re $s > 0$ |
| | 4 | $\frac{1}{s^{\nu}}\sin\frac{1}{as^{\frac{1}{2}}}$ | $\frac{t^{\nu-\frac{1}{2}}{}_0F_2\left[\begin{matrix} ; -\frac{t}{4a^2} \\ \nu+\frac{1}{2}, \frac{3}{2}; \end{matrix}\right]}{a\Gamma(\nu+\frac{1}{2})}$ | Re $\nu > -\frac{1}{2}$<br>Re $s > 0$ |
| | 5 | $\frac{1}{s^{\frac{1}{2}}}\cos\frac{a}{s}$ | $\frac{\cosh[(2at)^{\frac{1}{2}}]\cos[(2at)^{\frac{1}{2}}]}{(\pi t)^{\frac{1}{2}}}$ | Re $s > 0$ |
| | 6 | $\frac{1}{s^{\frac{3}{2}}}\cos\frac{a}{s}$ | $\frac{\sinh[(2at)^{\frac{1}{2}}]\cos[(2at)^{\frac{1}{2}}]}{(\pi a)^{\frac{1}{2}}}$ | Re $s > 0$ |
| | 7 | $\frac{1}{s^{\nu}}\cos\frac{a}{s}$ | $\left(\frac{t}{a}\right)^{\frac{\nu-1}{2}}\left[\cos\frac{3\pi(\nu-1)}{4}\mathrm{ber}_{\nu-1}[(4at)^{\frac{1}{2}}] + \sin\frac{3\pi(\nu-1)}{4}\mathrm{bei}_{\nu-1}[(4at)^{\frac{1}{2}}]\right]$ | Re $\nu > 0$<br>Re $s > 0$ |
| | 8 | $\frac{1}{s^{\nu}}\cos\frac{1}{as^{\frac{1}{2}}}$ | $\frac{t^{\nu-1}{}_0F_2\left[\begin{matrix} ; -\frac{t}{4a^2} \\ \nu, \frac{1}{2}; \end{matrix}\right]}{\Gamma(\nu)}$ | Re $\nu > 0$<br>Re $s > 0$ |
| 5.2.1 | 1 | $\frac{1}{s^{\nu+1}}\sin\left(\frac{a^2+3\nu\pi s}{4s}\right)$ | $\left(\frac{2}{a}\right)^{\nu} t^{\frac{\nu}{2}}\mathrm{bei}_{\nu}(at^{\frac{1}{2}})$ | Re $\nu > -1$<br>Re $s > 0$ |
| | 2 | $\frac{1}{s^{\nu+1}}\cos\left(\frac{a^2+3\nu\pi s}{4s}\right)$ | $\left(\frac{2}{a}\right)^{\nu} t^{\frac{\nu}{2}}\mathrm{ber}_{\nu}(at^{\frac{1}{2}})$ | Re $\nu > -1$<br>Re $s > 0$ |

| | | g(s) | f(t) | |
|---|---|---|---|---|
| 5.3 | 1 | $\operatorname{cosec}(s\pi)\left[\int_0^{\pi} e^{a\cos\theta}\cos(s\theta)\,d\theta - \pi I_s(a)\right]$ | $e^{-a\cosh t}$ | Re a > o<br>Re s > −∞ |
| | 2 | $\frac{e^{-\frac{a^2+b^2}{4s}}}{s^{\nu+1}}\int_0^{\pi} e^{\frac{ab}{2s}\cos\theta}\sin^{2\nu}\theta\,d\theta$ | $\frac{\pi^{\frac{1}{2}}2^{2\nu}\Gamma(\nu+\frac{1}{2})}{(ab)^{\nu}}J_{\nu}(at^{\frac{1}{2}})J_{\nu}(bt^{\frac{1}{2}})$ | Re $\nu > -\frac{1}{2}$<br>Re s > o |
| | 3 | $\operatorname{cosec}(s\pi)\left[\int_0^{\pi} e^{i a\sin\beta\cos\theta}\cdot\right.$<br>$\cdot\cos(s\theta - a\cos\beta\sin\theta)\,d\theta$<br>$\left.-\pi e^{i\beta s}J_s(a)\right]$ | $e^{-a\sinh(t+i\beta)}$ | $-\frac{\pi}{2}<\beta<\frac{\pi}{2}$<br>$\lvert\arg a\rvert<\frac{\pi}{2}-\beta$<br>Re s > −∞ |
| 5.3.2 | 1 | $\frac{1}{s^{\frac{1}{2}}}e^{-as^{\frac{1}{2}}}\sin(as^{\frac{1}{2}})$ | $\frac{\sin\frac{a^2}{2t}}{(\pi t)^{\frac{1}{2}}}$ | Re s > o |
| | 2 | $\frac{1}{s^{\frac{1}{2}}}e^{-as^{\frac{1}{2}}}\cos(as^{\frac{1}{2}})$ | $\frac{\cos\frac{a^2}{2t}}{(\pi t)^{\frac{1}{2}}}$ | Re s > o |
| 6 | 1 | $\tan^{-1}\frac{a}{s}$ | $\left(\frac{\pi a}{2t}\right)^{\frac{1}{2}}H_{-\frac{1}{2}}(at)$<br>$=\frac{\sin(at)}{t}$ | Re s > \|Im a\| |
| | 2 | $s\tan^{-1}\frac{a}{s}-a$ | $\frac{at\cos(at)-\sin(at)}{t^2}$ | Re s > \|Im a\| |
| | 3 | $\frac{1}{s}\tan^{-1}\frac{s}{a}$ | $-\operatorname{si}(at)$ | Re s > \|Im a\| |

| | | g(s) | f(t) | |
|---|---|---|---|---|
| 6(Contd.) | 4 | $\frac{1}{s}\cot^{-1}\frac{s}{a}$ | $\mathrm{Si}(at)$ | $\mathrm{Re}\, s > 0$ |
| | 5 | $3\tan^{-1}\frac{a}{s} - \tan^{-1}\frac{3a}{s}$ | $\frac{4\sin^3(at)}{t}$ | $\mathrm{Re}\, s > 3\lvert \mathrm{Im}\, a\rvert$ |
| | 6 | $5\tan^{-1}\frac{a}{s} - \frac{5}{2}\tan^{-1}\frac{3a}{s} + \frac{1}{2}\tan^{-1}\frac{5a}{s}$ | $\frac{8\sin^5(at)}{t}$ | $\mathrm{Re}\, s > 5\lvert \mathrm{Im}\, a\rvert$ |
| 6.1 | 1 | $\tan^{-1}\frac{s^2-as+b}{ab}$ | $\frac{e^{at}-1}{t}\sin bt$ | $\mathrm{Re}\, s > \mathrm{Max}\lvert \mathrm{Im}\, b\rvert, \lvert \mathrm{Im}\, b\rvert + \mathrm{Re}\, a$ |
| | 2 | $\tan^{-1}\frac{2as}{s^2-a^2+b^2}$ | $\frac{2\sin(at)\cos(bt)}{t}$ | $\mathrm{Re}\, s > \lvert \mathrm{Im}(\pm a \pm b)\rvert$ |
| | 3 | $\tan^{-1}\frac{s^2-a^2}{2bs}$ | $\frac{2\sin(bt)\cosh[(a^2-b^2)^{\frac{1}{2}}t]}{t}$ | $\mathrm{Re}\, s > \lvert \mathrm{Im}\, b\rvert + \lvert \mathrm{Re}(a^2-b^2)^{\frac{1}{2}}\rvert$ |
| | 4 | $\frac{s}{s^2+a^2} - \frac{1}{a}\tan^{-1}\frac{a}{s}$ | $\left(\frac{a\pi t}{2}\right)^{\frac{1}{2}} H_{-\frac{3}{2}}(at)$ | $\mathrm{Re}\, s > \lvert \mathrm{Im}\, a\rvert$ |
| | 5 | $2\tan^{-1}\frac{a}{s} - \tan^{-1}\frac{2as}{s^2+3a^2}$ | $\frac{4}{t}\sin(at)$ | $\mathrm{Re}\, s > 3\lvert \mathrm{Im}\, a\rvert$ |
| 6.2 | 1 | $\frac{\sin^{-1}\frac{a}{s}}{(s^2-a^2)^{\frac{1}{2}}}$ | $\frac{\pi}{2}L_0(at)$ | $\mathrm{Re}\, s > \lvert \mathrm{Re}\, a\rvert$ |
| | 2 | $\sin^{-1}\frac{a}{(s^2+a^2)^{\frac{1}{2}}}$ | $\frac{\sin(at)}{t}$ | $\mathrm{Re}\, s > \lvert \mathrm{Im}\, a\rvert$ |

| | | g(s) | f(t) | |
|---|---|---|---|---|
| 6.2 (Contd.) | 3 | $1-\left(\frac{s^2}{a^2}-1\right)^{\frac{1}{2}}\sin^{-1}\frac{a}{s}$ | $\frac{\pi}{2t}L_1(at)$ | $\mathrm{Re}\, s>\lvert\mathrm{Re}\, a\rvert$ |
| | 4 | $\frac{s}{(s^2-a^2)^{\frac{1}{2}}}\sin^{-1}\frac{a}{s}-\frac{a}{s}$ | $\frac{\pi a}{2}L_1(at)$ | $\mathrm{Re}\, s>\lvert\mathrm{Re}\, a\rvert$ |
| | 5 | $\cos^{-1}\frac{s}{(s^2+a^2)^{\frac{1}{2}}}$ | $\frac{\sin(at)}{t}$ | $\mathrm{Re}\, s>\lvert\mathrm{Im}\, a\rvert$ |
| | 6 | $\frac{\cos^{-1}\frac{s}{a}}{(a^2-s^2)^{\frac{1}{2}}}$ | $K_0(at)$ | $\mathrm{Re}\, s>-\mathrm{Re}\, a$ |
| 6.2.1 | 1 | $\frac{3s^2-a^2}{3s}-\frac{s(s^2-a^2)^{\frac{1}{2}}}{a}\sin^{-1}\frac{a}{s}$ | $\frac{a\pi}{2t^2}L_2(at)$ | $\mathrm{Re}\, s>\lvert\mathrm{Re}\, a\rvert$ |
| | 2 | $\frac{2s^2-a^2}{a(s^2-a^2)^{\frac{1}{2}}}\sin^{-1}\frac{a}{s}-2-\frac{a^2}{3s^2}$ | $\frac{a\pi}{2}L_2(at)$ | $\mathrm{Re}\, s>\lvert\mathrm{Re}\, a\rvert$ |
| | 3 | $\frac{5a^2s^2-60s^4-2a^4}{15s^3}+\frac{4s^3-3as}{a(s^2-a^2)^{\frac{1}{2}}}\sin^{-1}\frac{a}{s}$ | $\frac{\pi a^2}{2}L_3(at)$ | $\mathrm{Re}\, s>\lvert\mathrm{Re}\, a\rvert$ |
| | 4 | $\frac{60s^4-35a^2s^2-3a^4}{15s^2}-\frac{(4s^2-a^2)(s^2-a^2)^{\frac{1}{2}}}{a}\sin^{-1}\frac{a}{s}$ | $\frac{3\pi a^2}{2t}L_3(at)$ | $\mathrm{Re}\, s>\lvert\mathrm{Re}\, a\rvert$ |
| 6.4.1 | 1 | $\log(s^2+a^2)\tan^{-1}\frac{a}{s}$ | $-\frac{2}{t}\log(\gamma t)\sin(at)$ | $\mathrm{Re}\, s>\lvert\mathrm{Im}\, a\rvert$ |
| | 2 | $2a\tan^{-1}\frac{a}{s}-s\log(1+\frac{a^2}{s^2})$ | $\frac{4}{t^2}\sin^2\frac{at}{2}$ | $\mathrm{Re}\, s\geqslant\lvert\mathrm{Im}\, a\rvert$ |

| | | g(s) | f(t) | |
|---|---|---|---|---|
| 6.4.1 (Contd.) | 3 | $\dfrac{s\tan^{-1}\frac{2}{s}-\frac{1}{2}\log(1+\frac{4}{s^2})}{s^2+1}$ | $2\cos t\,\mathrm{si}(t)$ | Re $s > 0$ |
| | 4 | $\dfrac{\tan^{-1}\frac{2}{s}+\frac{s}{2}\log[s^2(s^2+4)]}{s^2+1}$ | $2\cos t\,\mathrm{ci}(t)$ | Re $s > 0$ |
| | 5 | $\dfrac{s\tan^{-1}\frac{2}{s}-\frac{1}{2}\log[s^2(s^2+4)]}{s^2+1}$ | $-2\sin t\,\mathrm{ci}(t)$ | Re $s > 0$ |
| | 6 | $\dfrac{\tan^{-1}\frac{1}{s-1}+\frac{s}{2}\log(s^2-2s+2)}{s^2+1}$ | $-\cos t\,\overline{\mathrm{Ei}}(t)$ | Re $s > 1$ |
| | 7 | $\dfrac{s\tan^{-1}\frac{1}{s-1}-\frac{1}{2}\log(s^2-2s+2)}{s^2+1}$ | $\sin t\,\overline{\mathrm{Ei}}(t)$ | Re $s > 1$ |
| | 8 | $\dfrac{\tan^{-1}\frac{2}{s}+\frac{s}{2}\log(s^2+4)}{s^2+1}$ | $\sin t\,\mathrm{si}(t)+\cos t\,\mathrm{ci}(t)$ | Re $s > 0$ |
| | 9 | $\dfrac{s\tan^{-1}\frac{2}{s}-\frac{1}{2}\log(s^2+4)}{s^2+1}$ | $-\sin t\,\mathrm{ci}(t)+\cos t\,\mathrm{si}(t)$ | Re $s > 0$ |
| | 10 | $\dfrac{a\tan^{-1}\frac{a}{s}+\frac{s}{2}\log[\gamma^2(s^2+a^2)]}{s^2+a^2}$ | $-\log t\cos(at)$ | Re $s > \lvert\mathrm{Im}\,a\rvert$ |
| | 11 | $\dfrac{s\tan^{-1}\frac{a}{s}-\frac{a}{2}\log[\gamma^2(s^2+a^2)]}{s^2+a^2}$ | $\log t\sin(at)$ | Re $s > \lvert\mathrm{Im}\,a\rvert$ |

| | | g(s) | f(t) | |
|---|---|---|---|---|
| 6.4.1 (Contd.) | 12 | $\dfrac{a\tan^{-1}\frac{a}{s+1}+\frac{s}{2}\log[(s+1)^2+a^2]}{s^2+a^2}$ | $-\cos(at)Ei(-t)$ | $Re\ s > \lvert Im\ a\rvert$ |
| | 13 | $\dfrac{s\tan^{-1}\frac{a}{s+1}-\frac{a}{2}\log[(s+1)^2+a^2]}{s^2+a^2}$ | $\sin(at)Ei(-t)$ | $Re\ s > \lvert Im\ a\rvert$ |
| | 14 | $\dfrac{s\tan^{-1}\frac{2bs}{b^2-a^2-s^2}+\frac{a}{2}\log\frac{(b+a)^2+s^2}{(b-a)^2+s^2}}{s^2+a^2}$ | $-\frac{2}{b}\cos(at)\,si(bt)$ | $Re\ s > \lvert Im\ a\rvert$ <br> $b \neq o$ |
| | 15 | $\dfrac{s\tan^{-1}\frac{2as}{s^2+b^2-a^2}-\frac{a}{2}\log\frac{(s^2+b^2-a^2)^2+4a^2s^2}{b^2}}{s^2+a^2}$ | $-\frac{2}{b}\sin(at)\,ci(bt)$ | $Re\ s > \lvert Im\ a\rvert$ <br> $b \neq o$ |
| | 16 | $\dfrac{a\tan^{-1}\frac{a}{s}}{s^2+a^2}+\dfrac{s\log(s^2+a^2)}{2(s^2+a^2)}-\dfrac{\log s}{s}-\dfrac{a^2\log\gamma}{s(s^2+a^2)}$ | $\log t\sin^2\frac{at}{2}$ | $Re\ s > \lvert Im\ a\rvert$ |
| | 17 | $2s\tan^{-1}\frac{3a}{s}-6s\tan^{-1}\frac{a}{s}+3a\log\frac{s^2+3a^2}{s^2+a^2}$ | $\dfrac{8\sin^3(at)}{t^2}$ | $Re\ s \geqslant 3\lvert Im\ a\rvert$ |
| | 18 | $\frac{s}{2}\log\frac{s^2+a^2}{s^2+b^2}+b\tan^{-1}\frac{b}{s}-a\tan^{-1}\frac{a}{s}$ | $\dfrac{\cos(at)-\cos(bt)}{t^2}$ | $Re\ s \geqslant Max\lvert Im\ a\rvert,$ <br> $\lvert Im\ b\rvert$ |
| 6.5.2 | 1 | $\dfrac{\sin(b+\tan^{-1}\frac{a}{s})}{(s^2+a^2)^{\frac{1}{2}}}$ | $\sin(at+b)$ | $Re\ s > \lvert Im\ a\rvert$ |
| | 2 | $\dfrac{\cos(b+\tan^{-1}\frac{a}{s})}{(s^2+a^2)^{\frac{1}{2}}}$ | $\cos(at+b)$ | $Re\ s > \lvert Im\ a\rvert$ |

| | | g(s) | f(t) | |
|---|---|---|---|---|
| 6.5.2 (Contd.) | 3 | $\dfrac{\sin[\nu \tan^{-1}\frac{a}{s}]}{(s^2+a^2)^{\frac{\nu}{2}}}$ | $\dfrac{t^{\nu-1}\sin(at)}{\Gamma(\nu)}$ | $\mathrm{Re}\,\nu > -1$<br>$\mathrm{Re}\,s > \lvert \mathrm{Im}\,a \rvert$ |
| | 4 | $\dfrac{\cos[\nu \tan^{-1}\frac{a}{s}]}{(s^2+a^2)^{\frac{\nu}{2}}}$ | $\dfrac{t^{\nu-1}\cos(at)}{\Gamma(\nu)}$ | $\mathrm{Re}\,\nu > 0$<br>$\mathrm{Re}\,s > \lvert \mathrm{Im}\,a \rvert$ |
| | 5 | $\dfrac{1}{s^a}\cos\left[2n\sin^{-1}\left(\dfrac{1}{s^{\frac{1}{2}}}\right)\right]$ | $\dfrac{t^{a-1}}{\Gamma(a)}\,{}_2F_2\left[\begin{matrix}-n,n\,; \\ a,\frac{1}{2}\,;\end{matrix}\; t\right]$ | $n=0,1,2,\ldots$<br>$\mathrm{Re}\,a>0$<br>$\mathrm{Re}\,s>0$ |
| | 6 | $\dfrac{1}{s^a}\sin\left[(2n+1)\sin^{-1}\left(\dfrac{1}{s^{\frac{1}{2}}}\right)\right]$ | $\dfrac{(2n+1)\,t^{a-1}}{\Gamma(a)}\,{}_2F_2\left[\begin{matrix}-n,n+1\,; \\ a,\ \frac{3}{2}\,;\end{matrix}\; t\right]$ | $n=0,1,2,\ldots$<br>$\mathrm{Re}\,a>0$<br>$\mathrm{Re}\,s>0$ |
| 6.5.4.2.1 | 1 | $\dfrac{\sin(\nu\tan^{-1}\frac{a}{s})}{(s^2+a^2)^{\frac{\nu}{2}}}[\psi(\nu)-\frac{1}{2}\log(s^2+a^2)$ $+\tan^{-1}\frac{a}{s}\cot(\nu\tan^{-1}\frac{a}{s})]$ | $\dfrac{t^{\nu-1}}{\Gamma(\nu)}\log t\sin(at)$ | $\mathrm{Re}\,\nu > -1$<br>$\mathrm{Re}\,s > \lvert \mathrm{Im}\,a \rvert$ |
| | 2 | $\dfrac{\cos(\nu\tan^{-1}\frac{a}{s})}{(s^2+a^2)^{\frac{\nu}{2}}}[\psi(\nu)-\frac{1}{2}\log(s^2+a^2)$ $-\tan^{-1}\frac{a}{s}\tan(\nu\tan^{-1}\frac{a}{s})]$ | $\dfrac{t^{\nu-1}}{\Gamma(\nu)}\log t\cos(at)$ | $\mathrm{Re}\,\nu > 0$<br>$\mathrm{Re}\,s > \lvert \mathrm{Im}\,a \rvert$ |
| 7 | 1 | $\dfrac{1}{s}\,\mathrm{cosech}(as)$ | $0 \quad 0<t<a$<br>$2n \quad (2n-1)a<t<(2n+1)a$ | $a>0$<br>$\mathrm{Re}\,s>0$<br>$n=1,2,3,\ldots$ |
| | 2 | $\dfrac{1}{s}\,\mathrm{sech}(as)$ | $0 \quad 0<t<a$<br>$2 \quad (4n+1)a<t<(4n+3)a$<br>$0 \quad (4n+3)a<t<(4n+5)a$ | $a>0$<br>$\mathrm{Re}\,s>0$<br>$n=1,2,3,\ldots$ |

| | | g(s) | f(t) | | |
|---|---|---|---|---|---|
| 7(Contd.) | 3 | $\frac{1}{s}[1-\operatorname{sech}(as)]$ | 1 | $0<t<a$ | Re $s>0$ |
| | | | -1 | $(4n-3)a<t<(4n-1)a$ | $n=1,2,3,\ldots$ |
| | | | 1 | $(4n-1)a<t<(4n+1)a$ | $a>0$ |
| | 4 | $\frac{\cosh(as)}{s\cosh(2as)}$ | 1 | $(4n-3)a<t<(4n-1)a$ | Re $s>0$ |
| | | | 2 | $(8n-5)a<t<(8n-3)a$ | $n=1,2,3,\ldots$ |
| | | | 0 | otherwise | $a>0$ |
| | 5 | $\frac{\cosh(bs)}{s\cosh(as)}$ | $1+\frac{2}{\pi}\sum_{n=1}^{\infty}\frac{(-1)^n}{n-\frac{1}{2}}\cos\frac{(n-\frac{1}{2})\pi b}{a}\cos\frac{(n-\frac{1}{2})\pi t}{a}$ | | $-a\leqslant b\leqslant a$<br>Re $s>0$ |
| | 6 | $\frac{\sinh(as)}{s\cosh(2as)}$ | 1 | $(8n-7)a<t<(8n-5)a$ | Re $s>0$ |
| | | | -1 | $(8n-3)a<t<(8n-1)a$ | $n=1,2,3,\ldots$ |
| | | | 0 | otherwise | $a>0$ |
| | 7 | $\frac{\sinh(bs)}{s\cosh(as)}$ | $\frac{2}{\pi}\sum_{n=1}^{\infty}\frac{(-1)^{n-1}}{n-\frac{1}{2}}\sin\frac{(n-\frac{1}{2})\pi b}{a}\sin\frac{(n-\frac{1}{2})\pi t}{a}$ | | $0\leqslant b\leqslant a$<br>Re $s>0$ |
| | 8 | $\frac{\sinh(as)}{s\cosh^2(as)}$ | 0 | $0<t<a$ | Re $s>0$ |
| | | | $4n-2$ | $(4n-3)a<t<(4n-1)a$ | $n=1,2,3,\ldots$ |
| | | | $-4n$ | $(4n-1)a<t<(4n+1)a$ | $a>0$ |
| | 9 | $\frac{1}{s}\tanh\frac{as}{2}$ | 1 | $2na<t<(2n+1)a$ | $a>0$<br>Re $s>0$ |
| | | | -1 | $(2n+1)a<t<(2n+2)a$ | $n=0,1,2,\ldots$ |
| | 10 | $\frac{1}{s}\coth as$ | $2n+1$ | $2na<t<2(n+1)a$ | $a>0$<br>Re $s>0$<br>$n=0,1,2,\ldots$ |

| | | g(s) | f(t) | | |
|---|---|---|---|---|---|
| 7.1 | 1 | $\frac{1}{s^2}\operatorname{cosech}(as)$ | $0$ | $0 < t < a$ | $a > 0$ |
| | | | $2n(t-an)$ | $(2n-1)a < t < (2n+1)a$ | $\mathrm{Re}\, s > 0$<br>$n = 1,2,3,\ldots$ |
| | 2 | $\dfrac{\operatorname{cosech}\frac{\pi s}{2a}}{s^2+a^2}$ | $\dfrac{\lvert\cos(at)\rvert - \cos(at)}{a}$ | | $\mathrm{Re}\, s > \lvert \mathrm{Im}\, a \rvert$ |
| | 3 | $\dfrac{s+a\operatorname{cosech}(\frac{\pi s}{2a})}{s^2+a^2}$ | $\lvert\cos(at)\rvert$ | | $\mathrm{Re}\, s > \lvert \mathrm{Im}\, a \rvert$ |
| | 4 | $\frac{1}{s^2}\operatorname{sech}(as)$ | $0$ | $0 < t < a$ | $a > 0$ |
| | | | $t-(-1)^n(t-2na)$ | $(2n-1)a < t < (2n+1)a$ | $\mathrm{Re}\, s > 0$<br>$n = 1,2,3,\ldots$ |
| | 5 | $\dfrac{\cosh(bs)}{s^2\cosh(as)}$ | $t + \dfrac{2a}{\pi^2}\sum_{n=1}^{\infty}\dfrac{(-1)^n}{(n-\frac{1}{2})^2}\cos\dfrac{(n-\frac{1}{2})\pi b}{a}\sin\dfrac{(n-\frac{1}{2})\pi t}{a}$ | | $-a \leq b \leq a$<br>$\mathrm{Re}\, s > 0$ |
| | 6 | $\dfrac{\sinh(as)}{s^2\cosh(2as)}$ | $0$ | $0 < t < a$ | $a > 0$ |
| | | | $t-(8n+1)a$ | $(8n+1)a < t < (8n+3)a$ | $\mathrm{Re}\, s > 0$<br>$n = 0,1,2,\ldots$ |
| | | | $2a$ | $(8n+3)a < t < (8n+5)a$ | |
| | | | $-t+(8n+7)a$ | $(8n+5)a < t < (8n+7)a$ | |
| | | | $0$ | $(8n+7)a < t < (8n+9)a$ | |
| | 7 | $\dfrac{\sinh(bs)}{s^2\cosh(as)}$ | $b + \dfrac{2a}{\pi^2}\sum_{n=1}^{\infty}\dfrac{(-1)^n}{(n-\frac{1}{2})^2}\sin\dfrac{(n-\frac{1}{2})\pi b}{a}\cos\dfrac{(n-\frac{1}{2})\pi t}{a}$ | | $0 \leq b \leq a$<br>$\mathrm{Re}\, s > 0$ |
| | 8 | $\frac{1}{s^2}\tanh(as)$ | $a-(-1)^n(2an+a-t)$ | $2na < t < 2(n+1)a$ | $a > 0$<br>$\mathrm{Re}\, s > 0$<br>$n = 0,1,2,\ldots$ |

| | | $g(s)$ | $f(t)$ | |
|---|---|---|---|---|
| 7.1 (Contd.) | 9 | $\frac{1}{s^2}\coth(as)$ | $(2n+1)t-2an(n+1) \quad 2na < t < 2(n+1)a$ | $a > 0$, Re $s > 0$, $n = 0,1,2,\ldots$ |
| | 10 | $\dfrac{\coth\frac{\pi s}{2a}}{s^2+a^2}$ | $\dfrac{\lvert\sin(at)\rvert}{a}$ | Re $s > \lvert \text{Im } a\rvert$ |
| | 11 | $\dfrac{s\coth\frac{\pi s}{2a}}{s^2+a^2}$ | $\cos(at) \quad \frac{2n\pi}{a} < t < \frac{(2n+1)\pi}{a}$<br>$-\cos(at) \quad \frac{(2n+1)\pi}{a} < t < \frac{(2n+2)\pi}{a}$ | $a > 0$, Re $s > 0$, $n = 0,1,2,\ldots$ |
| | 12 | $\frac{b}{s^2} - \frac{ab}{2s}\left(\coth\frac{as}{2} - 1\right)$ | $b(t-na) \quad na < t < (n+1)a$ | $a > 0$, Re $s > 0$, $n = 0,1,2,\ldots$ |
| | 13 | $\dfrac{1+as\tanh(as)}{s^2\cosh(as)}$ | $2t \quad (4n-3)a < t < (4n-1)a$<br>$0 \quad$ otherwise | $a > 0$, Re $s > 0$, $n = 1,2,3,\ldots$ |
| 7.2 | 1 | $\frac{1}{s^{\frac{1}{2}}}\sinh\frac{a}{s}$ | $\dfrac{\cosh(2a^{\frac{1}{2}}t^{\frac{1}{2}})-\cos(2a^{\frac{1}{2}}t^{\frac{1}{2}})}{2(\pi t)^{\frac{1}{2}}}$ | Re $s > 0$ |
| | 2 | $\frac{1}{s^{\frac{3}{2}}}\sinh\frac{a}{s}$ | $\dfrac{\sinh(2a^{\frac{1}{2}}t^{\frac{1}{2}})-\sin(2a^{\frac{1}{2}}t^{\frac{1}{2}})}{2(a\pi)^{\frac{1}{2}}}$ | Re $s > 0$ |
| | 3 | $\frac{1}{s^{\frac{5}{2}}}\sinh\frac{a}{s}$ | $\frac{t^{\frac{1}{2}}}{2a\pi^{\frac{1}{2}}}[\cosh(2a^{\frac{1}{2}}t^{\frac{1}{2}})+\cos(2a^{\frac{1}{2}}t^{\frac{1}{2}})]$<br>$-\frac{1}{4a^{\frac{3}{2}}\pi^{\frac{1}{2}}}[\sinh(2a^{\frac{1}{2}}t^{\frac{1}{2}})+\sin(2a^{\frac{1}{2}}t^{\frac{1}{2}})]$ | Re $s > 0$ |
| | 4 | $\frac{1}{s^{\nu}}\sinh\frac{a}{s}$ | $\frac{1}{2}(\frac{t}{a})^{\frac{\nu-1}{2}}[I_{\nu-1}(2a^{\frac{1}{2}}t^{\frac{1}{2}})-J_{\nu-1}(2a^{\frac{1}{2}}t^{\frac{1}{2}})]$ | Re $\nu > -1$, Re $s > 0$ |

| | | g(s) | f(t) | |
|---|---|---|---|---|
| 7.2 (Contd.) | 5 | $\operatorname{cosech}(as^{\frac{1}{2}})$ | $-\frac{1}{a^2}\left[\frac{\partial}{\partial\nu}\theta_4\left(\frac{\nu}{2}\middle\vert\frac{t}{a^2}\right)\right]_{\nu=0}$ | Re s > 0 |
| | 6 | $\frac{1}{s^{\frac{1}{2}}}\operatorname{cosech}(as^{\frac{1}{2}})$ | $a^{-1}\theta_4\left(0\middle\vert\frac{t}{a^2}\right)$ | Re s > 0 |
| | 7 | $\sinh(\nu s^{\frac{1}{2}})\operatorname{cosech}(as^{\frac{1}{2}})$ | $a^{-1}\frac{\partial}{\partial\nu}\theta_4\left(\frac{\nu}{2a}\middle\vert\frac{t}{a^2}\right)$ $= a^{-1}\frac{\partial}{\partial\nu}\theta_3\left(\frac{1}{2}+\frac{\nu}{2a}\middle\vert\frac{t}{a^2}\right)$ | $-a<\nu<a$ Re s > 0 |
| | 8 | $\frac{1}{s^{\frac{1}{2}}}\sinh(\nu s^{\frac{1}{2}})\operatorname{cosech}(as^{\frac{1}{2}})$ | $-a^{-1}\hat{\theta}_4\left(\frac{\nu}{2a}\middle\vert\frac{t}{a^2}\right)$ $= -a^{-1}\hat{\theta}_3\left(\frac{1}{2}+\frac{\nu}{2a}\middle\vert\frac{t}{a^2}\right)$ | $-a\leqslant\nu\leqslant a$ Re s > 0 |
| | 9 | $\frac{1}{s}\sinh(\nu s^{\frac{1}{2}})\operatorname{cosech}(as^{\frac{1}{2}})$ | $\frac{1}{a}\int_a^{\nu+a}\theta_3\left(\frac{u}{2a}\middle\vert\frac{t}{a^2}\right)du$ $= -\frac{1}{a}\int_0^{\nu}\theta_4\left(\frac{u}{2a}\middle\vert\frac{t}{a^2}\right)du$ | $-a\leqslant\nu\leqslant a$ Re s > 0 |
| | 10 | $\frac{\sinh(as^{\frac{1}{2}})\sinh(bs^{\frac{1}{2}})}{s^{\frac{1}{2}}\sinh(cs^{\frac{1}{2}})}$ | $\frac{2}{c}\sum_{n=1}^{\infty}(-1)^{n+1}\sin\frac{n\pi a}{c}\sin\frac{n\pi b}{c}e^{-\frac{n^2\pi^2}{c^2}t}$ | a < c b < c Re s > 0 |
| | 11 | $\frac{1}{s^{\frac{1}{2}}}\cosh\frac{a}{s}$ | $\frac{\cos(2a^{\frac{1}{2}}t^{\frac{1}{2}})+\cosh(2a^{\frac{1}{2}}t^{\frac{1}{2}})}{2(\pi t)^{\frac{1}{2}}}$ | Re s > 0 |
| | 12 | $\frac{1}{s^{\frac{3}{2}}}\cosh\frac{a}{s}$ | $\frac{\sinh(2a^{\frac{1}{2}}t^{\frac{1}{2}})+\sin(2a^{\frac{1}{2}}t^{\frac{1}{2}})}{2(a\pi)^{\frac{1}{2}}}$ | Re s > 0 |

| | | $g(s)$ | $f(t)$ | |
|---|---|---|---|---|
| 7.2 (Contd.) | 13 | $\frac{1}{s^{\frac{3}{2}}} \cosh \frac{a}{s}$ | $\frac{t^{\frac{1}{2}}}{2a\pi^{\frac{1}{2}}}[\cosh(2a^{\frac{1}{2}}t^{\frac{1}{2}})-\cos(2a^{\frac{1}{2}}t^{\frac{1}{2}})]$ $-\frac{1}{4a^{\frac{3}{2}}\pi^{\frac{1}{2}}}[\sinh(2a^{\frac{1}{2}}t^{\frac{1}{2}})-\sin(2a^{\frac{1}{2}}t^{\frac{1}{2}})]$ | $\mathrm{Re}\, s > 0$ |
| | 14 | $\frac{1}{s^{\nu}} \cosh \frac{a}{s}$ | $\frac{1}{2}\left(\frac{t}{a}\right)^{\frac{\nu-1}{2}}[I_{\nu-1}(2a^{\frac{1}{2}}t^{\frac{1}{2}})+J_{\nu-1}(2a^{\frac{1}{2}}t^{\frac{1}{2}})]$ | $\mathrm{Re}\, \nu > 0$ <br> $\mathrm{Re}\, s > 0$ |
| | 15 | $\mathrm{sech}(as^{\frac{1}{2}})$ | $-\frac{1}{a^2}\left[\frac{\partial}{\partial\nu}\theta_1\left(\frac{\nu}{2}\middle\vert\frac{t}{a^2}\right)\right]_{\nu=0}$ | $\mathrm{Re}\, s > 0$ |
| | 16 | $\frac{1}{s^{\frac{1}{2}}} \mathrm{sech}(as^{\frac{1}{2}})$ | $a^{-1}\hat{\theta}_2\left(\frac{1}{2}\middle\vert\frac{t}{a^2}\right)$ | $\mathrm{Re}\, s > 0$ |
| | 17 | $\frac{1}{s} \mathrm{sech}(as^{\frac{1}{2}})$ | $1-\frac{1}{a}\int_0^a \theta_1\left(\frac{u}{2a}\middle\vert\frac{t}{a^2}\right)du$ | $\mathrm{Re}\, s > 0$ |
| | 18 | $\cosh(\nu s^{\frac{1}{2}})\,\mathrm{sech}(as^{\frac{1}{2}})$ | $-a^{-1}\frac{\partial}{\partial\nu}\theta_2\left(\frac{1}{2}+\frac{\nu}{2a}\middle\vert\frac{t}{a^2}\right)$ $= -a^{-1}\frac{\partial}{\partial\nu}\theta_1\left(\frac{\nu}{2a}\middle\vert\frac{t}{a^2}\right)$ | $-a < \nu < a$ <br> $\mathrm{Re}\, s > 0$ |
| | 19 | $\frac{1}{s^{\frac{1}{2}}} \cosh(\nu s^{\frac{1}{2}})\,\mathrm{sech}(as^{\frac{1}{2}})$ | $-a^{-1}\hat{\theta}_1\left(\frac{\nu}{2a}\middle\vert\frac{t}{a^2}\right)$ | $-a \leqslant \nu \leqslant a$ <br> $\mathrm{Re}\, s > 0$ |
| | 20 | $\frac{1}{s} \cosh(\nu s^{\frac{1}{2}})\,\mathrm{sech}(as^{\frac{1}{2}})$ | $1+\frac{1}{a}\int_a^{\nu} \theta_1\left(\frac{u}{2a}\middle\vert\frac{t}{a^2}\right)du$ $= 1-\frac{1}{a}\int_0^{\nu+a} \theta_2\left(\frac{u}{2a}\middle\vert\frac{t}{a^2}\right)du$ | $-a \leqslant \nu \leqslant a$ <br> $\mathrm{Re}\, s > 0$ |

| | | g(s) | f(t) | |
|---|---|---|---|---|
| 7.2 (Contd.) | 21 | $\sinh(\nu s^{\frac{1}{2}})\,\mathrm{sech}(a s^{\frac{1}{2}})$ | $-\frac{1}{a}\frac{\partial}{\partial\nu}\hat{\theta}_1\left(\frac{\nu}{2a}\middle\vert\frac{t}{a^2}\right)$ | $-a<\nu<a$ <br> $\mathrm{Re}\, s>0$ |
| | 22 | $\frac{1}{s^{\frac{1}{2}}}\sinh(\nu s^{\frac{1}{2}})\,\mathrm{sech}(a s^{\frac{1}{2}})$ | $-a^{-1}\theta_1\left(\frac{\nu}{2a}\middle\vert\frac{t}{a^2}\right)$ <br> $= -a^{-1}\theta_2\left(\frac{1}{2}+\frac{\nu}{2a}\middle\vert\frac{t}{a^2}\right)$ | $-a\leqslant\nu\leqslant a$ <br> $\mathrm{Re}\, s>0$ |
| | 23 | $\frac{1}{s}\sinh(\nu s^{\frac{1}{2}})\,\mathrm{sech}(a s^{\frac{1}{2}})$ | $-\frac{1}{a}\int_0^{\nu}\hat{\theta}_1\left(\frac{u}{2a}\middle\vert\frac{t}{a^2}\right)du$ <br> $= \frac{1}{a}\int_a^{\nu+a}\hat{\theta}_2\left(\frac{u}{2a}\middle\vert\frac{t}{a^2}\right)du$ | $-a\leqslant\nu\leqslant a$ <br> $\mathrm{Re}\, s>0$ |
| | 24 | $\cosh(\nu s^{\frac{1}{2}})\,\mathrm{cosech}(a s^{\frac{1}{2}})$ | $-a^{-1}\frac{\partial}{\partial\nu}\theta_1\left(\frac{\nu}{2a}\middle\vert\frac{t}{a^2}\right)$ <br> $= -a^{-1}\frac{\partial}{\partial\nu}\hat{\theta}_4\left(\frac{\nu}{2a}\middle\vert\frac{t}{a^2}\right)$ | $-a<\nu<a$ <br> $\mathrm{Re}\, s>0$ |
| | 25 | $\frac{1}{s^{\frac{1}{2}}}\cosh(\nu s^{\frac{1}{2}})\,\mathrm{cosech}(a s^{\frac{1}{2}})$ | $a^{-1}\theta_4\left(\frac{\nu}{2a}\middle\vert\frac{t}{a^2}\right)$ <br> $= a^{-1}\theta_3\left(\frac{1}{2}+\frac{\nu}{2a}\middle\vert\frac{t}{a^2}\right)$ | $-a\leqslant\nu\leqslant a$ <br> $\mathrm{Re}\, s>0$ |
| | 26 | $\frac{1}{s}\cosh(\nu s^{\frac{1}{2}})\,\mathrm{cosech}(a s^{\frac{1}{2}})$ | $\frac{1}{a}\int_0^{\nu}\hat{\theta}_4\left(\frac{u}{2a}\middle\vert\frac{t}{a^2}\right)du+\frac{1}{a}\int_0^{t}\left[\frac{\partial}{\partial w}\hat{\theta}_4\left(\frac{w}{2a}\middle\vert\frac{u}{a^2}\right)\right]du$ | $-a<\nu<a$ <br> $\mathrm{Re}\, s>0$ |
| | 27 | $\frac{1}{s^{\frac{1}{2}}}\tanh(a s^{\frac{1}{2}})$ | $a^{-1}\theta_2\left(0\middle\vert\frac{t}{a^2}\right)$ | $\mathrm{Re}\, s>0$ |
| | 28 | $\frac{1}{s}\tanh(a s^{\frac{1}{2}})$ | $\int_0^{1}\hat{\theta}_2\left(\frac{u}{2}\middle\vert\frac{t}{a^2}\right)du$ | $\mathrm{Re}\, s>0$ |

| | | g(s) | f(t) | |
|---|---|---|---|---|
| 7.2 (Contd.) | 29 | $\frac{1}{s^{\frac{1}{2}}} \coth(as^{\frac{1}{2}})$ | $a^{-1}\theta_3\left(0\middle\|\frac{t}{a^2}\right)$ | Re s > o |
| | 30 | $\frac{1}{s^{\frac{1}{2}}} \tanh(as^{\frac{1}{2}}+b)$ | $\frac{e^{\frac{b^2}{a^2}t}}{a}\left[\theta_3\left(\frac{bt}{a^2}\middle\|\frac{t}{a^2}\right)+\hat{\theta}_3\left(\frac{bt}{a^2}\middle\|\frac{t}{a^2}\right)\right]-\frac{1}{(\pi t)^{\frac{1}{2}}}$ | Re s > o |
| | 31 | $\frac{1}{s^{\frac{1}{2}}}\left[\tanh(s^{\frac{1}{2}}+a^{\frac{1}{2}})+\tanh(s^{\frac{1}{2}}-a^{\frac{1}{2}})\right]$ | $2e^{at}\theta_3(a^{\frac{1}{2}}t\|t)$ | Re s > o |
| | 32 | $\frac{1}{s^{\frac{1}{2}}}\left[\tanh(s^{\frac{1}{2}}+a^{\frac{1}{2}})-\tanh(s^{\frac{1}{2}}-a^{\frac{1}{2}})+2\right]$ | $2e^{at}\hat{\theta}_3(a^{\frac{1}{2}}t\|t)$ | Re s > o |
| 7.2.1 | 1 | $\frac{1}{s-ic}\,\frac{\sinh(bs^{\frac{1}{2}})}{\sinh(as^{\frac{1}{2}})}$ | $\frac{\sinh(bi^{\frac{1}{2}}c^{\frac{1}{2}})}{\sinh(ai^{\frac{1}{2}}c^{\frac{1}{2}})}e^{ict} + 2\pi\sum_{n=1}^{\infty}\frac{n(-1)^n\sin\frac{n\pi b}{a}}{n^2\pi^2+ia^2c}e^{-\frac{n^2\pi^2}{a^2}t}$ | a ⩾ b > o<br>Re s > Max o, −Im c |
| | 2 | $\frac{1}{s-ic}\,\frac{\cosh(bs^{\frac{1}{2}})}{\cosh(as^{\frac{1}{2}})}$ | $\frac{\cosh(bi^{\frac{1}{2}}c^{\frac{1}{2}})}{\cosh(ai^{\frac{1}{2}}c^{\frac{1}{2}})}e^{ict} - 2s\sum_{n=0}^{\infty}\frac{(n+\frac{1}{2})(-1)^n\cos\frac{(n+\frac{1}{2})\pi b}{a}}{(n+\frac{1}{2})^2\pi^2+ia^2c}e^{-\frac{(n+\frac{1}{2})^2\pi^2t}{a^2}}$ | a ⩾ b > o<br>Re s > Max o, − Im c |
| 7.3.1 | 1 | $\frac{(as+\frac{1}{2})e^{-as}}{s^2\sinh(as)}$ | $2na-t \quad 2na < t < 2(n+1)a$ | Re s > o<br>n = 0, 1, 2, ... |
| 7.3.2 | 1 | $\frac{1}{s^{\frac{1}{2}}}e^{-as^{\frac{1}{2}}}\sinh(bs^{\frac{1}{2}})$ | $\frac{e^{-\frac{(a-b)^2}{4t}}-e^{-\frac{(a+b)^2}{4t}}}{2\pi^{\frac{1}{2}}t^{\frac{1}{2}}}$ | Re s > o |

| | | g(s) | f(t) | |
|---|---|---|---|---|
| 7.3.2 (Contd.) | 2 | $\dfrac{e^{-\frac{a^2+b^2}{4s}}\sinh(\frac{ab}{2s})}{s^{\frac{1}{2}}}$ | $\dfrac{\sin(at^{\frac{1}{2}})\sin(bt^{\frac{1}{2}})}{(\pi t)^{\frac{1}{2}}}$ | Re s > 0 |
| | 3 | $\dfrac{e^{-\frac{a^2+b^2}{4s}}\cosh(\frac{ab}{2s})}{s^{\frac{1}{2}}}$ | $\dfrac{\cos(at^{\frac{1}{2}})\cos(bt^{\frac{1}{2}})}{(\pi t)^{\frac{1}{2}}}$ | Re s > 0 |
| 8 | 1 | $\coth^{-1}\dfrac{s}{a}$ | $\left(\dfrac{a\pi}{2t}\right)^{\frac{1}{2}} L_{-\frac{1}{2}}(at)$ <br> $= t^{-1}\sin(at)$ | Re s > \|Re a\| |
| | 2 | $\dfrac{1}{s}\sinh^{-1}(\frac{s}{a})$ | $-Ji_0(at)$ | Re s > 0 |
| | 3 | $\dfrac{1}{s}(\sinh^{-1}\frac{s}{a})^2$ | $\int_{at}^{\infty} u^{-1}\, Y_0(u)\,du$ | Re s > 0 |
| 8.1 | 1 | $\dfrac{as}{s^2-a^2}-\coth^{-1}\dfrac{s}{a}$ | $\left(\dfrac{\pi a^3}{2}\right)^{\frac{1}{2}} t^{\frac{1}{2}} L_{-\frac{3}{2}}(at)$ | Re s > \|Re a\| |
| 8.2 | 1 | $\dfrac{\sinh^{-1}(\frac{s}{a})}{(s^2+a^2)^{\frac{1}{2}}}$ | $-\frac{\pi}{2} Y_0(at)$ | Re s > \|Im a\| |
| | 2 | $\dfrac{\sinh^{-1}\frac{a}{s}}{(s^2+a^2)^{\frac{1}{2}}}$ | $\frac{\pi}{2} H_0(at)$ | Re s > \|Im a\| |
| | 3 | $\dfrac{\frac{\pi}{2}+i\sinh^{-1}(\frac{s}{a})}{(s^2+a^2)^{\frac{1}{2}}}$ | $\frac{\pi}{2} H_0^{(2)}(at)$ | Re s > \|Im a\| |
| | 4 | $\dfrac{\frac{\pi}{2}-i\sinh^{-1}\frac{s}{a}}{(s^2+a^2)^{\frac{1}{2}}}$ | $\frac{\pi}{2} H_0^{(1)}(at)$ | Re s > \|Im a\| |

| | | $g(s)$ | $f(t)$ | |
|---|---|---|---|---|
| 8.2 (Contd.) | 5 | $\dfrac{\cosh^{-1}\frac{s}{a}}{(s^2-a^2)^{\frac{1}{2}}}$ | $K_0(at)$ | Re $s > -$Re $a$ |
| 8.3.2 | 1 | $\dfrac{e^{-\nu\sinh^{-1}\frac{s}{a}}}{(s^2+a^2)^{\frac{1}{2}}}$ | $J_\nu(at)$ | Re $\nu > -1$<br>Re $s > \lvert$Im $a\rvert$ |
| 8.4.1 | 1 | $\dfrac{s\tanh^{-1}\frac{a}{s}-\frac{a}{2}\log(s^2-a^2)}{s^2-a^2}$ | $\log(\gamma t)\sinh(at)$ | Re $s > \lvert$Re $a\rvert$ |
| | 2 | $\dfrac{\frac{s}{2}\log(s^2-a^2)-a\tanh^{-1}\frac{a}{s}}{s^2-a^2}$ | $\log\frac{\gamma}{t}\cosh(at)$ | Re $s > \lvert$Re $a\rvert$ |
| 8.7.2 | 1 | $\dfrac{\sinh(\nu\cosh^{-1}s)}{(s^2-1)^{\frac{1}{2}}}$ | $\dfrac{\sin(\nu\pi)}{\pi}K_\nu(t)$ | $\lvert$Re $\nu\rvert < 1$<br>Re $s > 1$ |
| 9 | 1 | $\frac{1}{s}A_n(1,\frac{1}{s})$ | $P_n(1-2t)$ | $n=0,1,2,\ldots$<br>Re $s > 0$ |
| | 2 | $\frac{1}{s}A_n(a,-\frac{1}{s})$ | $t^{n+a-1}(1+t)^n$ | $n=0,1,2,\ldots$<br>Re $s > 0$ |
| | 3 | $A_{n,\nu}(s)$ | $2^\nu i^n(n+\nu)\Gamma(\nu)C_n^\nu(-it)$ | $n=0,1,2,\ldots$<br>Re $s > 0$ |
| | 4 | $\displaystyle\sum_{n=0}^{\infty}\frac{b^{n+1}L_n^a(s)}{(b+1)^{n+1}(n+1)}$ | $(1+t)^{a-1}$ $\quad 0<t<b$<br>$0$ $\quad t>b$ | $b>0$<br>Re $s > -\infty$ |

| | | $g(s)$ | $f(t)$ | |
|---|---|---|---|---|
| 9(Contd.) | 5 | $\sum_{n=0}^{\infty} L_n^{a-n}(s)\frac{b^{n+1}}{n+1}$ | $(1+t)^a \quad 0<t<b$; $0 \quad t>b$ | $0<b<1$, $\mathrm{Re}\, s > -\infty$ |
| | 6 | $O_n(\frac{s}{a})$ | $\frac{a}{2}[at+(1+a^2t^2)^{\frac{1}{2}}]^n + \frac{a}{2}[at-(1+a^2t^2)^{\frac{1}{2}}]^n$ | $n=0,1,2,\ldots$ $\mathrm{Re}\, s>0$ |
| | 7 | $O_{2n}(s)$ | $\cosh(2n\sinh^{-1}t)$ | $n=0,1,2,\ldots$ $\mathrm{Re}\, s>0$ |
| | 8 | $O_{2n+1}(s)$ | $\sinh[(2n+1)\sinh^{-1}t]$ | $n=0,1,2,\ldots$ $\mathrm{Re}\, s>0$ |
| | 9 | $S_n(\frac{s}{a})$ | $\frac{[at+(1+a^2t^2)^{\frac{1}{2}}]^n - [at-(1+a^2t^2)^{\frac{1}{2}}]^n}{(1+a^2t^2)^{\frac{1}{2}}}$ | $n=0,1,2,\ldots$ $\mathrm{Re}\, s>0$ |
| 9.1 | 1 | $\frac{1}{s}A_n\left(1-n,\frac{2}{s^2}\right)$ | $\frac{(-2)^n(n-1)!}{(2n-1)!}H_{2n}(t)$ | $n=0,1,2,\ldots$ $\mathrm{Re}\, s>0$ |
| | 2 | $\frac{1}{s^2}A_n\left(1-n,\frac{2}{s^2}\right)$ | $\frac{(-2)^n n!}{(2n+1)!}He_{2n+1}(t)$ | $n=0,1,2,\ldots$ $\mathrm{Re}\, s>0$ |
| | 3 | $\frac{1}{s^{n+1}}L_n(s)$ | $\frac{(t+1)^n}{n!}P_n\left(\frac{t-1}{t+1}\right)$ | $n=0,1,2,\ldots$ $\mathrm{Re}\, s>0$ |
| | 4 | $\sum_{n=0}^{\infty}\frac{(-s)^n b^{n+1} L_n^{(a)}(-\frac{1}{s})}{(n+1)\Gamma(a+n+1)}$ | $\frac{J_a(2t^{\frac{1}{2}})}{t^{\frac{a}{2}}} \quad 0<t<b$; $0 \quad t>b$ | $b>0$, $\mathrm{Re}\, s>-\infty$ |
| | 5 | $\frac{1}{s}P_n(1-\frac{a}{s})$ | ${}_2F_2\left[\begin{matrix}-n, & n+1; & \frac{at}{2}\\ 1, & 1; & \end{matrix}\right]$ | $n=0,1,2,\ldots$ $\mathrm{Re}\, s>0$ |

| | | $g(s)$ | $f(t)$ | |
|---|---|---|---|---|
| 9.1 (Contd.) | 6 | $\dfrac{P_n(1-\frac{2}{s})}{s^{n+1}}$ | $\dfrac{t^n}{n!} L_n(t)$ | $n=0,1,2,\ldots$ Re $s>0$ |
| | 7 | $\dfrac{P_n\left(\frac{s-1}{s+1}\right)}{s+1}$ | $e^{-t}\sum_{m=0}^{n} a_{mn} L_m(2t)$ where $a_{mn}$ is given by $P_n(x) = \sum_{m=0}^{n} a_{mn} x^m$ | $n=0,1,2,\ldots$ Re $s>-1$ |
| | 8 | $\dfrac{P_n\left(\frac{s+a}{s+b}\right)}{(s+b)^{n+1}}$ | $\dfrac{t^n}{n!} e^{-bt} L_n\left[\dfrac{(b-a)t}{2}\right]$ | $n=0,1,2,\ldots$ Re $s>-$ Re $b$ |
| | 9 | $\dfrac{P_m\left(\frac{s-a}{s+a}\right) P_n\left(\frac{s-a}{s+a}\right)}{s+a}$ | $U^{m,n}(at)$ | $m,n=0,1,2,\ldots$ Re $s>-$ Re $a$ |
| | 10 | $\dfrac{(s-a)^n}{s^{n+1}} P_n\left[\dfrac{s^2-as+b}{s(s-a)}\right]$ | $L_n\left[\left\{\frac{a}{2}-\left(\frac{a^2}{4}-\frac{b}{2}\right)^{\frac{1}{2}}\right\}t\right] L_n\left[\left\{\frac{a}{2}+\left(\frac{a^2}{4}-\frac{b}{2}\right)^{\frac{1}{2}}\right]t\right]$ | $n=0,1,2,\ldots$ Re $s>0$ |
| | 11 | $\dfrac{Q_n\left(\frac{s+a}{s-a}\right)}{s-a}$ | $\frac{1}{2} V_n(at)$ | Re $s>0$ |
| | 12 | $\dfrac{1}{s^n} T_n(1-\frac{1}{s})$ | $\dfrac{(-1)^n(2t)^{n-1}}{\Gamma(2n)} He_{2n}(t^{\frac{1}{2}})$ | $n=0,1,2,\ldots$ Re $s>0$ |
| | 13 | $\dfrac{1}{s^{n+1}} U_n(\frac{1}{s}-1)$ | $\dfrac{2^{n-1} t^{n-\frac{1}{2}}}{(2n-1)!} He_{2n-1}(t^{\frac{1}{2}})$ | $n=1,2,3,\ldots$ Re $s>0$ |
| 9.2 | 1 | $\dfrac{1}{s^{\frac{1}{2}}} A_n(0,\frac{1}{s})$ | $\dfrac{1}{(\pi t)^{\frac{1}{2}}} T_n(1-2t)$ | $n=0,1,2,\ldots$ Re $s>0$ |

| | | $g(s)$ | $f(t)$ | |
|---|---|---|---|---|
| 9.2 (Contd.) | 2 | $\frac{1}{s^{\frac{1}{2}}} A_n(\frac{1}{2}, \frac{1}{s})$ | $\frac{(-1)^n}{(2n)!(\pi t)^{\frac{1}{2}}} P_{2n}(t^{\frac{1}{2}})$ | $n = 0,1,2,\ldots$ Re $s > 0$ |
| | 3 | $\frac{1}{s^{\frac{1}{2}}} A_n(\nu, \frac{1}{s})$ | $(-1)^n \frac{n!\Gamma(\nu)}{\Gamma(n+\nu)} \frac{1}{(\pi t)^{\frac{1}{2}}} C_{2n}^{\nu}(t^{\frac{1}{2}})$ | $n = 0,1,2,\ldots$ Re $s > 0$ |
| | 4 | $\frac{1}{s^{\frac{3}{2}}} A_n(\frac{3}{2}, \frac{1}{s})$ | $\frac{(-1)^n 2}{\pi^{\frac{1}{2}}(2n+1)!} P_{2n+1}(t^{\frac{1}{2}})$ | $n = 0,1,2,\ldots$ Re $s > 0$ |
| | 5 | $\frac{1}{s^{\frac{3}{2}}} A_n(2, \frac{1}{s})$ | $(-1)^n \frac{2t^{\frac{1}{2}}}{(n+1)\pi^{\frac{1}{2}}} U_{n+1}(2t-1)$ | $n = 0,1,2,\ldots$ Re $s > 0$ |
| | 6 | $\frac{1}{s^{\frac{3}{2}}} A_n(\nu, \frac{1}{s})$ | $\frac{(-1)^n n!\Gamma(\nu-1)}{\pi^{\frac{1}{2}}\Gamma(n+\nu)\, t^{\frac{1}{2}}} C_{2n+1}^{\nu-1}(t^{\frac{1}{2}})$ | $n = 0,1,2,\ldots$ Re $s > 0$ |
| | 7 | $\frac{1}{s^{\frac{\nu+1}{2}}} A_n(\nu, \frac{1}{s})$ | $\frac{(-1)^n n!\Gamma(\nu)}{\Gamma(\nu+n)\Gamma(\frac{\nu+1}{2})} t^{\frac{\nu-1}{2}} C_n^{\frac{\nu}{2}}(2t-1)$ | $n = 0,1,2,\ldots$ Re $s > 0$ |
| | 8 | $\frac{1}{s^{a}} A_n(b, \frac{1}{s})$ | $\frac{t^{a-1}}{\Gamma(a)} {}_2F_1[-n, n+b; a; t]$ | $n = 0,1,2,\ldots$ Re $s > 0$ |
| | 9 | $\frac{C_n^{\nu}\left(\frac{1}{s^{\frac{1}{2}}}\right)}{s^{\frac{n}{2}+\nu}}$ | $\frac{2^{\frac{n}{2}} t^{\frac{n}{2}+\nu-1}}{n!\Gamma(\nu)} He_n[(2t)^{\frac{1}{2}}]$ | $n = 0,1,2,\ldots$ Re $s > 0$ |
| | 10 | $\frac{He_n[(2s)^{\frac{1}{2}}]}{s^{\frac{n+1}{2}}}$ | $\frac{2^{\frac{n}{2}-1}}{(\pi t)^{\frac{1}{2}}}[(1+it^{\frac{1}{2}})^n+(1-it^{\frac{1}{2}})^n]$ | $n = 0,1,2,\ldots$ Re $s > 0$ |

| | | $g(s)$ | $f(t)$ | |
|---|---|---|---|---|
| 9.2 (Contd.) | 11 | $\dfrac{He_{2n}[(2s)^{\frac{1}{2}}]}{s^{n+\frac{1}{2}}}$ | $\dfrac{2^n}{(\pi t)^{\frac{1}{2}}}(1+t)^n\, T_n\left(\dfrac{1-t}{1+t}\right)$ | $n=0,1,2,\ldots$ Re $s>0$ |
| | 12 | $\dfrac{1}{s^{\frac{1}{2}}}\left(1-\dfrac{1}{2b^2 s}\right)^{\frac{n}{2}} He_n\left[\dfrac{a}{(b^2-\frac{1}{2s})^{\frac{1}{2}}}\right]$ | $\dfrac{1}{(2\pi t)^{\frac{1}{2}}}\left[He_n\left(\dfrac{a+t^{\frac{1}{2}}}{b}\right)+He_n\left(\dfrac{a-t^{\frac{1}{2}}}{b}\right)\right]$ | $n=0,1,2,\ldots$ Re $s>0$ |
| | 13 | $\dfrac{L_n^a(s)}{s^{n+b}}$ | $\dfrac{t^{b-1}(1+t)^n}{\Gamma(n+b)} P_n^{a,b-1}\left(\dfrac{t-1}{t+1}\right)$ | $n=0,1,2,\ldots$ Re $s>0$ |
| | 14 | $\dfrac{1}{s^b} L_n^a\left(\dfrac{c}{s}\right)$ | $\dfrac{(a+1)_n\, t^{b-1}}{n!\Gamma(b)}\, {}_1F_2\left[\begin{matrix} -n; \\ a+1,\ b;\end{matrix}\ ct\right]$ | Re $b>0$ $n=0,1,2,\ldots$ Re $s>0$ |
| | 15 | $\dfrac{1}{s^{\frac{1}{2}}} P_n\left(\dfrac{a}{s}\right)$ | $\dfrac{He_n[(2at)^{\frac{1}{2}}]\, He_n[(-2at)^{\frac{1}{2}}]}{n!\, i^n \pi^{\frac{1}{2}} t^{\frac{1}{2}}}$ | $n=0,1,2,\ldots$ Re $s>0$ |
| | 16 | $\dfrac{1}{s^{\frac{n+1}{2}}} P_n\left[\dfrac{1}{(2s)^{\frac{1}{2}}}\right]$ | $\dfrac{2^{\frac{n}{2}}\, t^{\frac{n-1}{2}}}{n!\,\pi^{\frac{1}{2}}} He_n(t^{\frac{1}{2}})$ | $n=0,1,2,\ldots$ Re $s>0$ |
| | 17 | $Q_n\left(\dfrac{s^{\frac{1}{2}}}{a^{\frac{1}{2}}}\right)$ | $\dfrac{n\Gamma(\frac{n}{2})\, e^{\frac{at}{2}}}{4\Gamma(n+\frac{3}{2})\, a^{\frac{1}{4}} t^{\frac{5}{4}}} M_{-\frac{1}{4},\frac{n}{2}+\frac{1}{4}}(at)$ | $n=1,2,3,\ldots$ Re $s>\lvert$Re $a\rvert$ |
| 9.2.1 | 1 | $\dfrac{C_n^{\nu}(1-\frac{2}{s})}{s^{n+2\nu}}$ | $\dfrac{\Gamma(\nu+\frac{1}{2})\, t^{n+2\nu-1}}{\Gamma(2\nu)\Gamma(n+\nu+\frac{1}{2})} L_n^{\nu-\frac{1}{2}}(t)$ | $n=0,1,2,\ldots$ Re $s>0$ |
| | 2 | $\dfrac{1}{s^a} C_n^{\nu}\left(1-\dfrac{b}{s}\right)$ | $\dfrac{t^{a-1}}{nB(n,2\nu)\Gamma(a)}\, {}_2F_2\left[\begin{matrix} -n, n+2\nu; \\ \nu+\frac{1}{2},\quad a;\end{matrix}\ \dfrac{bt}{2}\right]$ | Re $a>0$ $n=0,1,2,\ldots$ Re $s>0$ |

| | | $g(s)$ | $f(t)$ | |
|---|---|---|---|---|
| 9.2.1 (Contd.) | 3 | $\dfrac{C_n^{\nu}\left(\frac{s+a}{s+b}\right)}{(s+b)^{\mu}}$ | $\dfrac{t^{\mu-1}e^{-bt}}{nB(n,2\nu)\Gamma(\mu)}\,{}_2F_2\left[\begin{matrix}-n,n+2\nu; & \frac{(b-a)t}{2}\\ \mu,\nu+\frac{1}{2}; & \end{matrix}\right]$ | $\operatorname{Re}\mu>0$<br>$\operatorname{Re}\nu>0$<br>$n=0,1,2,\ldots$<br>$\operatorname{Re}s>-\operatorname{Re}b$ |
| | 4 | $\dfrac{He_{2n+1}[(2s)^{\frac{1}{2}}]}{s^{n+2}}$ | $2^{n+\frac{3}{2}}\left(\frac{t}{\pi}\right)^{\frac{1}{2}}\dfrac{(t+1)^n}{n+1}U_{n+1}\left(\frac{1-t}{1+t}\right)$ | $n=0,1,2,\ldots$<br>$\operatorname{Re}s>0$ |
| | 5 | $\frac{1}{s^a}P_n(1-\frac{b}{s})$ | $t^{a-1}\,{}_2F_2\left[\begin{matrix}-n,n+1; & \frac{bt}{2}\\ 1,\ a; & \end{matrix}\right]$ | $\operatorname{Re}a>0$<br>$n=0,1,2,\ldots$<br>$\operatorname{Re}s>0$ |
| | 6 | $\dfrac{P_n^{a,b}(1-\frac{2}{s})}{s^{a+b+n+1}}$ | $\dfrac{t^{a+b+n}}{\Gamma(a+b+n+1)}L_n^a(t)$ | $n=0,1,2,\ldots$<br>$\operatorname{Re}s>0$ |
| | 7 | $\dfrac{P_n\left(\frac{s+a}{s+b}\right)}{(s+b)^{\nu}}$ | $\dfrac{t^{\nu-1}}{\Gamma(\nu)}e^{-bt}\,{}_2F_2\left[\begin{matrix}-n,n+1; & (b-a)t\\ 1,\ \nu; & 2\end{matrix}\right]$ | $\operatorname{Re}\nu>0$<br>$n=0,1,2,\ldots$<br>$\operatorname{Re}s>-\operatorname{Re}b$ |
| | 8 | $\dfrac{(a+b-s)^{\frac{n}{2}}}{(a+b+s)^{\frac{n+1}{2}}}P_n\left[2\left\{\dfrac{ab}{(a+b)^2-s^2}\right\}^{\frac{1}{2}}\right]$ | $\dfrac{D_n(2a^{\frac{1}{2}}t^{\frac{1}{2}})\,D_n(2b^{\frac{1}{2}}t^{\frac{1}{2}})}{n!(\pi t)^{\frac{1}{2}}}$ | $n=0,1,2,\ldots$<br>$\operatorname{Re}s>-\operatorname{Re}(a+b)$ |
| 9.3.2 | 1 | $\dfrac{e^{-\frac{a}{s}}}{s^{n+\frac{1}{2}}}He_{2n}\left[\left(\frac{2a}{s}\right)^{\frac{1}{2}}\right]$ | $\dfrac{(-2)^n}{\pi^{\frac{1}{2}}}t^{n-\frac{1}{2}}\cos(2a^{\frac{1}{2}}t^{\frac{1}{2}})$ | $n=0,1,2,\ldots$<br>$\operatorname{Re}s>0$ |
| | 2 | $\dfrac{e^{-\frac{a}{s}}}{s^{n+\nu+1}}L_n^{\nu}(\frac{a}{s})$ | $\dfrac{t^{\frac{\nu}{2}+n}}{n!a^{\frac{\nu}{2}}}J_{\nu}(2a^{\frac{1}{2}}t^{\frac{1}{2}})$ | $\operatorname{Re}(\nu+n)>-1$<br>$n=0,1,2,\ldots$<br>$\operatorname{Re}s>0$ |
| 9.3.2.1 | 1 | $\dfrac{e^{-\frac{a}{s}}}{s^{n+1}}He_{2n+1}\left[\left(\frac{2a}{s}\right)^{\frac{1}{2}}\right]$ | $(-1)^n2^{n+\frac{1}{2}}\pi^{-\frac{1}{2}}t^n\sin(2a^{\frac{1}{2}}t^{\frac{1}{2}})$ | $n=0,1,2,\ldots$<br>$\operatorname{Re}s>0$ |

| | | g(s) | f(t) | |
|---|---|---|---|---|
| 9.3.2.1 (Contd.) | 2 | $e^{-\frac{a}{s}} \frac{(s-1)^n}{s^{\nu+n+1}} L_n^{\nu}\left[\frac{a}{s(1-s)}\right]$ | $\left(\frac{t}{a}\right)^{\frac{\nu}{2}} L_n^{\nu}(t) J_{\nu}(2a^{\frac{1}{2}}t^{\frac{1}{2}})$ | $n=0,1,2,\dots$ <br> $\mathrm{Re}\,\nu > -1$ <br> $\mathrm{Re}\,s > 0$ |
| 10 | 1 | $\frac{1}{s} J_{\nu}(\frac{a}{s})$ | $J_{\nu}[(2at)^{\frac{1}{2}}] I_{\nu}[(2at)^{\frac{1}{2}}]$ | $\mathrm{Re}\,\nu > -1$ <br> $\mathrm{Re}\,s > 0$ |
| | 2 | $Y_s(a) \frac{\partial J_s(a)}{\partial s} - J_s(a) \frac{\partial Y_s(a)}{\partial s}$ | $\frac{2}{\pi} K_0[2a \sinh \frac{t}{2}]$ | $\mathrm{Re}\,a > 0$ <br> $\mathrm{Re}\,s > -\infty$ |
| 10.1 | 1 | $J_{\nu-s}(a) Y_{-\nu-s}(a) - J_{-\nu-s}(a) Y_{\nu-s}(a)$ | $2\pi^{-2} \sin(2\nu\pi) K_{2\nu}[2a \sinh \frac{t}{2}]$ | $\mathrm{Re}\,a > 0$ <br> $\lvert\mathrm{Re}\,\nu\rvert < \frac{1}{2}$ <br> $\mathrm{Re}\,s > -\infty$ |
| 10.2 | 1 | $s^{\mu} J_{\nu}(\frac{a}{s})$ | $\frac{a^{\nu} t^{\nu-\mu-1}}{2^{\nu}\Gamma(\nu+1)\Gamma(\nu-\mu)} {}_0F_3\left[\begin{matrix} & ; -\frac{a^2t^2}{16} \\ \nu+1, \frac{\nu-\mu}{2}, \frac{\nu-\mu+1}{2}; & \end{matrix}\right]$ | $\mathrm{Re}(\nu-\mu) > 0$ <br> $\mathrm{Re}\,s > 0$ |
| | 2 | $\frac{1}{s^{\mu}} J_{\nu}[(\frac{a}{s})^{\frac{1}{2}}]$ | $\frac{a^{\frac{\nu}{2}} t^{\mu+\frac{\nu}{2}-1}}{2^{\nu}\Gamma(\mu+\frac{\nu}{2})\Gamma(\nu+1)} {}_0F_2\left[\begin{matrix} & ; -\frac{at}{4} \\ \mu+\frac{\nu}{2}, \nu+1; & \end{matrix}\right]$ | $\mathrm{Re}(\mu+\frac{\nu}{2}) > 0$ <br> $\mathrm{Re}\,s > 0$ |
| | 3 | $s^{\frac{1}{2}}[J_{\nu+\frac{1}{4}}(as) J_{\nu-\frac{1}{4}}(as) + Y_{\nu+\frac{1}{4}}(as) Y_{\nu-\frac{1}{4}}(as)]$ | $\left(\frac{2}{\pi}\right)^{\frac{3}{2}} \frac{e^{2\nu \sinh^{-1}\frac{t}{2a}}}{t^{\frac{1}{2}}(t^2+4a^2)^{\frac{1}{2}}}$ | $\mathrm{Re}\,a > 0$ <br> $\mathrm{Re}\,s > 0$ |
| | 4 | $s^{\frac{1}{2}}[J_{\frac{1}{4}+\nu}(as) J_{\frac{1}{4}-\nu}(as) + Y_{\frac{1}{4}+\nu}(as) Y_{\frac{1}{4}-\nu}(as)]$ | $\frac{2^{\frac{3}{2}}}{\pi^{\frac{3}{2}} t^{\frac{1}{2}}(t^2+4a^2)^{\frac{1}{2}}} \left\{ \cos[(\nu+\frac{1}{4})\pi] e^{-2\nu \sinh^{-1}\frac{t}{2a}} + \sin[(\nu+\frac{1}{4})\pi] e^{2\nu \sinh^{-1}\frac{t}{2a}} \right\}$ | $\mathrm{Re}\,a > 0$ <br> $\mathrm{Re}\,s > 0$ |

| | | g(s) | f(t) | |
|---|---|---|---|---|
| 10.2 (Contd.) | 5 | $s^{\frac{1}{2}}[J_{\nu+\frac{1}{4}}(as)Y_{\nu-\frac{1}{4}}(as)-J_{\nu-\frac{1}{4}}(as)Y_{\nu+\frac{1}{4}}(as)]$ | $\frac{2^{2\nu+\frac{3}{2}}a^{2\nu}[t+(t^2+4a^2)^{\frac{1}{2}}]^{-2\nu}}{\pi^{\frac{3}{2}}(t^3+4a^2t)^{\frac{1}{2}}}$ $=\left(\frac{2}{\pi}\right)^{\frac{3}{2}}\frac{e^{-2\nu\sinh^{-1}\frac{t}{2a}}}{(t^3+4a^2t)^{\frac{1}{2}}}$ | Re a > 0 Re s > 0 |
| | 6 | $s^{\frac{1}{2}}[J_{\frac{1}{4}+\nu}(as)Y_{\frac{1}{4}-\nu}(as)-J_{\frac{1}{4}-\nu}(as)Y_{\frac{1}{4}+\nu}(as)]$ | $\frac{2^{\frac{3}{2}}}{\pi^{\frac{3}{2}}t^{\frac{1}{2}}(t^2+4a^2)^{\frac{1}{2}}}\left\{\sin[(\nu+\frac{1}{4})\pi]e^{-2\nu\sinh^{-1}\frac{t}{2a}} - \cos[(\nu+\frac{1}{4})\pi]e^{2\nu\sinh^{-1}\frac{t}{2a}}\right\}$ | Re a > 0 Re s > 0 |
| 10.3 | 1 | $\frac{1}{s}e^{\frac{a^2-b^2}{s}}J_\nu(\frac{2ab}{s})$ | $J_\nu(2bt^{\frac{1}{2}})I_\nu(2at^{\frac{1}{2}})$ | Re $\nu > -1$ Re s > 0 |
| | 2 | $e^{-bs}[\frac{\pi}{2}Y_0(ibs)-\log\frac{\gamma}{2}J_0(ibs)]$ | $\frac{\log\frac{4t(2b-t)}{b^2}}{\pi t^{\frac{1}{2}}(2b-t)^{\frac{1}{2}}}$ $0 < t < 2b$; 0 $t > 2b$ | b > 0 Re s > $-\infty$ |
| 10.3.2 | 1 | $e^{-s}J_0[(a^2-s^2)^{\frac{1}{2}}]$ | $\frac{\cos[a(2t-t^2)^{\frac{1}{2}}]}{\pi(2t-t^2)^{\frac{1}{2}}}$ $0 < t < 2$; 0 $t > 2$ | Re s > $-\infty$ |
| 10.3.2.1 | 1 | $\frac{e^{-\frac{as}{s^2+1}}}{(s^2+1)^{\frac{1}{2}}}J_\nu\left(\frac{a}{s^2+1}\right)$ | $J_\nu(t)J_{2\nu}(2a^{\frac{1}{2}}t^{\frac{1}{2}})$ | Re $\nu > -\frac{1}{2}$ Re s > 0 |
| 10.5 | 1 | $\cos(as)J_0(as)+\sin(as)Y_0(as)$ | $\frac{2^{\frac{1}{2}}}{\pi}\left[\frac{(t^2+4a^2)^{\frac{1}{2}}-t}{t(t^2+4a^2)}\right]^{\frac{1}{2}}$ | Re a > 0 Re s > 0 |

| | | g(s) | f(t) | |
|---|---|---|---|---|
| 10.5 (Contd.) | 2 | $\sin(as)\, J_0(as) - \cos(as)\, Y_0(as)$ | $\frac{2^{\frac{1}{2}}}{\pi}\left[\frac{t+(t^2+4a^2)^{\frac{1}{2}}}{t(t^2+4a^2)}\right]^{\frac{1}{2}}$ | Re a > 0<br>Re s > 0 |
| | 3 | $\cos(as)\, J_1(as) + \sin(as)\, Y_1(as)$ | $-\frac{[(t^2+4a^2)^{\frac{1}{2}}-t]^{\frac{3}{2}}}{2^{\frac{1}{2}}\pi a[t(t^2+4a^2)]^{\frac{1}{2}}}$ | Re a > 0<br>Re s > 0 |
| | 4 | $\sin(as)\, J_1(as) - \cos(as)\, Y_1(as)$ | $\frac{[t+(t^2+4a^2)^{\frac{1}{2}}]^{\frac{3}{2}}}{2^{\frac{1}{2}}\pi a[t(t^2+4a^2)]^{\frac{1}{2}}}$ | Re a > 0<br>Re s > 0 |
| 10.5.2.1 | 1 | $\frac{1}{s^{\nu}}[\cos(as+b) J_{\nu}(as) + \sin(as+b) Y_{\nu}(as)]$ | $-\frac{2\, t^{\nu-\frac{1}{2}}(t^2+4a^2)^{\frac{\nu}{2}-\frac{1}{4}}}{\pi^{\frac{1}{2}}(2a)^{\nu}\Gamma(\nu+\frac{1}{2})} \cdot \sin[(\nu-\frac{1}{2})\cot^{-1}(\frac{t}{2a})+b]$ | Re a > 0<br>Re $\nu$ > $-\frac{1}{2}$<br>Re s > 0 |
| | 2 | $\frac{1}{s^{\nu}}[\sin(as+b) J_{\nu}(as) - \cos(as+b) Y_{\nu}(as)]$ | $\frac{2\, t^{\nu-\frac{1}{2}}(t^2+4a^2)^{\frac{\nu}{2}-\frac{1}{4}}}{\pi^{\frac{1}{2}}(2a)^{\nu}\Gamma(\nu+\frac{1}{2})} \cdot \cos[(\nu-\frac{1}{2})\cot^{-1}(\frac{t}{2a})+b]$ | Re a > 0<br>Re $\nu$ > $-\frac{1}{2}$<br>Re s > 0 |
| 11.2 | 1 | $\frac{1}{s^{\frac{1}{2}}} H_{\nu}^{(1)}(\frac{s}{a}) H_{\nu}^{(2)}(\frac{s}{a})$ | $a\left(\frac{2}{\pi}\right)^{\frac{1}{2}} t^{\frac{1}{2}} P_{\nu-\frac{1}{2}}^{\frac{1}{4}}\left[\left(1+\frac{a^2t^2}{4}\right)^{\frac{1}{2}}\right] P_{\nu-\frac{1}{2}}^{-\frac{1}{4}}\left[\left(1+\frac{a^2t^2}{4}\right)^{\frac{1}{2}}\right]$ | Re s > 0 |
| | 2 | $\frac{1}{s^{\nu}} H_{\nu}^{(1)}(as^{\frac{1}{2}}) H_{\nu}^{(2)}(as^{\frac{1}{2}})$ | $\frac{2\, t^{\frac{3\nu-1}{2}} e^{\frac{a^2}{2t}}}{\Gamma(\nu+\frac{1}{2}) a^{2\nu+1}} W_{\frac{\nu}{2},\frac{\nu}{2}}\left(\frac{a^2}{t}\right)$ | $\lvert\arg a\rvert < \pi$<br>Re $\nu$ > $-\frac{1}{2}$<br>Re s > 0 |
| | 3 | $s^{\frac{1}{2}} H_{\frac{1}{2}+\nu}^{(1)}(as)\, H_{\frac{1}{2}-\nu}^{(2)}(as)$ | $\frac{4e^{-\nu\pi i}\left\{\cosh\left(2\nu\sinh^{-1}\frac{t}{2a}\right)+i\sinh\left(2\nu\sinh^{-1}\frac{t}{2a}\right)\right\}}{[\pi^3 t(t^2+4a^2)]^{\frac{1}{2}}}$ | Re a > 0<br>Re s > 0 |

| | | g(s) | f(t) | |
|---|---|---|---|---|
| 11.2 (Contd.) | 4 | $\frac{1}{s^b} H_\mu^{(1)}(\frac{s}{a}) H_\nu^{(2)}(\frac{s}{a})$ | $\frac{2a\, e^{\frac{\nu-\mu}{2}\pi i}\, t^b}{\pi\Gamma(b+1)}\, {}_4F_3\left[\begin{matrix}\frac{1+\mu+\nu}{2}, \frac{1-\mu+\nu}{2}, \frac{1+\mu-\nu}{2}, \frac{1-\mu-\nu}{2}; \\ \frac{1}{2}, \frac{b+1}{2}, \frac{b}{2}+1\end{matrix}\; ; -\frac{a^2t^2}{4}\right]$ $+ \frac{i a^2(\mu^2-\nu^2) e^{\frac{\nu-\mu}{2}\pi i}\, t^{b+1}}{\pi\Gamma(b+2)} \cdot {}_4F_3\left[\begin{matrix}1+\frac{\mu+\nu}{2}, 1+\frac{\nu-\mu}{2}, 1-\frac{\mu+\nu}{2}, 1+\frac{\mu-\nu}{2}; \\ \frac{3}{2}, \frac{b}{2}+1, \frac{b+3}{2}\end{matrix}\; ; -\frac{a^2t^2}{4}\right]$ | $\mathrm{Re}\, b > -1$<br>$\mathrm{Re}\, s > 0$ |
| | 5 | $s^{\frac{1}{2}}\left[e^{\nu\pi i} H^{(1)}_{\frac{1}{2}+\nu}(as)\, H^{(2)}_{\frac{1}{2}-\nu}(as) + e^{-\nu\pi i} H^{(1)}_{\frac{1}{2}-\nu}(as)\, H^{(2)}_{\frac{1}{2}+\nu}(as)\right]$ | $\frac{8\cosh(2\nu \sinh^{-1}\frac{t}{2a})}{\pi^{\frac{3}{2}} t^{\frac{1}{2}} (t^2+4a^2)^{\frac{1}{2}}}$ | $\lvert\arg a\rvert < \pi$<br>$\mathrm{Re}\, s > 0$ |
| | 6 | $s^{\frac{1}{2}}\left[e^{\nu\pi i} H^{(1)}_{\frac{1}{2}+\nu}(as)\, H^{(2)}_{\frac{1}{2}-\nu}(as) - e^{-\nu\pi i} H^{(1)}_{\frac{1}{2}-\nu}(as)\, H^{(2)}_{\frac{1}{2}+\nu}(as)\right]$ | $\frac{8\, i \sinh(2\nu \sinh^{-1}\frac{t}{2a})}{\pi^{\frac{3}{2}} t^{\frac{1}{2}} (t^2+4a^2)^{\frac{1}{2}}}$ | $\lvert\arg a\rvert < \pi$<br>$\mathrm{Re}\, s > 0$ |
| | 7 | $s^{\frac{1}{2}}\left[H^{(1)}_{\mu+\frac{1}{2}}(as^{\frac{1}{2}})\, H^{(2)}_{\mu-\frac{1}{2}}(as^{\frac{1}{2}}) + H^{(1)}_{\mu-\frac{1}{2}}(as^{\frac{1}{2}})\, H^{(2)}_{\mu+\frac{1}{2}}(as^{\frac{1}{2}})\right]$ | $\frac{4\mu}{a\pi^{\frac{3}{2}}}\, \frac{e^{\frac{a^2}{2t}}}{t}\, W_{-\frac{1}{2},\mu}\left(\frac{a^2}{t}\right)$ | $\lvert\arg a^2\rvert < \pi$<br>$\mathrm{Re}\, s > 0$ |
| | 8 | $s^a\left[e^{(\mu-\nu)\pi i} H^{(1)}_{2\mu}(\frac{s}{b})\, H^{(2)}_{2\nu}(\frac{s}{b}) + e^{(\nu-\mu)\pi i} H^{(2)}_{2\mu}(\frac{s}{b})\, H^{(1)}_{2\nu}(\frac{s}{b})\right]$ | $\frac{4b}{\pi\Gamma(1-a)\, t^a}\, {}_4F_3\left[\begin{matrix}\frac{1}{2}+\mu+\nu, \frac{1}{2}-\mu+\nu, \frac{1}{2}+\mu-\nu, \frac{1}{2}-\mu-\nu; \\ \frac{1}{2}, \frac{1-a}{2}, 1-\frac{a}{2}\end{matrix}\; ; -\frac{b^2t^2}{4}\right]$ | $\mathrm{Re}(1-a) > 0$<br>$\mathrm{Re}\, b > 0$<br>$\mathrm{Re}\, s > 0$ |
| | 9 | $s^a\left[e^{(\mu-\nu)\pi i} H^{(1)}_{2\mu}(\frac{s}{b})\, H^{(2)}_{2\nu}(\frac{s}{b}) - e^{(\nu-\mu)\pi i} H^{(2)}_{2\mu}(\frac{s}{b})\, H^{(1)}_{2\nu}(\frac{s}{b})\right]$ | $\frac{8\, i\, b^2(\mu^2-\nu^2)}{\pi\,\Gamma(2-a)}\, t^{1-a} \cdot {}_4F_3\left[\begin{matrix}1+\mu+\nu, 1-\mu+\nu, 1+\mu-\nu, 1-\mu-\nu; \\ \frac{3}{2}, 1-\frac{a}{2}, \frac{3-a}{2}\end{matrix}\; ; -\frac{b^2t^2}{4}\right]$ | $\mathrm{Re}\, b > 0$<br>$\mathrm{Re}(1-\frac{a}{2}) > 0$<br>$\mathrm{Re}\, s > 0$ |

| | | g(s) | f(t) | |
|---|---|---|---|---|
| 11.2.1 | 1 | $s^{\frac{1}{2}} H^{(1)}_{\frac{1}{8}}(\frac{s^2}{a}) H^{(2)}_{\frac{1}{8}}(\frac{s^2}{a})$ | $\frac{2^{\frac{1}{2}} a \cos(\frac{\pi}{8})}{\pi^{\frac{1}{2}}} t^{\frac{1}{2}} J_{\frac{1}{8}}\left(\frac{at^2}{16}\right) J_{-\frac{1}{8}}\left(\frac{at^2}{16}\right)$ | $a>0$<br>$\mathrm{Re}\, s > 0$ |
| 11.3.2 | 1 | $\frac{1}{s^\nu} e^{-ias} H^{(1)}_\nu(as)$ | $-\frac{2i(t^2-2ait)^{\nu-\frac{1}{2}}}{\pi^{\frac{1}{2}}(2a)^\nu \Gamma(\nu+\frac{1}{2})}$<br>$= -\frac{2i\, t^{\nu-\frac{1}{2}}(4a^2+t^2)^{\frac{\nu}{2}-\frac{1}{4}}}{\pi^{\frac{1}{2}}\,(2a)^\nu \Gamma(\nu+\frac{1}{2})} e^{-i(\nu-\frac{1}{2})\cot^{-1}\frac{t}{2a}}$ | $\mathrm{Re}\,\nu > -\frac{1}{2}$<br>$-\frac{\pi}{2} < \arg a < \frac{3\pi}{2}$<br>$\mathrm{Re}\, s > 0$ |
| | 2 | $\frac{1}{s^\nu} e^{ias} H^{(2)}_\nu(as)$ | $\frac{i(t^2+2ait)^{\nu-\frac{1}{2}}}{\pi^{\frac{1}{2}} 2^{\nu-1} a^\nu \Gamma(\nu+\frac{1}{2})}$ | $\mathrm{Re}\,\nu > -\frac{1}{2}$<br>$-\frac{3\pi}{2} < \arg a < \frac{\pi}{2}$<br>$\mathrm{Re}\, s > 0$ |
| | 3 | $\frac{e^{is} H^{(2)}_\nu[(s^2+a^2)^{\frac{1}{2}}]}{(s^2+a^2)^{\frac{\nu}{2}}}$ | $\frac{i 2^{\frac{1}{2}}}{\pi^{\frac{1}{2}} a^{\nu-\frac{1}{2}}} (t^2+2it)^{\frac{\nu}{2}-\frac{1}{4}} J_{\nu-\frac{1}{2}}[a(t^2+2it)^{\frac{1}{2}}]$ | $\mathrm{Re}\,\nu > -\frac{1}{2}$<br>$\mathrm{Re}\, s > \lvert \mathrm{Im}\, a \rvert$ |
| 12 | 1 | $I_\nu(\frac{a}{s})$ | $\left(\frac{a}{2t}\right)^{\frac{1}{2}} Z^{(b)}_\nu[(2at)^{\frac{1}{2}}]$ | $\mathrm{Re}\,\nu > 0$<br>$\mathrm{Re}\, s > 0$ |
| | 2 | $s I_\nu(\frac{a}{s})$ | $\frac{a^2}{4} V^{(b)}_\nu[(2at)^{\frac{1}{2}}]$ | $\mathrm{Re}\,\nu > 1$<br>$\mathrm{Re}\, s > 0$ |
| | 3 | $\frac{1}{s} I_\nu(\frac{a}{s})$ | $X^{(b)}_\nu[(2at)^{\frac{1}{2}}]$<br>$= J_\nu[(-2iat)^{\frac{1}{2}}] J_\nu[(2iat)^{\frac{1}{2}}]$ | $\mathrm{Re}\,\nu > -1$<br>$\mathrm{Re}\, s > 0$ |

| | | g(s) | f(t) | | |
|---|---|---|---|---|---|
| 12 (Contd.) | 4 | $I_{-\nu}(s)-I_{\nu}(s)$ | $0$ | $0<t<1$ | Re s > 0 |
| | | | $\frac{2\sin(\nu\pi)\cosh(\nu\cosh^{-1}t)}{\pi(t^2-1)^{\frac{1}{2}}}$ | $t>1$ | |
| 12.1 | 1 | $\frac{1}{s^2}\, I_{\nu}(\frac{a}{s})$ | $(\frac{2t}{a})^{\frac{1}{2}}\, W_{\nu}^{(b)}[(2at)^{\frac{1}{2}}]$ | | Re $\nu > -2$<br>Re s > 0 |
| | 2 | $s^n\, I_{\nu}(\frac{2}{s})$ | $\frac{d^{n+1}}{dt^{n+1}}\, X_{\nu}^{(b)}(2t^{\frac{1}{2}})$ | | Re $\nu > n$<br>$n=0,1,2,\ldots$<br>Re s > 0 |
| 12.2 | 1 | $\frac{1}{s^{\nu}}\, I_{\nu}(\frac{a}{s})$ | $\frac{a^{\nu}t^{\mu+\nu-1}}{2^{\nu}\Gamma(\nu+1)\Gamma(\mu+\nu)}\, {}_0F_3\left[\begin{matrix} ;\frac{a^2t^2}{16} \\ \nu+1,\frac{\mu+\nu}{2},\frac{\mu+\nu+1}{2}; \end{matrix}\right]$ | | Re$(\mu+\nu) > 0$<br>Re s > 0 |
| | 2 | $s^{\frac{1}{2}}[I_{\nu-\frac{1}{4}}(as)I_{-\nu-\frac{1}{4}}(as)-I_{\nu+\frac{1}{4}}(as)I_{-\nu+\frac{1}{4}}(as)]$ | $(\frac{2}{\pi})^{\frac{3}{2}}\, \frac{\cos(2\nu\cos^{-1}\frac{t}{2a})}{t^{\frac{1}{2}}(4a^2-t^2)^{\frac{1}{2}}}$ | $0<t<2a$ | Re s > $-\infty$ |
| | | | $0$ | $t>2a$ | |
| 12.3 | 1 | $e^{-as}\, I_0(as)$ | $\frac{1}{\pi(2at-t^2)^{\frac{1}{2}}}$ | $0<t<2a$ | $a>0$<br>Re s > $-\infty$ |
| | | | $0$ | $t>2a$ | |
| | 2 | $e^{-as}\, I_1(as)$ | $\frac{a-t}{\pi a(2at-t^2)^{\frac{1}{2}}}$ | $0<t<2a$ | $a>0$<br>Re s > $-\infty$ |
| | | | $0$ | $t>2a$ | |
| | 3 | $\frac{1}{s}\, e^{-\frac{a^2+b^2}{4s}}\, I_{\frac{1}{2}}(\frac{ab}{2s})$ | $\frac{2}{\pi}\, \frac{\sin(at^{\frac{1}{2}})\sin(bt^{\frac{1}{2}})}{(abt)^{\frac{1}{2}}}$ | | Re s > 0 |

| | | g(s) | f(t) | | |
|---|---|---|---|---|---|
| 12.3 (Contd.) | 4 | $\frac{1}{s}\, e^{-\frac{a^2+b^2}{4s}}\, I_{-\frac{1}{2}}\left(\frac{ab}{2s}\right)$ | $\frac{2}{\pi}\,\frac{\cos(at^{\frac{1}{2}})\cos(bt^{\frac{1}{2}})}{(abt)^{\frac{1}{2}}}$ | | Re s > 0 |
| | 5 | $e^{-\frac{1}{2}(a+b)s}\, I_n\left[\frac{1}{2}(b-a)s\right]$ | $0$ | $0 < t < a$ | $b > a \geq 0$ <br> Re s > $-\infty$ |
| | | | $\frac{\cos\left(n \cos^{-1}\frac{2t-a-b}{b-a}\right)}{\pi(t-a)^{\frac{1}{2}}(b-t)^{\frac{1}{2}}}$ | $a < t < b$ | |
| | | | $0$ | $t > b$ | |
| | 6 | $\frac{1}{s}\, e^{\frac{a}{s}}\, I_\nu\left(\frac{a}{s}\right)$ | $I_\nu^2\left[(2at)^{\frac{1}{2}}\right]$ | | Re $\nu > -$ <br> Re s > 0 |
| | 7 | $\frac{1}{s}\, e^{-\frac{a}{s}}\, I_\nu\left(\frac{a}{s}\right)$ | $J_\nu^2\left[(2at)^{\frac{1}{2}}\right]$ | | Re $\nu > -$ <br> Re s > 0 |
| | 8 | $\frac{1}{s}\, e^{-\frac{a^2+b^2}{s}}\, I_\nu\left(\frac{2ab}{s}\right)$ | $J_\nu(2at^{\frac{1}{2}})\, J_\nu(2bt^{\frac{1}{2}})$ | | Re $\nu > -1$ <br> Re s > 0 |
| | 9 | $\frac{1}{s}\, e^{\frac{a^2+b^2}{s}}\, I_\nu\left(\frac{2ab}{s}\right)$ | $I_\nu(2at^{\frac{1}{2}})\, I_\nu(2bt^{\frac{1}{2}})$ | | Re $\nu > -1$ <br> Re s > 0 |
| | 10 | $e^{-\frac{a}{s}}\left[I_\nu\left(\frac{a}{s}\right) + 2\sum_{n=1}^{\infty} I_{\nu+n}\left(\frac{a}{s}\right)\right]$ | $\frac{\nu}{t}\, J_\nu^2\left[(2at)^{\frac{1}{2}}\right]$ | | Re $\nu > 0$ <br> Re s > 0 |
| 12.3.1 | 1 | $\frac{1}{s}\, e^{-\frac{1}{s^2}}\, I_\nu\left(\frac{1}{s^2}\right)$ | $\frac{2^{\frac{7}{6}-\nu}}{\Gamma(2\nu+1)\Gamma(\nu+1)\, t^{\frac{1}{3}}}\, \frac{d}{dt}\left\{t^{2\nu}\, {}_0F_2\left[\begin{matrix} ; \\ 2\nu+1, \nu+1 ; \end{matrix} -\frac{t^2}{2}\right]\right\}$ | | Re $\nu > 0$ <br> Re s > 0 |
| | 2 | $\frac{1}{s^2}\, e^{-\frac{1}{s^2}}\, I_\nu\left(\frac{1}{s^2}\right)$ | $\frac{t^{2\nu}}{2^{\nu-\frac{1}{2}}\Gamma(2\nu+1)\Gamma(\nu+1)}\, {}_0F_2\left[\begin{matrix} ; \\ 2\nu+1, \nu+1 ; \end{matrix} -\frac{t^2}{2}\right]$ | | Re $\nu > -1$ <br> Re s > 0 |

12.3.2

| | g(s) | f(t) | |
|---|---|---|---|
| 1 | $\frac{1}{s^{\frac{1}{2}}} e^{\frac{a}{s}} I_0(\frac{a}{s})$ | $\frac{I_0[(8at)^{\frac{1}{2}}]}{(\pi t)^{\frac{1}{2}}}$ | Re s > 0 |
| 2 | $e^{-s} I_0[(s^2-a^2)^{\frac{1}{2}}]$ | $\frac{\cos[a(2t-t^2)^{\frac{1}{2}}]}{\pi(2t-t^2)^{\frac{1}{2}}}$ $0 < t < 2$ <br> 0 $t > 2$ | Re s > $-\infty$ |
| 3 | $\frac{1}{s^{\frac{1}{2}}} e^{\frac{a}{s}} I_{\frac{1}{4}}(\frac{a}{s})$ | $\frac{\sinh[(8at)^{\frac{1}{2}}]}{\pi(2a)^{\frac{1}{4}} t^{\frac{3}{4}}}$ | Re s > 0 |
| 4 | $\frac{1}{s^{\frac{1}{2}}} e^{-\frac{a}{s}} I_{\frac{1}{4}}(\frac{a}{s})$ | $\frac{\sin[(8at)^{\frac{1}{2}}]}{\pi(2a)^{\frac{1}{4}} t^{\frac{3}{4}}}$ | Re s > 0 |
| 5 | $\frac{1}{s^{\frac{1}{2}}} e^{\frac{a}{s}} I_{-\frac{1}{4}}(\frac{a}{s})$ | $\frac{\cosh[(8at)^{\frac{1}{2}}]}{\pi(2a)^{\frac{1}{4}} t^{\frac{3}{4}}}$ | Re s > 0 |
| 6 | $\frac{1}{s^{\frac{1}{2}}} e^{-\frac{a}{s}} I_{-\frac{1}{4}}(\frac{a}{s})$ | $\frac{\cos[(8at)^{\frac{1}{2}}]}{\pi(2a)^{\frac{1}{4}} t^{\frac{3}{4}}}$ | Re s > 0 |
| 7 | $\frac{1}{s^{\frac{1}{2}}} e^{\frac{a}{s}} I_{\frac{3}{4}}(\frac{a}{s})$ | $\frac{\cosh[(8at)^{\frac{1}{2}}]}{\pi(2a)^{\frac{1}{4}} t^{\frac{3}{4}}} - \frac{\sinh[(8at)^{\frac{1}{2}}]}{2\pi(2a)^{\frac{3}{4}} t^{\frac{5}{4}}}$ | Re s > 0 |
| 8 | $\frac{1}{s^{\frac{1}{2}}} e^{-\frac{a}{s}} I_{\frac{3}{4}}(\frac{a}{s})$ | $\frac{\sin[(8at)^{\frac{1}{2}}]}{2\pi(2a)^{\frac{3}{4}} t^{\frac{5}{4}}} - \frac{\cos[(8at)^{\frac{1}{2}}]}{\pi(2a)^{\frac{1}{4}} t^{\frac{3}{4}}}$ | Re s > 0 |
| 9 | $\frac{1}{s^{\frac{1}{2}}} e^{\frac{a}{s}} I_{-\frac{3}{4}}(\frac{a}{s})$ | $\frac{\sinh[(8at)^{\frac{1}{2}}]}{\pi(2a)^{\frac{1}{4}} t^{\frac{3}{4}}} - \frac{\cosh[(8at)^{\frac{1}{2}}]}{2\pi(2a)^{\frac{3}{4}} t^{\frac{5}{4}}}$ | Re s > 0 |

| | | g(s) | f(t) | |
|---|---|---|---|---|
| 12.3.2 (Contd.) | 10 | $\frac{1}{s^{\frac{1}{2}}} e^{-\frac{a}{s}} I_{-\frac{3}{4}}\left(\frac{a}{s}\right)$ | $-\frac{\sin[(8at)^{\frac{1}{2}}]}{\pi(2a)^{\frac{1}{4}}t^{\frac{3}{4}}} - \frac{\cos[(8at)^{\frac{1}{2}}]}{2\pi(2a)^{\frac{3}{4}}t^{\frac{5}{4}}}$ | Re s > o |
| | 11 | $\frac{1}{s^{\frac{1}{2}}} e^{\frac{1}{s}} I_{\frac{5}{4}}\left(\frac{1}{s}\right)$ | $\left(\frac{3}{8t}+1\right)\frac{\sinh[(8t)^{\frac{1}{2}}]}{\pi 2^{\frac{1}{4}}t^{\frac{3}{4}}} - \frac{3\cosh[(8t)^{\frac{1}{2}}]}{2^{\frac{7}{4}}\pi t^{\frac{5}{4}}}$ | Re s > o |
| | 12 | $\frac{1}{s^{\frac{1}{2}}} e^{-\frac{1}{s}} I_{\frac{5}{4}}\left(\frac{1}{s}\right)$ | $\left(\frac{3}{8t}-1\right)\frac{\sin[(8t)^{\frac{1}{2}}]}{\pi 2^{\frac{1}{4}}t^{\frac{3}{4}}} - \frac{3\cos[(8t)^{\frac{1}{2}}]}{2^{\frac{7}{4}}\pi t^{\frac{5}{4}}}$ | Re s > o |
| | 13 | $\frac{1}{s^{\frac{1}{2}}} e^{\frac{1}{s}} I_{-\frac{5}{4}}\left(\frac{1}{s}\right)$ | $\left(\frac{3}{8t}+1\right)\frac{\cosh[(8t)^{\frac{1}{2}}]}{\pi 2^{\frac{1}{4}}t^{\frac{3}{4}}} - \frac{3\sinh[(8t)^{\frac{1}{2}}]}{2^{\frac{7}{4}}\pi t^{\frac{5}{4}}}$ | Re s > o |
| | 14 | $\frac{1}{s^{\frac{1}{2}}} e^{-\frac{1}{s}} I_{-\frac{5}{4}}\left(\frac{1}{s}\right)$ | $\left(\frac{3}{8t}-1\right)\frac{\cos[(8t)^{\frac{1}{2}}]}{\pi 2^{\frac{1}{4}}t^{\frac{3}{4}}} + \frac{3\sin[(8t)^{\frac{1}{2}}]}{2^{\frac{7}{4}}\pi t^{\frac{5}{4}}}$ | Re s > o |
| | 15 | $\frac{e^{-s}}{s^{\frac{1}{2}}} I_{n+\frac{1}{2}}(s)$ | $\frac{1}{(2\pi)^{\frac{1}{2}}}P_n(1-t)$    $0 < t < 2$<br>$0$    $t > 2$ | n = 0,1,2,...<br>Re s > −∞ |
| | 16 | $e^{-bs}s^{\nu}I_{\nu}(bs)$ | $\frac{\Gamma(\nu+\frac{1}{2})(2b)^{\nu}\cos(2\pi\nu)}{\pi^{\frac{3}{2}}(2bt-t^2)^{\nu+\frac{1}{2}}}$    $0 < t < 2b$<br>$\frac{-\Gamma(\nu+\frac{1}{2})(2b)^{\nu}\sin(2\pi\nu)}{\pi^{\frac{3}{2}}(t^2-2bt)^{\nu+\frac{1}{2}}}$    $t > 2b$ | Re $\nu < \frac{1}{2}$<br>b > o<br>Re s > o |
| | 17 | $\frac{1}{s^{\nu}} e^{-bs} I_{\nu}(bs)$ | $\frac{(2bt-t^2)^{\nu-\frac{1}{2}}}{\pi^{\frac{1}{2}}\Gamma(\nu+\frac{1}{2})(2b)^{\nu}}$    $0 < t < 2b$<br>$0$    $t > 2b$ | b > o<br>Re $\nu > -\frac{1}{2}$<br>Re s > −∞ |

| | | g(s) | f(t) | | |
|---|---|---|---|---|---|
| 12.3.2 (Contd.) | 18 | $\frac{1}{s^{\frac{1}{2}}} e^{\frac{a}{s}} I_\nu(\frac{a}{s})$ | $\frac{I_{2\nu}[(8at)^{\frac{1}{2}}]}{(\pi t)^{\frac{1}{2}}}$ | | $Re\ \nu > -\frac{1}{2}$ <br> $Re\ s > 0$ |
| | 19 | $\frac{1}{s^{\frac{1}{2}}} e^{-\frac{a}{s}} I_\nu(\frac{a}{s})$ | $\frac{J_{2\nu}[(8at)^{\frac{1}{2}}]}{(\pi t)^{\frac{1}{2}}}$ | | $Re\ \nu > -\frac{1}{2}$ <br> $Re\ s > 0$ |
| | 20 | $\frac{1}{s^{\frac{3}{2}}} e^{-\frac{1}{s}} I_\nu(\frac{1}{s})$ | $\frac{1}{\pi^{\frac{1}{2}}} \int_0^t \frac{J_{2\nu}[(8u)^{\frac{1}{2}}]du}{u^{\frac{1}{2}}}$ <br> $= \frac{1}{\pi^{\frac{1}{2}}} \sum_{n=0}^{\infty} J_{2\nu+2n+1}[(8t)^{\frac{1}{2}}]$ | | $Re\ \nu > -\frac{3}{2}$ <br> $Re\ s > 0$ |
| | 21 | $\frac{1}{s^{\frac{3}{2}}} e^{\frac{1}{s}} I_\nu(\frac{1}{s})$ | $\frac{1}{\pi^{\frac{1}{2}}} \int_0^t \frac{I_{2\nu}[(8u)^{\frac{1}{2}}]du}{u^{\frac{1}{2}}}$ <br> $= \frac{1}{\pi^{\frac{1}{2}}} \sum_{n=0}^{\infty} I_{2\nu+2n+1}[(8t)^{\frac{1}{2}}]$ | | $Re\ \nu > -\frac{3}{2}$ <br> $Re\ s > 0$ |
| | 22 | $\frac{1}{s^\mu} e^{\frac{a}{s}} I_\nu(\frac{a}{s})$ | $\frac{a^\nu t^{\mu+\nu-1}}{2^\nu \Gamma(\nu+1)\Gamma(\mu+\nu)} {}_1F_2\left[\begin{matrix} \nu+\frac{1}{2}; & 2at \\ 2\nu+1, \ \mu+\nu; & \end{matrix}\right]$ | | $Re(\mu+\nu) > 0$ <br> $Re\ s > 0$ |
| | 23 | $\frac{e^{-\frac{a}{s}}}{s^\mu} I_\nu(\frac{a}{s})$ | $\frac{a^\nu t^{\mu+\nu-1}}{2^\nu \Gamma(\nu+1)\Gamma(\mu+\nu)} {}_1F_2\left[\begin{matrix} \nu+\frac{1}{2}; & -2at \\ 2\nu+1, \ \mu+\nu; & \end{matrix}\right]$ | | $Re(\mu+\nu) > 0$ <br> $Re\ s > 0$ |
| | 24 | $\frac{1}{s^\nu} e^{-as} I_{\nu+n}(as)$ | $\frac{(-1)^n n!\Gamma(\nu)2^\nu}{\pi\Gamma(2\nu+n)a^\nu}[t(2a-t)]^{\nu-\frac{1}{2}} C_n^\nu\left(\frac{t}{a}-1\right)$ <br> $0$ | $0 < t < 2a$ <br> $t > 2a$ | $a > 0$ <br> $Re\ \nu > -\frac{1}{2}$ <br> $n = 0,1,2,\ldots$ <br> $Re\ s > -\infty$ |
| | 25 | $\frac{1}{s^{\frac{3}{2}}} e^{\frac{a}{s}} [I_{\nu-\frac{1}{2}}(\frac{a}{s}) - I_{\nu+\frac{1}{2}}(\frac{a}{s})]$ | $\left(\frac{2}{a\pi}\right)^{\frac{1}{2}} I_{2\nu}[(8at)^{\frac{1}{2}}]$ | | $Re\ \nu > -1$ <br> $Re\ s > 0$ |

| | | g(s) | f(t) | |
|---|---|---|---|---|
| 12.3.2 (Contd.) | 26 | $\frac{1}{s^{\frac{3}{2}}} e^{-\frac{a}{s}} [I_{\nu-\frac{1}{2}}(\frac{a}{s}) - I_{\nu+\frac{1}{2}}(\frac{a}{s})]$ | $\left(\frac{2}{a\pi}\right)^{\frac{1}{2}} J_{2\nu}[(8at)^{\frac{1}{2}}]$ | Re $\nu > -1$ <br> Re $s > 0$ |
| 12.4 | 1 | $\frac{1}{s} I_0(\log s)$ | $\frac{1}{\pi}\int_0^2 \frac{t^{u-1}du}{\Gamma(u)u^{\frac{1}{2}}(2-u)^{\frac{1}{2}}}$ | Re $s > -\infty$ |
| 12.7 | 1 | $\frac{I_1(as)\operatorname{cosech}(as)}{s}$ | $\frac{2}{a\pi}[2a(t-2an)-(t-2an)^2]^{\frac{1}{2}}$ $\quad 2an < t < 2a(n+1)$ | Re $s > 0$ <br> $n = 0,1,2,\ldots$ |
| | 2 | $\frac{1}{s}\sinh\left(\frac{a^2+b^2}{s}\right) I_\nu\left(\frac{2ab}{s}\right)$ | $\frac{1}{2}[I_\nu(2at^{\frac{1}{2}})I_\nu(2bt^{\frac{1}{2}}) - J_\nu(2at^{\frac{1}{2}})J_\nu(2bt^{\frac{1}{2}})]$ | Re $\nu > -1$ <br> Re $s > 0$ |
| | 3 | $\frac{1}{s}\cosh\left(\frac{a^2+b^2}{s}\right) I_\nu\left(\frac{2ab}{s}\right)$ | $\frac{1}{2}[I_\nu(2at^{\frac{1}{2}})I_\nu(2bt^{\frac{1}{2}}) + J_\nu(2at^{\frac{1}{2}})J_\nu(2bt^{\frac{1}{2}})]$ | Re $\nu > -1$ <br> Re $s > 0$ |
| 12.7.2 | 1 | $\frac{\sinh\frac{1}{s} I_{\frac{1}{4}}(\frac{1}{s})}{s^{\frac{1}{2}}}$ | $\frac{\sinh[(8t)^{\frac{1}{2}}] - \sin[(8t)^{\frac{1}{2}}]}{2^{\frac{5}{4}}\pi t^{\frac{3}{4}}}$ | Re $s > 0$ |
| | 2 | $\frac{\cosh\frac{1}{s} I_{\frac{1}{4}}(\frac{1}{s})}{s^{\frac{1}{2}}}$ | $\frac{\sinh[(8t)^{\frac{1}{2}}] + \sin[(8t)^{\frac{1}{2}}]}{2^{\frac{5}{4}}\pi t^{\frac{3}{4}}}$ | Re $s > 0$ |
| | 3 | $\frac{\sinh\frac{1}{s} I_{-\frac{1}{4}}(\frac{1}{s})}{s^{\frac{1}{2}}}$ | $\frac{\cosh[(8t)^{\frac{1}{2}}] - \cos[(8t)^{\frac{1}{2}}]}{2^{\frac{5}{4}}\pi t^{\frac{3}{4}}}$ | Re $s > 0$ |
| | 4 | $\frac{\cosh\frac{1}{s} I_{-\frac{1}{4}}(\frac{1}{s})}{s^{\frac{1}{2}}}$ | $\frac{\cosh[(8t)^{\frac{1}{2}}] + \cos[(8t)^{\frac{1}{2}}]}{2^{\frac{5}{4}}\pi t^{\frac{3}{4}}}$ | Re $s > 0$ |
| | 5 | $\frac{1}{s^{\frac{1}{2}}}\sinh\frac{a}{s} I_\nu(\frac{a}{s})$ | $\frac{I_{2\nu}[(8at)^{\frac{1}{2}}] - J_{2\nu}[(8at)^{\frac{1}{2}}]}{2(\pi t)^{\frac{1}{2}}}$ | Re $\nu > -\frac{1}{2}$ <br> Re $s > 0$ |

| | | g(s) | f(t) | | |
|---|---|---|---|---|---|
| 12.7.2 (Contd.) | 6 | $\frac{1}{s^{\frac{1}{2}}} \cosh \frac{a}{s} I_{\nu}(\frac{a}{s})$ | $\frac{I_{2\nu}[(8at)^{\frac{1}{2}}] + J_{2\nu}[(8at)^{\frac{1}{2}}]}{2(\pi t)^{\frac{1}{2}}}$ | | $\mathrm{Re}\,\nu > -\frac{1}{2}$<br>$\mathrm{Re}\, s > 0$ |
| | 7 | $\frac{1}{s^{\nu}} \operatorname{cosech}(as) I_{\nu}(as)$ | $\frac{2^{\nu}\Gamma(\nu)}{\pi a^{\nu}\Gamma(2\nu)}[2a(t-2na)-(t-2na)^2]^{\nu-\frac{1}{2}}$ | $2na < t < 2(n+1)a$ | $a > 0$<br>$\mathrm{Re}\,\nu > -\frac{1}{2}$<br>$\mathrm{Re}\, s > 0$<br>$n = 0,1,2,\ldots$ |
| 12.9.3.2 | 1 | $\frac{e^{-s}}{(s^2+a^2)^{\frac{\nu}{2}}} C_n^{\nu}\left[\frac{s}{(s^2+a^2)^{\frac{1}{2}}}\right] \cdot I_{\nu+n}[(s^2+a^2)^{\frac{1}{2}}]$ | $\frac{(-1)^n}{(2\pi)^{\frac{1}{2}} a^{\nu-\frac{1}{2}}}(2t-t^2)^{\frac{\nu}{2}-\frac{1}{4}} C_n^{\nu}(t-1) I_{\nu-\frac{1}{2}}[a(2t-t^2)^{\frac{1}{2}}]$ | $0 < t < 2$ | $n = 0,1,2,\ldots$<br>$\mathrm{Re}\,\nu > -\frac{1}{2}$<br>$\mathrm{Re}\, s > -\infty$ |
| | | | $0$ | $t > 2$ | |
| 13 | 1 | $K_0(as)$ | $0$ | $0 < t < a$ | $a > 0$<br>$\mathrm{Re}\, s > 0$ |
| | | | $\frac{1}{(t^2-a^2)^{\frac{1}{2}}}$ | $t > a$ | |
| | 2 | $\frac{1}{s} K_0(as)$ | $0$ | $0 < t < a$ | $a > 0$<br>$\mathrm{Re}\, s > 0$ |
| | | | $\cosh^{-1}\frac{t}{a}$ | $t > a$ | |
| | 3 | $K_1(as)$ | $0$ | $0 < t < a$ | $a > 0$<br>$\mathrm{Re}\, s > 0$ |
| | | | $\frac{t}{a(t^2-a^2)^{\frac{1}{2}}}$ | $t > a$ | |
| | 4 | $K_n(as)$ | $0$ | $0 < t < a$ | $n = 0,1,2,\ldots$<br>$\mathrm{Re}\, s > 0$ |
| | | | $\frac{T_n(\frac{t}{a})}{(t^2-a^2)^{\frac{1}{2}}}$ | $t > a$ | |

| | | g(s) | f(t) | | |
|---|---|---|---|---|---|
| 13 (Contd.) | 5 | $\frac{1}{s}K_n(as)$ | $0$ | $0<t<a$ | $n=0,1,2,\ldots$ Re $s>0$ |
| | | | $\frac{(t^2-a^2)^{\frac{1}{2}}}{an}U_n(\frac{t}{a})$ | $t>a$ | |
| | 6 | $K_\nu(as)$ | $0$ | $0<t<a$ | $a>0$ Re $s>0$ |
| | | | $\frac{\cosh(\nu\cosh^{-1}\frac{t}{a})}{(t^2-a^2)^{\frac{1}{2}}} = \frac{a^{-\nu}[(t^2-a^2)^{\frac{1}{2}}+t]^{\nu}+[(t^2-a^2)^{\frac{1}{2}}+t]^{-\nu}a^{\nu}}{2(t^2-a^2)^{\frac{1}{2}}}$ | $t>a$ | |
| | 7 | $\frac{1}{s}K_\nu(as)$ | $0$ | $0<t<a$ | $a>0$ Re $s>0$ |
| | | | $\frac{[(t+a)^{\frac{1}{2}}+(t-a)^{\frac{1}{2}}]^{2\nu}-[(t+a)^{\frac{1}{2}}-(t-a)^{\frac{1}{2}}]^{2\nu}}{2^{\nu+1}\nu a^{\nu}} = \nu^{-1}\sinh[\nu\cosh^{-1}\frac{t}{a}]$ | $t>a$ | |
| | 8 | $\frac{1}{s}\int_s^\infty K_0(au)\,du$ | $0$ | $0<t<a$ | Re $s>0$ |
| | | | $\frac{1}{a}\cos^{-1}\frac{a}{t}$ | $t>a$ | |
| 13.2 | 1 | $K_0(as^{\frac{1}{2}})$ | $\frac{e^{-\frac{a^2}{4t}}}{2t}$ | | Re $a^2\geqslant 0$ $a\neq 0$ Re $s>0$ |
| | 2 | $s^{\frac{1}{2}}K_1(as^{\frac{1}{2}})$ | $a\frac{e^{-\frac{a^2}{4t}}}{4t^2}$ | | Re $a^2>0$ Re $s>0$ |
| | 3 | $\frac{K_{\frac{1}{2}}[b(s^2+a^2)^{\frac{1}{2}}]}{(s^2+a^2)^{\frac{1}{4}}}$ | $0$ | $0<t<b$ | $b\geqslant 0$ Re $s>0$ |
| | | | $\left(\frac{\pi}{2t}\right)^{\frac{1}{2}}J_0[a(t^2-b^2)^{\frac{1}{2}}]$ | $t>b$ | |

| | | g(s) | f(t) | | |
|---|---|---|---|---|---|
| 13.2 (Contd.) | 4 | $\frac{1}{s^{\frac{1}{2}}} K_1(as^{\frac{1}{2}})$ | $\frac{e^{-\frac{a^2 t}{4}}}{a}$ | | Re $a^2 \geqslant 0$<br>Re $s > 0$ |
| | 5 | $\frac{K_1[b(s^2+a^2)^{\frac{1}{2}}]}{(s^2+a^2)^{\frac{1}{2}}}$ | $0$<br>$\frac{\sin[a(t^2-b^2)^{\frac{1}{2}}]}{ab}$ | $0 < t < b$<br>$t > b$ | $b > 0$<br>Re $s > \lvert \mathrm{Im}\, a \rvert$ |
| | 6 | $\frac{K_\nu(as)}{s^\nu}$ | $0$<br>$\frac{\pi^{\frac{1}{2}}(t^2-a^2)^{\nu-\frac{1}{2}}}{(2a)^\nu \Gamma(\nu+\frac{1}{2})}$ | $0 < t < a$<br>$t > a$ | Re $\nu > -\frac{1}{2}$<br>Re $s > 0$ |
| | 7 | $\frac{K_\nu(as)}{s^\mu}$ | $0$<br>$\left(\frac{\pi}{2a}\right)^{\frac{1}{2}}(t^2-a^2)^{\frac{\mu}{2}-\frac{1}{4}} P^{-\mu+\frac{1}{2}}_{\nu-\frac{1}{2}}(\frac{t}{a})$ | $0 < t < a$<br>$t > a$ | $a > 0$<br>Re $\mu > -\frac{1}{2}$<br>Re $s > 0$ |
| | 8 | $s^\mu K_\nu(\frac{a}{s})$ | $\frac{2^\mu \pi^{\frac{1}{2}}}{t^{\mu+1}} S_2\left(\frac{\nu-1}{2}, \frac{-\nu-1}{2}, \frac{\mu+1}{2}, \frac{\mu}{2}; \frac{at}{4}\right)$ | | Re$(\mu \pm \nu) < 0$<br>Re $s > 0$ |
| | 9 | $\frac{1}{s^{\frac{1}{2}}} K_\nu(as^{\frac{1}{2}})$ | $\frac{e^{-\frac{a^2}{8t}} K_{\frac{\nu}{2}}(\frac{a^2}{8t})}{2\pi^{\frac{1}{2}} t^{\frac{1}{2}}}$ | | Re $a^2 > 0$<br>Re $s > 0$ |
| | 10 | $s^\mu K_\nu(as^{\frac{1}{2}})$ | $\frac{e^{-\frac{a^2}{8t}} W_{\mu+\frac{1}{2},\frac{\nu}{2}}(\frac{a^2}{4t})}{a\, t^{\mu+\frac{1}{2}}}$ | | Re $a^2 > 0$<br>Re $s > 0$ |
| | 11 | $s^{\frac{\nu}{2}+n} K_\nu(as^{\frac{1}{2}})$ | $\frac{(-1)^n n!\, a^\nu}{2^{\nu+1} t^n} e^{-\frac{a^2}{4t}} L_n^\nu(\frac{a^2}{4t})$ | | Re $a^2 > 0$<br>Re $s > 0$ |

| | | g(s) | f(t) | | |
|---|---|---|---|---|---|
| 13.2 (Contd.) | 12 | $s^{\frac{\nu}{2}} K_\nu(as^{\frac{1}{2}})$ | $\dfrac{a^\nu e^{-\frac{a^2}{4t}}}{(2t)^{\nu+1}}$ | | Re $a^2 > 0$<br>Re $s > 0$ |
| | 13 | $\dfrac{1}{s^{\frac{\nu}{2}}} K_\nu(as^{\frac{1}{2}})$ | $\dfrac{(2t)^{\nu-1} e^{-\frac{a^2}{4t}}}{a^\nu}$ | | Re $a^2 > 0$<br>Re $s > 0$ |
| | 14 | $s^{\frac{\nu}{2}-1} K_\nu(as^{\frac{1}{2}})$ | $\dfrac{2^{\nu-1}\Gamma(\nu, \frac{a^2}{4t})}{a^\nu}$ | | Re $a^2 > 0$<br>Re $s > 0$ |
| | 15 | $\dfrac{K_\nu[b(s^2+a^2)^{\frac{1}{2}}]}{(s^2+a^2)^{\frac{\nu}{2}}}$ | $0$<br>$\left(\dfrac{\pi}{2}\right)^{\frac{1}{2}} \dfrac{(t^2-b^2)^{\frac{\nu}{2}-\frac{1}{4}} J_{\nu-\frac{1}{2}}[a(t^2-b^2)^{\frac{1}{2}}]}{a^{\nu-\frac{1}{2}} b^\nu}$ | $0 < t < b$<br>$t > b$ | Re $\nu > -\frac{1}{2}$<br>Re $s > \vert \text{Im } a \vert$<br>$b > 0$ |
| | 16 | $\dfrac{K_\nu[b(s^2-a^2)^{\frac{1}{2}}]}{(s^2-a^2)^{\frac{\nu}{2}}}$ | $0$<br>$\left(\dfrac{\pi}{2}\right)^{\frac{1}{2}} \dfrac{(t^2-b^2)^{\frac{\nu}{2}-\frac{1}{4}}}{a^{\nu-\frac{1}{2}} b^\nu} I_{\nu-\frac{1}{2}}[a(t^2-b^2)^{\frac{1}{2}}]$ | $0 < t < b$<br>$t > b$ | $b > 0$<br>Re $\nu > -\frac{1}{2}$<br>Re $s > \vert \text{Re } a \vert$ |
| | 17 | $s^\nu [K_\nu(as^{\frac{1}{2}})]^2$ | $\dfrac{\pi^{\frac{1}{2}} a^{\nu-1}}{2t^{\frac{3\nu+1}{2}}} e^{-\frac{a^2}{2t}} W_{\frac{\nu}{2},\frac{\nu}{2}}\left(\frac{a^2}{t}\right)$ | | Re $a^2 > 0$<br>Re $s > 0$ |
| | 18 | $s^{\frac{1}{2}} K_{\nu+\frac{1}{4}}(as)\, K_{\nu-\frac{1}{4}}(as)$ | $0$<br>$\dfrac{(2\pi)^{\frac{1}{2}} \cosh(2\nu \cosh^{-1} \frac{t}{2a})}{t^{\frac{1}{2}}(t^2-4a^2)^{\frac{1}{2}}}$<br>$= \left(\dfrac{\pi}{2}\right)^{\frac{1}{2}} \dfrac{[t+(t^2-4a^2)^{\frac{1}{2}}]^{2\nu} + [t-(t^2-4a^2)^{\frac{1}{2}}]^{2\nu}}{(2a)^{2\nu} t^{\frac{1}{2}} (t^2-4a^2)^{\frac{1}{2}}}$ | $0 < t < 2a$<br>$t > 2a$ | $a > 0$<br>Re $s > 0$ |

| | | g(s) | f(t) | |
|---|---|---|---|---|
| 13.2 (Contd.) | 19 | $s^{\frac{1}{2}} K_{\nu+\frac{1}{2}}(as^{\frac{1}{2}}) K_{\nu-\frac{1}{2}}(as^{\frac{1}{2}})$ | $\frac{\pi^{\frac{1}{2}}}{2^{\frac{3}{2}} a t} e^{-\frac{a^2 t}{2}} W_{\frac{1}{2},\nu}(\frac{a^2}{t})$ | $\text{Re } a^2 > 0$ <br> $\text{Re } s > 0$ |
| | 20 | $K_\nu(as^{\frac{1}{2}}) K_\nu(bs^{\frac{1}{2}})$ | $\frac{e^{-\frac{a^2+b^2}{4t}}}{2t} K_\nu(\frac{ab}{2t})$ | $\text{Re}(a+b)^2 > \text{Re}(a-b)^2 > 0$ <br> $\text{Re } s > 0$ |
| | 21 | $K_\nu[s^{\frac{1}{2}}+(s-1)^{\frac{1}{2}}] K_\nu[s^{\frac{1}{2}}-(s-1)^{\frac{1}{2}}]$ | $\frac{e^{\frac{t}{2}-\frac{1}{t}} K_\nu(\frac{t}{2})}{2t}$ | $\text{Re } s > 1$ |
| | 22 | $K_\nu[\{as+a(s^2-b^2)^{\frac{1}{2}}\}^{\frac{1}{2}}] K_\nu\left[\frac{ab}{\{as+a(s^2-b^2)^{\frac{1}{2}}\}^{\frac{1}{2}}}\right]$ | $\frac{e^{-\frac{a}{2t}}}{2t} K_\nu(ab^2 t)$ | $\text{Re } a > 0$ <br> $\text{Re } s > -\text{Re } ab^2$ |
| 13.3 | 1 | $e^{as} K_0(as)$ | $\frac{1}{(t^2+2at)^{\frac{1}{2}}}$ | $\|\arg a\| < \pi$ <br> $\text{Re } s > 0$ |
| | 2 | $\frac{1}{s} e^{as} K_0(as)$ | $2 \log \frac{t^{\frac{1}{2}}+(t+2a)^{\frac{1}{2}}}{(2a)^{\frac{1}{2}}}$ <br> $= \cosh^{-1}(1+\frac{t}{a})$ | $\|\arg a\| < \pi$ <br> $\text{Re } s > 0$ |
| | 3 | $e^{as} K_1(as)$ | $\frac{t+a}{a(t^2+2at)^{\frac{1}{2}}}$ | $\|\arg a\| < \pi$ <br> $\text{Re } s > 0$ |
| | 4 | $\frac{1}{s} e^{as} K_1(as)$ | $\frac{(t^2+2at)^{\frac{1}{2}}}{a}$ | $\|\arg a\| < \pi$ <br> $\text{Re } s > 0$ |
| | 5 | $e^{as} K_\nu(as)$ | $\frac{\cosh[\nu \cosh^{-1}(1+\frac{t}{a})]}{(t^2+2at)^{\frac{1}{2}}}$ | $\|\arg a\| < \pi$ <br> $\text{Re } s > 0$ |

| | | g(s) | f(t) | |
|---|---|---|---|---|
| 13.3 (Contd.) | 6 | $\frac{1}{s} e^{as} K_\nu(as)$ | $\frac{[(t+2a)^{\frac{1}{2}}+t^{\frac{1}{2}}]^{2\nu}-[(t+2a)^{\frac{1}{2}}-t^{\frac{1}{2}}]^{2\nu}}{2^{\nu+1}\,\nu\, a^\nu}$ $= \nu^{-1}\sinh[\nu\cosh^{-1}(1+\frac{t}{a})]$ | $\lvert\arg a\rvert < \pi$ Re s > 0 |
| | 7 | $e^{(a+b)s} K_\nu(as)\, K_\nu(bs)$ | $\frac{\pi(4ab)^\nu}{[(2a+t)(2b+t)]^{\nu+\frac{1}{2}}}\,{}_2F_1\left[\frac{1}{2}+\nu,\frac{1}{2}+\nu;1;\frac{t(2a+2b+t)}{(2a+t)(2b+t)}\right]$ $= \frac{[(2a+t)(2b+t)]^{\frac{\nu}{2}-\frac{1}{4}}}{\pi(4ab)^{\frac{\nu}{2}+\frac{1}{4}}} P_{\nu-\frac{1}{2}}\left[\frac{(2a+t)(2b+t)}{2ab}-1\right]$ | $\lvert\arg a\rvert < \pi$ $\lvert\arg b\rvert < \pi$ $\lvert\arg as\rvert < \pi$ $\lvert\arg bs\rvert < \pi$ Re s > 0 |
| | 8 | $e^{2s\cos^2\frac{\theta}{2}}\left[\theta-\sin\theta\int_0^s K_0(u)e^{-u\cos\theta}\,du\right]$ | $\frac{\sin\theta}{(1+t+\cos\theta)(t^2+2t)^{\frac{1}{2}}}$ | Re s > 0 |
| 13.3.1 | 1 | $e^{as^2} K_0(as^2)$ | $\left(\frac{\pi}{2a}\right)^{\frac{1}{2}} e^{-\frac{t^2}{16a}} I_0\left(\frac{t^2}{16a}\right)$ | Re a ⩾ 0 Re s > 0 |
| 13.3.2 | 1 | $\frac{1}{s^{\frac{1}{2}}} e^{\frac{a}{s}} K_0(\frac{a}{s})$ | $\frac{2}{(\pi t)^{\frac{1}{2}}} K_0[(8at)^{\frac{1}{2}}]$ | Re s > 0 |
| | 2 | $\frac{1}{s^{\frac{1}{2}}} e^{-\frac{a}{s}} K_0(\frac{a}{s})$ | $-\left(\frac{\pi}{t}\right)^{\frac{1}{2}} Y_0[(8at)^{\frac{1}{2}}]$ | Re s > 0 |
| | 3 | $\frac{1}{s^{\frac{1}{2}}} e^{\frac{a}{s}} K_{\frac{1}{4}}(\frac{a}{s})$ | $\frac{e^{-(8at)^{\frac{1}{2}}}}{a^{\frac{1}{2}}(2t)^{\frac{3}{4}}}$ | Re s > 0 |
| | 4 | $\frac{e^{bs} K_{\frac{1}{2}}[b(s^2+a^2)^{\frac{1}{2}}]}{(s^2+a^2)^{\frac{1}{4}}}$ | $\left(\frac{\pi}{2b}\right)^{\frac{1}{2}} J_0[a(t^2+2bt)^{\frac{1}{2}}]$ | Re s > $\lvert$Im a$\rvert$ |

| | | g(s) | f(t) | |
|---|---|---|---|---|
| 13.3.2 (Contd.) | 5 | $\frac{1}{s^{\frac{3}{2}}} e^{\frac{a}{s}} [K_1(\frac{a}{s}) - K_0(\frac{a}{s})]$ | $\left(\frac{8}{a\pi}\right)^{\frac{1}{2}} K_1[(8at)^{\frac{1}{2}}]$ | Re s > 0 |
| | 6 | $\frac{e^{as}}{s^{\frac{1}{2}}} K_{n+\frac{1}{2}}(as)$ | $\left(\frac{\pi}{2a}\right)^{\frac{1}{2}} P_n(1+\frac{t}{a})$ | n = 0,1,2,... <br> Re s > 0 |
| | 7 | $\frac{1}{s^{\frac{1}{2}}} e^{\frac{a}{s}} K_\nu(\frac{a}{s})$ | $\frac{2\cos(\nu\pi)}{(\pi t)^{\frac{1}{2}}} K_{2\nu}[(8at)^{\frac{1}{2}}]$ | $\lvert Re\,\nu \rvert < \frac{1}{2}$ <br> Re s > 0 |
| | 8 | $\frac{1}{s^{\frac{1}{2}}} e^{-\frac{a}{s}} K_\nu(\frac{a}{s})$ | $-\left(\frac{\pi}{t}\right)^{\frac{1}{2}} \left\{\sin(\nu\pi) J_{2\nu}[(8at)^{\frac{1}{2}}] + \cos(\nu\pi) Y_{2\nu}[(8at)^{\frac{1}{2}}]\right\}$ | $\lvert Re\,\nu \rvert < \frac{1}{2}$ <br> Re s > 0 |
| | 9 | $s^\mu e^{as} K_\nu(as)$ | $\frac{\pi^{\frac{1}{2}} P^{\mu+\frac{1}{2}}_{\nu-\frac{1}{2}}(1+\frac{t}{a})}{(2a)^{\frac{1}{2}}(t^2+2at)^{\frac{\mu}{2}+\frac{1}{4}}}$ | Re $\mu < \frac{1}{2}$ <br> $\lvert \arg a \rvert < \pi$ <br> Re s > 0 |
| | 10 | $\frac{1}{s^\nu} e^{as} K_\nu(as)$ | $\frac{\pi^{\frac{1}{2}}(t^2+2at)^{\nu-\frac{1}{2}}}{(2a)^\nu \Gamma(\nu+\frac{1}{2})}$ | Re $\nu > -\frac{1}{2}$ <br> $\lvert \arg a \rvert < \pi$ <br> Re s > 0 |
| | 11 | $\frac{e^{bs} K_\nu[b(s^2+a^2)^{\frac{1}{2}}]}{(s^2+a^2)^{\frac{\nu}{2}}}$ | $\left(\frac{\pi}{2}\right)^{\frac{1}{2}} \frac{(t^2+2bt)^{\frac{\nu}{2}-\frac{1}{4}}}{a^{\nu-\frac{1}{2}} b^\nu} J_{\nu-\frac{1}{2}}[a(t^2+2bt)^{\frac{1}{2}}]$ | Re $\nu > -\frac{1}{2}$ <br> $\lvert \arg b \rvert < \pi$ <br> Re s > $\lvert$ Im a $\rvert$ |
| | 12 | $\frac{e^{bs} K_\nu[b(s^2-a^2)^{\frac{1}{2}}]}{(s^2-a^2)^{\frac{\nu}{2}}}$ | $\left(\frac{\pi}{2}\right)^{\frac{1}{2}} \frac{(t^2+2bt)^{\frac{\nu}{2}-\frac{1}{4}}}{a^{\nu-\frac{1}{2}} b^\nu} I_{\nu-\frac{1}{2}}[a(t^2+2bt)^{\frac{1}{2}}]$ | Re $\nu > -\frac{1}{2}$ <br> $\lvert \arg b \rvert < \pi$ <br> Re s > $\lvert$ Re a $\rvert$ |

| | | g(s) | f(t) | |
|---|---|---|---|---|
| 13.3.2 (Contd.) | 13 | $s^{\frac{1}{2}}e^{2as}K_{\nu+\frac{1}{4}}(as)\,K_{\nu-\frac{1}{4}}(as)$ | $\dfrac{(2\pi)^{\frac{1}{2}}\cosh[2\nu\cosh^{-1}(1+\frac{t}{2a})]}{[t(t+2a)(t+4a)]^{\frac{1}{2}}}$ | $\lvert\arg a\rvert<\pi$<br>$\mathrm{Re}\, s>0$ |
| | 14 | $\dfrac{2^{\frac{n+1}{2}}\pi^{\frac{n}{2}}}{s}e^{-\frac{1}{2}a^{\frac{1}{n}}s^{\frac{1}{n}}}K_{n\nu}\left(\frac{1}{2}a^{\frac{1}{n}}s^{\frac{1}{n}}\right)$ | $\sum_{i,-i}\frac{1}{i}E\left[\Delta(n;n\nu),\Delta(n;-n\nu):\Delta(n;\tfrac{1}{2}):\frac{ae^{i\pi}}{n^n t}\right]$<br>$\sum_{i,-i}$ denotes that in the expression following the $\Sigma$ sign i is to be replaced by -i and the two expressions are to be added. | $n=2,3,4,\ldots$<br>$\mathrm{Re}\, a>0$<br>$\mathrm{Re}\, s>0$ |
| 13.3.2.1 | 1 | $s^{\frac{1}{2}}e^{as^2}K_{\frac{1}{4}}(as^2)$ | $\dfrac{e^{-\frac{t^2}{8a}}}{(2at)^{\frac{1}{2}}}$ | $\mathrm{Re}\, a>0$<br>$\mathrm{Re}\, s>0$ |
| | 2 | $\dfrac{1}{s^{\frac{1}{2}}}e^{as^2}K_{\frac{1}{4}}(as^2)$ | $(8a)^{-\frac{1}{4}}\gamma\left(\frac{1}{4},\frac{t^2}{8a}\right)$ | $\mathrm{Re}\, a>0$<br>$\mathrm{Re}\, s>0$ |
| | 3 | $\dfrac{1}{s^{2\nu}}e^{as^2}K_{\nu}(as^2)$ | $\dfrac{2\pi^{\frac{1}{2}}(8a)^{\frac{\nu}{2}}}{\Gamma(2\nu+1)}t^{\nu-1}e^{-\frac{t^2}{16a}}M_{-\frac{3\nu}{2},\frac{\nu}{2}}\left(\frac{t^2}{8a}\right)$ | $\mathrm{Re}\, a>0$<br>$\mathrm{Re}\,\nu>-\frac{1}{2}$<br>$\mathrm{Re}\, s>0$ |
| 13.7.2 | 1 | $\dfrac{1}{s^{\frac{1}{2}}}\sinh\frac{a}{s}K_0(\frac{a}{s})$ | $\dfrac{K_0[(8at)^{\frac{1}{2}}]}{(\pi t)^{\frac{1}{2}}}+\dfrac{\pi^{\frac{1}{2}}Y_0[(8at)^{\frac{1}{2}}]}{2t^{\frac{1}{2}}}$ | $\mathrm{Re}\, s>0$ |
| | 2 | $\dfrac{1}{s^{\frac{1}{2}}}\cosh\frac{a}{s}K_0(\frac{a}{s})$ | $\dfrac{K_0[(8at)^{\frac{1}{2}}]}{(\pi t)^{\frac{1}{2}}}-\dfrac{\pi^{\frac{1}{2}}Y_0[(8at)^{\frac{1}{2}}]}{2t^{\frac{1}{2}}}$ | $\mathrm{Re}\, s>0$ |
| 13.10.2 | 1 | $J_{\nu}(as^{\frac{1}{2}})\,K_{\nu}(as^{\frac{1}{2}})$ | $\dfrac{J_{\nu}(\frac{a^2}{2t})}{2t}$ | $a^2>0$<br>$\mathrm{Re}\, s>0$ |

| | | g(s) | f(t) | | |
|---|---|---|---|---|---|
| 13.10.2 (Contd.) | 2 | $Y_\nu(as^{\frac{1}{2}})\, K_\nu(as^{\frac{1}{2}})$ | $\dfrac{Y_\nu(\frac{a^2}{2t})}{2t}$ | | $a^2 > 0$<br>$\operatorname{Re} s > 0$ |
| 13.11.2 | 1 | $H_\nu^{(1)}(as^{\frac{1}{2}})\, K_\nu(as^{\frac{1}{2}})$ | $\dfrac{H_\nu^{(1)}(\frac{a^2}{2t})}{2t}$ | | $a^2 > 0$<br>$\operatorname{Re} s > 0$ |
| | 2 | $H_\nu^{(2)}(as^{\frac{1}{2}})\, K_\nu(as^{\frac{1}{2}})$ | $\dfrac{H_\nu^{(2)}(\frac{a^2}{2t})}{2t}$ | | $a^2 > 0$<br>$\operatorname{Re} s > 0$ |
| 13.12 | 1 | $K_s(a)\, I_s(a)$ | $\frac{1}{2} J_0(2a \sinh \frac{t}{2})$ | | $\operatorname{Re} a > 0$<br>$\operatorname{Re} s > -\frac{1}{2}$ |
| 13.12.1 | 1 | $I_{\nu+s}(a) K_{\nu-s}(a)$ | $\frac{1}{2} J_{2\nu}(2a \sinh \frac{t}{2})$ | | $\operatorname{Re} \nu > -\frac{1}{2}$<br>$\operatorname{Re} a > 0$<br>$\operatorname{Re} s > -\frac{1}{2}$ |
| 13.12.2 | 1 | $K_0(as^{\frac{1}{2}})\, I_0(as^{\frac{1}{2}})$ | $\dfrac{e^{-\frac{a^2}{2t}} I_0(\frac{a^2}{2t})}{2t}$ | | $\operatorname{Re} s > 0$ |
| | 2 | $s^{\frac{1}{2}} I_n(as)\, K_{n+\frac{1}{2}}(as)$ | $(-1)^n (\frac{2}{\pi})^{\frac{1}{2}} \dfrac{\cos[(2n+\frac{1}{2})\cos^{-1}(\frac{t}{2a})]}{t^{\frac{1}{2}}(4a^2-t^2)^{\frac{1}{2}}}$ | $0 < t < 2a$ | $n = 0,1,2,\ldots$<br>$\operatorname{Re} s > -\infty$ |
| | | | $0$ | $t > 2a$ | |
| | 3 | $K_\nu(as^{\frac{1}{2}})\, I_\nu(bs^{\frac{1}{2}})$ | $\dfrac{e^{-\frac{a^2+b^2}{4t}}}{2t} I_\nu\left(\dfrac{ab}{2t}\right)$ | | $\operatorname{Re}(a+b)^2 \geqslant \operatorname{Re}(a-b)^2 > 0$<br>$\operatorname{Re} s > 0$ |
| | 4 | $I_\nu\{b[(s^2+a^2)^{\frac{1}{2}}-s]\}\, K_\nu\{b[(s^2+a^2)^{\frac{1}{2}}+s]\}$ | $0$ | $0 < t < 2b$ | $b > 0$<br>$\operatorname{Re} \nu > -\frac{1}{2}$ |
| | | | $\dfrac{J_{2\nu}[a(t^2-4b^2)^{\frac{1}{2}}]}{(t^2-4b^2)^{\frac{1}{2}}}$ | $t > 2b$ | $\operatorname{Re} s > \lvert \operatorname{Im} a \rvert$ |

| | | g(s) | f(t) | |
|---|---|---|---|---|
| 13.12.3.2 | 1 | $s^{-\frac{1}{2}} e^{-\frac{a}{s}} [\tan(\nu\pi)\, I_\nu(\frac{a}{s}) + \frac{\sec(\nu\pi)}{\pi} K_\nu(\frac{a}{s})]$ | $-\frac{Y_{2\nu}[(8at)^{\frac{1}{2}}]}{(\pi t)^{\frac{1}{2}}}$ | $\lvert Re\,\nu \rvert < \frac{1}{2}$<br>$Re\, s > 0$ |
| | 2 | $\frac{1}{s^{\frac{1}{2}}} e^{-\frac{a}{s}} [e^{i\nu\pi} I_\nu(\frac{a}{s}) + \frac{i}{\pi} K_\nu(\frac{a}{s})]$ | $\frac{\cos(\nu\pi)}{(\pi t)^{\frac{1}{2}}} H^{(2)}_{2\nu}[(8at)^{\frac{1}{2}}]$ | $\lvert Re\,\nu \rvert < \frac{1}{2}$<br>$Re\, s > 0$ |
| | 3 | $\frac{1}{s^{\frac{1}{2}}} e^{-\frac{a}{s}} [e^{-i\nu\pi} I_\nu(\frac{a}{s}) - \frac{i}{\pi} K_\nu(\frac{a}{s})]$ | $\frac{\cos(\nu\pi)}{(\pi t)^{\frac{1}{2}}} H^{(1)}_{2\nu}[(8at)^{\frac{1}{2}}]$ | $\lvert Re\,\nu \rvert < \frac{1}{2}$<br>$Re\, s > 0$ |
| 14 | 1 | $\frac{1}{s} K(\frac{a}{s})$ | $\frac{\pi}{2} I_0^2(\frac{at}{2})$ | $Re\, s > \lvert Re\, a \rvert$ |
| | 2 | $K(\frac{a}{s}) - \frac{\pi}{2}$ | $\frac{\pi a}{2} I_0(\frac{at}{2})\, I_1(\frac{at}{2})$ | $Re\, s > \lvert Re\, a \rvert$ |
| | 3 | $s[K(\frac{a}{s}) - \frac{\pi}{2}]$ | $\frac{\pi a^2}{8} \left\{ [I_0(\frac{at}{2})]^2 + 2[I_1(\frac{at}{2})]^2 + I_0(\frac{at}{2})\, I_2(\frac{at}{2}) \right\}$ | $Re\, s > \lvert Re\, a \rvert$ |
| | 4 | $s[\frac{\pi}{2} - E(\frac{a}{s})]$ | $\frac{\pi a}{2t} I_0(\frac{at}{2})\, I_1(\frac{at}{2})$ | $Re\, s > \lvert Re\, a \rvert$ |
| | 5 | $s[K(\frac{a}{s}) - E(\frac{a}{s})]$ | $\frac{\pi a^2}{4} [I_0^2(\frac{at}{2}) + I_1^2(\frac{at}{2})]$ | $Re\, s > \lvert Re\, a \rvert$ |
| 14.1 | 1 | $\frac{s}{s^2 - a^2} E(\frac{a}{s})$ | $\frac{\pi}{2} I_0(\frac{at}{2})[I_0(\frac{at}{2}) + at\, I_1(\frac{at}{2})]$ | $Re\, s > \lvert Re\, a \rvert$ |
| | 2 | $\frac{s^2}{s^2 - a^2} E(\frac{a}{s}) - K(\frac{a}{s})$ | $\frac{\pi a^2 t}{4} [I_0^2(\frac{at}{2}) + I_1^2(\frac{at}{2})]$ | $Re\, s > \lvert Re\, a \rvert$ |

| | | g(s) | f(t) | |
|---|---|---|---|---|
| 14.1 (Contd.) | 3 | $\frac{s}{s^2-a^2}E\left(\frac{a}{s}\right)-\frac{1}{s}K\left(\frac{a}{s}\right)$ | $\frac{\pi a}{2}tI_0\left(\frac{at}{2}\right)I_1\left(\frac{at}{2}\right)$ | Re s > \|Re a\| |
| | 4 | $\frac{2s^2-a^2}{s}K\left(\frac{a}{s}\right)-2s\,E\left(\frac{a}{s}\right)$ | $\frac{\pi a^2}{2}I_1^2\left(\frac{at}{2}\right)$ | Re s > \|Re a\| |
| 14.2 | 1 | $\frac{B\left[\frac{a}{(s^2+a^2)^{\frac{1}{2}}}\right]}{(s^2+a^2)^{\frac{1}{2}}}$ | $\frac{\pi}{4}\left[J_0^2\left(\frac{at}{2}\right)-J_1^2\left(\frac{at}{2}\right)\right]$ | Re s > \|Im a\| |
| | 2 | $\frac{G\left[\frac{a}{(s^2+a^2)^{\frac{1}{2}}}\right]}{(s^2+a^2)^{\frac{3}{2}}}$ | $\frac{\pi}{2a^2}J_1^2\left(\frac{at}{2}\right)$ | Re s > \|Im a\| |
| | 3 | $\frac{D\left[\frac{a}{(s^2+a^2)^{\frac{1}{2}}}\right]}{(s^2+a^2)^{\frac{1}{2}}}$ | $\frac{\pi}{4}\left[J_0^2\left(\frac{at}{2}\right)+J_1^2\left(\frac{at}{2}\right)\right]$ | Re s > \|Im a\| |
| | 4 | $\frac{E\left[\frac{a}{(s^2+a^2)^{\frac{1}{2}}}\right]}{(s^2+a^2)^{\frac{1}{2}}}$ | $\frac{\pi}{2}J_0\left(\frac{at}{2}\right)\left[J_0\left(\frac{at}{2}\right)-at\,J_1\left(\frac{at}{2}\right)\right]$ | Re s > \|Im a\| |
| | 5 | $\frac{K\left[\frac{a}{(s^2+a^2)^{\frac{1}{2}}}\right]}{(s^2+a^2)^{\frac{1}{2}}}$ | $\frac{\pi}{2}J_0^2\left(\frac{at}{2}\right)$ | Re s > \|Im a\| |
| | 6 | $\frac{K\left[\frac{a}{(s^2+a^2)^{\frac{1}{2}}}\right]-E\left[\frac{a}{(s^2+a^2)^{\frac{1}{2}}}\right]}{(s^2+a^2)^{\frac{1}{2}}}$ | $\frac{\pi a}{2}tJ_0\left(\frac{at}{2}\right)J_1\left(\frac{at}{2}\right)$ | Re s > \|Im a\| |
| 14.2.1 | 1 | $\frac{2s^2+a^2}{(s^2+a^2)^{\frac{1}{2}}}K\left[\frac{a}{(s^2+a^2)^{\frac{1}{2}}}\right]-2(s^2+a^2)E\left[\frac{a}{(s^2+a^2)^{\frac{1}{2}}}\right]$ | $\frac{\pi a^2}{2}J_1^2\left(\frac{at}{2}\right)$ | Re s > \|Im a\| |

| | | g(s) | f(t) | |
|---|---|---|---|---|
| 14.6.2 | 1 | $F\left(a, \sin^{-1}\frac{1}{s^{\frac{1}{2}}}\right)$ | $\frac{e^t}{2\pi^{\frac{1}{2}}t}\left[\frac{1}{t^{\frac{1}{2}}} * e^{(\frac{a^2}{2}-1)t}\, I_0\left(\frac{a^2}{2}t\right)\right]$ | Re s > 0 |
| 15 | 1 | $\frac{1}{s}\theta_1(a\vert s)$ | $\frac{1}{\pi}\sum_{n=-\infty}^{\infty}(-1)^n\frac{\sin[2(a+n-\frac{1}{2})t^{\frac{1}{2}}]}{a+n-\frac{1}{2}}$ | $\vert\mathrm{Re}\, a\vert < \frac{1}{2}$<br>Re s > 0 |
| | 2 | $\frac{1}{s}\theta_2(0\vert s)$ | 0 $\quad 0 < t < \frac{\pi^2}{4}$<br>2n+2 $\quad \pi^2(n+\frac{1}{2})^2 < t < \pi^2(n+\frac{3}{2})^2$ | Re s > 0<br>n = 0,1,2,... |
| | 3 | $\frac{1}{s}\theta_2(a\vert s)$ | $\frac{1}{\pi}\sum_{n=-\infty}^{\infty}(-1)^n\frac{\sin[2(a+n)t^{\frac{1}{2}}]}{a+n}$ | 0 < Re a < 1<br>Re s > 0 |
| | 4 | $\frac{1}{s}\theta_3(0\vert s)$ | 2n+1 $\quad \pi^2 n^2 < t < \pi^2(n+1)^2$ | Re s > 0<br>n = 0,1,2,... |
| | 5 | $\frac{1}{s}\theta_3(a\vert s)$ | $\frac{1}{\pi}\sum_{n=-\infty}^{\infty}\frac{\sin[2(a+n)t^{\frac{1}{2}}]}{a+n}$ | 0 < Re a < 1<br>Re s > 0 |
| | 6 | $\frac{1}{s}\theta_4(0\vert s)$ | 1 $\quad (2n)^2\pi^2 < t < (2n+1)^2\pi^2$<br>-1 $\quad (2n+1)^2\pi^2 < t < (2n+2)^2\pi^2$ | Re s > 0<br>n = 0,1,2,... |
| | 7 | $\frac{1}{s}\theta_4(a\vert s)$ | $\frac{1}{\pi}\sum_{n=-\infty}^{\infty}\frac{\sin[2(a+n+\frac{1}{2})t^{\frac{1}{2}}]}{a+n+\frac{1}{2}}$ | $\vert\mathrm{Re}\, a\vert < \frac{1}{2}$<br>Re s > 0 |
| 15.2 | 1 | $\frac{1}{s^{\frac{1}{2}}}\theta_1(a\vert s)$ | $\frac{1}{\pi^{\frac{1}{2}}}\sum_{n=-\infty}^{\infty}(-1)^n J_0[2(a+n-\frac{1}{2})t^{\frac{1}{2}}]$ | Re s > 0 |

| | | g(s) | f(t) | |
|---|---|---|---|---|
| 15.2 (Contd.) | 2 | $\frac{1}{s^{\nu}}\theta_1(a\|s)$ | $\frac{t^{\frac{\nu}{2}-\frac{1}{4}}}{\pi^{\frac{1}{2}}}\sum_{n=-\infty}^{\infty}\frac{(-1)^n J_{\nu-\frac{1}{2}}[2(a+n-\frac{1}{2})t^{\frac{1}{2}}]}{(a+n-\frac{1}{2})^{\nu-\frac{1}{2}}}$ | $\mathrm{Re}\,\nu \geqslant \frac{1}{2}$ <br> $\|\mathrm{Re}\,a\| < \frac{1}{2}$ <br> $\mathrm{Re}\,s > 0$ |
| | 3 | $\frac{1}{s^{\frac{1}{2}}}\theta_2(a\|s)$ | $\frac{1}{\pi^{\frac{1}{2}}}\sum_{n=-\infty}^{\infty}(-1)^n J_0[2(a+n)t^{\frac{1}{2}}]$ | $\mathrm{Re}\,s > 0$ |
| | 4 | $\frac{1}{s^{\nu}}\theta_2(a\|s)$ | $\frac{t^{\frac{\nu}{2}-\frac{1}{4}}}{\pi^{\frac{1}{2}}}\sum_{n=-\infty}^{\infty}\frac{(-1)^n J_{\nu-\frac{1}{2}}[2(a+n)t^{\frac{1}{2}}]}{(a+n)^{\nu-\frac{1}{2}}}$ | $\mathrm{Re}\,\nu \geqslant \frac{1}{2}$ <br> $0 < \mathrm{Re}\,a < 1$ <br> $\mathrm{Re}\,s > 0$ |
| | 5 | $\frac{1}{s^{\frac{1}{2}}}\theta_3(a\|s)$ | $\frac{1}{\pi^{\frac{1}{2}}}\sum_{n=-\infty}^{\infty}J_0[2(a+n)t^{\frac{1}{2}}]$ | $\mathrm{Re}\,s > 0$ |
| | 6 | $\frac{1}{s^{\nu}}\theta_3(a\|s)$ | $\frac{t^{\frac{\nu}{2}-\frac{1}{4}}}{\pi^{\frac{1}{2}}}\sum_{n=-\infty}^{\infty}\frac{J_{\nu-\frac{1}{2}}[2(a+n)t^{\frac{1}{2}}]}{(a+n)^{\nu-\frac{1}{2}}}$ | $\mathrm{Re}\,\nu \geqslant \frac{1}{2}$ <br> $0 < \mathrm{Re}\,a < 1$ <br> $\mathrm{Re}\,s > 0$ |
| | 7 | $\frac{1}{s^{\frac{1}{2}}}\theta_4(a\|s)$ | $\frac{1}{\pi^{\frac{1}{2}}}\sum_{n=-\infty}^{\infty}J_0[2(a+n+\frac{1}{2})t^{\frac{1}{2}}]$ | $\mathrm{Re}\,s > 0$ |
| | 8 | $\frac{1}{s^{\nu}}\theta_4(a\|s)$ | $\frac{t^{\frac{\nu}{2}-\frac{1}{4}}}{\pi^{\frac{1}{2}}}\sum_{n=-\infty}^{\infty}\frac{J_{\nu-\frac{1}{2}}[2(a+n+\frac{1}{2})t^{\frac{1}{2}}]}{(a+n+\frac{1}{2})^{\nu-\frac{1}{2}}}$ | $\mathrm{Re}\,\nu \geqslant \frac{1}{2}$ <br> $\|\mathrm{Re}\,a\| < \frac{1}{2}$ <br> $\mathrm{Re}\,s > 0$ |
| 15.3.2 | 1 | $e^{a^2 s}[\theta_3(2as\|4s)+\hat{\theta}_3(2as\|4s)] - \frac{1}{2\pi^{\frac{1}{2}}s^{\frac{1}{2}}}$ | $\frac{\sinh a}{2\pi t^{\frac{1}{2}}[\cosh a - \cos(t^{\frac{1}{2}})]}$ | $\mathrm{Re}\,a > 0$ <br> $\mathrm{Re}\,s > 0$ |

| | | $g(s)$ | $f(t)$ | |
|---|---|---|---|---|
| 16.2 | 1 | $\mathrm{Erfc}(a^{\frac{1}{2}}s^{\frac{1}{2}})$ | $0 \quad 0<t<a$<br>$\dfrac{a^{\frac{1}{2}}}{\pi t(t-a)^{\frac{1}{2}}} \quad t>a$ | $a>0$<br>$\mathrm{Re}\, s \geqslant 0$ |
| | 2 | $\dfrac{1}{s^{\frac{1}{2}}}\mathrm{Erf}(a^{\frac{1}{2}}s^{\frac{1}{2}})$ | $\dfrac{1}{(\pi t)^{\frac{1}{2}}} \quad 0<t<a$<br>$0 \quad t>a$ | $a>0$<br>$\mathrm{Re}\, s > -\infty$ |
| | 3 | $\dfrac{1}{s^{\frac{1}{2}}}\mathrm{Erfc}(a^{\frac{1}{2}}s^{\frac{1}{2}})$ | $0 \quad 0<t<a$<br>$\dfrac{1}{(\pi t)^{\frac{1}{2}}} \quad t>a$ | $a>0$<br>$\mathrm{Re}\, s > 0$ |
| | 4 | $\mathrm{Erf}\left(\dfrac{a}{s^{\frac{1}{2}}}\right)$ | $\dfrac{\sin(2at^{\frac{1}{2}})}{\pi t}$ | $\mathrm{Re}\, s>0$ |
| 16.3.1 | 1 | $e^{a^2s^2}\mathrm{Erfc}(as)$ | $\dfrac{e^{-\frac{t^2}{4a^2}}}{(\pi a^2)^{\frac{1}{2}}}$ | $\mathrm{Re}\, a^2>0$<br>$\mathrm{Re}\, s > -\infty$ |
| | 2 | $\dfrac{1}{s}e^{a^2s^2}\mathrm{Erfc}(as)$ | $\mathrm{Erf}\left(\dfrac{t}{2a}\right)$ | $\mathrm{Re}\, a^2>0$<br>$\mathrm{Re}\, s>0$ |
| | 3 | $1-\pi^{\frac{1}{2}}as\, e^{a^2s^2}\mathrm{Erfc}(as)$ | $\dfrac{1}{2a^2}\, te^{-\frac{t^2}{4a^2}}$ | $\mathrm{Re}\, a^2>0$<br>$\mathrm{Re}\, s > -\infty$ |
| | 4 | $\dfrac{1-e^{a^2s^2}\mathrm{Erfc}(as)}{s}$ | $\mathrm{Erfc}\left(\dfrac{t}{2a}\right)$ | $\mathrm{Re}\, a^2>0$<br>$\mathrm{Re}\, s > -\infty$ |
| | 5 | $\dfrac{e^{s^2}\mathrm{Erfc}(s)}{s-a}$ | $e^{a(t+a)}[\mathrm{Erf}(\frac{t}{2}+a)-\mathrm{Erf}(a)]$ | $\mathrm{Re}\, s>\mathrm{Re}\, a$ |

| | | g(s) | f(t) | |
|---|---|---|---|---|
| 16.3.1 (Contd.) | 6 | $\frac{e^{\frac{s^2}{4a^2}}\mathrm{Erfc}(\frac{s}{2a})}{s-a}$ | $e^{at+\frac{1}{4}}[\mathrm{Erf}(at+\frac{1}{2})-\mathrm{Erf}(\frac{1}{2})]$ | Re s > Re a |
| | 7 | $\frac{e^{s^2}}{s}\mathrm{Erfc}(s+a)$ | $0 \quad 0<t<2a$<br>$\mathrm{Erf}(\frac{t}{2})-\mathrm{Erf}(a) \quad t>2a$ | $a>0$<br>Re $s>0$ |
| | 8 | $e^{a^2s^2}\mathrm{Erfc}(as+\frac{b}{2a})$ | $0 \quad 0<t<b$<br>$\frac{e^{-\frac{t^2}{4a^2}}}{(\pi a^2)^{\frac{1}{2}}} \quad t>b$ | Re $a^2>0$<br>$b>0$<br>Re $s>-\infty$ |
| | 9 | $\frac{1}{s}e^{\frac{s^2}{a^2}}[\mathrm{Erf}(\frac{s}{a})-\mathrm{Erf}(\frac{s}{a}+b)]$ | $\mathrm{Erf}(\frac{at}{2}) \quad 0<t<\frac{2b}{a}$<br>$\mathrm{Erf}(b) \quad t>\frac{2b}{a}$ | $b>0$<br>Re $s>0$ |
| 16.3.2 | 1 | $e^{as}\mathrm{Erfc}(a^{\frac{1}{2}}s^{\frac{1}{2}})$ | $\frac{a^{\frac{1}{2}}}{\pi t^{\frac{1}{2}}(t+a)}$ | $\lvert\arg a\rvert<\pi$<br>Re $s\geqslant 0$ |
| | 2 | $\frac{1}{s^{\frac{1}{2}}}e^{as}\mathrm{Erfc}(a^{\frac{1}{2}}s^{\frac{1}{2}})$ | $\frac{1}{\pi^{\frac{1}{2}}(t+a)^{\frac{1}{2}}}$ | $\lvert\arg a\rvert<\pi$<br>Re $s>0$ |
| | 3 | $\frac{e^{as}}{s^{\frac{3}{2}}}\mathrm{Erfc}(a^{\frac{1}{2}}s^{\frac{1}{2}})$ | $\frac{2}{\pi^{\frac{1}{2}}}[(t^2+a)^{\frac{1}{2}}-a^{\frac{1}{2}}]$ | $\lvert\arg a\rvert<\pi$<br>Re $s>0$ |
| | 4 | $(\frac{s}{\pi})^{\frac{1}{2}}e^{-bs}-a^{\frac{1}{2}}\mathrm{Erfc}(a^{\frac{1}{2}}s^{\frac{1}{2}})$ | $0 \quad 0<t<a$<br>$\frac{(t-a)^{\frac{1}{2}}}{\pi t} \quad t>a$ | $a>0$<br>Re $s>0$ |

| | | g(s) | f(t) | |
|---|---|---|---|---|
| 16.3.2 (Contd.) | 5 | $e^{-as}-(\pi as)^{\frac{1}{2}}\text{Erfc}[(as)^{\frac{1}{2}}]$ | $0 \quad 0<t<a$<br>$\frac{a^{\frac{1}{2}}}{2t^{\frac{3}{2}}} \quad t>a$ | $a>0$<br>$\text{Re } s>0$ |
| | 6 | $\frac{1}{(\pi s)^{\frac{1}{2}}}-a^{\frac{1}{2}}e^{as}\text{Erfc}(a^{\frac{1}{2}}s^{\frac{1}{2}})$ | $\frac{t^{\frac{1}{2}}}{\pi(t+a)}$ | $\lvert\arg a\rvert<\pi$<br>$\text{Re } s>0$ |
| | 7 | $1-(\pi as)^{\frac{1}{2}}e^{as}\text{Erfc}(a^{\frac{1}{2}}s^{\frac{1}{2}})$ | $\frac{a^{\frac{1}{2}}}{2(t+a)^{\frac{3}{2}}}$ | $\lvert\arg a\rvert<\pi$<br>$\text{Re } s\geqslant 0$ |
| | 8 | $\frac{1}{a^{\frac{1}{2}}}e^{-as}-\pi^{\frac{1}{2}}s^{\frac{1}{2}}\text{Erfc}(a^{\frac{1}{2}}s^{\frac{1}{2}})$ | $0 \quad 0<t<a$<br>$\frac{1}{2t^{\frac{3}{2}}} \quad t>a$ | $a>0$<br>$\text{Re } s\geqslant 0$ |
| | 9 | $\frac{e^{\frac{1}{s}}}{s^{\frac{1}{2}}}\text{Erfc}\left(\frac{1}{s^{\frac{1}{2}}}\right)$ | $\frac{e^{-2t^{\frac{1}{2}}}}{(\pi t)^{\frac{1}{2}}}$ | $\text{Re } s>0$ |
| | 10 | $\frac{e^{\frac{1}{s}}}{s^{\frac{1}{2}}}\text{Erfc}\left(-\frac{1}{s^{\frac{1}{2}}}\right)$ | $\frac{e^{2t^{\frac{1}{2}}}}{(\pi t)^{\frac{1}{2}}}$ | $\text{Re } s>0$ |
| | 11 | $\frac{e^{-\frac{a^2}{s}}}{s^{\frac{1}{2}}}\text{Erf}\left(\frac{ia}{s^{\frac{1}{2}}}\right)$ | $\frac{i\sin(2at^{\frac{1}{2}})}{(\pi t)^{\frac{1}{2}}}$ | $\text{Re } s>0$ |
| | 12 | $\frac{e^{\frac{1}{4s}}}{s^{\frac{3}{2}}}\text{Erfc}\left(-\frac{1}{2s^{\frac{1}{2}}}\right)$ | $\frac{2}{\pi^{\frac{1}{2}}}(e^{t^{\frac{1}{2}}}-1)$ | $\text{Re } s>0$ |
| | 13 | $\frac{1}{s^{\frac{3}{2}}}e^{\frac{a^2}{s}}\text{Erf}\left(\frac{a}{s^{\frac{1}{2}}}\right)+\frac{1}{\pi^{\frac{1}{2}}as}$ | $\frac{\cosh(2at^{\frac{1}{2}})}{\pi^{\frac{1}{2}}a}$ | $\text{Re } s>0$ |

| | | g(s) | f(t) | |
|---|---|---|---|---|
| 16.3.2 (Contd.) | 14 | $\frac{1}{s}+\frac{i\pi^{\frac{1}{2}}a}{s^{\frac{3}{2}}}e^{-\frac{a^2}{s}}\operatorname{Erf}\left(\frac{ia}{s^{\frac{1}{2}}}\right)$ | $\cos(2a\,t^{\frac{1}{2}})$ | Re s > 0 |
| | 15 | $\frac{1}{s^{\nu}}e^{\frac{a}{s}}\operatorname{Erfc}[(\frac{a}{s})^{\frac{1}{2}}]$ | $\left(\frac{t}{a}\right)^{\frac{\nu-1}{2}}\left[I_{\nu-1}(2a^{\frac{1}{2}}t^{\frac{1}{2}})-L_{\nu-1}(2a^{\frac{1}{2}}t^{\frac{1}{2}})\right]$ | Re ν > 0<br>Re s > 0 |
| | 16 | $\frac{e^{\frac{a}{s}}}{s^{\nu}}\operatorname{Erf}[(\frac{a}{s})^{\frac{1}{2}}]$ | $\left(\frac{t}{a}\right)^{\frac{\nu-1}{2}}L_{\nu-1}(2a^{\frac{1}{2}}t^{\frac{1}{2}})$ | Re ν > $-\frac{1}{2}$<br>Re s > 0 |
| | 17 | $\frac{1}{s^{\frac{1}{2}}}e^{\frac{a}{s}}\operatorname{Erfc}[(\frac{a}{s})^{\frac{1}{2}}]$ | $\frac{e^{-2a^{\frac{1}{2}}t^{\frac{1}{2}}}}{(\pi t)^{\frac{1}{2}}}$ | \|arg a\| < π<br>Re s > 0 |
| | 18 | $\frac{1}{s^{\frac{3}{2}}}e^{\frac{a}{s}}\operatorname{Erfc}[(\frac{a}{s})^{\frac{1}{2}}]$ | $\frac{1-e^{-2a^{\frac{1}{2}}t^{\frac{1}{2}}}}{(a\pi)^{\frac{1}{2}}}$ | \|arg a\| < π<br>Re s > 0 |
| | 19 | $\frac{1}{s^{\nu}}e^{as}\operatorname{Erfc}[(as)^{\frac{1}{2}}]$ | $\frac{t^{\nu-\frac{1}{2}}{}_2F_1[1,\frac{1}{2};\nu+\frac{1}{2};-\frac{t}{a}]}{(\pi a)^{\frac{1}{2}}\Gamma(\nu+\frac{1}{2})}$ | Re ν > $-\frac{1}{2}$<br>\|arg a\| < π<br>Re s > 0 |
| | 20 | $\frac{1}{s^{\frac{1}{2}}}e^{\frac{a}{s}}\operatorname{Erf}[(\frac{a}{s})^{\frac{1}{2}}]$ | $\frac{\sinh(2a^{\frac{1}{2}}t^{\frac{1}{2}})}{(\pi t)^{\frac{1}{2}}}$ | Re s > 0 |
| | 21 | $\frac{1}{s^{\frac{3}{2}}}e^{\frac{a}{s}}\operatorname{Erf}[(\frac{a}{s})^{\frac{1}{2}}]$ | $\frac{\cosh(2a^{\frac{1}{2}}t^{\frac{1}{2}})-1}{(\pi a)^{\frac{1}{2}}}$ | Re s > 0 |
| | 22 | $\frac{1}{s}-\frac{\pi^{\frac{1}{2}}a^{\frac{1}{2}}}{s^{\frac{3}{2}}}e^{\frac{a}{s}}\operatorname{Erfc}[(\frac{a}{s})^{\frac{1}{2}}]$ | $e^{-2a^{\frac{1}{2}}t^{\frac{1}{2}}}$ | \|arg a\| < π<br>Re s > 0 |

| | | g(s) | f(t) | |
|---|---|---|---|---|
| 16.3.2 (Contd.) | 23 | $\frac{1}{s^{\frac{5}{2}}} e^{\frac{a}{s}} \mathrm{Erf}\,[\,(\frac{a}{s})^{\frac{1}{2}}]$ | $\frac{t^{\frac{1}{2}}}{a\pi^{\frac{1}{2}}} \sinh(2a^{\frac{1}{2}}t^{\frac{1}{2}}) - \frac{t}{a^{\frac{1}{2}}\pi^{\frac{1}{2}}} - \frac{\cosh(2a^{\frac{1}{2}}t^{\frac{1}{2}})-1}{2a^{\frac{3}{2}}\pi^{\frac{1}{2}}}$ | Re s > 0 |
| 16.3.2.1 | 1 | $e^{as^2}\mathrm{Erfc}(a^{\frac{1}{2}}s^{\frac{1}{2}})$ | $\frac{e^{-\frac{t^2}{4a}}}{(\pi a)^{\frac{1}{2}}}$ | Re s > -∞ |
| | 2 | $1-(\pi a)^{\frac{1}{2}}\, s\, e^{as^2}\mathrm{Erfc}(a^{\frac{1}{2}}s^{\frac{1}{2}})$ | $\frac{t}{2a} e^{-\frac{t^2}{4a}}$ | Re s > -∞ |
| | 3 | $\frac{1}{s^2} - \frac{i\pi^{\frac{1}{2}}}{as^{\frac{5}{2}}}(\frac{s}{2} - a^2)\, e^{-\frac{a^2}{s}} \mathrm{Erf}\left(\frac{ia}{s^{\frac{1}{2}}}\right)$ | $\frac{t^{\frac{1}{2}}}{a}\sin(2at^{\frac{1}{2}})$ | Re s > 0 |
| | 4 | $\frac{(\frac{s}{2}+a)\, e^{\frac{a}{s}}}{s^{\frac{5}{2}}} \mathrm{Erf}\left(\frac{a^{\frac{1}{2}}}{s^{\frac{1}{2}}}\right) - \frac{a^{\frac{1}{2}}}{\pi^{\frac{1}{2}}s^2}$ | $\frac{t^{\frac{1}{2}}}{\pi^{\frac{1}{2}}} \sinh(2a^{\frac{1}{2}}t^{\frac{1}{2}})$ | Re s > 0 |
| | 5 | $\frac{(\frac{s}{2}+a)\, e^{\frac{a}{s}}}{s^{\frac{5}{2}}} \mathrm{Erfc}\left(\frac{a^{\frac{1}{2}}}{s^{\frac{1}{2}}}\right) - \frac{a^{\frac{1}{2}}}{\pi^{\frac{1}{2}}s^2}$ | $\frac{t^{\frac{1}{2}}}{\pi^{\frac{1}{2}}} e^{-2a^{\frac{1}{2}}t^{\frac{1}{2}}}$ | $\lvert \arg a \rvert < \pi$<br>Re s > 0 |
| 17.1 | 1 | $[\frac{1}{2} - C(\frac{s^2}{4})]^2 + [\frac{1}{2} - S(\frac{s^2}{4})]^2$ | $\frac{2}{\pi}\,\frac{\sin(t^2)}{t}$ | Re s > 0 |
| | 2 | $\frac{1}{s}\{[\frac{1}{2} - C(\frac{s^2}{4a})]^2 + [\frac{1}{2} - S(\frac{s^2}{4a})]^2\}$ | $\frac{1}{\pi}\,\mathrm{Si}(at^2)$ | Re s > 0 |
| 17.5.1 | 1 | $\cos(\frac{s^2}{4})[\frac{1}{2} - C(\frac{s^2}{4})] + \sin(\frac{s^2}{4})[\frac{1}{2} - S(\frac{s^2}{4})]$ | $(\frac{2}{\pi})^{\frac{1}{2}}\sin(t^2)$ | Re s > 0 |
| | 2 | $\cos(\frac{s^2}{4})[\frac{1}{2} - S(\frac{s^2}{4})] - \sin(\frac{s^2}{4})[\frac{1}{2} - C(\frac{s^2}{4})]$ | $(\frac{2}{\pi})^{\frac{1}{2}}\cos(t^2)$ | Re s > 0 |

| | | g(s) | f(t) | |
|---|---|---|---|---|
| 17.5.1 (Contd.) | 3 | $\frac{1}{s}\left[\cos\left(\frac{s^2}{a}\right)\left\{\frac{1}{2}-C\left(\frac{s^2}{a}\right)\right\}+\sin\left(\frac{s^2}{a}\right)\left\{\frac{1}{2}-S\left(\frac{s^2}{a}\right)\right\}\right]$ | $S\left(\frac{at^2}{4}\right)$ | Re s > 0 |
| | 4 | $\frac{1}{s}\left[\cos\left(\frac{s^2}{a}\right)\left\{\frac{1}{2}-S\left(\frac{s^2}{a}\right)\right\}-\sin\left(\frac{s^2}{a}\right)\left\{\frac{1}{2}-C\left(\frac{s^2}{a}\right)\right\}\right]$ | $C\left(\frac{at^2}{4}\right)$ | Re s > 0 |
| 18 | 1 | $[\mathrm{ci}(as)]^2+[\mathrm{si}(as)]^2$ | $\frac{1}{t}\log\left(1+\frac{t^2}{a^2}\right)$ | Re s > 0 |
| 18.5 | 1 | $\mathrm{ci}(as)\sin(as)+\mathrm{si}(as)\cos(as)$ | $-\frac{a}{t^2+a^2}$ | Re a > 0<br>Re s > 0 |
| | 2 | $\mathrm{ci}(as)\cos(as)-\mathrm{si}(as)\sin(as)$ | $\frac{t}{t^2+a^2}$ | Re a > 0<br>Re s > 0 |
| | 3 | $\frac{1}{s}[\mathrm{ci}(as)\sin(as)+\mathrm{si}(as)\cos(as)]$ | $-\tan^{-1}\left(\frac{t}{a}\right)$ | Re a > 0<br>Re s > 0 |
| | 4 | $\frac{1}{s}[\mathrm{ci}(as)\cos(as)-\mathrm{si}(as)\sin(as)]$ | $\frac{1}{2}\log\left(1+\frac{t^2}{a^2}\right)$ | Re a > 0<br>Re s > 0 |
| | 5 | $\frac{1}{s}\left[\frac{\pi}{2}+\mathrm{ci}(as)\sin(as)+\mathrm{si}(as)\cos(as)\right]$ | $\cot^{-1}\frac{t}{a}$ | Re s > 0 |
| | 6 | $\frac{1}{s}[\log a+\mathrm{ci}(as)\cos(as)-\mathrm{si}(as)\sin(as)]$ | $\frac{1}{2}\log(t^2+a^2)$ | Re s > 0 |
| | 7 | $[b\cos(as)-c\sin(as)]\mathrm{ci}(as)-[b\sin(as)+c\cos(as)]\mathrm{si}(as)$ | $\frac{bt+ac}{t^2+a^2}$ | $\lvert\arg(\pm ia)\rvert<\pi$<br>Re s > 0 |
| 18.5.1 | 1 | $\frac{1}{s^2}\left[\frac{\pi}{2}+\mathrm{ci}(as)\sin(as)+\mathrm{si}(as)\cos(as)\right]+\frac{a}{s}[\mathrm{si}(as)\sin(as)-\mathrm{ci}(as)\cos(as)]$ | $t\cot^{-1}\frac{t}{a}$ | Re s > 0 |

| | | g(s) | f(t) | | |
|---|---|---|---|---|---|
| 18.5.1 (Contd.) | 2 | $\frac{1}{s^2}[\mathrm{ci}(as)\sin(as)+\mathrm{si}(as)\cos(as)]$ $-\frac{a}{s}[\mathrm{ci}(as)\cos(as)-\mathrm{si}(as)\sin(as)]$ | $-t\tan^{-1}(\frac{t}{a})$ | | Re $s>0$ |
| 19 | 1 | $\mathrm{Ei}(-as)$ | $0$<br>$-\frac{1}{t}$ | $0<t<a$<br>$t>a$ | $a>0$<br>Re $s>0$ |
| | 2 | $\frac{1}{s}\mathrm{Ei}(-as)$ | $0$<br>$\log\frac{a}{t}$ | $0<t<a$<br>$t>a$ | $a>0$<br>Re $s>0$ |
| | 3 | $\frac{1}{s}[\log a-\mathrm{Ei}(-as)]$ | $\log a$<br>$\log t$ | $0<t<a$<br>$t>a$ | $a>0$<br>Re $s>0$ |
| | 4 | $[\mathrm{Ei}(-\frac{s}{2})]^2$ | $0$<br>$\frac{2}{t}\log(2t-1)$ | $0<t<1$<br>$t>1$ | Re $s>0$ |
| | 5 | $\frac{1}{s}\mathrm{Ei}(-\frac{a}{s})$ | $2\,\mathrm{Ji}_0(2a^{\frac{1}{2}}t^{\frac{1}{2}})$ | | Re $s>0$ |
| | 6 | $\mathrm{Ei}(-as)\mathrm{Ei}(-bs)$ | $0$<br>$\frac{1}{t}\log\frac{(t-a)(t-b)}{ab}$ | $0<t<a+b$<br>$t>a+b$ | $a>0$<br>$b>0$<br>Re $s>0$ |
| | 7 | $\overline{\mathrm{Ei}}(\frac{s}{a})\mathrm{Ei}(-\frac{s}{a})$ | $\frac{1}{t}\log\lvert 1-a^2t^2\rvert$ | | Re $s>0$ |
| 19.1 | 1 | $\frac{1}{s}\mathrm{Ei}[-b(s+a)]$ | $0$<br>$\mathrm{Ei}(-ba)-\mathrm{Ei}(-at)$ | $0<t<b$<br>$t>b$ | $b>0$<br>$a\neq 0$<br>Re $s>-$Re $a$ |

| | | g(s) | f(t) | |
|---|---|---|---|---|
| 19.1 (Contd.) | 2 | $Ei(a-s)+Ei(-a-s)$ | $0 \quad 0<t<1$<br>$-\frac{2\cosh(at)}{t} \quad t>1$ | $\mathrm{Re}\, s > \lvert \mathrm{Re}\, a \rvert$ |
| | 3 | $-Ei(a-s)+Ei(-a-s)$ | $0 \quad 0<t<1$<br>$\frac{2\sinh(at)}{t} \quad t>1$ | $\mathrm{Re}\, s > \lvert \mathrm{Re}\, a \rvert$ |
| 19.2 | 1 | $\frac{1}{s^{\nu}}\, Ei(-\frac{a}{s})$ | $2t^{\nu-1}\int_{\infty}^{a^{\frac{1}{2}}t^{\frac{1}{2}}} u^{-\nu} J_{\nu-1}(2u)\,du$ | $\mathrm{Re}\,\nu>0$<br>$\mathrm{Re}\, a>0$<br>$\mathrm{Re}\, s>0$ |
| 19.3 | 1 | $e^{as}\, Ei(-as)$ | $-\frac{1}{t+a}$ | $\lvert \arg a \rvert < \pi$<br>$\mathrm{Re}\, s>0$ |
| | 2 | $\frac{1}{s}\, e^{as}\, Ei(-as)$ | $-\log(1+\frac{t}{a})$ | $\lvert \arg a \rvert < \pi$<br>$\mathrm{Re}\, s>0$ |
| | 3 | $\frac{1}{s}\, e^{\frac{a}{s}}\, Ei(-\frac{a}{s})$ | $-2K_0(2a^{\frac{1}{2}}t^{\frac{1}{2}})$ | $\mathrm{Re}\, s>0$ |
| | 4 | $e^{as}\, Ei[-(a+b)s]$ | $0 \quad 0<t<b$<br>$-\frac{1}{t+a} \quad t>b$ | $a \neq 0$<br>$b>0$<br>$\lvert \arg(a+b) \rvert < \pi$<br>$\mathrm{Re}\, s>0$ |
| | 5 | $se^{as}\, Ei(-as)+\frac{1}{a}$ | $\frac{1}{(t+a)^2}$ | $\lvert \arg a \rvert < \pi$<br>$a \neq 0$<br>$\mathrm{Re}\, s>0$ |
| | 6 | $e^{-as}+asEi(-as)$ | $0 \quad 0<t<a$<br>$\frac{a}{t^2} \quad t>a$ | $a>0$<br>$\mathrm{Re}\, s>0$ |
| | 7 | $\frac{1}{s}\, e^{-as}\, \overline{Ei}(as)$ | $-\log\lvert 1-\frac{t}{a} \rvert$ | $a>0$<br>$\mathrm{Re}\, s>0$ |

| | | g(s) | f(t) | |
|---|---|---|---|---|
| 19.3 (Contd.) | 8 | $e^{-as}\,\overline{Ei}(as)$ | $\frac{1}{a-t}$ Cauchy Principal Value of integral | $a \geq 0$<br>$Re\ s > 0$ |
| | 9 | $\frac{1}{s}[\log a - e^{as}\,Ei(-as)]$ | $\log(t+a)$ | $\lvert\arg a\rvert < \pi$<br>$Re\ s > 0$ |
| | 10 | $\frac{1}{s}[e^{-as}\log a - Ei(-as)]$ | $0 \qquad 0 < t < a$<br>$\log t \qquad t > a$ | $a > 0$<br>$Re\ s > 0$ |
| | 11 | $e^{as}\{Ei[-(a+c)s] - Ei[-(a+b)s]\}$ | $0 \qquad 0 < t < b$<br>$\frac{1}{t+a} \qquad b < t < c$<br>$0 \qquad t > c$ | $Re\ s > -\infty$<br>$-a$ not between $b$ and $c$ |
| | 12 | $b e^{as}\,Ei(-as) + c e^{-as}\,Ei(as)$ | $-\frac{(b+c)t-(b-c)a}{t^2-a^2}$ | $\lvert\arg(\pm a)\rvert < \pi$<br>$Re\ s > 0$ |
| | 13 | $b e^{as}\,Ei(-as) + c e^{-as}\,\overline{Ei}(as)$ | $-\frac{(b+c)t-(b-c)a}{t^2-a^2}$ Cauchy Principal Value of integral | $a > 0$<br>$Re\ s > 0$ |
| | 14 | $\frac{1}{s}[\log(a^2) - e^{as}\,Ei(-as) - e^{-as}\,Ei(as)]$ | $\log(t^2-a^2)$ | $Im\ a > 0$<br>$Re\ s > 0$ |
| | 15 | $\frac{1}{s}[\log(a^2) - e^{as}\,Ei(-as) - e^{-as}\,\overline{Ei}(as)]$ | $\log\lvert t^2-a^2\rvert$ | $Re\ a > 0$<br>$Re\ s > 0$ |
| | 16 | $e^{as}\,[Ei(-as)]^2$ | $0 \qquad 0 < t < a$<br>$\frac{2\log\frac{t}{a}}{t+a} \qquad t > a$ | $a > 0$<br>$Re\ s > 0$ |

| | | $g(s)$ | $f(t)$ | |
|---|---|---|---|---|
| 19.3 (Contd.) | 17 | $e^{as}\{[\mathrm{Ei}(-as)]^2 - 2\log a\,\mathrm{Ei}(-2as)\}$ | $0 \quad 0<t<a$<br>$\dfrac{2\log t}{t+a} \quad t>a$ | $a>0$<br>$\mathrm{Re}\, s>0$ |
| | 18 | $e^{(a+b)s}\mathrm{Ei}(-as)\mathrm{Ei}(-bs)$ | $\dfrac{\log\dfrac{(t+a)(t+b)}{ab}}{t+a+b}$ | $\lvert\arg(a+b)\rvert<\pi$<br>$a,b\neq 0$<br>$\mathrm{Re}\, s>0$ |
| | 19 | $e^{(a+b)s}[\mathrm{Ei}(-as)\mathrm{Ei}(-bs) - \log(ab)\mathrm{Ei}(-as-bs)]$ | $\dfrac{\log[(t+a)(t+b)]}{t+a+b}$ | $\lvert\arg(a+b)\rvert<\pi$<br>$a,b\neq 0$<br>$\mathrm{Re}\, s>0$ |
| 19.3.1 | 1 | $e^{\frac{s^2}{4a^2}}\,\mathrm{Ei}\left(-\dfrac{s^2}{4a^2}\right)$ | $\dfrac{2ai}{\pi^{\frac{1}{2}}}e^{-a^2t^2}\,\mathrm{Erf}(iat)$ | $\lvert\arg a\rvert<\dfrac{\pi}{4}$<br>$\mathrm{Re}\, s>0$ |
| | 2 | $\sum\limits_{m=1}^{n}(m-1)!(-a)^{n-m}s^{-m} + (-1)^{n-1}a^n e^{as}\,\mathrm{Ei}(-as)$ | $\dfrac{t^n}{t+a}$ | $\lvert\arg a\rvert<\pi$<br>$n=1,2,3,\ldots$<br>$\mathrm{Re}\, s>0$ |
| | 3 | $\sum\limits_{m=1}^{n-1}(m-1)!\,\dfrac{(-s)^{n-m-1}}{a^m} - (-s)^{n-1}e^{as}\,\mathrm{Ei}(-as)$ | $\dfrac{(n-1)!}{(t+a)^n}$ | $\lvert\arg a\rvert<\pi$<br>$n=2,3,4,\ldots$<br>$\mathrm{Re}\, s\geq 0$ |
| | 4 | $e^{-bs}\sum\limits_{m=1}^{n-1}(m-1)!\,\dfrac{(-s)^{n-m-1}}{(a+b)^m} - (-s)^{n-1}e^{as}\,\mathrm{Ei}[-(a+b)s]$ | $0 \quad 0<t<b$<br>$\dfrac{(n-1)!}{(t+a)^n} \quad t>b$ | $n=2,3,4,\ldots$<br>$\lvert\arg(a+b)\rvert<\pi$<br>$\mathrm{Re}\, s>0$ |
| 19.3.2 | 1 | $\dfrac{1}{s^\nu}e^{\frac{a}{s}}\,\mathrm{Ei}(-\tfrac{a}{s})$ | $t^{\nu-1}\displaystyle\int_\infty^{at} u^{-\frac{\nu+1}{2}} J_{\nu-1}[2(u-at)^{\frac{1}{2}}]\,du$ | $\mathrm{Re}\,\nu>0$<br>$\mathrm{Re}\, s>0$ |
| 19.4 | 1 | $\dfrac{1}{s}[\mathrm{Ei}(-as) - \log(\gamma s)]$ | $\log t \quad 0<t<a$<br>$\log a \quad t>a$ | $a>0$<br>$\mathrm{Re}\, s>-\infty$ |

| | | g(s) | f(t) | |
|---|---|---|---|---|
| 19.4.1 (Contd.) | 1 | $\log\frac{s+a}{s-a} + \mathrm{Ei}(a-s) - \mathrm{Ei}(-a-s)$ | $\frac{2\sinh(at)}{t}$ $\quad 0<t<1$; $\quad 0 \quad t>1$ | $\mathrm{Re}\, s > -\infty$ |
| 19.16.3.1 | 1 | $e^{\frac{s^2}{a^2}}\left[\mathrm{Erfc}(\frac{s}{a}) + \frac{i}{\pi}\,\mathrm{Ei}\left(-\frac{s^2}{a^2}\right)\right]$ | $\frac{a}{\pi^{\frac{1}{2}}}\, e^{-\frac{a^2t^2}{4}}\,\mathrm{Erfc}(\frac{iat}{2})$ | $\mathrm{Re}\, s > 0$ |
| 21 | 1 | $\frac{\psi^2(s)}{s}$ | $[\log\{\gamma(e^t-1)\}]^2 - \frac{\pi^2}{6} - t\log(e^t-1) + 1*\log(e^t-1)$ | $\mathrm{Re}\, s > 0$ |
| | 2 | $B(as,\nu)$ | $\frac{1}{a}(1-e^{-\frac{t}{a}})^{\nu-1}$ | $\mathrm{Re}\, a > 0$; $\mathrm{Re}\,\nu > 0$; $\mathrm{Re}\, s > 0$ |
| | 3 | $\Gamma(-\nu, as)$ | $0 \quad 0<t<a$; $\quad \frac{(t-a)^\nu}{\Gamma(\nu+1)a^\nu t} \quad t>a$ | $a>0$; $\mathrm{Re}\,\nu > -1$; $\mathrm{Re}\, s > 0$ |
| | 4 | $\Gamma(-s,1)$ | $e^{-e^t}$ | $\mathrm{Re}\, s > -\infty$ |
| | 5 | $\Gamma(-s,a) - \Gamma(-s,b)$ | $0 \quad 0<t<\log a$; $\quad e^{-e^t} \quad \log a < t < \log b$; $\quad 0 \quad t>\log b$ | $1 \leq a < b$; $\mathrm{Re}\, s > -\infty$ |
| | 6 | $\gamma(\nu, \frac{a}{s})$ | $a^{\frac{\nu}{2}}\, t^{\frac{\nu}{2}-1}\, J_\nu(2a^{\frac{1}{2}}t^{\frac{1}{2}})$ | $\mathrm{Re}\,\nu > 0$; $\mathrm{Re}\, s > 0$ |
| | 7 | $\gamma(\nu, -\frac{a}{s})$ | $a^{\frac{\nu}{2}}(-1)^\nu t^{\frac{\nu}{2}-1}\, I_\nu(2a^{\frac{1}{2}}t^{\frac{1}{2}})$ | $\mathrm{Re}\,\nu > 0$; $\mathrm{Re}\, s > 0$ |

| | | g(s) | f(t) | |
|---|---|---|---|---|
| 21 (Contd.) | 8 | $\gamma(s,1)$ | $e^{-e^{-t}}$ | Re s > 0 |
| | 9 | $\gamma(-s,b)-\gamma(-s,a)$ | 0 $\quad 0 < t < \log a$<br>$e^{-e^{t}}$ $\quad \log a < t < \log b$<br>0 $\quad t > \log b$ | $1 \leq a < b$<br>Re s > $-\infty$ |
| | 10 | $\frac{1}{s}\,\psi(as)$ | $-\log[\gamma(e^{\frac{t}{a}}-1)]$ | Re a > 0<br>Re s > 0 |
| | 11 | $\psi^{(n)}(as)$ | $\dfrac{t^n}{(-a)^{n+1}(1-e^{-\frac{t}{a}})}$ | Re a > 0<br>n = 0,1,2,...<br>Re s > 0 |
| 21.1 | 1 | $B(\nu,s-ia)+B(\nu,s+ia)$ | $2(1-e^{-t})^{\nu-1}\cos(at)$ | Re $\nu$ > 0<br>Re s > \|Im a\| |
| | 2 | $B(\nu,s-ia)-B(\nu,s+ia)$ | $2i(1-e^{-t})^{\nu-1}\sin(at)$ | Re $\nu$ > − 1<br>Re s > \|Im a\| |
| | 3 | $B\left(\frac{s}{2a}-\frac{\nu}{2},\nu+1\right)$ | $2^{\nu+1}a^{\nu}\sinh^{\nu}(at)$ | Re a > 0<br>Re $\nu$ > − 1<br>Re s > Re($a\nu$) |
| | 4 | $B\left(\frac{s}{a}-\nu,2\nu+1\right)$ | $2^{\nu}a[\cosh(at)-1]^{\nu}$ | Re a > 0<br>Re $\nu$ > $-\frac{1}{2}$<br>Re s > Re($a\nu$) |
| | 5 | $\dfrac{B(\frac{s}{a},\nu+n+1)B(\frac{s}{a},b+n-\frac{s}{a})}{B(\frac{s}{a},b-\frac{s}{a})}$ | $a(1-e^{-at})^{\nu}{}_2F_1[-n,\nu+b+n;b;e^{-at}]$ | Re $\nu$ > − 1<br>Re s > 0 |
| | 6 | $B(s,a)[\psi(s+a)-\psi(s)]$ | $t(1-e^{-t})^{a-1}$ | Re a > 0<br>Re s > 0 |

| | | g(s) | f(t) | |
|---|---|---|---|---|
| 21.1 (Contd.) | 7 | $\psi(\frac{s+1}{2}) - \psi(\frac{s}{2})$ | $\frac{2}{1+e^{-t}}$ | Re s > o |
| | 8 | $\frac{1}{s}[\psi(\frac{s+1}{2}) - \psi(\frac{s}{2})]$ | $2 \log \frac{1+e^{t}}{2}$ | Re s > o |
| | 9 | $s[\psi(\frac{s+2}{4}) - \psi(\frac{s}{4})]-2$ | $2 \operatorname{sech}^2 t$ | Re s > - 2 |
| | 10 | $\psi(\frac{s+2}{4}) - \psi(\frac{s}{4}) - \frac{2}{s}$ | $2 \tanh t$ | Re s > o |
| | 11 | $\frac{1}{s}[\psi(\frac{s+2}{4}) - \psi(\frac{s}{4})] - \frac{2}{s^2}$ | $2 \log \cosh t$ | Re s > o |
| | 12 | $\psi(s+a)-\psi(s)$ | $\frac{1-e^{-at}}{1-e^{-t}}$ | Re s > Max o, - Re a |
| | 13 | $\psi\left(\frac{s+3a}{4a}\right) - \psi\left(\frac{s+a}{4a}\right)$ | $2a \operatorname{sech}(at)$ | Re s > Max - Re a, - Re 3a |
| | 14 | $\psi(s-ia) - \psi(s+ia)$ | $-2i \frac{\sin(at)}{1-e^{-t}}$ | Re s > \|Im a\| |
| | 15 | $\psi(s-ia+1) - \psi(s+ia+1)$ | $-2i \frac{\sin(at)}{e^{t}-1}$ | Re s > \|Im a\| - 1 |
| | 16 | $\psi(as+b) - \psi(as+c)$ | $\frac{e^{-\frac{ct}{a}} - e^{-\frac{bt}{a}}}{a(1-e^{-\frac{t}{a}})}$ | Re a > o<br>Re s > Max - Re $\frac{c}{a}$, - Re $\frac{c}{b}$ |
| | 17 | $\psi(s+a) + \psi(s+b) - \psi(s+a+b) - \psi(s)$ | $\frac{(1-e^{-at})(1-e^{-bt})}{1-e^{-t}}$ | Re s > Max o, - Re a, - Re b, - Re(a+b) |

| | | g(s) | f(t) | |
|---|---|---|---|---|
| 21.1 (Contd.) | 18 | $\dfrac{\Gamma\left(-\frac{ab+is}{2b}\right)}{\Gamma\left(1+\frac{ab-is}{2b}\right)}$ | $\dfrac{(2i)^{a+1}\sin^a(bt)}{\Gamma(a+1)}$ | Re a > − 1<br>Re s > Max 2 Im b + Im(ab), − Im(ab) |
| | 19 | $\dfrac{\Gamma(-\frac{1}{4}-\frac{is}{2})}{(1-2is)\Gamma(\frac{1}{4}-\frac{is}{2})}$ | $(i-1)\left(\dfrac{\sin t}{\pi}\right)^{\frac{1}{2}}$ | Re s > o |
| | 20 | $\dfrac{\Gamma(s+a)}{\Gamma(s+b)}(s+c)_n$ | $\dfrac{e^{-at}}{\Gamma(b-a-n)}(1-e^{-t})^{b-a-n-1}\,{}_2F_1[-n,b-c-n;b-a-n;1-e^{-t}]$ | Re(b−a) > n<br>n = 0,1,2,...<br>Re s > − Re a |
| | 21 | $\dfrac{\Gamma(s)\Gamma(c+s)}{\Gamma(a+s)\Gamma(b+s)}$ | $\dfrac{(1-e^{-t})^{a-b-c-1}}{\Gamma(a+b-c)}\,{}_2F_1[a-c,b-c;a+b-c;1-e^{-t}]$ | Re(a+b−c) > o<br>Re s > Max o, − Re c |
| | 22 | $\dfrac{\Gamma(1+\frac{is}{2a})\Gamma(1-\frac{is}{2a})}{s\Gamma(\nu+1+\frac{is}{2a})\Gamma(\nu+1-\frac{is}{2a})}$ | $\dfrac{2^{2\nu}}{\Gamma(2\nu+1)}\lvert\sin(at)\rvert^{2\nu}$ | a> o<br>Re $\nu$ > $-\frac{1}{2}$<br>Re s > o |
| | 23 | $\dfrac{\Gamma(s-n-\mu)\Gamma(s+n-\mu+\frac{1}{2})}{\Gamma(s+n+\mu+1)\Gamma(s-n+\mu+\frac{1}{2})}$ | $\dfrac{4^{\mu}\pi^{\frac{1}{2}}}{\Gamma(2\mu+\frac{1}{2})}\sinh^{2\mu}(\frac{t}{2})P_{2n}^{-2\mu}(\cosh\frac{t}{2})$ | Re $\mu$ > $-\frac{1}{4}$<br>n = 0,1,2,...<br>Re s > n + Re $\mu$ |
| | 24 | $\dfrac{\Gamma(s+a)\Gamma(s+b)}{\Gamma(s+c)\Gamma(s+d)}$ | $\dfrac{e^{-at}(1-e^{-t})^{c+d-a-b-1}}{\Gamma(c+d-a-b)}\,{}_2F_1[d-b,c-b;c+d-a-b;1-e^{-t}]$ | Re(c+d−a−b) > o<br>Re s > − Re a, −Re b |
| | 25 | $\displaystyle\int_0^\infty\frac{du}{(s+au)\Gamma(u+1)}$ | $\nu(e^{-at})$ | Re s > o |
| 21.2 | 1 | $\dfrac{\Gamma(\nu,as)}{s^\nu}$ | 0    0 < t < a<br>$t^{\nu-1}$    t > a | a> o<br>Re s > o |

| | | g(s) | f(t) | |
|---|---|---|---|---|
| 21.2 (Contd.) | 2 | $s^{\mu}\Gamma(\nu,\frac{a}{s})$ | $t^{-\mu-1}\int_{at}^{\infty} u^{\frac{\mu+\nu-1}{2}} J_{\nu-\mu-1}(2u^{\frac{1}{2}})\,du$ | $\mathrm{Re}(\mu+\nu) < -\frac{1}{2}$<br>$\mathrm{Re}\,\mu > 0$<br>$\mathrm{Re}\,s > 0$ |
| | 3 | $\frac{\gamma(\nu,as)}{s^{\nu}}$ | $t^{\nu-1} \quad 0 < t < a$<br>$0 \quad t > a$ | $\mathrm{Re}\,\nu > 0$<br>$a > 0$<br>$\mathrm{Re}\,s > -\infty$ |
| | 4 | $s^{\mu}\gamma(\nu,\frac{a}{s})$ | $t^{-\mu-1}\int_{0}^{at} u^{\frac{\mu+\nu-1}{2}} J_{\nu-\mu-1}(2u^{\frac{1}{2}})\,du$ | $\mathrm{Re}\,\nu > 0$<br>$\mathrm{Re}(\nu-\mu) > 0$<br>$\mathrm{Re}\,s > 0$ |
| | 5 | $\gamma\left(\nu,\frac{(s^2+a^2)^{\frac{1}{2}}-s}{2}\right)$ | $(\frac{a}{2})^{\nu}\frac{t^{\frac{\nu}{2}-1}}{(t+1)^{\frac{\nu}{2}}} J_{\nu}[a(t^2+t)^{\frac{1}{2}}]$ | $\mathrm{Re}\,\nu > 0$<br>$\mathrm{Re}\,s > \lvert \mathrm{Im}\,a \rvert$ |
| 21.2.1 | 1 | $\frac{\Gamma(\nu,bs)}{(s-a)s^{\nu}}$ | $0 \quad 0 < t < a$<br>$e^{at}\int_{b}^{t} e^{-au}u^{\nu-1}\,du \quad t > a$ | $a \geqslant 0$<br>$\mathrm{Re}\,s > b$ |
| 21.3 | 1 | $\frac{B(s,a)}{b^{s}}$ | $0 \quad 0 < t < \log b$<br>$(1-be^{-t})^{a-1} \quad t > \log b$ | $\mathrm{Re}\,a > 0$<br>$b > 0$<br>$\mathrm{Re}\,s > 0$ |
| | 2 | $a^{s}\Gamma(-s,a)$ | $\exp(-a\,e^{t})$ | $\mathrm{Re}\,a > 0$<br>$\mathrm{Re}\,s > -\infty$ |
| | 3 | $e^{as}\Gamma(\nu,as)$ | $\frac{a^{\nu}}{\Gamma(1-\nu)(t+a)t^{\nu}}$ | $\mathrm{Re}\,\nu < 1$<br>$\mathrm{Re}\,s > 0$ |
| | 4 | $\frac{\gamma(s,a)}{a^{s}}$ | $\exp(-ae^{-t})$ | $\mathrm{Re}\,s > 0$ |

| | | g(s) | f(t) | |
|---|---|---|---|---|
| 21.3.1 | 1 | $\dfrac{1}{2^s\, s\, B\left(\frac{s+n+1}{2}, \frac{s-n+1}{2}\right)}$ | $\dfrac{T_n(e^{-t})}{\pi(1-e^{-2t})^{\frac{1}{2}}}$ | $n=0,1,2,\ldots$ <br> $\operatorname{Re} s > 0$ |
| | 2 | $\dfrac{1}{2^s\, s\, B\left(\frac{s+\nu+1}{2}, \frac{s-\nu+1}{2}\right)}$ | $\dfrac{\cos[\nu \cos^{-1}(e^{-t})]}{\pi(1-e^{-2t})^{\frac{1}{2}}}$ | $\operatorname{Re} s > 0$ |
| | 3 | $e^{as^2}\,\Gamma(\nu, as^2)$ | $\dfrac{2^{2\nu} e^{i\pi(\nu-\frac{1}{2}) - \frac{t^2}{4a}}\, \gamma\left(\frac{1}{2}-\nu, \frac{e^{i\pi} t^2}{4a}\right)}{a^{\frac{1}{2}}\,\Gamma(1-2\nu)}$ | $\operatorname{Re} a > 0$ <br> $\operatorname{Re} \nu < 1$ <br> $\operatorname{Re} s > 0$ |
| | 4 | $\dfrac{e^{-\pi s}}{\Gamma(a+is)\Gamma(a-is)}$ | $\dfrac{(2 \sin \frac{t}{2})^{2a-2}}{2\pi\Gamma(2a-1)}$ $\quad 0 < t < 2\pi$ <br> $0 \quad t > 2\pi$ | $\operatorname{Re} a > \frac{3}{2}$ <br> $\operatorname{Re} s > -\infty$ |
| | 5 | $\dfrac{b^{-as}\,\Gamma(as)}{\Gamma(as+n+1)}$ | $0 \quad 0 < t < a \log b$ <br> $\dfrac{(1-b\, e^{-\frac{t}{a}})^n}{n!\, a} \quad t > a \log b$ | $n=0,1,2,\ldots$ <br> $a > 0$ <br> $b \geq 1$ <br> $\operatorname{Re} s > 0$ |
| | 6 | $\dfrac{\Gamma(s)}{2^s\,\Gamma\left(\frac{s+n+1}{2}\right)\Gamma\left(\frac{s-n+1}{2}\right)}$ | $\dfrac{T_n(e^{-t})}{\pi(1-e^{-2t})^{\frac{1}{2}}}$ | $n=0,1,2,\ldots$ <br> $\operatorname{Re} s > 0$ |
| | 7 | $\dfrac{\Gamma(s-\mu+1)}{\Gamma(s+\mu+1)}\, e^{\pm s i\theta}$ | $\dfrac{\pi^{\frac{1}{2}}\, e^{\mp[\frac{\theta}{2}+(\frac{\mu}{2}-\frac{1}{4})\pi] i}\, \operatorname{cosec}^{\mu}\theta}{2^{\mu-1}\,\Gamma(\mu+\frac{1}{2})[\pi P_\nu^\mu(\cos\theta) \pm 2i\, Q_\nu^\mu(\cos\theta)]} \cdot$ <br> $e^{(\mu-1)t}(1-e^{-t})^{\mu-\frac{1}{2}}[(1-e^{-t})\sin\theta \mp i(1-e^{-t})\cos\theta]^{\mu-\frac{1}{2}}$ | $\operatorname{Re}\mu > -\frac{1}{2}$ <br> $\operatorname{Re} s > \operatorname{Re}(\mu-1)$ |
| | 8 | $\dfrac{2^s\,\Gamma\left(\frac{s+\nu+1}{2}\right)\Gamma\left(\frac{s-\nu}{2}\right)}{\Gamma(s+\mu+1)}$ | $2\pi^{\frac{1}{2}}(1-e^{-2t})^{\frac{\mu}{2}}\, P_\nu^{-\mu}(e^t)$ | $\operatorname{Re} u > -1$ <br> $\operatorname{Re} s > \operatorname{Max} \operatorname{Re} \nu,$ <br> $-\operatorname{Re}(1+\nu)$ |

| | | g(s) | f(t) | |
|---|---|---|---|---|
| 21.3.2 | 1 | $\dfrac{e^{as}\,\Gamma(\nu,as)}{s^{\nu}}$ | $(t+a)^{\nu-1}$ | $\lvert\arg a\rvert < \pi$<br>$\mathrm{Re}\, s > 0$ |
| | 2 | $\dfrac{e^{\frac{a}{s}}\,\Gamma(-\nu,\frac{a}{s})}{s^{\nu+1}}$ | $2\left(\frac{t}{a}\right)^{\frac{\nu}{2}}\dfrac{K_{\nu}(2a^{\frac{1}{2}}t^{\frac{1}{2}})}{\Gamma(\nu+1)}$ | $\mathrm{Re}\,\nu > -1$<br>$\mathrm{Re}\, s > 0$ |
| | 3 | $s^{\nu-\frac{3}{2}}\,e^{\frac{a}{s}}\,\Gamma(\nu,\frac{a}{s})$ | $\Gamma(\nu)\left(\frac{a}{t}\right)^{\frac{\nu}{2}-\frac{1}{4}}\left[I_{\frac{1}{2}-\nu}(2a^{\frac{1}{2}}t^{\frac{1}{2}}) - \mathbf{L}_{\nu-\frac{1}{2}}(2a^{\frac{1}{2}}t^{\frac{1}{2}})\right]$ | $\mathrm{Re}\,\nu < \frac{3}{2}$<br>$\mathrm{Re}\, s > 0$ |
| | 4 | $s^{\nu-1}e^{-\frac{a}{s}}\,\Gamma(\nu,e^{i\pi}\frac{a}{s})$ | $-\dfrac{\pi i}{\Gamma(1-\nu)}\left(\frac{a}{t}\right)^{\frac{\nu}{2}}H_{\nu}^{(2)}(2a^{\frac{1}{2}}t^{\frac{1}{2}})$ | $\mathrm{Re}\,\nu < 1$<br>$\mathrm{Re}\, s > 0$ |
| | 5 | $s^{\nu-1}e^{-\frac{a}{s}}\,\Gamma(\nu,e^{-i\pi}\frac{a}{s})$ | $\dfrac{\pi i}{\Gamma(1-\nu)}\left(\frac{a}{t}\right)^{\frac{\nu}{2}}H_{\nu}^{(1)}(2a^{\frac{1}{2}}t^{\frac{1}{2}})$ | $\mathrm{Re}\,\nu < 1$<br>$\mathrm{Re}\, s > 0$ |
| | 6 | $\dfrac{e^{-as}\,\gamma(\nu,-as)}{s^{\nu}}$ | $(a-t)^{\nu-1}$ $\quad 0 < t < a$<br>$0$ $\quad t > a$ | $\mathrm{Re}\,\nu > 0$<br>$a > 0$<br>$\mathrm{Re}\, s > -\infty$ |
| | 7 | $s^{\nu-1}e^{\frac{a}{s}}\,\gamma(\nu,\frac{a}{s})$ | $\Gamma(\nu)\left(\frac{a}{t}\right)^{\frac{\nu}{2}}I_{\nu}(2a^{\frac{1}{2}}t^{\frac{1}{2}})$ | $\mathrm{Re}\,\nu > 0$<br>$\mathrm{Re}\, s > 0$ |
| | 8 | $s^{\nu-1}e^{-\frac{a}{s}}\,\gamma(\nu,\frac{a}{s}e^{-i\pi})$ | $\Gamma(\nu)\left(\frac{a}{t}\right)^{\frac{\nu}{2}}e^{-i\nu\pi}J_{\nu}(2a^{\frac{1}{2}}t^{\frac{1}{2}})$ | $\mathrm{Re}\, s > 0$ |
| | 9 | $s^{\nu-\frac{3}{2}}\,e^{\frac{a}{s}}\,\gamma(\nu,\frac{a}{s})$ | $\Gamma(\nu)\left(\frac{a}{t}\right)^{\frac{\nu}{2}-\frac{1}{4}}\mathbf{L}_{\nu-\frac{1}{2}}(2a^{\frac{1}{2}}t^{\frac{1}{2}})$ | $\mathrm{Re}\, s > 0$ |
| | 10 | $s^{\mu}e^{\frac{a}{s}}\,\gamma(\nu,\frac{a}{s})$ | $\dfrac{a^{\nu}t^{\nu-\mu-1}}{\nu\Gamma(\nu-\mu)}\,{}_1F_2\left[\begin{matrix}1; \\ \nu+1,\nu-\mu;\end{matrix}\ at\right]$ | $\mathrm{Re}\,\nu > 0$<br>$\mathrm{Re}\,\mu > 0$<br>$\mathrm{Re}\, s > 0$ |

| | | g(s) | f(t) | |
|---|---|---|---|---|
| 21.3.2.1 | 1 | $\frac{1}{s^{\frac{1}{2}}} e^{as^2} \Gamma(\frac{1}{4}, as^2)$ | $\frac{\Gamma(\frac{1}{4}) t^{\frac{1}{2}}}{2a^{\frac{1}{2}}} e^{-\frac{t^2}{8a}} I_{\frac{1}{4}}\left(\frac{t^2}{8a}\right)$ | Re a > o<br>Re s > o |
| | 2 | $\frac{e^{\frac{a^2 s^2}{2}} \Gamma(\nu, \frac{a^2 s^2}{2})}{s^{2\nu}}$ | $\frac{\Gamma(\nu) a^{2\nu-1} e^{-\frac{t^2}{4a^2}}}{(2\pi)^{\frac{1}{2}}} \left[D_{-2\nu}(-\frac{t}{a}) - D_{-2\nu}(\frac{t}{a})\right]$ | Re s > o |
| | 3 | $\frac{e^{-as}\Gamma(\nu, ab)}{s} - \frac{b^{\nu}\Gamma[\nu, a(s+b)]}{s(s+b)^{\nu}}$ | 0 $\quad 0 < t < a$<br>$\Gamma(\nu, bt) \quad t > a$ | Re s > - Re b |
| 1.4 | 1 | $\psi(\frac{s}{a}) - \log \frac{s}{a}$ | $\frac{1}{t} - \frac{a}{1-e^{-at}}$ | Re s > o |
| | 2 | $\frac{1}{s}[\psi(\frac{s}{a}) - \log \frac{s}{a}]$ | $\log \frac{at}{e^{at}-1}$ | Re s > o |
| | 3 | $\psi(\frac{s}{2}) + \frac{1}{s} - \log \frac{s}{2}$ | $\frac{1}{t} - \coth t$ | Re s > o |
| | 4 | $\frac{1}{s}[\log \frac{s}{2} - \frac{1}{2s} - \psi(\frac{s}{2})]$ | $\log \sinh t - \log t$ | Re s > o |
| | 5 | $s + \log\Gamma(s) - s \log s + \frac{1}{2} \log \frac{s}{2\pi}$ | $\frac{1}{t(1-e^{-t})} - \frac{1}{t^2} - \frac{1}{2t}$ | Re s > o |
| | 6 | $\log \frac{(2\pi)^{\frac{1}{2}}}{B(\frac{s}{2}, \frac{1}{2})} - \frac{1}{2}\psi(s)$ | $\frac{1}{1+e^{-t}}\left(\frac{1}{2} - \frac{1}{t} + \frac{1}{e^t - 1}\right)$ | Re s > o |
| 1.4.1 | 1 | $\log\left[\frac{s}{4}\left\{\frac{\Gamma(\frac{s}{4})}{\Gamma(\frac{s+2}{4})}\right\}^2\right]$ | $\frac{\tanh t}{t}$ | Re s >o |

| | | g(s) | f(t) | |
|---|---|---|---|---|
| 21.4.1 (Contd.) | 2 | $\log\left[\frac{s}{4}\left\{\frac{\Gamma(\frac{s+3}{4})}{\Gamma(\frac{s+1}{4})}\right\}^2\right]$ | $\frac{1-\operatorname{sech} t}{t}$ | Re s > o |
| | 3 | $\log\left[(s+a)\left(\frac{\Gamma(s+a)}{\Gamma(s+a+\frac{1}{2})}\right)^2\right]$ | $\frac{1}{t}e^{-at}\tanh\frac{t}{4}$ | Re s > - Re a |
| | 4 | $\log\left[\frac{1}{s+a}\left(\frac{\Gamma(s+a+\frac{3}{4})}{\Gamma(s+a+\frac{1}{4})}\right)^2\right]$ | $\frac{1}{t}e^{-at}[1-\operatorname{sech}\frac{t}{4}]$ | Re s > - Re a |
| | 5 | $\log\frac{\Gamma(\frac{s}{2})\Gamma(\frac{a+s+1}{2})}{\Gamma(\frac{s+1}{2})\Gamma(\frac{a+s}{2})}$ | $\frac{1-e^{-at}}{t(1+e^{-t})}$ | Re s > Max o, - Re a |
| | 6 | $\log\frac{\Gamma(s)\Gamma(s+a+b)}{\Gamma(s+a)\Gamma(s+b)}$ | $\frac{(1-e^{-at})(1-e^{-bt})}{t(1-e^{-t})}$ | Re s > Max o, - Re a, - Re b, - Re(a+b) |
| | 7 | $\log\frac{\Gamma(s+a)\Gamma(s+b+\frac{1}{2})}{\Gamma(s+a+\frac{1}{2})\Gamma(s+b)}$ | $\frac{e^{-at}-e^{-bt}}{t(1+e^{-\frac{t}{2}})}$ | Re s > Max - Re a, - Re b |
| | 8 | $\log\frac{\Gamma(s+a)\Gamma(s+b+c)}{\Gamma(s+a+c)\Gamma(s+b)}$ | $\frac{(e^{-at}-e^{-bt})(1-e^{-ct})}{t(1-e^{-t})}$ | Re s > Max - Re a, - Re(b+c), - Re b, - Re(a+c) |
| | 9 | $\log\frac{\Gamma(s)\Gamma(s+a+b)\Gamma(s+b+c)\Gamma(s+c+a)}{\Gamma(s+a)\Gamma(s+b)\Gamma(s+c)\Gamma(s+a+b+c)}$ | $\frac{(1-e^{-at})(1-e^{-bt})(1-e^{-ct})}{t(1-e^{-t})}$ | 2 Re s > \|Re a\| + \|Re b\| + \|Re c\| |
| | 10 | $\log\frac{\Gamma(as+b)}{\Gamma(as+c)} + (c-b)\psi(as+d)$ | $\frac{1}{1-e^{-\frac{t}{a}}}\left[\frac{e^{-\frac{bt}{a}}-e^{-\frac{ct}{a}}}{t} + \frac{(b-c)e^{-\frac{dt}{a}}}{a}\right]$ | Re s > Max - Re $\frac{b}{a}$, - Re $\frac{c}{a}$, - Re $\frac{d}{a}$; Re a > o |

| | | $g(s)$ | $f(t)$ | |
|---|---|---|---|---|
| 21.4.1 (Contd.) | 17 | $\psi(\frac{s+1}{2}) - \log\frac{s}{2}$ | $\frac{1}{t} - \operatorname{cosech} t$ | $\operatorname{Re} s > 0$ |
| | 18 | $\log\frac{\Gamma(\frac{s+1}{2})}{\Gamma(\frac{s}{2})} - \frac{1}{2}\psi(\frac{s+1}{2})$ | $\frac{t-e^{t}+1}{2t\sinh t}$ | $\operatorname{Re} s > 0$ |
| | 19 | $\log\frac{\Gamma(\frac{s+1}{2})}{\Gamma(\frac{s}{2})} - \frac{1}{2}\psi(\frac{s-1}{2})$ | $\frac{t-e^{t}+1}{2t\sinh t} + e^{t}$ | $\operatorname{Re} s > 1$ |
| | 20 | $\log\frac{\Gamma(\frac{s}{2})}{\Gamma(\frac{s-1}{2})} - \frac{1}{2}\psi(\frac{s}{2})$ | $\frac{e^{t}(t-2e^{\frac{t}{2}}\cosh\frac{t}{2})}{2t(\cosh t+1)}$ | $\operatorname{Re} s > 1$ |
| | 21 | $\log\frac{\Gamma(1+\frac{s}{2})}{\Gamma(\frac{1+s}{2})} - \frac{1}{2}\psi(\frac{s}{2})$ | $\frac{1-e^{t}+t\,e^{2t}}{t(e^{2t}-1)}$ | $\operatorname{Re} s > 0$ |
| | 22 | $\sum_{n=0}^{\infty}\left[\log(s+n) - \psi(s+n) - \frac{1}{2(s+n)}\right]$ | $\frac{1}{1-e^{-t}}\left(\frac{1}{e^{t}-1} - \frac{1}{t} + \frac{1}{2}\right)$ | $\operatorname{Re} s > 0$ |
| 21.4.3.1 | 1 | $\log\frac{e^{s}\Gamma(s)}{(2\pi)^{\frac{1}{2}}s^{s-\frac{1}{2}}}$ | $\frac{1}{t}\left(\frac{1}{1-e^{-t}} - \frac{1}{t} - \frac{1}{2}\right)$ | $\operatorname{Re} s > 0$ |
| | 2 | $\frac{1}{s}\frac{d}{ds}\log\frac{e^{s}\Gamma(s)}{(2\pi)^{\frac{1}{2}}s^{s-\frac{1}{2}}}$ | $-\log\frac{2\sinh\frac{t}{2}}{t}$ | $\operatorname{Re} s > 0$ |
| 1.9.1 | 1 | $B(s,n+\frac{3}{2})L_n^{s+\frac{1}{2}}(a)$ | $\frac{He_{2n+1}[(2a)^{\frac{1}{2}}(1-e^{-t})^{\frac{1}{2}}]}{(-2)^{n}(2a)^{\frac{1}{2}}n!}$ | $n=0,1,2,\ldots$ <br> $\operatorname{Re} s > 0$ |
| | 2 | $B(s+\frac{1}{2},n+\frac{1}{2})\,L_n^{s}(a)$ | $\frac{He_{2n}[(2a)^{\frac{1}{2}}(1-e^{-t})^{\frac{1}{2}}]}{(-2)^{n}n!(e^{t}-1)^{\frac{1}{2}}}$ | $n=0,1,2,\ldots$ <br> $\operatorname{Re} s > -\frac{1}{2}$ |

| | | g(s) | f(t) | |
|---|---|---|---|---|
| 21.10.3.1 | 1 | $\Gamma(s+\frac{1}{2})(\frac{2}{a})^s J_s(a)$ | $\frac{\cos[a(1-e^{-t})^{\frac{1}{2}}]}{\pi^{\frac{1}{2}}(e^t-1)^{\frac{1}{2}}}$ | $\mathrm{Re}\, s > -\frac{1}{2}$ |
| | 2 | $\Gamma(s)(\frac{2}{a})^s J_{\nu+s}(a)$ | $(1-e^{-t})^{\frac{\nu}{2}} J_\nu[a(1-e^{-t})^{\frac{1}{2}}]$ | $\mathrm{Re}\, \nu > -1$<br>$\mathrm{Re}\, s > 0$ |
| 21.12.3.1 | 1 | $\Gamma(s+\frac{1}{2})(\frac{2}{a})^s I_s(a)$ | $\frac{\cosh[a(1-e^{-t})^{\frac{1}{2}}]}{\pi^{\frac{1}{2}}(e^t-1)^{\frac{1}{2}}}$ | $\mathrm{Re}\, s > -\frac{1}{2}$ |
| 21.13.3.1 | 1 | $(\frac{a}{2})^s \frac{K_s(a)}{\Gamma(s+\frac{1}{2})}$ | $\frac{\cos[a(e^t-1)^{\frac{1}{2}}]}{2\pi^{\frac{1}{2}}(1-e^{-t})^{\frac{1}{2}}}$ | $a > 0$<br>$\mathrm{Re}\, s > -\frac{1}{2}$ |
| | 2 | $\frac{a^s}{\Gamma(s+1)} K_{\nu-s}(2a)$ | $\frac{1}{2}(e^t-1)^{\frac{\nu}{2}} J_\nu[2a(e^t-1)^{\frac{1}{2}}]$ | $a > 0$<br>$\mathrm{Re}\, \nu > -1$<br>$\mathrm{Re}\, s > \frac{1}{2}\mathrm{Re}(\nu-\frac{3}{2}$ |
| 22 | 1 | $\frac{1}{s}\zeta(s)$ | $n \quad \log n < t < \log(n+1)$ | $\mathrm{Re}\, s > 0$<br>$n = 1,2,3,\ldots$ |
| | 2 | $\zeta(\nu, as)$ | $\frac{t^{\nu-1}}{a^\nu \Gamma(\nu)(1-e^{-\frac{t}{a}})}$ | $\mathrm{Re}\, \nu > 1$<br>$\mathrm{Re}\, a > 0$<br>$\mathrm{Re}\, s > 0$ |
| | 3 | $\frac{\zeta'(s)}{s\zeta(s)}$ | $-\psi(e^t)$ | $\mathrm{Re}\, s > 1$ |
| 22.1 | 1 | $\frac{1}{s}\zeta(s+a)$ | $\sum_{1 \leq n \leq e^t} n^{-a}$ | $\mathrm{Re}\, s > -\mathrm{Re}\, a - 1$ |
| | 2 | $\zeta(\nu, \frac{s}{2}+1)$ | $\frac{(2t)^{\nu-1}(\coth t - 1)}{\Gamma(\nu)}$ | $\mathrm{Re}\, \nu > 1$<br>$\mathrm{Re}\, s > -2$ |

| | | $g(s)$ | $f(t)$ | | |
|---|---|---|---|---|---|
| 22.1 (Contd.) | 3 | $\zeta(\nu, \frac{s+1}{2})$ | $\frac{(2t)^{\nu-1} \operatorname{cosech} t}{\Gamma(\nu)}$ | | Re $\nu > 1$<br>Re $s > -1$ |
| | 4 | $\int_0^\infty \zeta(u+1, \frac{s}{a})\, du$ | $\frac{a\,\nu(at)}{1-e^{-at}}$ | | Re $s >$ Re $a$ |
| 22.2 | 1 | $\frac{1}{s^a}\zeta(s)$ | $\frac{1}{\Gamma(a)} \sum_{1 \leq n \leq e^t} (t-\log n)^{a-1}$ | | Re $a > 0$<br>Re $s > 0$ |
| | 2 | $\zeta(\nu, \frac{s}{2}) - \frac{2^{\nu-1}}{s^\nu}$ | $\frac{(2t)^{\nu-1} \coth t}{\Gamma(\nu)}$ | | Re $\nu > 1$<br>Re $s > 0$ |
| 22.3.1 | 1 | $\frac{\zeta(s-1)}{2^s}$ | $\tanh[\frac{\pi}{2}(e^{2t}-1)^{\frac{1}{2}}]$ | | Re $s > 0$ |
| | 2 | $\frac{1}{s}(1-2^{2-s})\zeta(s-1)$ | $n$ | $\log(2n-1) < t < \log(2n+1)$ | Re $s > 0$<br>$n = 1,2,3,\ldots$ |
| 23 | 1 | $P_\nu(s)$ | $-\left(\frac{2}{\pi^3 t}\right)^{\frac{1}{2}} \sin(\nu\pi)\, K_{\nu+\frac{1}{2}}(t)$ | | $-1 <$ Re $\nu < 0$<br>Re $s > -1$ |
| | 2 | $\frac{1}{s} P_\nu(\frac{s}{a})$ | $-\frac{\sin(\nu\pi)\, W_{0,\nu+\frac{1}{2}}(2at)}{a\pi t}$ | | $0 <$ Re $\nu < 1$<br>Re $s > 0$ |
| | 3 | $Q_\nu(\frac{s}{a})$ | $\left(\frac{a\pi}{2t}\right)^{\frac{1}{2}} I_{\nu+\frac{1}{2}}(at)$ | | Re $\nu > -1$<br>Re $s > \|$Re $a\|$ |
| | 4 | $Q_s^\mu(a)$ | $0$ | $0 < t < \cosh^{-1} a$ | Re $\mu < \frac{1}{2}$<br>Re $s > -$ Re$(\mu+1)$ |
| | | | $\frac{\pi^{\frac{1}{2}} [-(a^2-1)^{\frac{1}{2}}]^\mu e^{-\frac{t}{2}}}{2^{\frac{1}{2}} \Gamma(\frac{1}{2}-\mu)(\cosh t - a)^{\mu+\frac{1}{2}}}$ | $t > \cosh^{-1} a$ | |

| | | g(s) | f(t) | |
|---|---|---|---|---|
| 23.1 | 1 | $Q_\nu\left(\frac{s^2+a^2+b^2}{2ab}\right)$ | $\pi a^{\frac{1}{2}} b^{\frac{1}{2}} J_{\nu+\frac{1}{2}}(at)\, J_{\nu+\frac{1}{2}}(bt)$ | $\mathrm{Re}\,\nu > -1$<br>$\mathrm{Re}\,s > \lvert \mathrm{Im}\,a\rvert + \lvert\mathrm{Im}\,b\rvert$ |
| 23.2 | 1 | $\dfrac{P_\nu^{-\mu}(\frac{s}{a})}{(s^2-a^2)^{\frac{\mu}{2}}}$ | $\left(\frac{2a}{\pi}\right)^{\frac{1}{2}} \dfrac{t^{\mu-\frac{1}{2}} K_{\nu+\frac{1}{2}}(at)}{\Gamma(\mu-\nu)\Gamma(\mu+\nu+1)}$ | $\mathrm{Re}(\mu+\nu) > -1$<br>$\mathrm{Re}(\mu-\nu) > 0$<br>$\mathrm{Re}\,s > -\mathrm{Re}\,a$ |
| | 2 | $s^\nu (a^2-s^2)^{\frac{\nu}{2}} P_\nu^\nu(\frac{a}{s})$ | $\dfrac{(\frac{\pi}{2})^{\frac{1}{2}}(\frac{a}{t})^{\nu+\frac{1}{2}}}{\Gamma(-2\nu)}\left[I_{-\nu-\frac{1}{2}}(at) - \mathbf{L}_{-\nu-\frac{1}{2}}(at)\right]$ | $\mathrm{Re}\,\nu < 0$<br>$\mathrm{Re}\,s > \lvert\mathrm{Re}\,a\rvert$ |
| | 3 | $s^{\nu+1}(a^2-s^2)^{\frac{\nu}{2}} P_\nu^\nu(\frac{a}{s})$ | $\dfrac{\pi^{\frac{1}{2}} a}{\Gamma(-2\nu)2^{\frac{1}{2}}}(\frac{a}{t})^{\nu+\frac{1}{2}}\left[I_{-\nu-\frac{3}{2}}(at) - \mathbf{L}_{-\nu-\frac{3}{2}}(at)\right]$ | $\mathrm{Re}\,\nu < -\frac{1}{2}$<br>$\mathrm{Re}\,s > \lvert\mathrm{Re}\,a\rvert$ |
| | 4 | $\left(\frac{s^2}{a^2-s^2}\right)^{\frac{\nu}{2}} P_\nu^\nu(\frac{a}{s}) - \dfrac{\Gamma(-\nu)(s^2-a^2)^\nu}{\Gamma(-2\nu)2^{\nu+1}}$ | $-(\frac{\pi}{2})^{\frac{1}{2}}(\frac{a}{t})^{\nu+\frac{1}{2}} \dfrac{\mathbf{L}_{-\nu-\frac{1}{2}}(at)}{\Gamma(-2\nu)}$ | $\mathrm{Re}\,\nu < 0$<br>$\mathrm{Re}\,s > \lvert\mathrm{Re}\,a\rvert$ |
| | 5 | $\dfrac{(s-a)^{\frac{\mu}{2}}}{s^{\frac{\nu+1}{2}}} P_\nu^\mu\left(\frac{a^{\frac{1}{2}}}{s^{\frac{1}{2}}}\right)$ | $\dfrac{t^{\frac{\nu-\mu-1}{2}} e^{\frac{at}{2}} D_{\mu+\nu}(2^{\frac{1}{2}} a^{\frac{1}{2}} t^{\frac{1}{2}})}{\pi^{\frac{1}{2}} 2^{\frac{\mu-\nu}{2}}\,\Gamma(\nu-\mu+1)}$ | $\mathrm{Re}\,\mu < 1$<br>$\mathrm{Re}(\nu-\mu) > -1$<br>$\mathrm{Re}\,s > 0$ |
| | 6 | $\dfrac{P_\mu^{-\nu}\left[\frac{s}{(s^2+a^2)^{\frac{1}{2}}}\right]}{(s^2+a^2)^{\frac{\mu+1}{2}}}$ | $\dfrac{t^\mu J_\nu(at)}{\Gamma(\mu+\nu+1)}$ | $\mathrm{Re}(\mu+\nu) > -1$<br>$\mathrm{Re}\,s > \lvert\mathrm{Im}\,a\rvert$ |
| | 7 | $\dfrac{P_\mu^{-\nu}\left[\frac{s}{(s^2-a^2)^{\frac{1}{2}}}\right]}{(s^2-a^2)^{\frac{\mu+1}{2}}}$ | $\dfrac{t^\mu I_\nu(at)}{\Gamma(\mu+\nu+1)}$ | $\mathrm{Re}(\mu+\nu) > -1$<br>$\mathrm{Re}\,s > \lvert\mathrm{Re}\,a\rvert$ |
| | 8 | $\dfrac{1}{s^{\frac{1}{2}}}\left\{P_{-\frac{1}{4}}^{-\nu}\left[\frac{(s^2+a^2)^{\frac{1}{2}}}{s}\right]\right\}^2$ | $\dfrac{2^{\nu+\frac{1}{2}}}{\Gamma(2\nu+\frac{1}{2})t^{\frac{1}{2}}} J_\nu^2(\frac{at}{2})$ | $\mathrm{Re}\,\nu > -\frac{1}{4}$<br>$\mathrm{Re}\,s > \lvert\mathrm{Im}\,a\rvert$ |

| | | g(s) | f(t) | |
|---|---|---|---|---|
| 23.2 (Contd.) | 9 | $\frac{1}{s^{\frac{1}{2}}} P^{\nu}_{-\frac{1}{4}}\left[\left(1+\frac{a^2}{s^2}\right)^{\frac{1}{2}}\right] P^{-\nu}_{-\frac{1}{4}}\left[\left(1+\frac{a^2}{s^2}\right)^{\frac{1}{2}}\right]$ | $\left(\frac{2}{\pi t}\right)^{\frac{1}{2}} J_{\nu}\left(\frac{at}{2}\right) J_{-\nu}\left(\frac{at}{2}\right)$ | Re s > \|Im a\| |
| | 10 | $\dfrac{P^{-\nu}_{\frac{1}{4}}\left[\frac{(s^2+a^2)^{\frac{1}{2}}}{s}\right] P^{-\nu}_{-\frac{1}{4}}\left[\frac{(s^2+a^2)^{\frac{1}{2}}}{s}\right]}{s^{\frac{1}{2}}(s^2+a^2)^{\frac{1}{2}}}$ | $\frac{2^{\nu+\frac{3}{2}}}{a\Gamma(2\nu+\frac{3}{2})} t^{\frac{1}{2}} J^2_{\nu}\left(\frac{at}{2}\right)$ | Re $\nu$ > $-\frac{3}{4}$<br>Re s > \|Im a\| |
| | 11 | $\dfrac{P^{-\nu}_{-\frac{1}{4}}\left[\left(1+\frac{a^2}{s^2}\right)^{\frac{1}{2}}\right] P^{-\nu-1}_{-\frac{1}{4}}\left[\left(1+\frac{a^2}{s^2}\right)^{\frac{1}{2}}\right]}{s^{\frac{1}{2}}(s^2+a^2)^{\frac{1}{2}}}$ | $\frac{2^{\nu+\frac{5}{2}}}{a\Gamma(2\nu+\frac{5}{2})} t^{\frac{1}{2}} J_{\nu}\left(\frac{at}{2}\right) J_{\nu+1}\left(\frac{at}{2}\right)$ | Re $\nu$ > $-\frac{5}{4}$<br>Re s > \|Im a\| |
| | 12 | $(s^2+a^2)^{-\frac{\mu+1}{2}}\left\{\Gamma(\mu+\nu+1)\cot(\nu\pi)\, P^{-\nu}_{\mu}\left[\left(\frac{s^2}{s^2+a^2}\right)^{\frac{1}{2}}\right] - \Gamma(\mu-\nu+1)\operatorname{cosec}(\nu\pi)\, P^{\nu}_{\mu}\left[\left(\frac{s^2}{s^2+a^2}\right)^{\frac{1}{2}}\right]\right\}$ | $t^{\mu} Y_{\nu}(at)$ | Re$(\mu\pm\nu)$ > − 1<br>Re s > \|Im a\| |
| | 13 | $s^{-\frac{1}{2}}(s^2+a^2)^{-\frac{1}{2}}\left\{(\nu+\frac{1}{4}) P^{\nu}_{-\frac{1}{4}}\left[\left(1+\frac{a^2}{s^2}\right)^{\frac{1}{2}}\right] P^{-\nu}_{\frac{1}{4}}\left[\left(1+\frac{a^2}{s^2}\right)^{\frac{1}{2}}\right] - (\nu-\frac{1}{4}) P^{\nu}_{\frac{1}{4}}\left[\left(1+\frac{a^2}{s^2}\right)^{\frac{1}{2}}\right] P^{-\nu}_{-\frac{1}{4}}\left[\left(1+\frac{a^2}{s^2}\right)^{\frac{1}{2}}\right]\right\}$ | $\frac{2}{a\pi^{\frac{1}{2}}} t^{\frac{1}{2}} J_{\nu}\left(\frac{at}{2}\right) J_{-\nu}\left(\frac{at}{2}\right)$ | Re s > \|Im a\| |
| | 14 | $\dfrac{Q^{\mu}_{\nu}(\frac{s}{a})}{(s^2-a^2)^{\frac{\mu}{2}}}$ | $\left(\frac{\pi a}{2}\right)^{\frac{1}{2}} \frac{\sin[(\mu+\nu)\pi]}{\sin(\nu\pi)} t^{\mu-\frac{1}{2}} I_{\nu+\frac{1}{2}}(at)$ | Re$(\mu+\nu)$ > − 1<br>Re s > \|Re a\| |
| | 15 | $\frac{1}{s^{\mu}} Q_{\nu}[(\frac{s}{a})^{\frac{1}{2}}]$ | $\frac{a^{\frac{\nu+1}{2}} \pi^{\frac{1}{2}} \Gamma(\nu+1) t^{\mu+\frac{\nu-1}{2}}}{2^{\nu+1}\Gamma(\nu+\frac{3}{2})\Gamma(\mu+\frac{\nu+1}{2})}\, {}_2F_2\left[\begin{matrix}\frac{\nu+1}{2}, \frac{\nu}{2}+1 ; \\ \nu+\frac{3}{2}, \mu+\frac{\nu+1}{2} ;\end{matrix} at\right]$ | Re$(\mu+\frac{\nu}{2})$ > $-\frac{1}{2}$<br>Re s > 0 |
| | 16 | $\dfrac{Q^{\nu}_{\mu}\left[\frac{s}{(s^2-a^2)^{\frac{1}{2}}}\right]}{(s^2-a^2)^{\frac{\mu+1}{2}}}$ | $\frac{\sin[(\mu+\nu)\pi]}{\sin(\mu\pi)\Gamma(\mu-\nu+1)} t^{\mu} K_{\nu}(at)$ | Re$(\mu\pm\nu)$ > − 1<br>Re s > − Re a |

| | | g(s) | f(t) | |
|---|---|---|---|---|
| 23.2.1 | 1 | $\dfrac{P^{1}_{2n+1}\left[\left(\dfrac{s-a}{s+a}\right)^{\frac{1}{2}}\right]}{(s+a)^{n+1}}$ | $\dfrac{(-1)^{n+1}}{(a\pi)^{\frac{1}{2}}}\ \dfrac{(n+1)!\,2^{2n+\frac{1}{2}}}{(2n)!}\,t^{n-\frac{1}{2}}\,k_{2n+2}(at)$ | $n=0,1,2,\ldots$<br>$\operatorname{Re} s>0$ |
| | 2 | $e^{as}\,Q^{\mu}_{s-\frac{1}{2}}(\cosh a)$ | $\dfrac{\pi^{\frac{1}{2}}\,e^{\mu\pi i}\sinh^{\mu}a}{\Gamma(\frac{1}{2}-\mu)\,2^{\mu+1}\left[\sinh\frac{t}{2}\,\sinh(a+\frac{t}{2})\right]^{\mu+\frac{1}{2}}}$ | $\operatorname{Re}\mu<\frac{1}{2}$<br>$\lvert\arg a\rvert<\pi$<br>$\operatorname{Re} s>-\operatorname{Re}\mu-\frac{1}{2}$ |
| 23.8.7 | 1 | $\dfrac{Q^{\mu}_{\nu}(s)}{\sinh^{\mu}(\cosh^{-1}s)}$ | $\left(\frac{\pi}{2}\right)^{\frac{1}{2}}\dfrac{\sin(\mu+\nu)\pi}{\sin(\nu\pi)}\,t^{\mu-\frac{1}{2}}\,I_{\nu+\frac{1}{2}}(t)$ | $\operatorname{Re}(\mu+\nu)>-1$<br>$\operatorname{Re} s>1$ |
| 23.21.3.1 | 1 | $2^{s+\frac{1}{2}}\Gamma(s)(\mu^2-1)^{\frac{1}{4}-\frac{s}{2}}P^{\frac{1}{2}-s}_{a+s-\frac{1}{2}}(\mu)$ | $\dfrac{[\mu+(\mu^2-1)^{\frac{1}{2}}(1-e^{-t})^{\frac{1}{2}}]^{a}+[\mu-(\mu^2-1)^{\frac{1}{2}}(1-e^{-t})^{\frac{1}{2}}]^{a}}{\pi^{\frac{1}{2}}(1-e^{-t})^{\frac{1}{2}}}$ | $\operatorname{Re} s>0$ |
| | 2 | $\dfrac{\Gamma(s-\mu+\nu+1)\Gamma(s-\mu-\nu)}{\Gamma(s+1)}\left(\dfrac{a}{a-2}\right)^{\frac{s}{2}}P^{\mu-s}_{\nu}(a-1)$ | $\left[(e^{t}-1)\left(\dfrac{a}{a-2}e^{t}-1\right)\right]^{\frac{\mu}{2}}P^{-\mu}_{\nu}(ae^{t}+1-a)$ | $\operatorname{Re} a>0$<br>$\operatorname{Re}\mu>-1$<br>$\operatorname{Re} s>\operatorname{Max}\operatorname{Re}(\mu+\nu),$<br>$\operatorname{Re}(\mu-\nu-1)$ |
| | 3 | $\dfrac{\Gamma(s)e^{-\frac{as}{2}}}{2^{\frac{s}{2}}\Gamma(\frac{s+\nu+1}{2})}P^{-\frac{s+\nu}{2}}_{\frac{\nu-s}{2}}[(1-e^{-2a})^{\frac{1}{2}}]$ | $0$, $\quad 0<t<a$<br>$\dfrac{2^{\frac{\nu}{2}}e^{\frac{a\nu}{2}}}{\pi^{\frac{1}{2}}\Gamma(\nu+1)}\ \dfrac{[e^{-a}(1-e^{-2t})^{\frac{1}{2}}-e^{-t}(1-e^{-2a})^{\frac{1}{2}}]^{\nu}}{(1-e^{-2t})^{\frac{1}{2}}}$, $\quad t>a$ | $\operatorname{Re}\nu>-1$<br>$a>0$<br>$\operatorname{Re} s>0$ |
| | 4 | $2^{s}e^{s\pi i}\Gamma(s)(a^2-1)^{\frac{s}{2}}Q^{\nu-s}_{s-1}(a)$ | $\Gamma(\nu)e^{\nu\pi i}(a^2-1)^{\frac{\nu}{2}}\dfrac{[a+(1-e^{-t})^{\frac{1}{2}}]^{-\nu}+[a-(1-e^{-t})^{\frac{1}{2}}]^{-\nu}}{2(1-e^{-t})^{\frac{1}{2}}}$ | $\operatorname{Re} s>0$ |
| 25.2 | 1 | $s^{\nu}H_{\nu}(\frac{a}{s})$ | $\dfrac{2^{\nu+\frac{3}{2}}\pi^{\frac{1}{2}}}{t^{\nu+1}}\,S_1\left(\frac{\nu}{2},\frac{\nu-1}{2},\frac{-\nu-1}{2},\frac{\nu+1}{2};\frac{at}{4}\right)$ | $\operatorname{Re} s>0$ |

| | | g(s) | f(t) | |
|---|---|---|---|---|
| 25.2 (Contd.) | 2 | $s^{\nu-1} H_\nu(\frac{a}{s})$ | $\frac{2^{\nu+\frac{1}{2}}\pi^{\frac{1}{2}}}{t^\nu} S_1(\frac{\nu}{2}, \frac{\nu-1}{2}, \frac{-\nu-1}{2}, \frac{\nu-1}{2}; \frac{at}{4})$ | Re s > 0 |
| | 3 | $\frac{H_\nu(\frac{a}{s})}{s^\mu}$ | $\frac{a^{\nu+1} t^{\mu+\nu}}{\pi^{\frac{1}{2}} 2^\nu \Gamma(\nu+\frac{3}{2})\Gamma(\mu+\nu+1)}\, {}_1F_4\left[\begin{matrix} 1; \\ \frac{3}{2}, \nu+\frac{3}{2}, \frac{\mu+\nu+1}{2}, \frac{\mu+\nu}{2}+1; \end{matrix} -\frac{a^2t^2}{16}\right]$ | $Re(\mu+\nu) > -1$<br>Re s > 0 |
| | 4 | $\frac{L_\nu(\frac{a}{s})}{s^\mu}$ | $\frac{a^{\nu+1} t^{\mu+\nu}}{\pi^{\frac{1}{2}} 2^\nu \Gamma(\nu+\frac{3}{2})\Gamma(\mu+\nu+1)}\, {}_1F_4\left[\begin{matrix} 1; \\ \frac{3}{2}, \nu+\frac{3}{2}, \frac{\mu+\nu+1}{2}, \frac{\mu+\nu}{2}+1; \end{matrix} \frac{a^2t^2}{16}\right]$ | $Re(\mu+\nu) > -1$<br>Re s > 0 |
| 25.3.2 | 1 | $\frac{e^{-as} L_\nu(as)}{s^\nu}$ | $\frac{(2at-t^2)^{\nu-\frac{1}{2}}}{\pi^{\frac{1}{2}}(2a)^\nu \Gamma(\nu+\frac{1}{2})}$   $0 < t < a$<br>$-\frac{(2at-t^2)^{\nu-\frac{1}{2}}}{\pi^{\frac{1}{2}}(2a)^\nu \Gamma(\nu+\frac{1}{2})}$   $a < t < 2a$<br>$0$   $t > 2a$ | $Re\,\nu > -\frac{1}{2}$<br>$Re\, s > -\infty$<br>$a > 0$ |
| 25.7.2 | 1 | $\frac{L_\nu(as)}{s^\nu \sinh(as)}$ | $\frac{1}{\pi}(\frac{2}{a})^\nu \frac{\Gamma(\nu)}{\Gamma(2\nu)}\left[2a(t-2na)-(t-2na)^2\right]^{\nu-\frac{1}{2}}$   $2na < t < (2n+1)a$<br>$-\frac{1}{\pi}(\frac{2}{a})^\nu \frac{\Gamma(\nu)}{\Gamma(2\nu)}\left[2a(t-2na)-(t-2na)^2\right]^{\nu-\frac{1}{2}}$   $(2n+1)a < t < (2n+2)a$ | $a > 0$<br>$Re\,\nu > -\frac{1}{2}$<br>Re s > 0<br>$n = 0, 1, 2, \ldots$ |
| 25.10 | 1 | $\frac{\pi}{2}[H_1(as) - Y_1(as)] - 1$ | $\frac{t}{a(t^2+a^2)^{\frac{1}{2}}}$ | $\lvert \arg a \rvert < \frac{\pi}{2}$<br>Re s > 0 |
| | 2 | $\frac{1}{s}[H_0(as) - Y_0(as)]$ | $\frac{4}{\pi} \log \frac{(t+ia)^{\frac{1}{2}} + (t-ia)^{\frac{1}{2}}}{(2a)^{\frac{1}{2}}} = \frac{2}{\pi} \sinh^{-1} \frac{t}{a}$ | $a > 0$<br>Re s > 0 |
| | 3 | $H_0(s) - Y_0(s)$ | $\frac{2}{\pi(t^2+1)^{\frac{1}{2}}}$ | Re s > 0 |

| | | g(s) | f(t) | |
|---|---|---|---|---|
| 25.10.1 | 1 | $\frac{1}{s}[H_1(as)-Y_1(as)]-\frac{2}{\pi a s^2}$ | $\frac{2}{\pi a}[(t^2+a^2)^{\frac{1}{2}}-t]$ | $\lvert\arg a\rvert<\frac{\pi}{2}$ <br> $\mathrm{Re}\, s>0$ |
| | 2 | $\frac{1}{s^2}[H_0(s)-Y_0(s)+sH_1(s)-sY_1(s)]-\frac{2}{\pi s}$ | $\frac{2}{\pi}t\sinh^{-1}t$ | $\mathrm{Re}\, s>0$ |
| 25.10.2 | 1 | $\frac{1}{s^{\frac{1}{2}}}[H_0(as^{\frac{1}{2}})-Y_0(as^{\frac{1}{2}})]$ | $\frac{2e^{\frac{a^2}{8t}}}{\pi^{\frac{3}{2}}t^{\frac{1}{2}}}K_0\left(\frac{a^2}{8t}\right)$ | $\mathrm{Re}\, s>0$ |
| | 2 | $Y_{-1}(as^{\frac{1}{2}})-H_{-1}(as^{\frac{1}{2}})$ | $\frac{a e^{\frac{a^2}{8t}}}{4(\pi t)^{\frac{3}{2}}}[K_1(\frac{a^2}{8t})-K_0(\frac{a^2}{8t})]$ | $\mathrm{Re}\, s>0$ |
| | 3 | $s^{\nu-1}[H_\nu(\frac{a}{s})-Y_\nu(\frac{a}{s})]$ | $\frac{\cos(\nu\pi)}{\pi^{\frac{3}{2}}}(\frac{2}{t})^\nu S_3(\frac{\nu}{2},\frac{\nu-1}{2},\frac{-\nu-1}{2},\frac{\nu-1}{2};\frac{at}{4})$ | $\mathrm{Re}\,\nu<1$ <br> $\mathrm{Re}\, s>0$ |
| | 4 | $\frac{1}{s^{\frac{\nu}{2}}}[H_{-\nu}(as^{\frac{1}{2}})-Y_{-\nu}(as^{\frac{1}{2}})]$ | $\frac{2^\nu\cos(\nu\pi)}{\pi a^\nu}t^{\nu-1}e^{\frac{a^2}{4t}}\mathrm{Erfc}\left(\frac{a}{2t^{\frac{1}{2}}}\right)$ | $\mathrm{Re}\,\nu>-\frac{1}{2}$ <br> $\mathrm{Re}\, s>0$ |
| | 5 | $\frac{1}{s^\nu}[H_\nu(as)-Y_\nu(as)]$ | $\frac{(t^2+a^2)^{\nu-\frac{1}{2}}}{2^{\nu-1}\pi^{\frac{1}{2}}a^\nu\Gamma(\nu+\frac{1}{2})}$ | $-\frac{3}{2}<\mathrm{Re}\,\nu<\frac{1}{2}$ <br> $\mathrm{Re}\, s>0$ <br> $\mathrm{Re}\, a>0$ |
| | 6 | $\frac{1}{s^{\frac{\nu+1}{2}}}[H_\nu(as^{\frac{1}{2}})-Y_\nu(as^{\frac{1}{2}})]$ | $\frac{2e^{\frac{a^2}{8t}}W_{\frac{\nu}{2},\frac{\nu}{2}}\left(\frac{a^2}{4t}\right)}{a\pi^{\frac{1}{2}}\Gamma(\nu+\frac{1}{2})t^{\frac{\nu}{2}}}$ | $-2<\mathrm{Re}\,\nu<\frac{1}{2}$ <br> $\mathrm{Re}\, s>0$ |
| 25.10.2.1 | 1 | $s^{\frac{1}{2}}[H_{\frac{1}{4}}(\frac{s^2}{a})-Y_{\frac{1}{4}}(\frac{s^2}{a})]$ | $\frac{a}{\pi^{\frac{1}{2}}}t^{\frac{1}{2}}J_{-\frac{1}{4}}(\frac{at^2}{4})$ | $a>0$ <br> $\mathrm{Re}\, s>0$ |
| | 2 | $s^{\frac{1}{2}}[H_{-\frac{1}{4}}(\frac{s^2}{a})-Y_{-\frac{1}{4}}(\frac{s^2}{a})]$ | $\frac{a}{\pi^{\frac{1}{2}}}t^{\frac{1}{2}}J_{\frac{1}{4}}(\frac{at^2}{4})$ | $a>0$ <br> $\mathrm{Re}\, s>0$ |

| | | $g(s)$ | $f(t)$ | | |
|---|---|---|---|---|---|
| 25.10.2.1 (Contd.) | 3 | $s^{\frac{3}{2}}[H_{-\frac{1}{4}}(\frac{s^2}{a})-Y_{-\frac{1}{4}}(\frac{s^2}{a})]$ | $\frac{a^2}{2\pi^{\frac{1}{2}}}t^{\frac{3}{2}}J_{-\frac{3}{4}}(\frac{at^2}{4})$ | | $a>0$<br>$Re\, s>0$ |
| | 4 | $s^{\frac{3}{2}}[H_{-\frac{3}{4}}(\frac{s^2}{a})-Y_{-\frac{3}{4}}(\frac{s^2}{a})]$ | $-\frac{a^2}{2\pi^{\frac{1}{2}}}t^{\frac{3}{2}}J_{-\frac{1}{4}}(\frac{at^2}{4})$ | | $a>0$<br>$Re\, s>0$ |
| 25.12 | 1 | $I_0(as)-L_0(as)$ | $\frac{2}{\pi(a^2-t^2)^{\frac{1}{2}}}$<br>$0$ | $0<t<a$<br>$t>a$ | $a>0$<br>$Re\, s>-\infty$ |
| | 2 | $\frac{1}{s}[I_0(as)-L_0(as)]$ | $\frac{2}{\pi}\sin^{-1}\frac{t}{a}$<br>$0$ | $0<t<a$<br>$t>a$ | $a>0$<br>$Re\, s>-\infty$ |
| | 3 | $\frac{\pi}{2}[L_1(as)-I_1(as)]+1$ | $\frac{t}{a(a^2-t^2)^{\frac{1}{2}}}$<br>$0$ | $0<t<a$<br>$t>a$ | $a>0$<br>$Re\, s>-\infty$ |
| 25.12.1 | 1 | $\frac{1}{s^2}[L_0(as)-I_0(as)+as\, L_1(as)-as\, I_1(as)]+\frac{2a}{\pi s}$ | $\frac{2}{\pi}t\sin^{-1}\frac{t}{a}$<br>$0$ | $0<t<a$<br>$t>a$ | $Re\, s>-\infty$ |
| 25.12.2 | 1 | $\frac{1}{s^{\frac{1}{2}}}[I_0(as^{\frac{1}{2}})-L_0(as^{\frac{1}{2}})]$ | $\frac{e^{-\frac{a^2}{8t}}I_0(\frac{a^2}{8t})}{(\pi t)^{\frac{1}{2}}}$ | | $Re\, a>0$<br>$Re\, s>0$ |
| | 2 | $\frac{1}{s^{\frac{1}{2}}}[I_{\frac{1}{2}}(as^{\frac{1}{2}})-L_{\frac{1}{2}}(as^{\frac{1}{2}})]$ | $\frac{e^{-\frac{a^2}{8t}}}{a(2\pi t)^{\frac{1}{2}}}[I_{\frac{1}{4}}(\frac{a^2}{8t})-I_{-\frac{1}{4}}(\frac{a^2}{8t})]+\frac{\Gamma(\frac{1}{4})}{a^{\frac{1}{2}}\pi^{\frac{3}{2}}t^{\frac{1}{4}}}$ | | $Re\, s>0$ |

| | | $g(s)$ | $f(t)$ | | |
|---|---|---|---|---|---|
| 25.12.2 (Contd.) | 3 | $\frac{1}{s^{\nu}}[I_{\nu}(as)-L_{\nu}(as)]$ | $\frac{(a^2-t^2)^{\nu-\frac{1}{2}}}{2^{\nu-1}\pi^{\frac{1}{2}}a^{\nu}\Gamma(\nu+\frac{1}{2})}$ | $0<t<a$ | $Re\,\nu>-\frac{1}{2}$ |
| | | | $0$ | $t>a$ | $a>0$ <br> $Re\,s>-\infty$ |
| | 4 | $s^{\nu-1}[I_{\nu}(\frac{a}{s})-L_{\nu}(\frac{a}{s})]$ | $\frac{1}{\pi^{\frac{1}{2}}}(\frac{2}{t})^{\nu}S_2(\frac{\nu}{2},\frac{\nu-1}{2},\frac{-\nu-1}{2},\frac{\nu-1}{2};\frac{at}{4})$ | | $Re\,s>0$ |
| | 5 | $s^{\nu}[I_{-\nu}(\frac{a}{s})-L_{\nu}(\frac{a}{s})]$ | $\frac{\cos(\nu\pi)}{\pi^{\frac{1}{2}}}(\frac{2}{t})^{\nu+1}S_2(\frac{\nu}{2},\frac{-\nu-1}{2},\frac{\nu-1}{2},\frac{\nu+1}{2};\frac{at}{4})$ | | $Re\,\nu<0$ <br> $Re\,s>0$ |
| | 6 | $s^{\nu-1}[I_{-\nu}(\frac{a}{s})-L_{\nu}(\frac{a}{s})]$ | $\frac{\cos(\nu\pi)}{\pi^{\frac{1}{2}}}(\frac{2}{t})^{\nu}S_2(\frac{\nu}{2},\frac{-\nu-1}{2},\frac{\nu-1}{2},\frac{\nu-1}{2};\frac{at}{4})$ | | $Re\,\nu<1$ <br> $Re\,s>0$ |
| | 7 | $\frac{1}{s^{\frac{\nu}{2}}}[L_{-\nu}(as^{\frac{1}{2}})-I_{\nu}(as^{\frac{1}{2}})]$ | $\frac{i\,2^{\nu}\cos(\nu\pi)}{\pi a^{\nu}}t^{\nu-1}e^{\frac{a^2}{4t}}\,\mathrm{Erf}\left(\frac{ia}{2t^{\frac{1}{2}}}\right)$ | | $Re\,\nu>-\frac{1}{2}$ <br> $Re\,s>0$ |
| 25.12.7.2 | 1 | $\frac{1}{s^{\nu}}\,\mathrm{cosech}\,\frac{s}{2}[I_{\nu}(s)-L_{\nu}(s)]$ | $0$ | $0<t<\frac{1}{2}$ | $Re\,\nu>-\frac{1}{2}$ <br> $Re\,s>0$ |
| | | | $\frac{4[\frac{3}{4}+t-n-(t-n)^2]^{\nu-\frac{1}{2}}}{\pi^{\frac{1}{2}}\Gamma(\nu+\frac{1}{2})}$ | $n+\frac{1}{2}<t<n+\frac{3}{2}$ | $n=0,1,2,\ldots$ |
| 25.21.3.1 | 1 | $\Gamma(s+\frac{1}{2})(\frac{2}{a})^{s}H_{s}(a)$ | $\frac{\sin[a(1-e^{-t})^{\frac{1}{2}}]}{\pi^{\frac{1}{2}}(e^{t}-1)^{\frac{1}{2}}}$ | | $Re\,s>-\frac{1}{2}$ |
| | 2 | $\Gamma(s+\frac{1}{2})(\frac{2}{a})^{s}L_{s}(a)$ | $\frac{\sinh[a(1-e^{-t})^{\frac{1}{2}}]}{\pi^{\frac{1}{2}}(e^{t}-1)^{\frac{1}{2}}}$ | | $Re\,s>-\frac{1}{2}$ |
| 25.21.12.3.1 | 1 | $\Gamma(\frac{1}{2}-s)(\frac{a}{2})^{s}[I_{s}(a)-L_{-s}(a)]$ | $\frac{\sin[a(e^{t}-1)^{\frac{1}{2}}]}{\pi^{\frac{1}{2}}(1-e^{-t})^{\frac{1}{2}}}$ | | $a>0$ <br> $Re\,s>-\frac{1}{2}$ |

| | | $g(s)$ | $f(t)$ | |
|---|---|---|---|---|
| 26.10 | 1 | $E_\nu(\frac{s}{a}) + Y_\nu(\frac{s}{a})$ | $-\frac{a}{(a^2t^2+1)^{\frac{1}{2}}}\left\{\left[a^2t^2+1)^{\frac{1}{2}}+at\right]^\nu + \cos(\nu\pi)\left[(a^2t^2+1)^{\frac{1}{2}}-at\right]^\nu\right\}$ | Re $s > 0$ |
| | 2 | $J_\nu(s) - J_\nu(s)$ | $\frac{\sin(\nu\pi)}{\pi}\frac{e^{-\nu\sinh^{-1}t}}{(1+t^2)^{\frac{1}{2}}} = \frac{\sin(\nu\pi)}{\pi}\frac{[(t^2+1)^{\frac{1}{2}}-t]^\nu}{(1+t^2)^{\frac{1}{2}}}$ | Re $s > 0$ |
| 26.10.5 | 1 | $\operatorname{cosec}(\pi s)\,[J_s(a) - J_s(a)]$ | $\frac{1}{\pi}e^{-a\sinh t}$ | Re $a \geq 0$<br>Re $s > -\infty$ |
| 26.10.9 | 1 | $S_n(s) - \pi E_n(s) - \pi Y_n(s)$ | $\frac{2e^{n\sinh^{-1}t}}{(1+t^2)^{\frac{1}{2}}} = \frac{2[t+(1+t^2)^{\frac{1}{2}}]^n}{(1+t^2)^{\frac{1}{2}}}$ | $n = 0,1,2,\ldots$<br>Re $s > 0$ |
| | 2 | $S_n(s) + \pi E_n(s) + \pi Y_n(s)$ | $\frac{2(-1)^{n+1}e^{-n\sinh^{-1}t}}{(1+t^2)^{\frac{1}{2}}} = \frac{2(-1)^{n+1}[(1+t^2)^{\frac{1}{2}}-t]^n}{(1+t^2)^{\frac{1}{2}}}$ | $n = 0,1,2,\ldots$<br>Re $s > 0$ |
| 27 | 1 | $D_{-1}\left[(\frac{i}{2})^{\frac{1}{2}}s\right]D_{-1}\left[\frac{s}{(2i)^{\frac{1}{2}}}\right]$ | $\frac{2\sin t^2}{t}$ | Re $s > 0$ |
| | 2 | $D_{-\nu}(s)\,D_{-\nu}(-s)$ | $\frac{(-1)^{\nu-1}\pi^{\frac{1}{2}}}{\Gamma(\nu)}I_{\nu-\frac{1}{2}}(\frac{t^2}{2})$ | Re $\nu > 0$<br>Re $s > 0$ |

| | | g(s) | f(t) | |
|---|---|---|---|---|
| 27 (Contd.) | 3 | $D_{-\nu}\left(\frac{s}{a}e^{\frac{\pi i}{4}}\right)D_{-\nu}\left(\frac{s}{a}e^{-\frac{\pi i}{4}}\right)$ | $\frac{\pi^{\frac{1}{2}}a}{\Gamma(\nu)}J_{\nu-\frac{1}{2}}\left(\frac{a^2t^2}{2}\right)$ | $Re\ \nu > 0$<br>$Re\ s > 0$ |
| 27.2 | 1 | $D_\nu[(2is)^{\frac{1}{2}}]\,D_\nu[(-2is)^{\frac{1}{2}}]$ | $\frac{[1+(t^2+1)^{\frac{1}{2}}]^{\nu+\frac{1}{2}}}{2^{\frac{1}{2}}\Gamma(-\nu)t^{\nu+1}(t^2+1)^{\frac{1}{2}}}$ | $Re\ \nu < 0$<br>$Re\ s \geqslant 0$ |
| | 2 | $D_{-\nu}(2^{\frac{1}{2}}s^{\frac{1}{2}}e^{\frac{\pi i}{4}})\,D_{-\nu}(2^{\frac{1}{2}}s^{\frac{1}{2}}e^{-\frac{\pi i}{4}})$ | $\frac{t^{\nu-1}[1+(1+t^2)^{\frac{1}{2}}]^{\frac{1}{2}-\nu}}{2^{\frac{1}{2}}\Gamma(\nu)(1+t^2)^{\frac{1}{2}}}$ | $Re\ \nu > 0$<br>$Re\ s > 0$ |
| | 3 | $\frac{1}{s^{\frac{1}{2}}}D_{-\nu}(as^{\frac{1}{2}})$ | $0 \qquad 0 < t < \frac{a^2}{4}$<br>$\frac{(t-\frac{a^2}{4})^{\frac{\nu-1}{2}}}{2^{\frac{\nu}{2}}\Gamma(\frac{\nu+1}{2})(t+\frac{a^2}{4})^{\frac{\nu}{2}}} \qquad t > \frac{a^2}{4}$ | $a > 0$<br>$Re\ \nu > -1$<br>$Re\ s > 0$ |
| | 4 | $D_{-\nu}(as^{\frac{1}{2}})$ | $0 \qquad 0 < t < \frac{a^2}{4}$<br>$\frac{a(t-\frac{a^2}{4})^{\frac{\nu}{2}-1}}{2^{\frac{\nu+1}{2}}\Gamma(\frac{\nu}{2})(t+\frac{a^2}{4})^{\frac{\nu+1}{2}}} \qquad t > \frac{a^2}{4}$ | $Re\ \nu > 0$<br>$Re\ a > 0$<br>$Re\ s > 0$ |
| 27.3.1 | 1 | $\frac{1}{s}e^{\frac{a^2s^2}{4}}D_{-\nu}(as)$ | $\frac{2^{\frac{\nu}{2}+1}}{\Gamma(\nu)}\gamma\left(\frac{\nu}{2},\frac{t^2}{2a^2}\right)$ | $Re\ \nu > 0$<br>$\lvert\arg a\rvert < \frac{\pi}{4}$<br>$Re\ s > 0$ |
| | 2 | $e^{\frac{a^2s^2}{4}}D_{-\nu}(as)$ | $\frac{t^{\nu-1}e^{-\frac{t^2}{2a^2}}}{\Gamma(\nu)a^\nu}$ | $Re\ s > \begin{cases} -\infty \text{ for } \lvert\arg a\rvert < \frac{\pi}{4}, \frac{3\pi}{4} < \arg a < \frac{5\pi}{4} \\ 0 \text{ for } \arg a = \frac{\pi}{4}, \frac{3\pi}{4}, \frac{5\pi}{4}, \frac{7\pi}{4} \\ \infty \text{ otherwise} \end{cases}$<br>$Re\ \nu > 0$ |

| | | g(s) | f(t) | |
|---|---|---|---|---|
| 27.3.1 (Contd.) | 3 | $s^n e^{\frac{s^2}{4}} D_{-n-1}(s)$ | $\frac{d^n}{dt^n}\left(e^{-\frac{t^2}{2}} \frac{t^n}{n!}\right)$ | $n=0,1,2,\ldots$<br>$\mathrm{Re}\, s > -\infty$ |
| | 4 | $e^{\frac{s^2}{4a^2}} D_{-\mu}(\frac{s}{a})\, D_{-\nu}(\frac{s}{a})$ | $\frac{a^{\mu+\nu}}{\Gamma(\mu+\nu)} t^{\mu+\nu-1} e^{-\frac{a^2t^2}{2}} {}_2F_2\left[\begin{matrix}\mu, \; \nu \; ; \frac{a^2t^2}{4} \\ \frac{\mu+\nu}{2}, \frac{\mu+\nu+1}{2} ;\end{matrix}\right]$ | $\mathrm{Re}(\mu+\nu) > 0$<br>$\mathrm{Re}\, s > -\infty$ |
| | 5 | $e^{\frac{a^2s^2}{4}}\left\{e^{\frac{ia^2bs}{2}} D_{-\nu}[a(s+ib)] - e^{-\frac{ia^2bs}{2}} \cdot D_{-\nu}[a(s-ib)]\right\}$ | $\frac{-i2t^{\nu-1}}{\Gamma(\nu)a^\nu} e^{-\frac{t^2}{2a^2}+\frac{a^2b^2}{4}} \sin(bt)$ | $\mathrm{Re}\, a^2 > 0$<br>$\mathrm{Re}\, \nu > -1$<br>$\mathrm{Re}\, s > -\infty$ |
| | 6 | $e^{\frac{a^2s^2}{4}}\left\{e^{-\frac{ia^2bs}{2}} D_{-\nu}[a(s-ib)] + e^{\frac{ia^2bs}{2}} D_{-\nu}[a(s+ib)]\right\}$ | $\frac{2t^{\nu-1}}{\Gamma(\nu)a^\nu} e^{-\frac{t^2}{2a^2}+\frac{a^2b^2}{4}} \cos(bt)$ | $\mathrm{Re}\, a^2 > 0$<br>$\mathrm{Re}\, \nu > 0$<br>$\mathrm{Re}\, s > -\infty$ |
| 27.3.2 | 1 | $e^{\frac{a^2s}{4}} D_{-\nu}(as^{\frac{1}{2}})$ | $\frac{a t^{\frac{\nu}{2}-1}}{\Gamma(\frac{\nu}{2})(2t+a^2)^{\frac{\nu+1}{2}}}$ | $\mathrm{Re}\, \nu > 0$<br>$\mathrm{Re}\, a > 0$<br>$\mathrm{Re}\, s \geq 0$ |
| | 2 | $\frac{1}{s^{\frac{1}{2}}} e^{\frac{a^2s}{4}} D_{-\nu}(as^{\frac{1}{2}})$ | $\frac{t^{\frac{\nu-1}{2}}}{\Gamma(\frac{\nu+1}{2})(2t+a^2)^{\frac{\nu}{2}}}$ | $\mathrm{Re}\, \nu > -1$<br>$\mathrm{Re}\, a > 0$<br>$\mathrm{Re}\, s > 0$ |
| | 3 | $\frac{e^{-\frac{1}{4s}}}{s^{n+\frac{1}{2}}} D_{2n}\left(\frac{1}{s^{\frac{1}{2}}}\right)$ | $\frac{(-2t)^n \cos[(2t)^{\frac{1}{2}}]}{(\pi t)^{\frac{1}{2}}}$ | $n=0,1,2,\ldots$<br>$\mathrm{Re}\, s > 0$ |
| | 4 | $\frac{1}{s^\nu} e^{-\frac{a^2}{4s}} D_{2\nu-1}\left(\frac{a}{s^{\frac{1}{2}}}\right)$ | $\frac{2^{\nu+\frac{1}{2}} t^{\nu-1}}{\pi^{\frac{1}{2}}} \sin(\nu\pi - 2^{\frac{1}{2}} a t^{\frac{1}{2}})$ | $\mathrm{Re}\, \nu > 0$<br>$\mathrm{Re}\, s > 0$ |

27.3.2 (Contd.)

| | $g(s)$ | $f(t)$ | |
|---|---|---|---|
| 5 | $\frac{1}{s^{\nu}} e^{\frac{a^2}{4s}} D_{-2\nu}\left(\frac{a}{s^{\frac{1}{2}}}\right)$ | $\frac{(2t)^{\nu-1} e^{-2^{\frac{1}{2}} a t^{\frac{1}{2}}}}{\Gamma(2\nu)}$ | $\mathrm{Re}\,\nu > 0$<br>$\mathrm{Re}\,s > 0$ |
| 6 | $e^{\frac{a^2}{4s}} \sum_{r=0}^{n-1} (-1)^r \binom{n-1}{r} \left(\frac{a^2}{s}\right)^{\frac{n+1-r}{2}} D_{-n+r-1}\left(\frac{a}{s^{\frac{1}{2}}}\right)$ | $\frac{a}{(2t)^{\frac{1}{2}}} e^{-\frac{at^{\frac{1}{2}}}{2^{\frac{1}{2}}}} k_{2n}\left(\frac{at^{\frac{1}{2}}}{2^{\frac{1}{2}}}\right)$ | $n = 1,2,3,\ldots$<br>$\mathrm{Re}\,s > 0$ |
| 7 | $\frac{1}{s^{\nu}} e^{\frac{a^2}{4s}} \left[D_{-2\nu}\left(-\frac{a}{s^{\frac{1}{2}}}\right) + D_{-2\nu}\left(\frac{a}{s^{\frac{1}{2}}}\right)\right]$ | $\frac{2^{\nu} t^{\nu-1} \cosh(2^{\frac{1}{2}} a t^{\frac{1}{2}})}{\Gamma(2\nu)}$ | $\mathrm{Re}\,\nu > 0$<br>$\mathrm{Re}\,s > 0$ |
| 8 | $\frac{1}{s^{\nu}} e^{\frac{a^2}{4s}} \left[D_{-2\nu}\left(-\frac{a}{s^{\frac{1}{2}}}\right) - D_{-2\nu}\left(\frac{a}{s^{\frac{1}{2}}}\right)\right]$ | $\frac{2^{\nu} t^{\nu-1} \sinh(2^{\frac{1}{2}} a t^{\frac{1}{2}})}{\Gamma(2\nu)}$ | $\mathrm{Re}\,\nu > -\frac{1}{2}$<br>$\mathrm{Re}\,s > 0$ |
| 9 | $\frac{1}{s^{\nu}} e^{-\frac{a^2}{4s}} \left[D_{2\nu-1}\left(\frac{a}{s^{\frac{1}{2}}}\right) + D_{2\nu-1}\left(-\frac{a}{s^{\frac{1}{2}}}\right)\right]$ | $\frac{2^{\nu+\frac{1}{2}} \sin(\nu\pi)}{\pi^{\frac{1}{2}}} t^{\nu-1} \cos(2^{\frac{1}{2}} a t^{\frac{1}{2}})$ | $\mathrm{Re}\,\nu > 0$<br>$\mathrm{Re}\,s > 0$ |
| 10 | $\frac{e^{-\frac{a^2}{4s}}}{s^{\nu}} \left[D_{2\nu-1}\left(-\frac{a}{s^{\frac{1}{2}}}\right) - D_{2\nu-1}\left(\frac{a}{s^{\frac{1}{2}}}\right)\right]$ | $\frac{2^{\nu+\frac{1}{2}} \cos(\nu\pi)}{\pi^{\frac{1}{2}}} t^{\nu-1} \sin(2^{\frac{1}{2}} a t^{\frac{1}{2}})$ | $\mathrm{Re}\,\nu > -\frac{1}{2}$<br>$\mathrm{Re}\,s > 0$ |
| 11 | $s^{\frac{\nu}{2}} e^{-\frac{1}{4s}} \left[D_{\nu}\left(\frac{i}{s^{\frac{1}{2}}}\right) + D_{\nu}\left(\frac{-i}{s^{\frac{1}{2}}}\right)\right]$ | $\frac{\cos[(2t)^{\frac{1}{2}}]}{\Gamma(-\nu)\, t\, (2t)^{\frac{\nu}{2}}}$ | $\mathrm{Re}\,\nu < 0$<br>$\mathrm{Re}\,s > 0$ |
| 12 | $e^{\frac{s}{2}} D_{\nu-\frac{1}{2}}(s^{\frac{1}{2}})\, D_{-\nu-\frac{1}{2}}(s^{\frac{1}{2}})$ | $\frac{\cos(\nu \cos^{-1} \frac{1}{1+2t})}{[\pi t(t+1)(2t+1)]^{\frac{1}{2}}}$ | $\mathrm{Re}\,s > 0$ |
| 13 | $\frac{1}{s^{\frac{1}{2}}} e^{\frac{a^2+b^2}{4} s} D_{\mu}(a s^{\frac{1}{2}})\, D_{\nu}(b s^{\frac{1}{2}})$ | $\frac{2^{\frac{\mu+\nu}{2}}}{\Gamma(\frac{1-\mu-\nu}{2})\, t^{\frac{1}{2}}} \left(1 + \frac{a^2}{2t}\right)^{\frac{\mu}{2}} \left(1 + \frac{b^2}{2t}\right)^{\frac{\nu}{2}} \cdot$<br>${}_2F_1\left[-\frac{\mu}{2}, -\frac{\nu}{2}; \frac{1-\mu-\nu}{2}; \frac{2t(a^2+b^2+2t)}{(a^2+2t)(b^2+2t)}\right]$ | $\lvert \arg a^2 \rvert < \frac{\pi}{2}$<br>$\lvert \arg b^2 \rvert < \frac{\pi}{2}$<br>$\mathrm{Re}(\mu+\nu) < 2$<br>$\lvert \arg a^2 s \rvert < \frac{\pi}{2}$<br>$\lvert \arg b^2 s \rvert < \frac{\pi}{2}$<br>$\mathrm{Re}\,s > 0$ |

| | | g(s) | f(t) | |
|---|---|---|---|---|
| 27.3.2.1 | 1 | $\frac{e^{-\frac{1}{4s}}}{s^{n+1}} D_{2n+1}\left(\frac{1}{s^{\frac{1}{2}}}\right)$ | $(\frac{2}{\pi})^{\frac{1}{2}}(-2t)^n \sin[(2t)^{\frac{1}{2}}]$ | Re s > o<br>n = 0,1,2,... |
| 27.21.3.1 | 1 | $2^s \Gamma(s+\nu) D_{-2s}(a)$ | $\frac{e^{\frac{t}{2}}}{2^{\nu}(e^t-1)^{\nu+\frac{1}{2}}} \exp\left[-\frac{a^2 e^{-t}}{4(1-e^{-t})}\right] D_{2\nu}\left[\frac{a}{(1-e^{-t})^{\frac{1}{2}}}\right]$ | $\lvert \arg a \rvert < \frac{\pi}{4}$<br>Re s > − Re ν |
| 28 | 1 | $S_{o,o}(s)$ | $\frac{1}{(t^2+1)^{\frac{1}{2}}}$ | Re s > o |
| | 2 | $S_{o,\nu}(s)$ | $\frac{\cosh(\nu \sinh^{-1} t)}{(1+t^2)^{\frac{1}{2}}}$<br>$= \frac{[(t^2+1)^{\frac{1}{2}}+t]^{\nu}+[(t^2+1)^{\frac{1}{2}}-t]^{\nu}}{2(t^2+1)^{\frac{1}{2}}}$ | Re s > o |
| | 3 | $\frac{1}{s} S_{o,\nu}(s)$ | $\frac{1}{\nu} \sinh(\nu \sinh^{-1} t)$<br>$= \frac{1}{2\nu}\left[[(t^2+1)^{\frac{1}{2}}+t]^{\nu} - [(t^2+1)^{\frac{1}{2}}-t]^{\nu}\right]$ | Re s > o |
| | 4 | $S_{-1,\nu}(s)$ | $\frac{\sinh(\nu \sinh^{-1} t)}{\nu(1+t^2)^{\frac{1}{2}}}$<br>$= \frac{[(t^2+1)^{\frac{1}{2}}+t]^{\nu} - [(t^2+1)^{\frac{1}{2}}-t]^{\nu}}{2\nu(t^2+1)^{\frac{1}{2}}}$ | Re s > o |
| | 5 | $\frac{1}{s} S_{1,\nu}(s)$ | $\cosh(\nu \sinh^{-1} t)$<br>$= \frac{1}{2}\left[[(t^2+1)^{\frac{1}{2}}+t]^{\nu} + [(t^2+1)^{\frac{1}{2}}-t]^{\nu}\right]$ | Re s > o |

| | | g(s) | f(t) | |
|---|---|---|---|---|
| 28 (Contd.) | 6 | $\frac{1}{s} S_{2,\nu}(s) - 1$ | $(\nu - \frac{1}{\nu}) \sinh(\nu \sinh^{-1} t)$ $= \frac{1}{2}(\nu - \frac{1}{\nu}) \left[ [(t^2+1)^{\frac{1}{2}} + t]^{\nu} - [(t^2+1)^{\frac{1}{2}} - t]^{\nu} \right]$ | Re s > o |
| | 7 | $S_{o,\nu}(s) - \nu S_{-1,\nu}(s)$ | $\frac{[(t^2+1)^{\frac{1}{2}} - t]^{\nu}}{(t^2+1)^{\frac{1}{2}}}$ | Re s > o |
| | 8 | $\frac{1}{s}[S_{1,\nu}(s) + \nu S_{o,\nu}(s)]$ | $[(t^2+1)^{\frac{1}{2}} + t]^{\nu}$ | Re s > o |
| | 9 | $\frac{1}{s}[S_{1,\nu}(s) - \nu S_{o,\nu}(s)]$ | $[(t^2+1)^{\frac{1}{2}} - t]^{\nu}$ | Re s > o |
| | 10 | $V_{\nu}(2s,o)$ | $\frac{t^{\nu-1} \sin(\nu\pi)}{\pi(1+t^2)}$ | Re ν > o<br>Re s > o |
| 28.1 | 1 | $\frac{1}{s^2} S_{2,o}(s)$ | $(1+t^2)^{\frac{1}{2}} - t \sinh^{-1} t$ | Re s > o |
| | 2 | $\frac{1}{s^2} S_{2,\nu}(s)$ | $1 + (\nu - \frac{1}{\nu}) \int_o^t \sinh(\nu \sinh^{-1} u) du$ | Re s > o |
| 28.2 | 1 | $\frac{1}{s^{\frac{\nu}{2}}} S_{\mu,\nu}(as^{\frac{1}{2}})$ | $\frac{2^{\mu+\nu-1} t^{\nu-1}}{a^{\nu}\Gamma(\frac{\nu-\mu+1}{2})} e^{\frac{a^2}{4t}} \Gamma\left(\frac{\mu+\nu+1}{2}, \frac{a^2}{4t}\right)$ | Re(μ−ν) < 1<br>$\|\arg a^2\| < \pi$<br>Re s > o |
| | 2 | $\frac{S_{\mu,\nu}(as^{\frac{1}{2}})}{s^{\frac{\mu+1}{2}}}$ | $2^{\mu} a^{-1} t^{\frac{\mu}{2}} e^{\frac{a^2}{8t}} W_{\frac{\mu}{2},\frac{\nu}{2}}\left(\frac{a^2}{4t}\right)$ | Re(μ±ν) > −1<br>$\|\arg a\| < \frac{\pi}{2}$<br>Re s > o |
| | 3 | $s^b S_{\mu,\nu}(as)$ | $\frac{a^{\mu-1}}{\Gamma(1-b-\mu) t^{b+\mu}} {}_3F_2\left[\begin{matrix} 1, \frac{1-\mu+\nu}{2}, \frac{1-\mu-\nu}{2}; \\ \frac{1-b-\mu}{2}, \frac{2-b-\mu}{2}; \end{matrix} -\frac{t^2}{a^2}\right]$ | Re a > o<br>Re(b+μ) < 1<br>Re s > o |

| | | g(s) | f(t) | |
|---|---|---|---|---|
| 28.2.1 | 1 | $s^{\frac{1}{2}} S_{\mu,\frac{1}{4}}(\frac{s^2}{a})$ | $\frac{a\, t^{\frac{1}{2}}}{2^{2\mu+2}\,\Gamma(-2\mu-\frac{1}{2})} s_{-\mu-1,\frac{1}{4}}\left(\frac{at^2}{4}\right)$ | $\mathrm{Re}\,\mu < -\frac{1}{4}$<br>$\mathrm{Re}\, s > 0$ |
| 28.3.1 | 1 | $\frac{s_{\nu+s-1,\,s-\nu}(a)}{a^s}$ | $\frac{2^{\nu}\Gamma(\nu) J_{\nu}[a(1-e^{-t})^{\frac{1}{2}}]}{(1-e^{-t})^{\frac{\nu}{2}}}$ | $\mathrm{Re}\, s > 0$ |
| 28.21.3 | 1 | $\frac{\Gamma(s)}{a^s} U_s(2a,0)$ | $\cos[a(1-e^{-t})]$ | $\mathrm{Re}\, s > 0$ |
| 28.21.3.1 | 1 | $\frac{\Gamma(s)}{a^s} U_{s+1}(2a,0)$ | $\sin[a(1-e^{-t})]$ | $\mathrm{Re}\, s > 0$ |
| | 2 | $\frac{\Gamma(s)}{a^s}[U_s(2a,0)\cos a + U_{s+1}(2a,0)\sin a]$ | $\cos(ae^{-t})$ | $\mathrm{Re}\, s > 0$ |
| | 3 | $\frac{\Gamma(s)}{a^s}[U_s(2a,0)\sin a - U_{s+1}(2a,0)\cos a]$ | $\sin(ae^{-t})$ | $\mathrm{Re}\, s > 0$ |
| 30 | 1 | $\frac{1}{s}\,{}_1F_1[\frac{1}{2};1;-\frac{1}{s}]$ | $J_0^2(t^{\frac{1}{2}})$ | $\mathrm{Re}\, s > 0$ |
| | 2 | $\frac{1}{s}\,{}_1F_1[1;n;\frac{1}{s}]$ | ${}_0F_1[\,;n;t]$ | $n = 1,2,3,\ldots$<br>$\mathrm{Re}\, s > 0$ |
| | 3 | ${}_1F_1[a;c;-s]$ | $\frac{\Gamma(c)\, t^{a-1}(1-t)^{c-a-1}}{\Gamma(a)\Gamma(c-a)}$ $\quad 0 < t < 1$<br>$0 \quad t > 1$ | $\mathrm{Re}\, c > \mathrm{Re}\, a > 0$<br>$\mathrm{Re}\, s > -\infty$ |
| | 4 | $\Phi_1(a,c,a+b;h,-s)$ | $\frac{t^{a-1}(1-t)^{b-1}}{B(a,b)(1-ht)^c}$ $\quad 0 < t < 1$<br>$0 \quad t > 1$ | $\mathrm{Re}\, a > 0$<br>$\mathrm{Re}\, b > 0$<br>$\lvert\arg(1-h)\rvert < \pi$<br>$\mathrm{Re}\, s > -\infty$ |

| | | g(s) | f(t) | | |
|---|---|---|---|---|---|
| 30 (Contd.) | 5 | $\frac{1}{s} W_{\mu,\nu}(s)$ | $0$ | $0 < t < \frac{1}{2}$ | $\mathrm{Re}\,\mu > 1$ <br> $\nu - \frac{1}{2} \neq 0, \pm 1, \pm 2, \ldots$ <br> $\mathrm{Re}\, s > 0$ |
| | | | $\left(\frac{2t+1}{2t-1}\right)^{\frac{\mu}{2}} P^{\mu}_{\nu-\frac{1}{2}}(2t)$ | $t > \frac{1}{2}$ | |
| 30.2 | 1 | $\frac{1}{s^{\nu+1}}\, {}_1F_1\left[\nu + \frac{1}{2}; 2\nu + 1; -\frac{1}{s}\right]$ | $4^{\nu}\Gamma(\nu+1)\, J^2_{\nu}(t^{\frac{1}{2}})$ | | $\mathrm{Re}\,\nu > -1$ <br> $\mathrm{Re}\, s > 0$ |
| | 2 | $\frac{1}{s^{\mu}}\, {}_1F_1\left[\mu; \nu; -\frac{a}{s}\right]$ | $\frac{\Gamma(\nu)}{\Gamma(\mu)\, a^{\frac{\nu-1}{2}}}\, t^{\frac{2\mu-\nu-1}{2}}\, J_{\nu-1}(2a^{\frac{1}{2}}t^{\frac{1}{2}})$ | | $\mathrm{Re}\,\mu > 0$ <br> $\mathrm{Re}\, s > 0$ |
| | 3 | $s^{\frac{1}{2}} M_{\frac{1}{4},\nu}\left(\frac{a}{s}\right) M_{-\frac{1}{4},\nu}\left(\frac{a}{s}\right)$ | $\frac{2^{2\nu} a}{t^{\frac{1}{2}}} \frac{[\Gamma(2\nu+1)]^2}{\Gamma(2\nu + \frac{1}{2})} J_{2\nu}\left[(2at)^{\frac{1}{2}} e^{\frac{i\pi}{4}}\right] J_{2\nu}\left[(2at)^{\frac{1}{2}} e^{-\frac{i\pi}{4}}\right]$ | | $\mathrm{Re}\,\nu > -\frac{1}{4}$ <br> $\mathrm{Re}\, s > 0$ |
| | 4 | $\frac{1}{s^{\nu+\frac{1}{2}}} W_{\mu,\nu}\left(\frac{s}{a}\right)$ | $0$ | $0 < t < \frac{1}{2a}$ | $\mathrm{Re}(\nu-\mu) > \frac{1}{2}$ <br> $\mathrm{Re}\, s > 0$ |
| | | | $\frac{a^{\frac{1}{2}-\nu}\,(at - \frac{1}{2})^{\nu-\mu-\frac{1}{2}}}{\Gamma(\nu + \frac{1}{2}-\mu)\,(at + \frac{1}{2})^{\frac{1}{2}-\nu-\mu}}$ | $t > \frac{1}{2a}$ | |
| | 5 | $s^{\frac{1}{2}} W_{\frac{1}{4},\nu}\left(\frac{ia}{s}\right) W_{\frac{1}{4},\nu}\left(-\frac{ia}{s}\right)$ | $-\frac{4a\pi^{\frac{1}{2}} K_{2\nu}[(2at)^{\frac{1}{2}}]}{(2t)^{\frac{1}{2}}\Gamma(\frac{1}{4}+\nu)\Gamma(\frac{1}{4}-\nu)} \left\{\sin\left[(\nu - \frac{1}{4})\pi\right] \cdot J_{2\nu}[(2at)^{\frac{1}{2}}] + \cos\left[(\nu - \frac{1}{4})\pi\right] Y_{2\nu}[(2at)^{\frac{1}{2}}]\right\}$ | | $\lvert\mathrm{Re}\,\nu\rvert < \frac{1}{4}$ <br> $\mathrm{Re}\, s > 0$ |
| | 6 | $\frac{1}{s^{b}} W_{\mu,\nu}(ias) W_{\mu,\nu}(-ias)$ | $\frac{a^{2\mu} t^{b-2\mu-1}}{\Gamma(b-2\mu)}\, {}_4F_3\left[\begin{matrix}\frac{1}{2}-\mu+\nu, \frac{1}{2}-\mu-\nu, \frac{1}{2}-\mu, 1-\mu; \\ 1-2\mu, \frac{b}{2}-\mu, \frac{b+1}{2}-\mu\ ;\end{matrix} -\frac{t^2}{a^2}\right]$ | | $\mathrm{Re}\, a > 0$ <br> $\mathrm{Re}(\frac{b}{2}-\mu) > 0$ <br> $\mathrm{Re}\, s > 0$ |
| | 7 | $\frac{1}{s^{a}} \Phi_1\left(a,b,c;\frac{x}{s},\frac{y}{s}\right)$ | $\frac{t^{a-1}}{\Gamma(a)} \Phi_3(b,c;xt,yt)$ | | $\mathrm{Re}\, a > 0$ <br> $\mathrm{Re}\, x > 0$ <br> $\mathrm{Re}\, s > 0$ |

| | | g(s) | f(t) | |
|---|---|---|---|---|
| 30.2 (Contd.) | 8 | $\frac{1}{s^a}\Phi_2(b,a,c;x,\frac{y}{s})$ | $\frac{t^{a-1}}{\Gamma(a)}\Phi_3(b,c;x,yt)$ | Re a > o<br>Re s > Max o, Re y |
| | 9 | $\frac{1}{s^b}\Psi_1(a,b,c,d;\frac{x}{s},y)$ | $\frac{t^{b-1}}{\Gamma(b)}\Psi_2(a,c,d;xt,y)$ | Re b > o<br>Re s > Max o, Re x |
| | 10 | $\frac{1}{s^{\mu+\nu}}\Psi_2\left(\nu+\mu;2\mu_1+1,\ldots,2\mu_n+1;\frac{a_1}{s},\ldots,\frac{a_n}{s}\right)$ | $\frac{t^{\nu-1}}{\Gamma(\nu+\mu)}\prod_{r=1}^{n}\left[\frac{\Gamma(2\mu_r+1)}{a_r^{\mu_r}}J_{2\mu_r}(2a_r^{\frac{1}{2}}t^{\frac{1}{2}})\right]$ | $\mu=\sum_{r=1}^{n}\mu_r$<br>Re$(\nu+\mu)$ > o<br>Re s > o |
| | 11 | $\frac{1}{s^b}\Xi_1(a,b,c,d;x,\frac{y}{s})$ | $\frac{t^{b-1}}{\Gamma(b)}\Xi_2(a,c,d;x,yt)$ | Re b > o<br>Re s > Max o, Re y |
| | 12 | $\frac{1}{s^d}\Xi_1(a,b,d,c;\frac{x}{s},y)$ | $\frac{t^{d-1}}{\Gamma(d)}\Phi_2(a,b,c;xt,y)$ | Re d > o<br>Re s > Max o, Re x |
| | 13 | $\frac{1}{s^a}\Xi_2(a,b,c;\frac{x}{s},y)$ | $\frac{t^{a-1}}{\Gamma(a)}\Phi_3(b,c;xt,y)$ | Re a > o<br>Re s > Max o, Re x |
| 30.2.1 | 1 | $\frac{1}{s^{2\nu+2}}{}_1F_1[\nu+\frac{1}{2};2\nu+1;-\frac{1}{s^2}]$ | $\frac{2t^{2\nu}}{\Gamma(2\nu+1)\Gamma(\nu+1)}{}_0F_2\left[\begin{matrix} ; -\frac{t^2}{4} \\ 2\nu+1,\nu+1; \end{matrix}\right]$ | Re $\nu$ > $-1$<br>Re s > o |
| | 2 | $\frac{1}{s^{2a}}\Xi_1(a,b,a+\frac{1}{2},c;\frac{4y}{s^2},x)$ | $\frac{t^{2a-1}}{\Gamma(2a)}\Phi_3(b,c;x,yt^2)$ | Re a > o<br>Re s > 2 $\lvert$Re $y^{\frac{1}{2}}\rvert$ |
| | 3 | $\frac{1}{s^{\frac{3}{2}}}W_{-\nu,\frac{1}{8}}\left(\frac{e^{\frac{\pi i}{2}}s^2}{a}\right)W_{-\nu,\frac{1}{8}}\left(\frac{e^{-\frac{\pi i}{2}}s^2}{a}\right)$ | $\frac{\pi^{\frac{3}{2}}}{2^{\frac{1}{2}}\Gamma(\nu+\frac{3}{8})\Gamma(\nu+\frac{5}{8})}t^{\frac{1}{2}}J_{\nu+\frac{1}{8}}(\frac{at^2}{8})J_{\nu-\frac{1}{8}}(\frac{at^2}{8})$ | Re $\nu$ > $-\frac{3}{8}$<br>a > o<br>Re s > o |

| | | $g(s)$ | $f(t)$ | |
|---|---|---|---|---|
| 30.3 | 1 | $\frac{1}{s} e^{\frac{as}{2}} W_{\nu,\mu}(as)$ | $(1+\frac{a}{t})^{\frac{\nu}{2}} P^{\nu}_{\mu-\frac{1}{2}}(1+\frac{2t}{a})$ | $\lvert\arg a\rvert < \pi$<br>$\mathrm{Re}\,\nu < 1$<br>$\mathrm{Re}\,s > 0$ |
| | 2 | $\frac{1}{s} e^{\frac{s}{a}} W_{\nu,0}(\frac{s}{a})\, W_{-\nu,0}(\frac{s}{a})$ | $\dfrac{P_{\nu-\frac{1}{2}}\left[\frac{2}{(1+at)^2}-1\right]}{1+at}$ | $\mathrm{Re}\,s > 0$ |
| | 3 | $\frac{1}{s} e^{\frac{a+b}{2}s} W_{\mu,\nu}(as)\, W_{\lambda,\nu}(bs)$ | $\frac{(ab)^{\nu+\frac{1}{2}}}{\Gamma(1-\mu-\lambda)} \frac{(a+t)^{\mu-\nu-\frac{1}{2}}(b+t)^{\lambda-\nu-\frac{1}{2}}}{t^{\mu+\lambda}} \cdot$<br>${}_2F_1\left[\nu+\frac{1}{2}-\mu, \nu+\frac{1}{2}-\lambda; 1-\mu-\lambda; \frac{t(a+b+t)}{(a+t)(b+t)}\right]$ | $\mathrm{Re}(1-\mu-\lambda) > 0$<br>$\lvert\arg a\rvert < \pi$<br>$\lvert\arg b\rvert < \pi$<br>$\lvert\arg as\rvert < \pi$<br>$\lvert\arg bs\rvert < \pi$<br>$\mathrm{Re}\,s > 0$ |
| 30.3.1 | 1 | $\frac{1}{s^n} e^{-\frac{a}{s}} k_{2n}(\frac{a}{s})$ | $\frac{(-1)^{n-1}(2a)^{\frac{1}{2}}}{n!} t^{n-\frac{1}{2}} J_1[(8at)^{\frac{1}{2}}]$ | $n = 0,1,2,\ldots$<br>$\mathrm{Re}\,s > 0$ |
| | 2 | $a^{\frac{s}{2}} W_{\mu-\frac{s}{2},\nu+\frac{s}{2}}(a)$ | $\dfrac{\exp\left[-(\frac{1}{2}-\nu+\mu)t - a(e^t-\frac{1}{2})\right]}{a^{\nu-\frac{1}{2}}\Gamma(\frac{1}{2}-\nu-\mu)(e^t-1)^{\frac{1}{2}+\mu+\nu}}$ | $\mathrm{Re}(\mu+\nu) < \frac{1}{2}$<br>$\mathrm{Re}\,a > 0$<br>$\mathrm{Re}\,s > -\infty$ |
| | 3 | $a^{\frac{s}{2}} W_{\frac{1-s-2\nu}{2},\frac{s}{2}}(a)$ | $\frac{a^{\frac{1}{2}} e^{\frac{a}{2}}}{\Gamma(\nu)} (1-e^{-t})^{\nu-1} \exp(-ae^t)$ | $\mathrm{Re}\,a > 0$<br>$\mathrm{Re}\,\nu > 0$<br>$\mathrm{Re}\,s > -\infty$ |
| 30.3.2 | 1 | $\frac{e^{-\frac{1}{s}}}{s^{\nu+1}} {}_1F_1[-\nu;1;\frac{1}{s}]$ | $\frac{t^{\nu}}{\Gamma(\nu+1)} J_0(2t^{\frac{1}{2}})$ | $\mathrm{Re}\,\nu > -1$<br>$\mathrm{Re}\,s > 0$ |
| | 2 | $\frac{e^{-\frac{1}{s}}}{s^{\nu-\mu}} {}_1F_1[\mu;\nu;\frac{1}{s}]$ | $\frac{\Gamma(\nu)}{\Gamma(\nu-\mu)} t^{\frac{\nu-1}{2}-\mu} J_{\nu-1}(2t^{\frac{1}{2}})$ | $\mathrm{Re}\,\nu > \mathrm{Re}\,\mu$<br>$\mathrm{Re}\,s > 0$ |
| | 3 | $\frac{1}{s^n} e^{-\frac{a}{s}} k_{2n}(\frac{a}{s})$ | $\frac{(-1)^{n-1}(2a)^{\frac{1}{2}} t^{n-\frac{1}{2}}}{n!} J_1[(8at)^{\frac{1}{2}}]$ | $n = 0,1,2,\ldots$<br>$\mathrm{Re}\,s > 0$ |

| | | g(s) | f(t) | | |
|---|---|---|---|---|---|
| 30.3.2 (Contd.) | 4 | $\frac{1}{s^{\nu}} e^{-\frac{a}{s}} k_{-2\nu}\left(\frac{a e^{i\pi}}{s}\right)$ | $-\frac{i \sin(\nu\pi)}{\Gamma(\nu+1)} t^{\nu-\frac{1}{2}} H_1^{(2)}[(8at)^{\frac{1}{2}}]$ | | $Re\,\nu > 0$<br>$Re\,s > 0$ |
| | 5 | $\frac{1}{s^{\nu}} e^{-\frac{a}{s}} k_{-2\nu}\left(\frac{a e^{-i\pi}}{s}\right)$ | $\frac{i \sin(\nu\pi)}{\Gamma(\nu+1)} t^{\nu-\frac{1}{2}} H_1^{(1)}[(8at)^{\frac{1}{2}}]$ | | $Re\,\nu > 0$<br>$Re\,s > 0$ |
| | 6 | $\frac{1}{s^{\frac{1}{2}}} e^{-\frac{1}{2s}} M_{0,0}(\frac{1}{s})$ | $J_0^2(t^{\frac{1}{2}})$ | | $Re\,s > 0$ |
| | 7 | $\frac{1}{s^{\mu}} e^{-\frac{a}{2s}} M_{\mu,\nu}(\frac{a}{s})$ | $\frac{a^{\frac{1}{2}}\Gamma(2\nu+1)}{\Gamma(\mu+\nu+\frac{1}{2})} t^{\mu-\frac{1}{2}} J_{2\nu}(2a^{\frac{1}{2}}t^{\frac{1}{2}})$ | | $Re(\mu+\nu) > -\frac{1}{2}$<br>$Re\,s > 0$ |
| | 8 | $\frac{1}{s^{\mu}} e^{\frac{a}{2s}} M_{-\mu,\nu}(\frac{a}{s})$ | $\frac{a^{\frac{1}{2}}\Gamma(2\nu+1)}{\Gamma(\mu+\nu+\frac{1}{2})} t^{\mu-\frac{1}{2}} I_{2\nu}(2a^{\frac{1}{2}}t^{\frac{1}{2}})$ | | $Re(\mu+\nu) > -\frac{1}{2}$<br>$Re\,s > 0$ |
| | 9 | $\frac{1}{s^{\mu+\nu}} e^{-\frac{(a+b)s}{2}} M_{\mu-\nu,\mu+\nu-\frac{1}{2}}[(b-a)s]$ | $0$ | $0 < t < a$ | $b > a \geqslant 0$<br>$Re\,\mu > 0$ |
| | | | $\frac{(t-a)^{2\mu-1}(b-t)^{2\nu-1}}{B(2\mu,2\nu)(b-a)^{\mu+\nu-1}}$ | $a < t < b$ | $Re\,\nu > 0$<br>$Re\,s > -\infty$ |
| | | | $0$ | $t > b$ | |
| | 10 | $\frac{e^{\frac{a}{2s}} W_{-\nu,\nu}(\frac{a}{s})}{s^{3\nu+\frac{1}{2}}}$ | $\frac{2t^{2\nu} K_{2\nu}(a^{\frac{1}{2}}t^{\frac{1}{2}}) I_{2\nu}(a^{\frac{1}{2}}t^{\frac{1}{2}})}{\Gamma(2\nu+\frac{1}{2}) a^{\nu-\frac{1}{2}}}$ | | $Re\,\nu > -\frac{1}{4}$<br>$Re\,s > 0$ |
| | 11 | $\frac{1}{s^{\mu}} e^{\frac{a}{2s}} W_{-\mu,\nu}(\frac{a}{s})$ | $\frac{2a^{\frac{1}{2}}t^{\mu-\frac{1}{2}}}{\Gamma(\mu+\nu+\frac{1}{2})\Gamma(\mu-\nu+\frac{1}{2})} K_{2\nu}(2a^{\frac{1}{2}}t^{\frac{1}{2}})$ | | $Re(\mu\pm\nu) > -\frac{1}{2}$<br>$Re\,s > 0$ |
| | 12 | $\frac{1}{s^{\mu}} e^{-\frac{a}{s}} W_{-\mu,\nu}\left(\frac{2a e^{i\pi}}{s}\right)$ | $\frac{\pi(2a)^{\frac{1}{2}} e^{-\nu\pi i}}{\Gamma(\mu+\nu+\frac{1}{2})\Gamma(\mu-\nu+\frac{1}{2})} t^{\mu-\frac{1}{2}} H_{2\nu}^{(2)}[(8at)^{\frac{1}{2}}]$ | | $Re(\mu\pm\nu) > -\frac{1}{2}$<br>$Re\,s > 0$ |

| | | g(s) | f(t) | | |
|---|---|---|---|---|---|
| 30.3.2 (Contd.) | 13 | $\frac{1}{s^{\mu}} e^{-\frac{a}{s}} W_{-\mu,\nu}\left(\frac{2ae^{-i\pi}}{s}\right)$ | $\frac{\pi(2a)^{\frac{1}{2}} e^{\nu\pi i}}{\Gamma(\mu+\nu+\frac{1}{2})\Gamma(\mu-\nu+\frac{1}{2})} t^{\mu-\frac{1}{2}} H^{(1)}_{2\nu}[(8at)^{\frac{1}{2}}]$ | | $Re(\mu\pm\nu) > -\frac{1}{2}$<br>$Re\, s > 0$ |
| | 14 | $\frac{1}{s^{\mu}} e^{-\frac{a}{2s}} W_{\mu,\nu}(\frac{a}{s})$ | $-a^{\frac{1}{2}} cosec(2\nu\pi) t^{\mu-\frac{1}{2}} \{ J_{2\nu}(2a^{\frac{1}{2}}t^{\frac{1}{2}}) \cdot \cos[(\mu+\nu)\pi] - J_{-2\nu}(2a^{\frac{1}{2}}t^{\frac{1}{2}}) \cos[(\mu-\nu)\pi] \}$ | | $Re(\mu\pm\nu) > -\frac{1}{2}$<br>$Re\, s > 0$ |
| | 15 | $\frac{1}{s^{\mu}} e^{\frac{a}{2s}} W_{\mu,\nu}(\frac{a}{s})$ | $-a^{\frac{1}{2}} t^{\mu-\frac{1}{2}} \{ \sin[(\nu-\mu)\pi] J_{2\nu}(2a^{\frac{1}{2}}t^{\frac{1}{2}}) + \cos[(\nu-\mu)\pi] Y_{2\nu}(2a^{\frac{1}{2}}t^{\frac{1}{2}}) \}$ | | $Re(\mu\pm\nu) > -\frac{1}{2}$<br>$Re\, s > 0$ |
| | 16 | $s^{\mu-\frac{1}{2}} e^{\frac{s}{2a}} W_{\mu,\nu}(\frac{s}{a})$ | $\frac{a^{\frac{1}{4}} P^{2\mu+\frac{1}{2}}_{2\nu-\frac{1}{2}}\left[(1+at)^{\frac{1}{2}}\right]}{2^{2\mu+\frac{1}{2}} t^{\mu+\frac{1}{4}} (1+at)^{\frac{1}{2}}}$ | | $Re\, \mu < \frac{1}{4}$<br>$Re\, s > 0$ |
| | 17 | $s^{\mu-1} e^{\frac{s}{2a}} W_{\mu,\nu}(\frac{s}{a})$ | $\frac{P^{2\mu-\frac{1}{2}}_{2\nu-\frac{1}{2}}\left[(1+at)^{\frac{1}{2}}\right]}{2^{2\mu-\frac{1}{2}} a^{\frac{1}{4}} t^{\mu-\frac{1}{4}}}$ | | $Re\, \mu < \frac{3}{4}$<br>$Re\, s > 0$ |
| | 18 | $\frac{e^{\frac{s}{2}}}{s^{\nu+\frac{1}{2}}} W_{\mu,\nu+n}(s)$ | $\frac{n!}{\Gamma(n+\nu-\frac{\mu-1}{2})} t^{\nu-\frac{\mu+1}{2}} (1+t)^{\nu+\frac{\mu-1}{2}} P_n^{\nu-\frac{\mu+1}{2},\, \nu+\frac{\mu-1}{2}}(1+2t)$ | | $n = 0,1,2,\ldots$<br>$Re\, s > 0$ |
| | 19 | $\frac{1}{s^{\nu+\frac{1}{2}}} e^{\frac{as}{2}} W_{\mu,\nu}(as)$ | $\frac{a^{\frac{1}{2}-\nu} t^{\nu-\mu-\frac{1}{2}} (a+t)^{\mu+\nu-\frac{1}{2}}}{\Gamma(\frac{1}{2}-\mu+\nu)}$ | | $\lvert \arg a \rvert < \pi$<br>$Re(\nu-\mu) > -\frac{1}{2}$<br>$Re\, s > 0$ |
| | 20 | $\frac{1}{s^{\mu+\nu}} e^{\frac{s(a-b)}{2}} W_{\mu-\nu,\mu+\nu-\frac{1}{2}}[(a+b)s]$ | $0$ | $0 < t < b$ | $b > 0$<br>$Re\, \nu > 0$<br>$\lvert \arg(a+b) \rvert < \pi$<br>$Re\, s > 0$ |
| | | | $\frac{(t+a)^{2\mu-1}(t-b)^{2\nu-1}}{\Gamma(2\nu)(a+b)^{\mu+\nu-1}}$ | $t > b$ | |

| | | $g(s)$ | $f(t)$ | |
|---|---|---|---|---|
| 30.3.2 (Contd.) | 21 | $\frac{1}{s^b} e^{\frac{s}{a}} W_{\mu,\nu}(\frac{s}{a})$ | $\frac{t^{b-\mu-1}}{a^{\mu}\Gamma(b-\mu)}\, {}_2F_1[\frac{1}{2}-\mu+\nu, \frac{1}{2}-\mu-\nu; b-\mu; -at]$ | $\lvert \arg a \rvert < \pi$<br>$Re(b-\mu) > 0$<br>$Re\, s > 0$ |
| | 22 | $\frac{1}{s^b} e^{\frac{a}{2s}} W_{\mu,\nu}(\frac{a}{s})$ | $\frac{\Gamma(-2\nu) a^{\nu+\frac{1}{2}} t^{\nu+b-\frac{1}{2}}}{\Gamma(\frac{1}{2}-\mu-\nu)\Gamma(\frac{1}{2}+\nu+b)}\, {}_1F_2\left[\begin{matrix}\frac{1}{2}-\mu+\nu; & at \\ 1+2\nu, \frac{1}{2}+\nu+b; & \end{matrix}\right]$<br>$+\frac{\Gamma(2\nu) a^{-\nu+\frac{1}{2}} t^{-\nu+b-\frac{1}{2}}}{\Gamma(\frac{1}{2}-\mu+\nu)\Gamma(\frac{1}{2}-\nu+b)}\, {}_1F_2\left[\begin{matrix}\frac{1}{2}-\mu-\nu; & at \\ 1-2\nu, \frac{1}{2}-\nu+b; & \end{matrix}\right]$ | $Re(\frac{1}{2}\pm\nu+b) > 0$<br>$Re\, s > 0$ |
| | 23 | $e^{bs} M_{-\mu,\nu}\left[\frac{a^2 b}{s+(s^2-a^2)^{\frac{1}{2}}}\right] \cdot$<br>$W_{-\mu,\nu}[b\{s+(s^2-a^2)^{\frac{1}{2}}\}]$ | $\frac{ab\Gamma(2\nu+1)}{\Gamma(\mu+\nu+\frac{1}{2})} \frac{t^{\mu-\frac{1}{2}}}{(t+2b)^{\mu+\frac{1}{2}}} I_{2\nu}[a(t^2+2bt)^{\frac{1}{2}}]$ | $Re(\mu+\nu) > -\frac{1}{2}$<br>$\lvert \arg b \rvert < \pi$<br>$Re\, s > \lvert Re\, a \rvert$ |
| | 24 | $\frac{1}{s^{\mu}} e^{-\frac{a}{2s}} \left\{\frac{\tan[(\mu-\nu)\pi]\Gamma(\mu+\nu+\frac{1}{2})}{\Gamma(2\nu+1)} \cdot\right.$<br>$\left. M_{\mu,\nu}(\frac{a}{s}) - \sec[(\mu-\nu)\pi] W_{\mu,\nu}(\frac{a}{s})\right\}$ | $a^{\frac{1}{2}} t^{\mu-\frac{1}{2}} Y_{2\mu}(2a^{\frac{1}{2}}t^{\frac{1}{2}})$ | $Re(\mu\pm\nu) > -\frac{1}{2}$<br>$Re\, s > 0$ |
| | 25 | $e^{bs} W_{-\mu,\nu}\left[\frac{a^2 b}{s+(s^2-a^2)^{\frac{1}{2}}}\right] \cdot$<br>$W_{-\mu,\nu}\left[b[s+(s^2-a^2)^{\frac{1}{2}}]\right]$ | $\frac{2ab}{\Gamma(\mu+\nu+\frac{1}{2})\Gamma(\mu-\nu+\frac{1}{2})} \frac{t^{\mu-\frac{1}{2}}}{(t+2b)^{\mu+\frac{1}{2}}} \cdot$<br>$K_{2\nu}[a(t^2+2bt)^{\frac{1}{2}}]$ | $Re(\frac{1}{2}+\mu\pm\nu) > 0$<br>$\lvert \arg b \rvert < \pi$<br>$Re\, s > \lvert Re\, a \rvert$ |
| 30.3.2.1 | 1 | $s^{n-\frac{3}{2}} e^{\frac{s^2}{2a}} W_{-\frac{3}{4}-\frac{n}{2}, \frac{1}{4}-\frac{n}{2}}(\frac{s^2}{a})$ | $(-1)^{n-1}\, 2 a^{\frac{n}{2}-\frac{1}{4}} e^{-\frac{at^2}{8}} k_{2n}(\frac{at^2}{8})$ | $n = 0,1,2,\ldots$<br>$Re\, s > -\infty$ |
| | 2 | $\frac{e^{\frac{as^2}{2}} W_{-3\nu,\nu}(as^2)}{s^{2\nu+1}}$ | $\frac{2^{8\nu}\Gamma(2\nu+1)}{a^{\nu}\Gamma(8\nu+1)} t^{4\nu} e^{-\frac{t^2}{8a}} I_{2\nu}\left(\frac{t^2}{8a}\right)$ | $Re\, a > 0$<br>$Re\, \nu > -\frac{1}{8}$<br>$Re\, s > 0$ |

| | | g(s) | f(t) | |
|---|---|---|---|---|
| 30.3.2.1 (Contd.) | 3 | $\frac{1}{s^{2\nu+1}} e^{\frac{as^2}{2}} W_{\mu,\nu}(as^2)$ | $\frac{2^{1-\mu+\nu} a^{\frac{\mu+\nu+1}{2}}}{\Gamma(1-2\mu+2\nu)} t^{\nu-\mu-1} e^{-\frac{t^2}{8a}} M_{-\frac{\mu+3\nu}{2},\frac{\nu-\mu}{2}}\left(\frac{t^2}{4a}\right)$ | Re a > o<br>$\mathrm{Re}(\mu-\nu) < \frac{1}{2}$<br>Re s > o |
| 30.5.3 | 1 | $\frac{1}{s^{\mu}} \int_0^{\pi} e^{-\frac{r}{4s}} {}_1F_1[1-\mu+\nu;1+\nu;\frac{r}{4s}] \sin^{2\nu}\theta \, d\theta$<br>where $r = a^2-2ab\cos\theta + b^2$ | $\frac{\pi\Gamma(2\nu+1)}{(ab)^{\nu}\Gamma(\mu)} t^{\mu-\nu-1} J_{\nu}(at^{\frac{1}{2}}) J_{\nu}(bt^{\frac{1}{2}})$ | $\mathrm{Re}\,\nu > -\frac{1}{2}$<br>$\mathrm{Re}\,\mu > o$<br>Re s > o |
| 30.21.1 | 1 | $\frac{\Gamma(\frac{1}{2}+\nu+s)\Gamma(\frac{1}{2}-\nu+s)}{\Gamma(1-\mu+s)} W_{-s,\nu}(a)$ | $e^{-\frac{a}{2}}(1-e^{-t})^{-\mu} \exp\left[-\frac{a}{2(e^t-1)}\right] W_{\mu,\nu}\left(\frac{a}{e^t-1}\right)$ | Re a > o<br>$\mathrm{Re}(\frac{1}{2}\pm\nu+s) > o$ |
| | 2 | $\Gamma(s-\nu+1)\, W_{\frac{\nu-1}{2}-s,\frac{\nu}{2}}(a)$ | $a^{\frac{1-\nu}{2}} e^{-\frac{a}{2}}(e^t-1)^{\nu-1} \exp\left[-\frac{a}{e^t-1}\right]$ | Re a > o<br>$\mathrm{Re}\, s > \mathrm{Re}(\nu-1)$ |
| | 3 | $\frac{\Gamma(\frac{1}{2}-\mu-\nu+s)}{\Gamma(s+1)} W_{\mu-\frac{s}{2},\nu-\frac{s}{2}}(a)$ | $\frac{(e^t-1)^{\nu-\frac{1}{2}}}{\Gamma(2\nu+1)} \exp(-\frac{a}{2}e^t)\, M_{-\mu,\nu}(ae^t-a)$ | $\mathrm{Re}\,\nu > -\frac{1}{2}$<br>$\mathrm{Re}\, s > \mathrm{Re}(\nu+\mu)-\frac{1}{2}$ |
| | 4 | $\Gamma(s-b)\left[W_{-s+\frac{1}{2},b}(a)-(s-b)\, W_{-s-\frac{1}{2},b}(a)\right]$ | $2^b a^{\frac{1-b}{2}} \sinh^{2b}\frac{t}{2}\, e^{-\frac{a}{2}\coth\frac{t}{2}}$ | Re a > o<br>Re s > Re b |
| | 5 | $\Gamma(\mu+s)\, W_{-s,\nu}(a)$ | $\frac{ae^t}{(e^t-1)^{\mu+1}} \exp\left[-\frac{a}{2(e^t-1)}\right] W_{\mu,\nu}\left(\frac{a}{e^t-1}\right)$ | Re a > o<br>$\mathrm{Re}\, s > -\mathrm{Re}\,\mu$ |
| | 6 | $\Gamma(\frac{1}{2}+\nu+s)\Gamma(\frac{1}{2}-\nu+s)\, W_{-s,\nu}(a)\, W_{s,\nu}(b)$ | $\frac{1}{2} a^{\frac{1}{2}} b^{\frac{1}{2}} \operatorname{cosech}\frac{t}{2}\, e^{-\frac{a+b}{2}\coth\frac{t}{2}} \cdot$<br>$K_{2\nu}[a^{\frac{1}{2}}b^{\frac{1}{2}}\operatorname{cosech}\frac{t}{2}]$ | Re a > o<br>Re b > o<br>$\mathrm{Re}(s\pm2\nu) > -1$ |
| | 7 | $\Gamma(s+\nu+\frac{1}{2})\Gamma(s-\nu+\frac{1}{2})\, W_{-s,\nu}(a)\, W_{-s,\nu}(b)$ | $\frac{a^{\frac{1}{2}}b^{\frac{1}{2}} e^{\frac{a-b}{2}}}{\sinh\frac{t}{2}} \exp\left(-\frac{ae^t+b}{e^t-1}\right) K_{2\nu}\left[\frac{a^{\frac{1}{2}}b^{\frac{1}{2}}}{\sinh\frac{t}{2}}\right]$ | Re a > o<br>Re b > o<br>$\mathrm{Re}(s\pm\nu) > -\frac{1}{2}$ |

| | | g(s) | f(t) | |
|---|---|---|---|---|
| 30.21.1 (Contd.) | 8 | $\Gamma(s+\nu+\frac{1}{2})\Gamma(s-\nu+\frac{1}{2})\, W_{-s,\nu}(ia)\, W_{-s,\nu}(-ia)$ | $a\,\mathrm{cosech}\,\frac{t}{2}\, K_{2\nu}[a\,\mathrm{cosech}\,\frac{t}{2}]$ | Re a > 0<br>Re(s ± ν) > − 1 |
| | 9 | $\Gamma(s+\nu+\frac{1}{2})\, W_{-s,\nu}(b)\, M_{s,\nu}(a)$ | $\frac{1}{2}a^{\frac{1}{2}}b^{\frac{1}{2}}\Gamma(2\nu+1)e^{\frac{a+b}{2}}\mathrm{cosech}\,\frac{t}{2}\exp\left(\frac{a-be^{t}}{e^{t}-1}\right)J_{2\nu}\left(\frac{a^{\frac{1}{2}}b^{\frac{1}{2}}}{\sinh\frac{t}{2}}\right)$ | Re a > 0<br>Re b > 0<br>Re s > − Re ν − $\frac{1}{2}$ |
| | 10 | $\frac{\Gamma(s)}{\Gamma(\nu+s)}\Phi_1(s,\mu,\nu;c,a)$ | $\frac{(1-e^{-t})^{\nu-1}}{\Gamma(\nu)(1-ce^{-t})^{\mu}}\exp(ae^{-t})$ | Re ν > 0<br>\|arg(1−c)\| < π<br>Re s > 0 |
| | 11 | $\frac{\Gamma(s)}{\Gamma(\nu+s)}a^{-\frac{s}{2}}M_{\frac{\nu-s}{2},\frac{\nu+s-1}{2}}(a)$ | $\frac{a^{\frac{\nu}{2}}}{\Gamma(\nu)e^{\frac{a}{2}}}(1-e^{-t})^{\nu-1}\exp(ae^{-t})$ | Re ν > 0<br>Re s > 0 |
| 31 | 1 | ${}_2F_1[a,b;c;-\frac{s}{d}]$ | $d^{\frac{a+b-5}{2}}t^{\frac{a+b-3}{2}}e^{-\frac{d}{2}t}W_{\frac{a+b+1}{2}-c,\frac{a-b}{2}}(dt)$ | Re s > − Re $\frac{d}{2}$ |
| | 2 | ${}_2F_1[a,b;c;\frac{1}{2}-\frac{s}{d}]$ | $\frac{d\Gamma(c)}{\Gamma(a)\Gamma(b)}(dt)^{\frac{a+b-3}{2}}W_{\frac{a+b+1}{2}-c,\frac{a-b}{2}}(dt)$ | Re a > 0<br>Re b > 0<br>Re s > − Re $\frac{d}{2}$ |
| 31.1 | 1 | ${}_2F_1[1,2;2-\nu;\frac{a-s}{2a}]$ | $\frac{2\pi a\nu(1-\nu)\, k_{2\nu}(at)}{\sin(\nu\pi)}$ | Re s > 0 |
| | 2 | $\frac{s^{m+n}}{(s+a)^{m+n+2}}{}_2F_1\left[-m,-n;2;\frac{a^2}{s^2}\right]$ | $\frac{(-1)^{m+n}}{a^2t}k_{2m+2}(\frac{at}{2})k_{2n+2}(\frac{at}{2})$ | m,n = 0,1,2,...<br>Re s > − Re a |
| | 3 | $\frac{(s-a)^m(s-b)^n}{s^{m+n+2}}{}_2F_1\left[-m,-n;-m-n-1;\frac{s(s-a-b)}{(s-a)(s-b)}\right]$ | $\frac{(-1)^{m+n}(m+1)!(n+1)!}{ab(m+n+1)!}\frac{e^{\frac{a+b}{2}t}}{t}\cdot k_{2m+2}(\frac{at}{2})\, k_{2n+2}(\frac{bt}{2})$ | m,n = 0,1,2,...<br>Re s > 0 |

| | | g(s) | f(t) | |
|---|---|---|---|---|
| 31.2 | 1 | $s^{n-a}\,{}_2F_1\left[-n,a-n;m-n+1;\frac{(s^2+a^2)^{\frac12}}{s}\right]$ | $\frac{(m-n)!}{m!\Gamma(a-n)}\,t^{a-1}p_n(m,t)$ | $n,m=0,1,2,\ldots$<br>$\mathrm{Re}\,a>\min(n,m)$<br>$\mathrm{Re}\,s>0$ |
| | 2 | $\frac{1}{s^a}\,{}_2F_1[-\frac{n}{2},\frac{1-n}{2};1-a;s]$<br>If a is an integer take the first $1+[\frac{n}{2}]$ terms of the series. | $\frac{t^{a-\frac{n}{2}-1}}{2^{\frac{n}{2}}\Gamma(a)}He_n[(2t)^{\frac12}]$ | $n=0,1,2,\ldots$<br>$\mathrm{Re}\,a>\frac{n}{2}$ for n even<br>$\mathrm{Re}\,a>\frac{n-1}{2}$ for n odd<br>$\mathrm{Re}\,s>0$ |
| | 3 | $\frac{1}{s^\nu}\,{}_2F_1[-n,b+n;c;\frac{a}{s}]$ | $\frac{t^{\nu-1}}{\Gamma(\nu)}\,{}_2F_2\left[\begin{matrix}-n,b+n;\\ c,\ \nu;\end{matrix}\ at\right]$ | $\mathrm{Re}\,\nu>0$<br>$n=0,1,2,\ldots$<br>$\mathrm{Re}\,s>\frac12\lvert\mathrm{Re}\,a\rvert$ |
| | 4 | $\frac{1}{s^\nu}\,{}_2F_1[-n,\nu;c;\frac{a}{s}]$ | $\frac{n!\Gamma(c)}{\Gamma(n+c)\Gamma(\nu)}\,t^{\nu-1}L_n^{c-1}(at)$ | $n=0,1,2,\ldots$<br>$\mathrm{Re}\,\nu>0$<br>$\mathrm{Re}\,s>\frac12\lvert\mathrm{Re}\,a\rvert$ |
| | 5 | $\frac{1}{s^\nu}\,{}_2F_1[\nu,b;c;\frac{a}{s}]$ | $\frac{t^{\nu-\frac{c}{2}-1}}{a^{\frac{c}{2}}}M_{\frac{c}{2}-b,\frac{c}{2}-\frac12}(at)$ | $\mathrm{Re}\,\nu>0$<br>$\mathrm{Re}\,s>\frac12\lvert\mathrm{Re}\,a\rvert$ |
| | 6 | $\frac{1}{s^\nu}\,{}_2F_1[\nu,b;2(\nu-1);\frac{a}{s}]$ | $\frac{e^{\frac{at}{2}}}{a^{\nu-1}\Gamma(\nu)}M_{\nu-b-1,\nu-\frac32}(at)$ | $\mathrm{Re}\,\nu>0$<br>$\mathrm{Re}\,s>\frac12\lvert\mathrm{Re}\,a\rvert$ |
| | 7 | $\frac{1}{s^{a+\nu+1}}\,{}_2F_1[a+\nu+1,\mu+\nu;2\nu;\frac{2a}{s}]$ | $\frac{t^a e^{at}M_{-\mu,\nu-\frac12}(2at)}{(2a)^\nu\Gamma(a+\nu+1)}$ | $\mathrm{Re}(a+\nu)>-1$<br>$\mathrm{Re}\,s>\lvert\mathrm{Re}\,a\rvert$ |
| | 8 | $\frac{1}{s^\nu}F_1(a,b,\nu,c;x,\frac{y}{s})$ | $\frac{t^{\nu-1}}{\Gamma(\nu)}\Phi_1(a,b,c;x,yt)$ | $\mathrm{Re}\,\nu>0$<br>$\mathrm{Re}\,s>\mathrm{Max}\ 0,\mathrm{Re}\,y$ |
| | 9 | $\frac{1}{s^\nu}F_1(\nu,a,b,c;\frac{x}{s},\frac{y}{s})$ | $\frac{t^{\nu-1}}{\Gamma(\nu)}\Phi_2(a,b,c;xt,yt)$ | $\mathrm{Re}\,\nu>0$<br>$\mathrm{Re}\,s>\mathrm{Max}\ 0,\mathrm{Re}\,x,$ $\mathrm{Re}\,y$ |

| | | g(s) | f(t) | |
|---|---|---|---|---|
| 31.2 (Contd.) | 10 | $\frac{1}{s^\nu} F_2(a,b,\nu,c,d;x,\frac{y}{s})$ | $\frac{t^{\nu-1}}{\Gamma(\nu)} \Psi_1(a,b,c,d;x,yt)$ | $\mathrm{Re}\,\nu > 0$<br>$\mathrm{Re}\,s > \mathrm{Max}\ 0, \mathrm{Re}\,y$ |
| | 11 | $\frac{1}{s^\nu} F_3(a,b,c,\nu;k;x,\frac{y}{s})$ | $\frac{t^{\nu-1}}{\Gamma(\nu)} \Xi_1(a,b,c,k;x,yt)$ | $\mathrm{Re}\,\nu > 0$<br>$\mathrm{Re}\,s > \mathrm{Max}\ 0, \mathrm{Re}\,y$ |
| | 12 | $\frac{1}{s^\nu} F_4(\nu,b,c,d;\frac{x}{s},\frac{y}{s})$ | $\frac{t^{\nu-1}}{\Gamma(\nu)} \Psi_2(b,c,d;xt,yt)$ | $\mathrm{Re}\,\nu > 0$<br>$\mathrm{Re}\,s > \mathrm{Max}\ 0, \mathrm{Re}\,x, \mathrm{Re}\,y$ |
| 31.2.1 | 1 | $\frac{(s-a)^n(s-b)^m}{s^{m+n+\frac{1}{2}}} {}_2F_1\left[-m,-n;-m-n+\frac{1}{2};\ \frac{s(s-a-b)}{(s-a)(s-b)}\right]$ | $\frac{(-2)^{m+n}(m+n)!}{\pi^{\frac{1}{2}}(2m+2n)!} t^{-\frac{1}{2}} \cdot He_{2n}[(2at)^{\frac{1}{2}}]\, He_{2m}[(2bt)^{\frac{1}{2}}]$ | $m,n = 0,1,2,\ldots$<br>$\mathrm{Re}\,s > 0$ |
| | 2 | $\frac{(s-a)^n(s-b)^m}{s^{m+n+\frac{3}{2}}} {}_2F_1\left[-m,-n;-m-n-\frac{1}{2};\ \frac{s(s-a-b)}{(s-a)(s-b)}\right]$ | $-\frac{(-2)^{m+n+1}(m+n+1)!}{(ab\pi)^{\frac{1}{2}}(2m+2n+2)!} t^{-\frac{1}{2}} \cdot He_{2n+1}[(2at)^{\frac{1}{2}}]\, He_{2m+1}[(2bt)^{\frac{1}{2}}]$ | $m,n = 0,1,2,\ldots$<br>$\mathrm{Re}\,s > 0$ |
| | 3 | $\frac{(s-b)^n(s-c)^m}{s^{m+n+a+1}} {}_2F_1\left[-m,-n;-m-n-a;\ \frac{s(s-b-c)}{(s-b)(s-c)}\right]$ | $\frac{m!n!}{\Gamma(m+n+a+1)} t^a L_n^a(bt)\, L_m^a(ct)$ | $\mathrm{Re}\,a > -1$<br>$n,m = 0,1,2,\ldots$<br>$\mathrm{Re}\,s > 0$ |
| | 4 | $\frac{1}{s^\nu} {}_2F_1[-n,\frac{\nu}{2};\frac{1}{2}-n;(1-\frac{1}{s})^2]$ | $\frac{\pi(n!)^2}{2^{\nu-1}\Gamma(\frac{\nu}{2})\Gamma(n+\frac{1}{2})} t^{\nu-1}[L_n^{\frac{\nu-1}{2}}(\frac{t}{2})]^2$ | $\mathrm{Re}\,\nu > 0$<br>$n = 0,1,2,\ldots$<br>$\mathrm{Re}\,s > 0$ |
| | 5 | $\frac{(a-s)^n}{s^{n+\nu}} {}_2F_1[n+\nu,\frac{1}{2}-\nu;n+1;1-\frac{a}{s}]$ | $\frac{2^{2n-\frac{1}{2}+\nu} n!}{\pi^{\frac{1}{2}}\Gamma(2n+2\nu)} t^{\nu-1} e^{\frac{at}{2}} D_{2\nu+2n-1}[(2at)^{\frac{1}{2}}]$ | $n = 0,1,2,\ldots$<br>$\mathrm{Re}\,\nu > 0$<br>$\mathrm{Re}\,s > 0$ |
| | 6 | $\frac{(s-1)^n}{s^\nu} {}_2F_1[-n,a;1-\nu;\frac{s}{s-1}]$ | $\frac{n!}{\Gamma(\nu)} t^{\nu-1-n} L_n^{\nu+a-1-n}(t)$ | $\mathrm{Re}\,\nu > \mathrm{Max}\ n, n-\mathrm{Re}\,a$<br>$n = 0,1,2,\ldots$<br>$\mathrm{Re}\,s > 0$ |

31.2.1 (Contd.)

| | | g(s) | f(t) | |
|---|---|---|---|---|
| | 7 | $\frac{1}{s^{2\nu+1}}\,{}_2F_1[\nu,\nu+1;2\nu;-\frac{a^2}{s^2}]$ | $\frac{\pi a^{1-2\nu}}{2\nu B(\nu,\nu)}\, t J^2_{\nu-\frac{1}{2}}(\frac{at}{2})$ | Re $\nu > -\frac{1}{2}$<br>Re s > \|Im a\| |
| | 8 | $\frac{1}{s^{4\nu-1}}\,{}_2F_1[\nu,2\nu-\frac{1}{2};\nu+\frac{1}{2};-\frac{a^2}{s^2}]$ | $\frac{\pi\Gamma(\nu+\frac{1}{2})}{\Gamma(\nu)\Gamma(2\nu-\frac{1}{2})}(\frac{t}{2a})^{2\nu-1} J^2_{\nu-\frac{1}{2}}(\frac{at}{2})$ | Re $\nu > \frac{1}{4}$<br>Re s > \|Im a\| |
| | 9 | $\frac{1}{s^{2\nu}}\,{}_2F_1[\nu,\nu+\frac{1}{2};\mu;\frac{a^2}{s^2}]$ | $\frac{\Gamma(\mu)(2t)^{2\nu-\mu} I_{\mu-1}(at)}{a^{\mu-1}\Gamma(2\nu)}$ | Re $\nu > 0$<br>Re $\mu > 0$<br>Re s > \|Re a\| |
| | 10 | $\frac{1}{s^{2\nu}}\,{}_2F_1[\nu,\nu+\frac{1}{2};\mu;-\frac{a^2}{s^2}]$ | $\frac{\Gamma(\mu)(2t)^{2\nu-\mu} J_{\mu-1}(at)}{a^{\mu-1}\Gamma(2\nu)}$ | Re $\nu > 0$<br>Re $\mu > 0$<br>Re s > \|Im a\| |
| | 11 | $\frac{1}{(s^2+c^2)^a}\,{}_2F_1[a,b;a+b+\frac{1}{2};\frac{c^2}{s^2+c^2}]$ | $(\frac{2}{c})^{2b}\frac{\Gamma(a+b+\frac{1}{2})}{\Gamma(2a)}(\frac{2t}{c})^{a-b-\frac{1}{2}} J_{a+b-\frac{1}{2}}(ct)$ | Re a > 0<br>Re s > \|Im c\| |
| | 12 | $\frac{1}{(s+h)^a}\,{}_2F_1[a,b;c;\frac{s-h}{s+h}]$ | $\frac{\Gamma(c)\, t^{\frac{a-b+c-3}{2}}}{\Gamma(a)\Gamma(c-b)(2h)^{\frac{a+b-c+1}{2}}} W_{\frac{a-b-c+1}{2},\frac{a+b-c}{2}}(2ht)$ | Re(c-b) > 0<br>Re a > 0<br>Re s > - Re h |
| | 13 | $\frac{{}_2F_1[a,b;c;\frac{2h}{s+h}]}{(s+h)^a}$ | $\frac{t^{a-\frac{c+2}{2}} M_{\frac{c}{2}-b,\frac{c-1}{2}}(2ht)}{(2h)^{\frac{c}{2}}\Gamma(a)}$ | Re a > 0<br>Re s > \|Re h\| |
| | 14 | $\frac{1}{s^{\nu}} F_3(a,\nu,b,\frac{\nu+1}{2},c;x,\frac{4y}{s^2})$ | $\frac{t^{\nu-1}}{\Gamma(\nu)}\Xi_2(a,b,c;x,yt^2)$ | Re $\nu > 0$<br>Re s > 2\|Re $y^{\frac{1}{2}}$ |
| | 15 | $\frac{1}{s^{c+\mu+\nu-2}} F_4\left(\frac{c+\mu+\nu}{2}-1,\frac{c+\mu+\nu-1}{2};\mu,\nu;\frac{a^2}{s^2},\frac{b^2}{s^2}\right)$ | $\frac{\pi^{\frac{1}{2}}\Gamma(\mu)\Gamma(\nu)}{2^{c-1}a^{\mu-1}b^{\nu-1}\Gamma(\frac{c+\mu+\nu}{2}-1)\Gamma(\frac{c+\mu+\nu-1}{2})}\cdot t^{c-1} I_{\mu-1}(at)\, I_{\nu-1}(bt)$ | Re$(c+\mu+\nu) > 2$<br>Re s > \|Re a\|<br>+\|Re b\| |

| | | g(s) | f(t) | |
|---|---|---|---|---|
| 31.5 | 1 | $\frac{1}{s^{\mu}}\int_0^{\pi} {}_2F_1\left[\frac{\mu}{2},\frac{\mu+1}{2};\nu+1;-\frac{r}{s^2}\right]\sin^{2\nu}\theta\, d\theta$ where $r=a^2-2ab\cos\theta+b^2$ | $\frac{\pi\Gamma(2\nu+1)}{(ab)^{\nu}\Gamma(\mu)}\, t^{\mu-2\nu-1}\, J_{\nu}(at)\, J_{\nu}(bt)$ | Re $\mu > 0$<br>Re $s > \lvert \text{Im}\, a\rvert + \lvert \text{Im}\, b\rvert$ |
| 31.21.1 | 1 | $\frac{\Gamma(s)}{\Gamma(s+\frac{1}{2})}\, {}_2F_1\left[-\mu-\nu,\frac{1}{2}-\mu+\nu;s+\frac{1}{2};a^2\right]$ | $\frac{\Gamma(\frac{1}{2}-\mu-\nu)\Gamma(1-\mu+\nu)}{2^{2\mu+1}\pi}\,\frac{(1-a^2+a^2e^{-t})^{\mu}}{(1-e^{-t})^{\frac{1}{2}}}\cdot\left\{P^{2\mu}_{2\nu}[a(1-e^{-t})^{\frac{1}{2}}]+P^{2\mu}_{2\nu}[-a(1-e^{-t})^{\frac{1}{2}}]\right\}$ | $\lvert a\rvert < 1$<br>Re $s > 0$ |
| | 2 | $\frac{\Gamma(s)}{\Gamma(s+\frac{3}{2})}\, {}_2F_1\left[\frac{1}{2}-\mu-\nu,1-\mu+\nu;s+\frac{3}{2};a^2\right]$ | $-\frac{\Gamma(-\mu-\nu)\Gamma(\frac{1}{2}-\mu+\nu)}{4^{\mu+\frac{1}{2}}\pi a}(1-a^2+a^2e^{-t})^{\mu}\cdot\left\{P^{2\mu}_{2\nu}[a(1-e^{-t})^{\frac{1}{2}}]-P^{2\mu}_{2\nu}[-a(1-e^{-t})^{\frac{1}{2}}]\right\}$ | $\lvert a\rvert < 1$<br>Re $s > 0$ |
| | 3 | $B(s,\nu)\, {}_2F_1[a,b;s+\nu;h]$ | $(1-e^{-t})^{\nu-1}\, {}_2F_1[a,b;\nu;h(1-e^{-t})]$ | Re $\nu > 0$<br>$\lvert \arg(1-h)\rvert < \pi$<br>Re $s > 0$ |
| | 4 | $B(s,\nu)\, {}_2F_1[\mu,s;s+\nu;h]$ | $\frac{(1-e^{-t})^{\nu-1}}{(1-he^{-t})^{\mu}}$ | Re $\nu > 0$<br>$\lvert \arg(1-h)\rvert < \pi$<br>Re $s > 0$ |
| | 5 | $B(\nu,s-\nu)\, {}_2F_1[a,\nu;s;c]$ | $\frac{e^{t}(e^{t}-1)^{\nu-1}}{[1-c(1-e^{-t})]^{a}}$ | $\lvert c\rvert < 1$<br>Re $\nu > 0$<br>Re $s >$ Re $\nu$ |
| 32 | 1 | $\frac{1}{s}\, {}_pF_q\left[\begin{matrix}(b); & \frac{a}{s}\\ (c); & \end{matrix}\right]$ | ${}_pF_{q+1}\left[\begin{matrix}(b) & ;at\\ (c),1; & \end{matrix}\right]$ | $q \geqslant p-1$<br>Re $s > \lvert \text{Re}\, a\rvert$ |
| | 2 | $\frac{1}{s}\, {}_pF_q\left[\begin{matrix}(b),1; & \frac{a}{s}\\ (c) & ;\end{matrix}\right]$ | ${}_{p-1}F_q\left[\begin{matrix}(b); & at\\ (c); & \end{matrix}\right]$ | $q \geqslant p-1$<br>Re $s > \lvert \text{Re}\, a\rvert$ |
| | 3 | $\frac{1}{s}\, {}_pF_q\left[\begin{matrix}(b),1,\frac{1}{2}; & \frac{a^2}{s^2}\\ (c) & ;\end{matrix}\right]$ | ${}_{p-2}F_q\left[\begin{matrix}(b); & (\frac{at}{2})^2\\ (c); & \end{matrix}\right]$ | $q \geqslant p-1$<br>Re $s > \lvert \text{Re}\, a\rvert$ |

| | | g(s) | f(t) | |
|---|---|---|---|---|
| 32.2 | 1 | $\frac{1}{s^{\nu}} E(a,b,\nu:c:\frac{s}{h})$ | $\frac{\Gamma(a)\Gamma(b)}{\Gamma(c)} t^{\nu-1} {}_2F_1[a,b;c;-ht]$ | Re $\nu > 0$<br>Re $s > 0$ |
| | 2 | $\frac{1}{s^{\nu}} E(c-a,c-b,\nu:c:\frac{s}{h})$ | $\frac{\Gamma(c-a)\Gamma(c-b)}{\Gamma(c)} t^{\nu-1}(1+ht)^{a+b-c}\ {}_2F_1[a,b;c;-ht]$ | Re $\nu > 0$<br>Re $s > 0$ |
| | 3 | $\frac{1}{s^{b+\mu}} E(-\nu,\nu+1,b+\mu:\mu+1:\frac{s}{a})$ | $-\frac{\pi \operatorname{cosec}(\nu\pi)}{a^{\frac{\mu}{2}}} t^{b+\frac{\mu}{2}-1}(at+1)^{\frac{\mu}{2}} P_{\nu}^{-\mu}(2at+1)$ | Re$(b+\mu) > 0$<br>Re $s > 0$ |
| | 4 | $\frac{1}{s^{b}} E(\mu+\nu+1,\mu-\nu,b:\mu+1:\frac{s}{a})$ | $\frac{\Gamma(\mu+\nu+1)\Gamma(\mu-\nu)}{a^{\frac{\mu}{2}}} \frac{t^{b-\frac{\mu}{2}-1}}{(at+1)^{\frac{\mu}{2}}} P_{\nu}^{-\mu}(2at+1)$ | Re $b > 0$<br>Re $s > 0$ |
| | 5 | $\frac{1}{s^{a_{m+1}}} E(m+1;a_r:n;b_k:s)$ | $t^{a_{m+1}-1} E(m;a_r:n;b_k:\frac{1}{t})$ | Re $a_{m+1} > 0$<br>Re $s > 0$ |
| | 6 | $\frac{1}{s^{b}}\ {}_3F_3\left[\begin{matrix}\frac{\mu+\nu-1}{2}, \frac{\mu+\nu}{2}, b\ ; \\ \mu, \nu, \mu+\nu-1;\end{matrix} -\frac{a}{s}\right]$ | $\frac{2^{\mu+\nu-3}\Gamma(\mu)\Gamma(\nu)}{a^{\frac{\mu+\nu-2}{2}}\Gamma(b)} t^{b-\frac{\mu+\nu}{2}} J_{\mu-1}(a^{\frac{1}{2}}t^{\frac{1}{2}}) J_{\nu-1}(a^{\frac{1}{2}}t^{\frac{1}{2}})$ | Re $b > 0$<br>Re $s > 0$ |
| | 7 | $\frac{1}{s^{\frac{1}{2}}}\ {}_pF_q\left[\begin{matrix}a_1,\dots,a_p; \\ b_1,\dots,b_q;\end{matrix} -ks^{\frac{1}{2}}\right]$ | $(\pi t)^{-\frac{1}{2}}\ {}_{2p}F_{2q}\left[\begin{matrix}\frac{a_1}{2}, \frac{a_1+1}{2}, \dots, \frac{a_p}{2}, \frac{a_p+1}{2}; \\ \frac{b_1}{2}, \frac{b_1+1}{2}, \dots, \frac{b_q}{2}, \frac{b_q+1}{2};\end{matrix} -2^{p-q-2}\frac{k^2}{t}\right]$ | $k > 0$<br>$p \leq q$<br>Re $s > 0$ |
| | 8 | $\frac{1}{s^{\nu}}\ {}_pF_q\left[\begin{matrix}a_1,\dots,a_p; \\ b_1,\dots,b_q;\end{matrix} \frac{k}{s}\right]$ | $\frac{t^{\nu-1}}{\Gamma(\nu)}\ {}_pF_{q+1}\left[\begin{matrix}a_1,\dots,a_p\ ; \\ b_1,\dots,b_q,\nu;\end{matrix} kt\right]$ | $p \leq q+1$<br>Re $\nu > 0$<br>Re $s > 0$ if $p < q+1$<br>Re $s > k$ if $p = q+1$ |
| | 9 | $\frac{1}{s^{a_p}}\ {}_pF_q\left[\begin{matrix}a_1,\dots,a_p; \\ b_1,\dots,b_q;\end{matrix} \frac{k}{s}\right]$ | $\frac{t^{a_p-1}}{\Gamma(a_p)}\ {}_{p-1}F_q\left[\begin{matrix}a_1,\dots,a_{p-1}; \\ b_1,\dots,b_q\ ;\end{matrix} kt\right]$ | $p-1 \leq q$<br>Re $a_p > 0$<br>Re $s > 0$ if $p-1 < q$<br>Re $s >$ Re $k$ if $p-1=q$ |

| | g(s) | f(t) | |
|---|---|---|---|
| 32.2.1 1 | $\frac{1}{s^{a+1}}\,{}_3F_2\left[\begin{matrix}\frac{a+1}{3},\frac{a+2}{3},\frac{a+3}{3}; & -\frac{1}{s^3}\\ \mu,\ \nu\ ; & \end{matrix}\right]$ | $\frac{t^a}{\Gamma(a+1)}\,{}_0F_2\left[\begin{matrix} ; & -\frac{t^3}{27}\\ \mu,\nu; & \end{matrix}\right]$ | Re $a > -1$<br>Re $s > \frac{1}{2}$ |
| 2 | $\frac{1}{s^\nu}\,{}_pF_q\left[\begin{matrix}(a); & \frac{4k^2}{s^2}\\ (b); & \end{matrix}\right]$ | $\frac{t^{\nu-1}}{\Gamma(\nu)}\,{}_pF_{q+2}\left[\begin{matrix}(a)\ ; & k^2t^2\\ (b),\frac{\nu}{2},\frac{\nu+1}{2}; & \end{matrix}\right]$ | $p \leq q+1$<br>Re $\nu > 0$<br>Re $s > 0$ if $p < q+1$<br>Re $s > \lvert \text{Re}\, k \rvert$ if $p = q+1$ |
| 3 | $\frac{1}{s^{2\nu}}\,{}_{p+2}F_q\left[\begin{matrix}a_1,\dots,a_p,\frac{\nu}{2},\frac{\nu+1}{2}; & \frac{4k^2}{s^2}\\ b_1,\dots,b_q\ ; & \end{matrix}\right]$ | $\frac{t^{2\nu-1}}{\Gamma(2\nu)}\,{}_pF_q\left[\begin{matrix}a_1,\dots,a_p; & k^2t^2\\ b_1,\dots,b_q; & \end{matrix}\right]$ | $p < q$<br>Re $\nu > 0$<br>Re $s > 0$ if $p < q-1$<br>Re $s > \lvert \text{Re}\, k \rvert$ if $p = q-1$ |
| 4 | $\frac{1}{s^c}\,{}_{p+n}F_q\left[\begin{matrix}a_1,\dots,a_p,\frac{c}{n},\frac{c+1}{n},\dots,\frac{c+n-1}{n}; & \left(\frac{nk}{s}\right)^n\\ b_1,\dots,b_q\ ; & \end{matrix}\right]$ | $\frac{t^{c-1}}{\Gamma(c)}\,{}_pF_q\left[\begin{matrix}a_1,\dots,a_p; & (kt)^n\\ b_1,\dots,b_q; & \end{matrix}\right]$ | $n = 1,2,3,\dots$<br>$p+n \leq q+1$<br>Re $c > 0$<br>Re $s > 0$ if $p+n \leq q$<br>Re$(s + nke^{2\pi ir/n}) > 0$<br>$(r = 0,1,\dots,n-1)$<br>if $p+n = q+1$ |
| 5 | $\frac{1}{(s+ia)^{\mu+\nu}}\,F_A\left(\mu+\nu;\nu_1+\frac{1}{2},\dots,\nu_n+\frac{1}{2};\ 2\nu_1+1,\dots,2\nu_n+1;\frac{2a_1 i}{s+ia},\dots,\frac{2a_n i}{s+ia}\right)$<br>If $n = 2$ replace $F_A$ by $F_2$ | $\frac{2^\nu t^{\mu-1}}{\Gamma(\mu+\nu)}\prod_{r=1}^{n}\left[\frac{\Gamma(\nu_r+1)}{a_r^{\nu_r}}J_{\nu_r}(a_r t)\right]$ | Re$(\mu+\nu) > 0$<br>$\nu = \sum_{r=1}^{n}\nu_r$<br>$a = \sum_{r=1}^{n} a_r$<br>$n = 1,2,3,\dots$<br>Re$(s \pm ia_1 \pm \dots \pm ia_n) > 0$ |
| 6 | $\frac{1}{(s+a)^{b+U}}\,F_A\left(b+U;\nu_1-\mu_1,\dots,\nu_n-\mu_n;\ 2\nu_1,\dots,2\nu_n;\ \frac{a_1}{s+a},\dots,\frac{a_n}{s+a}\right)$<br>$a = \frac{1}{2}\sum_{r=1}^{n} a_r \quad U = \sum_{r=1}^{n}\nu_r$ | $\frac{t^{b-1}\prod_{r=1}^{n} M_{\mu_r,\nu_r-\frac{1}{2}}(a_r t)}{\prod_{r=1}^{n} a_r^{\nu_r}\,\Gamma(b+U)}$ | Re$(b+U) > 0$<br>Re$(s \pm \frac{a_1}{2} \pm \dots \pm \frac{a_n}{2}) > 0$ |

| | | g(s) | f(t) | |
|---|---|---|---|---|
| 32.2.1 (Contd.) | 7 | $\frac{1}{(s+a)^{b+n}} F_A\left(b+n;-m_1,\ldots,-m_n;2,\ldots,2;\frac{2a_1}{s+a},\ldots,\frac{2a_n}{s+a}\right)$ | $\frac{(-1)^m t^{b-1} \prod_{r=1}^{n} k_{2m_r+2}(a_r t)}{2^n \prod_{r=1}^{n} a_r \Gamma(b+n)}$ | $\mathrm{Re}(b+n) > 0$<br>$n = 1,2,3,\ldots$<br>$m_r = 1,2,3,\ldots$<br>$m = \sum_{r=1}^{n} m_r$<br>$a = \sum_{r=1}^{n} a_r$<br>$\mathrm{Re}\, s > 0$ |
| 32.21.1 | 1 | $B(s,\nu)\,{}_3F_2\left[\begin{matrix} a,b,\nu; \\ c,s+\nu; \end{matrix} h\right]$ | $(1-e^{-t})^{\nu-1}\,{}_2F_1[a,b;c;h(1-e^{-t})]$ | $\mathrm{Re}\,\nu > 0$<br>$\lvert\arg(1-h)\rvert < \pi$<br>$\mathrm{Re}\, s > 0$ |
| | 2 | $B(s,\nu)\,{}_3F_2\left[\begin{matrix} a,b,s; \\ c,s+\nu; \end{matrix} h\right]$ | $(1-e^{-t})^{\nu-1}\,{}_2F_1[a,b;c;he^{-t}]$ | $\mathrm{Re}\,\nu > 0$<br>$\lvert\arg(1-h)\rvert < \pi$<br>$\mathrm{Re}\, s > 0$ |
| | 3 | $B(\nu,s)\,{}_{p+1}F_{q+1}\left[\begin{matrix} a_1,\ldots,a_p,\nu; \\ b_1,\ldots,b_q,s+\nu; \end{matrix} k\right]$ | $(1-e^{-t})^{\nu-1}\,{}_pF_q\left[\begin{matrix} a_1,\ldots,a_p; \\ b_1,\ldots,b_q; \end{matrix} k(1-e^{-t})\right]$ | $\mathrm{Re}\,\nu > 0$<br>$p \leq q$<br>Valid for $p=q+1$ if $\lvert k\rvert < 1$<br>$\mathrm{Re}\, s > 0$ |
| | 4 | $B(\nu,s)\,{}_{p+1}F_{q+1}\left[\begin{matrix} a_1,\ldots,a_p,s; \\ b_1,\ldots,b_q,s+\nu; \end{matrix} k\right]$ | $(1-e^{-t})^{\nu-1}\,{}_pF_q\left[\begin{matrix} a_1,\ldots,a_p; \\ b_1,\ldots,b_q; \end{matrix} ke^{-t}\right]$ | $\mathrm{Re}\,\nu > 0$<br>$p \leq q$<br>Valid for $p=q+1$ if $\lvert k\rvert < 1$<br>$\mathrm{Re}\, s > 0$ |
| | 5 | $\Gamma(s-a_m)E(m;a_r:n;b_j,s:k)$ | $(e^t-1)^{a_m}E\left(m-1;a_r:n;b_j:\frac{k}{1-e^{-t}}\right)$ | $\mathrm{Re}\, a_m > -1$<br>$n = 0,1,2,\ldots$<br>$m = 1,2,3,\ldots$<br>$\mathrm{Re}\, s > \mathrm{Re}\, a_m$ |
| 32.21.3.1 | 1 | $2^{2s}B(s,s+a)\,{}_3F_2\left[\begin{matrix} -n,n+1,s+a; \\ 1,2s+a; \end{matrix} 1\right]$ | $\frac{[1-(1-e^{-t})^{\frac{1}{2}}]^a+(-1)^n[1+(1-e^{-t})^{\frac{1}{2}}]^a}{2^a(1-e^{-t})^{\frac{1}{2}}} \cdot P_n[(1-e^{-t})^{\frac{1}{2}}]$ | $n = 0,1,2,\ldots$<br>$\mathrm{Re}\, s > 0$ |

| | | g(s) | f(t) | |
|---|---|---|---|---|
| 7 | 1 | $I(a,b;s)$ | $\frac{1}{2t}\frac{1}{[at^{\frac{1}{2}}J_1(t^{\frac{1}{2}})+bJ_0(t^{\frac{1}{2}})]^2+[at^{\frac{1}{2}}Y_1(t^{\frac{1}{2}})+bY_0(t^{\frac{1}{2}})]^2}$ | $\mathrm{Re}\, s > 0$ |
| | 2 | $S(1,s)S(1,-s)$ | $-\frac{1}{t}\log(1-t^2)$ | $\mathrm{Re}\, s > 0$ |
| | 3 | $S(1,is)S(1,-is)$ | $-\frac{\log(1+t^2)}{t}$ | $\mathrm{Re}\, s > 0$ |
| | 4 | $S(\nu,s)$ | $\frac{1}{(1+t)^{\nu}}$ | $\mathrm{Re}\, s > 0$ |
| 7.2 | 1 | $\frac{1}{s^{\frac{1}{2}}}Q^{1,\nu}(s)$ | $\pi(\frac{t}{2})^{\frac{1}{2}} I_{\frac{\nu}{2}+\frac{1}{4}}(\frac{t}{2}) I_{\frac{\nu}{2}+\frac{3}{4}}(\frac{t}{2})$ | $\mathrm{Re}\, s > 1$ |
| | 2 | $\frac{1}{s^{\nu-\frac{1}{2}}}Q^{\nu,\frac{1}{2}-\nu}(s)$ | $(2\pi)^{\frac{1}{2}}(2t)^{\nu-1}\sinh(\frac{t}{2}) I_{\nu-1}(\frac{t}{2})$ | $\mathrm{Re}\, s > 1$ |
| | 3 | $\frac{1}{s^{\nu-\frac{1}{2}}}Q^{\nu,-\nu-\frac{1}{2}}(s)$ | $(2\pi)^{\frac{1}{2}}(4t)^{\nu-1}\cosh(\frac{t}{2}) I_{\nu-1}(\frac{t}{2})$ | $\mathrm{Re}\, s > 1$ |
| | 4 | $\frac{1}{s^{\frac{1}{2}}}\mu(\frac{a}{s},b)$ | $\frac{\mu(2a^{\frac{1}{2}}t^{\frac{1}{2}},b)}{2^{b+1}\pi^{\frac{1}{2}}t^{\frac{1}{2}}}$ | $\mathrm{Re}\, s > 0$ |
| | 5 | $\frac{1}{s^{\frac{1}{2}}}\nu(\frac{a}{s})$ | $\frac{\nu(2a^{\frac{1}{2}}t^{\frac{1}{2}})}{2\pi^{\frac{1}{2}}t^{\frac{1}{2}}}$ | $\mathrm{Re}\, s > 0$ |
| | 6 | $\frac{1}{s^{\frac{1}{2}}}\nu(\frac{a}{s},b)$ | $\frac{1}{2(\pi t)^{\frac{1}{2}}}\nu(2a^{\frac{1}{2}}t^{\frac{1}{2}},2b)$ | $\mathrm{Re}\, b > -\frac{1}{2}$<br>$\mathrm{Re}\, s > 0$ |
| | 7 | $\frac{1}{s^{\frac{3}{2}}}\nu(\frac{a}{s},b)$ | $\frac{2}{(\pi a)^{\frac{1}{2}}}\nu(2a^{\frac{1}{2}}t^{\frac{1}{2}},2b+1)$ | $\mathrm{Re}\, b > -\frac{3}{2}$<br>$\mathrm{Re}\, s > 0$ |
| 7.21 | 1 | $\Gamma(\frac{s}{a})\nu(1,\frac{s}{a})$ | $a\nu(1-e^{-at})$ | $\mathrm{Re}\, s > 0$ |